SIMMS

INTEGRATED

MATHEMATICS

A Modeling Approach
Using Technology

Level 1, Third Edition

KENDALL/HUNT PUBLISHING COMPANY
4050 Westmark Drive   Dubuque   Iowa 52002

CONTRIBUTORS

Masha Albrecht ■ Glenn Allinger ■ Byron Anderson ■ Staci Auck ■ Shirley Bagwell ■ Cliff Bara ■ Gary Bauer ■ Jack Beal ■ Patricia Bean ■ Glenn Blake ■ Kyle Boyce ■ Monty Brekke ■ Ruth Brocklebank ■ Lee Brown ■ Maurice Burke ■ Clay Burkett ■ Randy Carspecken ■ John Carter ■ William Chalgren ■ Terri Dahl ■ Ted Drieth ■ Wendy Driscoll ■ Bonnie Eichenberger ■ Todd Fife ■ Jerry Fisher ■ John Freal ■ John Gebhart ■ Kimberley Girard ■ Janet Higgins ■ James Hirstein ■ Sherry Horyna ■ Jeffrey Hostetter ■ Alexander Johnson ■ Danny Jones ■ Russ Killingsworth ■ John Knudson-Martin ■ Robbie Korin ■ Pam Koterba ■ Janet Kuchenbrod ■ Phillip Lieske ■ Satinee Lightbourne ■ Fred Longhart ■ Karen Longhart ■ Johnny W. Lott ■ Franklin Lund ■ Mike Lundin ■ Joy Lustgraaf ■ Mark Lutz ■ Peggy Lynn ■ Douglas Mack ■ Pat Mauch ■ Patty Mazurek ■ Anne Merrifield ■ Mary Ann Miller ■ Susan Moore ■ Mindy Obert ■ Laurie Paladichuk ■ Roger Patterson ■ Arthur Perleberg ■ Margaret Plouvier ■ Dean Preble ■ Darlene Pugh ■ Peter Rasmussen ■ Howard Reinhardt ■ Kate Riley ■ Todd Robbins ■ Dick Sander ■ Lisa Schlange ■ Verne Schlepp ■ Lisa Scott ■ Dick Seitz ■ Mike Sinclair ■ Ed Sisolak ■ Tim Skinner ■ David Stabio ■ Paul Swenson ■ Thomas Teegarden ■ David Thiel ■ Otis Thompson ■ Michael Trudnowski ■ Deanna Turley ■ Karen Umbaugh ■ Sharon Walen ■ Anne Watkins ■ Marcia Weinhold ■ Daniel West ■ Teri Willard ■ James Williamson ■ Lisa Wood ■ Mike Wood ■ Steve Yockim

SERIES EDITOR

Terry A. Souhrada

TECHNICAL EDITOR

Peter W. Fong

This material is based upon work supported by the National Science Foundation under Cooperative Agreement No. OSR 9150055. Any opinions, findings, conclusions or recommendations expressed in this material are those of the author(s) and do not necessarily reflect the views of the National Science Foundation.

Cover Credits:
   © JupiterImages Corporation: top left skier and top right snowflake
   © Corbis: bottom left skiers and bottom right snow

ISBN 0-7575-2029-4

Printed in the United States of America.

1 2 3 4 5 6 7 8 9 10   10 09 08 07 06

Contents

Preface

In recent years, many voices have called for the reform of mathematics education. The concerns cited include international test scores in mathematics, the retention of students in mathematical and scientific career paths, and the production of mathematically literate adults. Attempts to identify the root causes of these concerns have targeted not only the methods used to instruct and assess students, but also the nature of the mathematics that students learn and the manner in which they are expected to learn.

The Systemic Initiative for Montana Mathematics and Science (SIMMS) began as a five-year, cooperative enterprise of the state of Montana and the National Science Foundation. Funded through the Montana Council of Teachers of Mathematics, and led by mathematics and science teachers from around the state, SIMMS had an ambitious list of objectives, including redesigning the 9–12 mathematics curriculum using an integrated, interdisciplinary approach for *all* students; incorporating the use of technology in all facets and at all levels of mathematics and science; and developing and publishing curriculum and assessment materials for grades 9–16.

With additional funding from the National Science Foundation and the support of teachers, students, and the Kendall/Hunt Publishing Company, these curricular objectives have continued for more than a decade.

What Is Integrated Mathematics?

An integrated mathematics program "consists of topics chosen from a wide variety of mathematical fields . . . . [It] emphasizes the relationships among topics within mathematics as well as between mathematics and other disciplines" (Beal, et al., 1992; Lott and Reeves, 1991).

In its 2000 document, *Principles and Standards for School Mathematics,* the National Council of Teachers of Mathematics addressed curricular reform with these recommendations:

> Mathematics comprises different topical strands, such as algebra and geometry, but the strands are highly interconnected. The interconnection should be displayed prominently in the curriculum and in instructional materials and lessons. A coherent curriculum effectively organizes and integrates important mathematical ideas so that students can see how the ideas build on, or connect with, other ideas, thus enabling them to develop new understandings and skills . . . .
>
> Big ideas encountered in a variety of contexts should be established carefully, with important elements such as terminology, definitions, notation, concepts, and skills emerging in the process . . . .
>
> In addition, the curriculum should offer experiences that allow students to see that mathematics has powerful uses in modeling and predicting real-world phenomena. (pp. 15–16)

SIMMS *Integrated Mathematics* offers this coherent curriculum, built around big ideas in a variety of contexts, while providing experiences that allow students to model and predict phenomena.

In order to create innovative and accessible materials, a diverse group of more than 80 secondary teachers of mathematics and science, mathematicians, and mathematics educators contributed their skills as writers and reviewers. The SIMMS *Integrated Mathematics* curriculum is expressly designed for use in heterogeneous classrooms, and seeks to encourage the participation of underrepresented groups in mathematics.

Each academic year of SIMMS *Integrated Mathematics* includes algebra, geometry, probability, statistics, and discrete mathematics. Essential mathematical concepts are explored more than once, each time at a slightly higher level—in different settings and in different years—to help students build both vital connections and critical competencies. Students investigate mathematics in the context of crucial social and environmental issues—such as population growth, oil spills, and earthquake damage—along with other real-world topics including map-making, business inventory, digital animation, and automobile insurance.

Technology in the Classroom

SIMMS *Integrated Mathematics* focuses on the future needs of mathematically literate adults. Because of this commitment, the use of technology is a fundamental part of curriculum.

In *Principles and Standards for School Mathematics,* the Council noted that "Technology is essential in teaching and learning mathematics; it influences the mathematics that is taught and enhances students' learning" (p. 24). Nearly all current research on the appropriate use of technology in the classroom indicates that students using technology become better problem solvers, without suffering a decline in their more traditional skills.

SIMMS *Integrated Mathematics* works best when students have access to a word processor, spreadsheet, graphing utility, geometry utility, statistics package, and computer algebra system. (Many reasonably priced graphing calculators now include all of these features, with the exception of word processing.)

Student Performance

During the development of SIMMS *Integrated Mathematics,* researchers conducted periodic assessments of student performances in pilot schools. After the publication of the first edition, a four-year longitudinal case study was completed. In these studies, two basic measures—a selection of open-ended mathematical tasks and the PSAT—were administered to experimental and control populations.

On the test of open-ended tasks, technology was made available to both groups. In a comparative analysis, SIMMS *Integrated Mathematics* students were more likely to provide justification for their solutions and made more and better use of graphs, charts, and diagrams. They also demonstrated a greater variety of problem-solving strategies and were more willing to attempt difficult problems.

For the PSAT, technology was not allowed for either group. Student mathematics scores indicated no significant differences in achievement. In other words, although SIMMS *Integrated Mathematics* students were denied access to the technology typically available for classroom work, their performance on the PSAT matched that of their peers.

A summary of the pilot study, as well as a larger National Science Foundation study involving students in selected U.S. cities, is now in print (Senk and Thompson, 2003).

A Look to the Future

Once again in *Principles and Standards for School Mathematics,* the Council argues that:

> When students can connect mathematical ideas, their understanding is deeper and more lasting. They can see mathematical connections in the rich interplay among mathematical topics, in contexts that relate mathematics to other subjects, and in their own interests and experience. Through instruction that emphasizes the interrelatedness of mathematical ideas, students not only learn mathematics, they also learn about the utility of mathematics. (p. 64)

This deep and lasting understanding is what all teachers desire for their students. The third edition of SIMMS *Integrated Mathematics* builds on reform middle-school curricula, and is designed to replace all currently offered secondary mathematics courses, with the possible exception of Advanced Placement Calculus.

—Johnny W. Lott, former co-director of The SIMMS Project and past
president of the National Council of Teachers of Mathematics

References

Beal, J., D. Dolan, J. Lott and J. Smith. *Integrated Mathematics: Definitions, Issues, and Implications; Report and Executive Summary*. ERIC Clearinghouse for Science, Mathematics, and Environmental Education. The Ohio State University, Columbus, OH: ED 34701, January 1990, 115 pp.

Lott, J., and A. Reeves. "The Integrated Mathematics Project." *Mathematics Teacher* 84 (April 1991): 334–35.

National Council of Teachers of Mathematics. *Curriculum and Evaluation Standards for School Mathematics*. Reston, VA; NCTM, 1989.

———. *Principles and Standards for School Mathematics*. Reston, VA: NCTM, 2000.

Senk, S., and D. Thompson (eds.). *Standards-Based School Mathematics Curricula: What Are They? What Do Students Learn?* Mahwah, NJ: Lawrence Erlbaum Associates, 2003.

The SIMMS Project. *Monograph I: Philosophies*. Missoula, MT: The Montana Council of Teachers of Mathematics, 1993.

Souhrada, T. "Secondary school mathematics in transition: A comparative study of mathematics curricula and student results." *Dissertation Abstracts International* 62.4 (October 2001): 1355A.

Introduction

When the first edition of SIMMS *Integrated Mathematics: A Modeling Approach Using Technology* was published more than a decade ago, it provided an innovative approach to teaching and learning high school mathematics. The third edition maintains this standard while representing a significant revision of previous versions.

SIMMS *Integrated Mathematics* now includes four levels, offering a comprehensive alternative to traditional secondary mathematics courses. Each year-long level contains 15 modules. All modules are divided into activities, typically including an exploration, a discussion, warm-up problems, a set of homework assignments, and a research project.

Assessment materials—including alternative assessments that emphasize writing and logical argument—are an integral part of the curriculum. Each activity includes one or more suggested assessment items, identified in the Teacher Edition, while each module closes with an open-ended summary assessment. A more traditional assessment, for use at the teacher's discretion, appears in the Teacher Resources, along with short quizzes and review problems, as well as blackline masters for classroom handouts.

Level 1: A First-Year Course

Level 1 concentrates on the knowledge and understanding that students need to become mathematically literate citizens, while providing the necessary foundation for those who wish to pursue careers involving mathematics and science. Each module presents the relevant mathematics in an applied context. These contexts include human nutrition, the properties of reflected light, population growth, structural physiology, and topographic maps, among others. Mathematical content includes data collection, presentation and interpretation; linear, quadratic, and exponential functions; probability; trigonometric ratios; and an introduction to graph theory.

Level 2: A Second-Year Course

Level 2 continues to build on the mathematics that students need to become mathematically literate citizens. While retaining an emphasis on the presentation and interpretation of data, Level 2 also introduces such topics as matrix operations, elementary polynomials, combinatorics, statistics, and fair division. Students investigate traditional geometry, including proof, within the context of home building. They explore transformational geometry through cartoon animation. Other contexts include genetics, business inventory, radioactive decay, and carnival games.

Level 3: A Third-Year Course

This level continues to build mathematical understanding and logical reasoning, based on the first two years of work. Students expand their knowledge of data analysis, algebraic functions, geometric proof, probability, and graph theory. Contexts include map coloring, logarithmic scales, navigation, and quality control, among others. Specific mathematical topics include trigonometric functions, the normal curve, spherical geometry, parametric equations, basic topology, and an introduction to limits.

Level 4: A Fourth-Year Course

For some students, this course represents the end of a high-school mathematical career. For others, this course represents a stepping-stone to advanced placement courses. Because of these different needs, this course is both mathematically and contextually challenging and engaging. Students explore complex numbers, conic sections, hypothesis testing, finite geometry, mathematical induction, and derivatives. Applied contexts include cartography, automobile insurance, and compound interest, among others.

The Student Edition

The third edition of SIMMS *Integrated Mathematics* contains all of the basic elements found in previous editions, along with some new features. For example, each activity now offers an additional problem set, designed to hone mathematical skills before students encounter more complicated assignments. Several individual modules were substantially revised, presenting fresh approaches to geometric proof, hypothesis testing, compositions of functions, and other topics.

Explorations

Nearly all activities contain at least one exploration, giving students a hands-on opportunity to develop their own understandings of mathematical concepts. To facilitate the exchange of ideas and strategies, explorations are designed for work in a variety of instructional formats, including small groups.

Discussions

Discussions give students a structured forum for sharing insights and communicating mathematical ideas, and give teachers a setting for assessing comprehension and reinforcing essential concepts.

Mathematics Notes

Mathematics Notes formally summarize the mathematics students are expected to understand and apply. Each typically includes a definition or explanation, a description of the appropriate notation, and an example or graph.

Warm-Ups

These problem sets—a new feature in the third edition—are designed to review essential mathematical skills and vocabulary before students proceed to the Assignment. Warm-up problems typically do not invoke a real-world context.

Assignments

As in previous editions, most assignment problems present mathematics in applied contexts. Some extend previously learned concepts to other mathematical settings. Students are encouraged to justify their solutions and describe their reasoning.

Research Projects

Many modules contain a Research Project, offering students an opportunity for further study of contemporary or historical mathematics.

Summary Assessment

Summary Assessments typically ask students to demonstrate their problem-solving skills in the same context used in the module. They are often project-oriented and suitable for collaborative work.

Module Summary

At the end of every module, a Module Summary repeats the important mathematics from each activity.

Glossary

The Glossary offers an alphabetical list of definitions for all of the terms and concepts in an entire level (also included in the Teacher Edition).

Selected References

This list provides a helpful compilation of print and other resources for the entire level (also included in the Teacher Edition).

The Teacher Edition

To facilitate the implementation of the curriculum, the Teacher Edition contains the following features, several of which have been newly incorporated in this revision.

Overview/Objectives/Prerequisites

Each module begins with a brief overview of its contents, outlined activity by activity. This overview is followed by a list of teaching objectives, each identified by the activity number (in parentheses), and a list of prerequisite skills and knowledge.

Planning Guide

The planning guide displays the materials and technology needed for the entire module in a single table. It also provides an estimated timeline for the module, assuming approximately 50-minute class periods.

For added convenience, necessary materials and technology also are listed at the beginning of each activity.

Student Outcomes

This new feature appears near the beginning of each activity. It briefly describes the mathematics that students should gain from each exploration and discussion.

Warm-Ups, Assignments, and Assessment Items

Warm-Ups and Assignments appear at the end of each activity. Warm-Ups allow students to practice individual mathematical skills before tackling more complicated problems or real-world applications.

Each Assignment is separated into two sections. The problems in the first section cover all the essential mathematics in the activity. The second section provides optional problems—often presented in different contexts—for additional homework or enrichment.

Suggested assessment items are identified in the Teacher Edition by an asterisk preceding the problem number. These items give teachers an opportunity to conduct formative assessments during each activity.

Sample Responses

Appropriate responses are given for each Exploration, Discussion, Warm-Up, Assignment, and assessment item. When correct answers may vary, sample responses offer one or more reasonable solutions with corresponding justifications.

Teacher Notes

Teacher Notes offer practical teaching tips from experienced teachers. These notes appear throughout the Teacher Edition, providing advice on classroom management, alternate materials, possible extensions, calculator programs, and other topics.

Teacher Resources

A Teacher Resources CD provides more tools and flexibility for classroom implementation, including Flashbacks, Periodic Assessments, Module Assessments, and blackline masters. When these materials are available, the Teacher Edition displays the following icon.

Flashbacks

These brief problem sets provide a review of the prerequisite skills for each activity.

Periodic Assessments

To assist in ongoing, formative assessment, these short quizzes cover the mathematical content in two or three activities.

Module Assessment

This typically provides a more traditional alternative to the Summary Assessment in the Student Edition. Like Flashbacks and Periodic Assessments, the Module Assessment is designed for use at the teacher's discretion.

Templates

Templates are provided for use as blackline masters for classroom handouts or visual aids. When required, the Teacher Edition includes instructions for their distribution during specific explorations or assignments.

Professional Development

SIMMS Integrated Mathematics was written, reviewed, and piloted by a diverse group of secondary teachers. Many of these teachers are knowledgeable and experienced consultants, available to help schools plan appropriate inservice programs. Please contact Kendall/Hunt Publishing Company for more information.

Reflect on This

1

module

Overview

In this module, students investigate reflections in a plane using mirrors (or other reflective materials) and a geometry utility.

Introduction: Students become familiar with the reflections created by two hinged mirrors (a kaleidoscope).

Activity 1:   Students develop the relationship between the number of sides of a regular polygon and the measure of its central angle.

Activity 2:   Students discover that light rays reflecting off a flat surface form congruent incoming and outgoing angles.

Activity 3:   Students find the images of reflections in a line and describe them using a coordinate grid. They use a geometry utility to model reflections, observe patterns, and make conjectures. Students are introduced to the terms *image* and *preimage* as they relate to transformational geometry. They also are introduced to the difference between conjectures and theorems.

Activity 4:   Students investigate the properties associated with double reflections. (This activity can be omitted without significant loss of mathematical content.)

Objectives

In this module, students will:

* identify regular polygons and central angles (1)
* use the relationship between the number of sides of a regular polygon and the measure of its central angles (1)
* use congruent, complementary, and supplementary angle relationships to make conjectures (1, 2)
* learn and use the relationship between the incoming and outgoing angles in the reflection of a light ray (2, 3)
* use congruent segments and the shortest distance between two points to make conjectures about the paths traveled by light rays (3)
* model reflections in a line (3)
* examine the perpendicular bisector relationships created by reflections (3)
* explore the relationship between the coordinates of a point and the coordinates of its image under a reflection in the x- or y-axis (3)
* be introduced to the relationship between theorems and conjectures (3)
* use mathematical terms and notation to describe reflections and double reflections (3, 4)
* use correct notation for representing reflected points (3, 4)
* identify the images of points reflected in both the x- and y-axes (4).

Prerequisites

For this module, students should know:

* the geometric notation for points, segments, lines, and angles
* how to measure and draw angles with a protractor

* the names of common polygons
* the definition of an isosceles triangle
* the sum of the measures of the interior angles of a triangle (180°)
* the concepts of distance, congruence, collinearity, perpendicularity, and parallelism
* how to plot points on a coordinate plane
* how to write an algebraic expression to generalize a pattern.

 Flashbacks, for use at your discretion, appear in the Teacher Resources for this module. These brief problem sets provide a review of some prerequisite skills for each activity.

Planning Guide

Activity	Materials	Technology	Time Line
Introduction	■ mirrors ■ plain white paper ■ colored paper or commercial confetti ■ tape ■ scissors	■ none	1 day
Activity 1	■ straightedge ■ protractor ■ mirrors ■ plain white paper ■ colored paper or commercial confetti ■ tape	■ none	1 day
Activity 2	■ straightedge ■ protractor ■ mirrors ■ fiberboard blocks ■ pushpins ■ graph paper ■ rubber bands	■ none	2 days
Activity 3	■ straightedge ■ tinted plastic reflectors (such as MIRAs™ or Reflectas™) ■ graph paper	■ geometry utility	3 days
Activity 4	■ straightedge ■ mirrors ■ tape ■ graph paper	■ none	2 days
Assessment Activities	■ none	■ none	3 days **Total: 12 days**

 teacher note

A blackline master for graph paper appears in the Teacher Resources for this module.

Introduction

Students build model kaleidoscopes using hinged mirrors, colored paper, and confetti. This model provides a preview of the types of reflections that students will study throughout the module. **Note:** You also might wish to show students some actual kaleidoscopes.

Materials List

- mirrors (about 10 cm × 12 cm; two per group)
- tape (one roll per group)
- colored paper (several sheets per group) or commercial confetti
- plain white paper (one sheet per group)
- scissors (one pair per group)

Student Outcomes

After completing the following exploration and discussion, students should be able to:

✳ recognize that a relationship exists between the angle formed by the mirrors and the number of reflections.

Exploration

a–d. Students build a model kaleidoscope.

e. As students open and close the mirrors, the number of reflections seen will vary. Students should observe images that consist of one or more isosceles triangles.

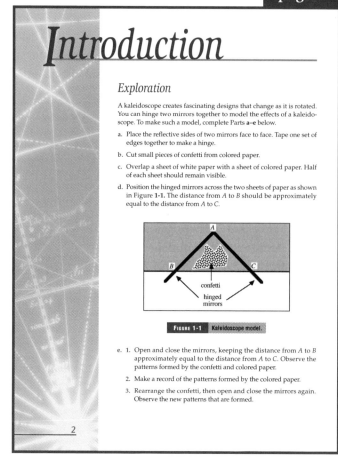

Introduction

Exploration

A kaleidoscope creates fascinating designs that change as it is rotated. You can hinge two mirrors together to model the effects of a kaleidoscope. To make such a model, complete Parts **a–e** below.

a. Place the reflective sides of two mirrors face to face. Tape one set of edges together to make a hinge.

b. Cut small pieces of confetti from colored paper.

c. Overlap a sheet of white paper with a sheet of colored paper. Half of each sheet should remain visible.

d. Position the hinged mirrors across the two sheets of paper as shown in Figure **1-1**. The distance from *A* to *B* should be approximately equal to the distance from *A* to *C*.

FIGURE 1-1   Kaleidoscope model.

e. 1. Open and close the mirrors, keeping the distance from *A* to *B* approximately equal to the distance from *A* to *C*. Observe the patterns formed by the confetti and colored paper.

2. Make a record of the patterns formed by the colored paper.

3. Rearrange the confetti, then open and close the mirrors again. Observe the new patterns that are formed.

Discussion

a. Describe the patterns created by the colored paper in your kaleidoscope.

b. What happened as you opened and closed the hinged mirrors?

c. What is the relationship between the size of the hinge angle and the number of reflections seen?

ACTIVITY
1

Opening and closing hinged mirrors causes multiple reflections. These reflections form patterns and shapes similar to those you created with a model kaleidoscope.

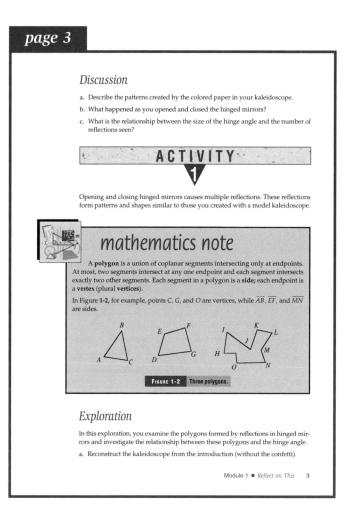

mathematics note

A **polygon** is a union of coplanar segments intersecting only at endpoints. At most, two segments intersect at any one endpoint and each segment intersects exactly two other segments. Each segment in a polygon is a **side**; each endpoint is a **vertex** (plural **vertices**).

In Figure **1-2**, for example, points C, G, and O are vertices, while $\overline{AB}$, $\overline{EF}$, and $\overline{MN}$ are sides.

FIGURE 1-2 Three polygons.

Exploration

In this exploration, you examine the polygons formed by reflections in hinged mirrors and investigate the relationship between these polygons and the hinge angle.

a. Reconstruct the kaleidoscope from the introduction (without the confetti).

Module 1 ■ *Reflect on This*   3

Discussion

a. The patterns consist of one or more isosceles triangles, with each overall pattern forming a regular polygon.

b. As the mirrors are opened and closed, the number of reflections seen changes.

c. As the measure of the hinge angle decreases, the number of reflections seen increases.

ACTIVITY
1

Students use multiple reflections to create regular polygons and determine the relationship between the number of sides in a regular polygon and the measure of its central angles.

Materials List

■ mirrors (about 12 cm × 12 cm; two per group)

■ tape (one roll per group)

■ colored paper (several sheets per group)

■ plain white paper (one sheet per group)

■ protractor (one per group)

■ straightedge (one per group)

Student Outcomes

After completing the following exploration and discussion, students should be able to:

✳ identify regular polygons and central angles

✳ use the relationship between the number of sides of a regular polygon and the measure of its central angles.

Exploration

a–b. Students should discover that a hinge angle of 120° is needed to form a triangle.

teacher note

Students might not obtain the exact measures of the hinge angles given in the Table **1-1** at the bottom of the next page. After students develop the relationship described in Part **d,** they might benefit from a discussion about the difficulty of exactly measuring the hinge angle for a heptagon.

c. See sample Table **1-1** below.

d. Students try to discover a relationship between the number of sides in a polygon and the measure of the hinge angle. All of the following relationships are true:

- (number of sides)(measure of hinge angle) = 360°

- $\dfrac{360°}{\text{number of sides}}$ = measure of hinge angle

- $\dfrac{360°}{\text{measure of hinge angle}}$ = number of sides

Discussion

a. As the measure of the hinge angle becomes smaller, the number of reflections seen increases. Hence, the number of sides seen also increases.

b. The polygons formed by the reflections are always regular polygons because a reflection in a flat mirror preserves all length and angle measures of the original object. In other words, the length of the reflected segment is always the same as the length of the original segment. Likewise, the measure of the reflected angle is always the same as the measure of the original angle. Mirrors that are not flat do not always preserve length and angle measures.

c. 1. The product of the number of sides in the polygon and the measure of its central angle is always 360°.

   2. This relationship may be expressed as follows, where *n* represents the number of sides and *a* represents the measure of the central angle:

   $$n \bullet a = 360° \quad \text{or} \quad \frac{360°}{a} = n \quad \text{or} \quad \frac{360°}{n} = a$$

d. Every regular polygon has the same number of central angles as its number of sides.

b. Begin with the mirrors completely open. Slowly close them until a triangle is formed by the colored paper and its reflections. As shown in Figure 1-3, the mirrors form a hinge angle at the center of the triangle. Draw this angle and determine its measure.

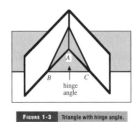

FIGURE 1-3 Triangle with hinge angle.

c. Continue to close the mirrors, keeping the distance from *A* to *B* equal to the distance from *A* to *C*. Other polygons will appear, such as a quadrilateral, a pentagon, and a hexagon. Record the measure of the hinge angle for each polygon that appears, up to a decagon, in Table 1-1.

TABLE 1-1 ■ Polygon Information

Polygon	No. of Sides	Measure of Hinge Angle
triangle	3	120°
quadrilateral		
pentagon		
hexagon		
heptagon		$51\frac{3}{7}°$
octagon		
nonagon		
decagon	10	

d. Use the patterns you observe in the table to describe a relationship between the number of sides of a polygon and the measure of the hinge angle.

Discussion

a. What appears to occur as the measure of the hinge angle becomes smaller?

4   Module 1 ■ *Reflect on This*

e. The congruent isosceles triangles in Figure **1-5** are △*AOB*, △*AOC*, and △*BOC*.

f. The vertex angle of any one of the isosceles triangles is congruent to a central angle of the polygon.

g. The measure of each base angle of the isosceles triangles is equal to one-half the measure of an interior angle of the polygon.

TABLE 1-1 ■ Polygon Information		
Polygon	**No. of Sides**	**Measure of Hinge Angle**
triangle	3	120°
quadrilateral	4	90°
pentagon	5	72°
hexagon	6	60°
heptagon	7	$51\frac{3}{7}°$
octagon	8	45°
nonagon	9	40°
decagon	10	36°

mathematics note

A polygon is **equiangular** if its interior angles are congruent. A polygon is **equilateral** if its sides are congruent. A polygon is **regular** if its sides are congruent and its interior angles are congruent.

For example, Figure 1-4 shows two regular polygons, a square and an equilateral triangle.

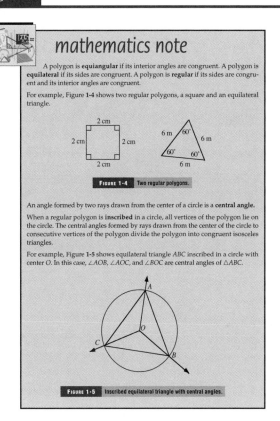

FIGURE 1-4   Two regular polygons.

An angle formed by two rays drawn from the center of a circle is a **central angle.**

When a regular polygon is **inscribed** in a circle, all vertices of the polygon lie on the circle. The central angles formed by rays drawn from the center of the circle to consecutive vertices of the polygon divide the polygon into congruent isosceles triangles.

For example, Figure 1-5 shows equilateral triangle *ABC* inscribed in a circle with center *O*. In this case, $\angle AOB$, $\angle AOC$, and $\angle BOC$ are central angles of $\triangle ABC$.

FIGURE 1-5   Inscribed equilateral triangle with central angles.

b. Are the polygons formed by the reflections in the exploration always regular polygons? Why or why not?

c. 1. What relationship exists between the number of sides of a regular polygon and the measure of its central angle?

   2. Express this relationship as an algebraic formula.

d. How many central angles are there in any regular polygon?

e. Identify the congruent isosceles triangles in Figure 1-5.

f. What is the relationship between the vertex angles of the isosceles triangles and the central angles of the polygon?

g. What is the relationship between the base angles of the isosceles triangles and the interior angles of the polygon?

Warm-Up

1. Determine the measure of the central angle for a regular polygon with:

   a. 4 sides

   b. 6 sides

   c. 15 sides

2. Describe the number of sides in a regular polygon with a central angle measure of:

   a. 45°

   b. 24°

   c. $32\frac{8}{11}°$

Assignment

1.1 a. Describe the measure of the central angle for a regular polygon with *n* sides.

   b. Describe the number of sides in a regular polygon with a central angle measure of 0°.

1.2 Explain how to draw each of the following figures using only a ruler and two hinged mirrors.

   a. two perpendicular lines

   b. a 120° angle

   c. a regular hexagon with sides 5 cm long

Warm-Up

1. a. 90°
   b. 60°
   c. 24°

2. a. 8 sides
   b. 15 sides
   c. 11 sides

teacher note

To complete this assignment, students must recognize that the sum of the interior angles of a triangle is 180°.

In Problem **1.7,** students identify a method for determining the area of a regular polygon. A formula for this area will be developed in the Level 1 module, "A New Look at Boxing."

Assignment

Problems suitable for use as assessment items are identified by an asterisk (*).

* **1.1 a.** $360°/n$

   b. If the measure of the central angle is 0°, a polygon is not formed. (This is the limiting case; the limit is a circle, not a polygon.)

1.2 Answers may vary. Some sample responses are given below.

   a. Reflect a point in a mirror. Draw one line along one mirror and another line that seems to connect the point and its reflection.

   b. Open the hinged mirrors until a triangle appears (as in Part **b** of the exploration). Because the hinge angle formed has a measure of 120°, tracing the angle formed by the two mirrors gives the desired angle.

   c. Draw a segment 5 cm long. Open the hinged mirrors until the segment is reflected into a regular hexagon. Sketch the isosceles triangle that is formed by the central angle and the segment. Keeping the hinge angle constant and the vertex of the hinge angle on the vertex of the isosceles triangle, rotate the mirrors left (or right) until only one mirror is on a side of the isosceles triangle. Sketch the central angle that is formed by the mirrors. Connect the endpoints of the angle to form the second side of the hexagon. Continue this process until all six sides have been sketched.

* **1.3** **a.** 60°; 60°; 120°; 120°

   b. Sample response: This is a quadrilateral and a trapezoid. It is not regular because the angle measures are not all the same. **Note:** Some students may recognize the shape as an isosceles trapezoid.

   c. Sample response: The central angle would decrease from 60° to 45° because the table would have 8 sides instead of 6. The angles on the edge piece would be 67.5°, 67.5°, 132.5°, and 132.5°.

✵ ✵ ✵ ✵ ✵

1.4 **a.** 72°

   b. 45°

   c. 36°

   d. 360°/n

1.5 **a.** 54°

   b. 67.5°

   c. 72°

   d. $\dfrac{180° - (360°/n)}{2}$

1.6 **a.** **1.** 108°

   2. 135°

   3. 144°

   4. $180° - \dfrac{360°}{n}$

   b. **1.** 540°

   2. 1080°

   3. 1440°

   4. $180°(n) - 360°$ or $180°(n - 2)$

1.7 **a.** The area of a regular pentagon is 5 times the area of one of the congruent isosceles triangles.

   b. The area of a regular octagon is 8 times the area of one of the congruent isosceles triangles.

   c. The area of a regular decagon is 10 times the area of one of the congruent isosceles triangles.

   d. The area of a regular n-gon is n times the area of one of the congruent isosceles triangles.

Students discover that the paths of light rays reflecting off a surface form congruent angles. The conventions introduced here for naming these angles are used for the remainder of the module. Students also discuss experimental error and its implications when making conclusions.

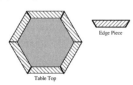

1.3 A carpenter wishes to make a tabletop in the shape of a regular hexagon. The edge of the table consists of six pieces like those shown below. The two longest sides of each edge piece are parallel to each other.

Edge Piece

Table Top

   a. Determine the measure of each interior angle in an edge piece.

   b. Identify the type of polygon represented by an edge piece. Is it a regular polygon? Explain your response.

   c. If the tabletop was a regular octagon, how would the measures of the angles in the edge pieces change? Explain your response.

✵ ✵ ✵ ✵ ✵

1.4 Determine the measure of a central angle for each of the following:

   a. a regular pentagon   **b.** a regular octagon

   c. a regular decagon   **d.** a regular n-gon

1.5 The following diagram shows square *ABCD* inscribed in a circle with center *O*. In this case, the measure of central angle *AOB* is 90°, while the measure of angle *OAB* is 45°.

What is the measure of angle *OAB* if the inscribed polygon is:

   a. a regular pentagon?   **b.** a regular octagon?

   c. a regular decagon?   **d.** a regular n-gon?

1.6 **a.** Find the measure of the interior angles in each of the following:

   1. a regular pentagon   **2.** a regular octagon

   3. a regular decagon   **4.** a regular n-gon

   b. Determine the sum of the measures of the interior angles for each regular polygon in Part **a.**

1.7 As mentioned in the mathematics note, the central angles of a regular polygon divide the polygon into congruent isosceles triangles. Describe how you could use the area of these triangles to find the area of each of the following:

   a. a regular pentagon   **b.** a regular octagon

   c. a regular decagon   **d.** a regular n-gon

ACTIVITY 2

When you look into your model kaleidoscope, the images you see are caused by light rays reflecting from the confetti, striking the hinged mirrors, then bouncing off the mirrors into your eyes. As you change the positions of the mirrors, the paths of the light rays also change. In this activity, you explore the paths that light rays follow in a reflection.

Exploration

   a. Draw an *x*-axis and a *y*-axis on a sheet of graph paper with the origin (0,0) near the center of the sheet. Label the origin as point *A* and a point on the positive *x*-axis as point *B*.

   b. As shown in Figure **1-6**, place a mirror tightly against one edge of a block of fiberboard and perpendicular to the broad face of the block.

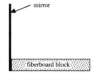

mirror

fiberboard block

FIGURE 1-6 Light-ray experiment (side view).

---

c. Carefully fold the graph paper along the x-axis. Place the folded sheet on top of the fiberboard block with the x-axis tightly against the mirror, as shown in Figure **1-7**.

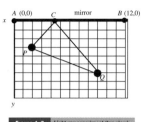

FIGURE 1-7 Light-ray experiment (top view).

d. Choose two points that fit the description below.

1. The x-coordinates are at least 3 units apart.

2. The y-coordinates are different and between –3 and –7.

e. 1. Label the point with the lesser x-coordinate as P and the other point as Q.

2. Place one pushpin through P and another through Q.

3. Sight through P toward the mirror with one eye closed. Looking at the reflection of Q, move your head until P aligns with the image of Q.

4. Mark a point C on the x-axis where P, C, and the reflection of Q are collinear (on the same line).

f. Place a rubber band around the pushpins. Using the point of a pencil, pull the side of the rubber band closer to the mirror until the pencil is at C. Check the position of C again to make sure P, C, and the reflection of Q are collinear. The side of the rubber band you stretched shows the path that light rays follow from Q to the mirror to P.

g. 1. Remove your graph paper from the fiberboard block and unfold it. Draw $\overline{PC}$ and $\overline{CQ}$. These segments show the path of light as it travels from the pushpin at Q to your eye at P by reflecting off the mirror.

2. Measure $\angle QCB$ and $\angle PCA$. Record these angle measures. **Note:** Save your graph paper for use in the assignment and in Activity **3**.

Module 1 ■ *Reflect on This*   9

Student Outcomes

After completing the following exploration and discussion, students should be able to:

✳ use congruent, complementary, and supplementary angle relationships to make conjectures

✳ use the relationship between the incoming and outgoing angles in the reflection of a light ray.

Exploration

a–c. Students draw axes and label points, and position the graph paper as indicated in Figure **1-7**.

d–e. Students choose points P and Q accordingly, label them, find the reflection of point P in the mirror, and determine the placement of point C.

f. Students use a rubber band to check the placement of point C.

g. Students draw the path of light from Q to the mirror to P, then measure the incoming and outgoing angles. Students should discover that these angles are congruent. **Note:** Remind students to save a copy of the graph for use in the assignment and in Activity **3**.

teacher note

A brief assessment of the mathematical content in Activities **1** and **2**, for use at your discretion, appears in the Teacher Resources for this module.

teacher note

You might wish to ask students to collect the class data for the angle measures in Part **g** and organize them in a table for the discussion.

Materials List

■ graph paper (one sheet per group; a blackline master appears in the Teacher Resources for this module)

■ half-inch fiberboard blocks (about 12 cm × 12 cm; one per group)

■ pushpins (two per group)

■ rubber bands (one per group)

■ flat mirrors (about 10 cm × 12 cm; one per group)

■ protractors (one per group)

■ straightedge (one per group)

Discussion

a. Because students look from point *P* to the mirror, the light rays travel from *Q* to the mirror, then from the mirror to the eye. Therefore, ∠*QCB* is the incoming angle, while ∠*PCA* is the outgoing angle.

b. Student data should suggest that the measures of the incoming and outgoing angles are congruent.

c. Due to inaccuracies in measurement, some pairs of angle measures might appear to contradict the conjecture.

d. Sample response: Errors might occur while aligning the mirror on the *x*-axis, locating the position of point *C*, and measuring the angles with a protractor. Such errors could make the relationship between the angle measures harder to discover.

e. Answers will vary. Some students may suggest using technology to test their conjecture.

f. The incoming angle is the complement of both the angle of incidence and the angle of reflection. The same is true of the outgoing angle.

Warm-Up

1. **a.** Complementary. The sum is 90°.
  b. Neither. The sum is 190°.
  c. Supplementary. The sum is 180°.
  d. Neither. The terms *supplementary* and *complementary* apply only to pairs of angles.

2. **a.** supplement = 140°; complement = 50°
  b. supplement = $(180 - m)°$; complement = $(90 - m)°$

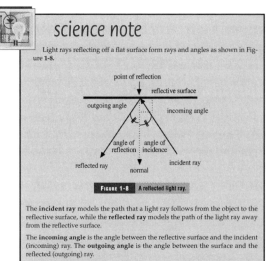

science note

Light rays reflecting off a flat surface form rays and angles as shown in Figure 1-8.

FIGURE 1-8   A reflected light ray.

The **incident ray** models the path that a light ray follows from the object to the reflective surface, while the **reflected ray** models the path of the light ray away from the reflective surface.

The **incoming angle** is the angle between the reflective surface and the incident (incoming) ray. The **outgoing angle** is the angle between the surface and the reflected (outgoing) ray.

The **normal** of the reflecting surface is the perpendicular line to the surface at the **point of reflection**. The **angle of incidence** is the angle formed by the normal and the incident ray, while the **angle of reflection** is the angle formed by the normal and the reflected ray.

Discussion

a. Using terms from the Science Note, describe the path traveled by a light ray that passes through *Q* and strikes the mirror before reaching your eye.

b. Make a conjecture about the relationship between the measures of the incoming angle and the outgoing angle.

c. Compare the angle measures you recorded with others in your group. Do any of these measurements contradict your conjecture? If so, do you still believe that your conjecture is correct? Explain your response.

---

d. Describe several ways in which an error in measurement could occur in the exploration. How might these errors affect your conclusions?

e. Suggest another method for confirming your conjecture in Part **c.**

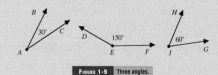

mathematics note

If the sum of the measures of two angles is 90°, then the two angles are **complementary**. In Figure **1-9**, for example, ∠*BAC* and ∠*HIG* are complementary angles because 30° + 60° = 90°.

FIGURE 1-9   Three angles.

If the sum of the measures of two angles is 180°, then the two angles are **supplementary**. In Figure **1-9**, ∠*BAC* and ∠*DEF* are supplementary angles because 30° + 150° = 180°.

f. Identify the pairs of angles in Figure **1-8** that are complementary.

Warm-Up

1. Identify each set of angle measures as supplementary, complementary, or neither. Justify your answers.
  a. 42°, 48°
  b. 63°, 127°
  c. 36°, 144°
  d. 120°, 40°, 20°

2. Determine the supplement and complement of each angle measure below:
  a. 40°
  b. $m°$, where $m < 90$

Assignment

2.1 Use your graph from the exploration to complete Parts **a–c** below.

  a. 1. Draw and label a normal on the graph at the point where the light rays were reflected.

    2. Measure and label the angle of incidence and the angle of reflection.

  b. Use the graph to make a conjecture about the relationship between each of the following pairs of angles:

    1. the angle of incidence and the angle of reflection

    2. the incoming angle and the angle of incidence

    3. the outgoing angle and the angle of reflection.

  c. Write an argument to convince a classmate that your conjectures are correct.

2.2 **a.** Consider a light ray bouncing off a mirror. Draw and label the normal to the surface at the point of reflection.

  b. Use a protractor to draw a light ray bouncing off the mirror with an angle of incidence of 55°.

  c. Label all angles and give their measures.

2.3 **a.** Prepare a labeled diagram that shows what happens when a ray of sunlight reflects off the surface of a watch.

  b. Write a summary of the mathematical ideas represented in the diagram.

          * * * * *

2.4 Using mathematical terms, describe what happens when a driver adjusts the side mirror on a car.

2.5 Reflections occur not only in mirrors, but also in other situations. In the game of pool, players use a cue stick to strike a white ball (the cue ball). When a player hits the cue ball correctly, it strikes one of the other balls and knocks it into one of six holes, or pockets, on the table. In a bank shot, a ball bounces off a side rail before falling into a pocket. The path of a ball bouncing off a side rail is like the path of light reflecting off a mirror.

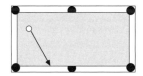

12   Module 1 ■ *Reflect on This*

teacher note

Students must complete Problem **2.1** before continuing on in this assignment. For Problem **2.1c,** you might wish to provide examples of acceptable arguments.

Assignment

Problems suitable for use as assessment items are identified by an asterisk (*).

2.1 a. Sample response:

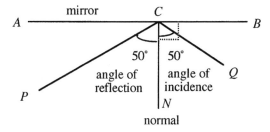

  b. 1. The angle of incidence is congruent to the angle of reflection.

    2. The incoming angle and angle of incidence are complementary.

    3. The outgoing angle and angle of reflection are complementary.

  c. Because the normal is perpendicular to the mirror, the sum of the measures of the incoming angle, $\angle BCQ$, and the angle of incidence, $\angle QCN$, is 90°, illustrative that the two angles are complementary. Likewise, the sum of the measures of the outgoing angle, $\angle ACP$, and the angle of reflection, $\angle PCN$, is 90°, therefore these two angles are complementary.

    Because $m\angle BCQ + m\angle QCN = 90°$ and $m\angle BCQ = m\angle ACP$, then $m\angle ACP + m\angle QCN = 90°$. Also, because $m\angle ACP + m\angle PCN = 90°$, then $m\angle QCN = m\angle PCN$, showing that the angle of incidence is congruent to the angle of reflection.

* 2.2 a–c. Sample response:

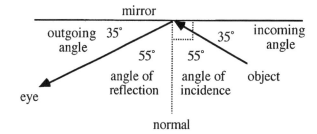

* 2.3 a. Student diagrams should resemble the sample given in Problem **2.2**.

  b. Sample response: When a ray of sunlight hits the watch, it reflects off the watch crystal. The angle at which the ray hits the watch (incoming angle) is congruent to the angle at which the ray reflects off the watch (outgoing angle). The angle of incidence is congruent to the angle of reflection. The incoming angle and angle of incidence are complementary, as are the outgoing angle and angle of reflection.

          * * * * *

2.4 Sample response: As the driver adjusts the mirror, the incoming and outgoing angles for light rays change. This changes the area to the side or behind the car that the driver can see.

2.5 Sample response: When the ball hits the side rail, it will bounce off with an outgoing angle congruent to its incoming angle. This path will not put the ball in the upper right corner pocket, as shown in the diagram below.

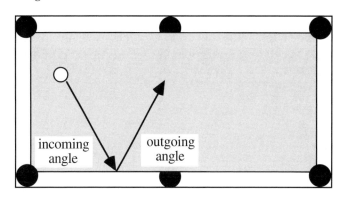

2.6 **a–b.** Sample response:

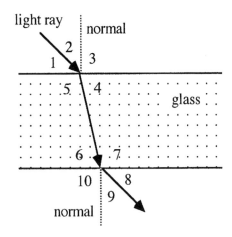

c. If the angles are numbered as shown in the diagram above ∠1 ≅ ∠8, ∠2 ≅ ∠9, ∠4 ≅ ∠6, ∠5 ≅ ∠7, and ∠3 ≅ ∠10.

Research Project

1. The length of the smallest mirror needed depends on the heights of the tallest and shortest members of the family. The tallest person must be able to see the reflection of the top of her head; therefore the top of the mirror must be placed at this point of reflection, as shown in the following diagram. Likewise, because the shortest person must be able to see the reflection of his feet, the bottom of the mirror must be placed at this point of reflection. The mirror length can be determined by finding the distance between these two points of reflection.

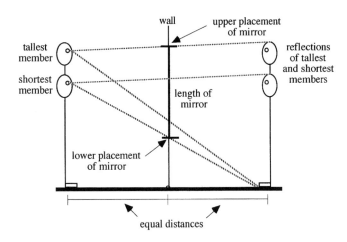

2. Student reports should include the following information.
   a. A periscope is an apparatus with a tube and mirrors.

Suppose a pool ball is hit along the path shown in the diagram. Will the ball fall into the upper right corner pocket after a single bounce off the side rail? Explain your response.

2.6 Light rays passing through glass are bent towards the normal. This bending of light rays is called **refraction**. For example, a stick in water appears bent because of refraction. The light ray enters and exits the glass as shown below.

light ray

glass

a. Copy the diagram above and draw the path of light from the entry point to the exit point.

b. Draw and label the normals at the entry and exit points.

c. In your drawing from Parts **a** and **b**, identify and label all pairs of angles that appear to be congruent.

Research Project

1. Describe how to determine the length of the smallest mirror that would allow every member of your family to see a complete reflection from head to toe. Include a diagram with your report.

2. Write a report about periscopes that answers the following questions.
   a. What is a periscope?
   b. In what types of situations are periscopes useful?
   c. How does a periscope work? (Include a diagram in your report.)
   d. How can you make a simple periscope using a tube and two mirrors? (Include a model with your report.)

b. Periscopes are used to see an otherwise obstructed field of view. For example, a submarine commander might use a periscope to see an object above the water, and someone in the back of a crowded concert hall might use a periscope to see the performers.

c–d. The mirrors in a periscope are placed so that incoming light reflects off each mirror and into the eye. A simple periscope may be made using mirrors and cardboard. Sample diagram:

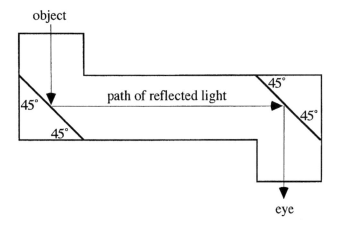

ACTIVITY 3

When you look in a mirror, your reflection sometimes appears to be behind the mirror's surface. This illusion, often called a **virtual image,** is created by light rays reflecting off the mirror. In this activity, you explore the relationship between the position of an object and the apparent position of its reflection in a mirror.

Exploration 1

a. Unfold your sheet of graph paper from the exploration in Activity **2** and lay it flat. Position a tinted plastic reflector along the *x*-axis with points *P* and *Q* on your side of the reflector.

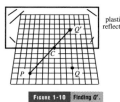

mathematics note

The reflection of an object is its **image.** The object itself is the **preimage.** If point *A* is the preimage, then the image of a point *A* can be represented as *A′* (read "A prime").

b. 1. Find the reflection of point *Q* in the reflector.

   2. Place your pencil behind the reflector and mark the point on the graph paper where the reflection of *Q* appears to be. This point is the image of *Q*. Label it *Q′*.

   3. Remove the reflector and draw $\overline{PQ'}$. As shown in Figure **1-10,** points *P, C,* and *Q′* should be collinear.

plastic reflector

FIGURE 1-10 Finding *Q′*.

14   Module 1 ■ *Reflect on This*

ACTIVITY 3

Students use a tinted plastic reflector and a coordinate grid to find the image of a reflection in a line. This process is then modeled on a geometry utility.

Materials List

■ tinted plastic reflectors (such as MIRAs™ or Reflectas™; one per group)

■ straightedge (one per group)

Technology

■ geometry utility

Student Outcomes

After completing the following exploration and discussion, students should be able to:

✳ use a geometry utility to investigate various geometric relationships

✳ relate constructions on a geometry utility to physical models of real phenomena

✳ explain the perpendicular bisector relationships created by reflections in a line

✳ explain the relationships between the coordinates of a point and the coordinates of its image under a reflection in the *x*- or *y*-axis

✳ explain the relationship between theorems and conjectures

✳ use correct notation for representing image points.

teacher note

Students must complete both explorations in this activity. Exploration **1** extends work from the sketches used in the previous activity. Exploration **2** allows students to better develop the objectives.

If your students have not used a geometry utility before, you might wish to allow some practice with the technology before beginning Exploration **2.** If access to geometry utilities is limited, the exploration may be conducted as a class demonstration.

Exploration 1

a–c. Students make additions to their sketches from the exploration in Activity **2.**

d. 1. Students should observe that the distance from the *x*-axis to *Q* is the same as the distance from the *x*-axis to *Q*′.

2. Students should discover that the distance from the *x*-axis to *P* is the same as the distance from the *x*-axis to *P*′.

e. The distance from the line of reflection to the object is the same as the distance from the line of reflection to the image.

Discussion 1

a. The pinholes should correspond with the locations of *P*′ and *Q*′ found using the reflector. (Some possible sources of error include the placement of the reflector, the thickness of the reflector, and the subjectivity involved in judging the position of the image.)

b. The two distances should be equal.

c. 1. Both segments should intersect at point *C*.

2. Sample response: This indicates that reflected light rays travel in the same way, regardless of direction. In other words, light travels from *P* to *Q* along the same path that it travels from *Q* to *P*.

d. Although some errors in measurement might occur, the class data should support the conjecture. You might wish to discuss how close two measurements should be to be considered equal in this situation.

Exploration 2

Students use a geometry utility to continue their investigations of reflections in a line. **Note:** For best results, students should set the measurement preferences on their geometry utilities so that angles are measured to the nearest degree and lengths to the nearest 0.1 units.

a. Student constructions should resemble the one shown in Figure **1-11**.

b. From Step **9**, students should observe that $m\angle QEB = 90°$. From Step **11**, they should observe that $EQ = EQ'$. This should lead to the conjecture that $\overline{AB}$ is the perpendicular bisector of $\overline{QQ'}$.

c. Students should note that, even as the lengths of the segments and positions of the points change, the relationships among them do not. For example, the measures of the incoming and outgoing angles remain congruent and $\overline{AB}$ remains the perpendicular bisector of $\overline{QQ'}$.

d. Students should discover that the shortest total distance occurs when *S* and *C* are concurrent.

---

c. 1. Use the plastic reflector to mark the image of point *P* on your graph paper. Label this point *P*′.

2. Remove the reflector and draw $\overline{QP'}$.

d. The **distance from a point to a line** is the distance along a path perpendicular to the line. Measure the distance from the *x*-axis to each of the following points:

1. *Q* and *Q*′.

2. *P* and *P*′.

e. Make a conjecture about the relationship between the distance from an object to the mirror line and the distance from its image to the mirror line.

Discussion 1

a. In Activity **2**, you pushed pins through two layers of folded graph paper at points *P* and *Q*. How do the locations of the pinholes in the second layer compare with the locations of *P*′ and *Q*′?

b. How is the distance from *Q* to the *x*-axis related to the distance from *Q*′ to the *x*-axis?

c. 1. Where do $\overline{PQ'}$ and $\overline{QP'}$ intersect?

2. What does this tell you about the paths traveled by reflected light?

d. Does the class data support the conjecture you made in Part **e** of Exploration **1**? Explain your response.

Exploration 2

In this exploration, you use technology to model the process described in Exploration **1**. Most geometry utilities have reflection tools for finding the images of objects. To use this feature, you must first define a mirror line and the points to be reflected.

a. 1. Construct a mirror line segment, $\overline{AB}$.

2. Construct two points, *P* and *Q*, on the same side of $\overline{AB}$.

3. Reflect points *P* and *Q* in $\overline{AB}$ and label the images *P*′ and *Q*′, respectively.

4. Construct $\overline{PQ'}$ and $\overline{QP'}$.

5. Construct a point *C* at the intersection of $\overline{AB}$ and $\overline{PQ'}$.

6. Measure $\angle PCA$ and $\angle QCB$.

---

7. Construct $\overline{PP'}$ and $\overline{QQ'}$.

8. Label the intersection of $\overline{AB}$ and $\overline{PP'}$ as point *D* and the intersection of $\overline{AB}$ and $\overline{QQ'}$ as point *E*. Your construction should now resemble the one in Figure **1-11** below.

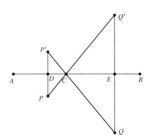

FIGURE 1-11   **Reflection modeled on a geometry utility.**

9. Measure $\angle PDA$ and $\angle QEB$.

10. Measure the distances from $\overline{AB}$ to points *P*, *P*′, *Q*, and *Q*′.

11. Measure $\overline{EQ}$ and $\overline{EQ'}$.

b. Use your measurements in Part **a** to make a conjecture about the relationship between $\overline{AB}$ and $\overline{QQ'}$.

c. Select and move various points on your construction. Note any relationships you observe among the measurements of angles and segments as you move the points.

d. Complete Steps **1–3** below using your construction from Part **a**.

1. Construct a point *S* anywhere on $\overline{AB}$.

2. Measure the total distance traveled when moving from *Q* to *S* and then from *S* to *P*.

3. By moving *S* along $\overline{AB}$, find the point where the total distance traveled in Step **2** is shortest.

mathematics note

The **perpendicular bisector** of a segment is the line that is perpendicular (⊥) to the segment and divides the segment into two congruent parts.

In Figure **1-12**, for example, line m is the perpendicular bisector of $\overline{CC'}$ because line m and $\overline{CC'}$ are perpendicular and $\overline{CM} \cong \overline{C'M}$.

A **reflection** in a line is a pairing of points in a plane so that the **line of reflection** (or **mirror line**) is the perpendicular bisector of every segment connecting a point in the preimage to its corresponding point in the image. Every point on the line of reflection is its own image.

In Figure **1-12**, parallelogram $C'D'E'F'$ is the image of parallelogram $CDEF$. Line m is the line of reflection because it is the perpendicular bisector of each segment joining a point in the preimage to its corresponding point in the image.

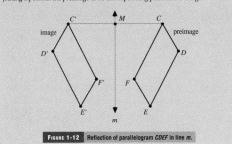

FIGURE 1-12 Reflection of parallelogram *CDEF* in line *m*.

Discussion 2

a. 1. Make a conjecture about the relationship between $\overline{AB}$ and $\overline{PP'}$ in Figure **1-11**.

   2. Do your measurements in Exploration **2** support this conjecture?

b. What conjecture can you make about the path that results in the shortest total distance in Part **c** of Exploration **2** and the point of reflection?

c. Imagine that $\overline{AB}$ in Figure **1-11** is on the x-axis.

   1. What does the measure of $\angle QEB$ tell you about the x-coordinates of points Q and Q'?

   2. What do the lengths of $\overline{EQ}$ and $\overline{EQ'}$ tell you about the y-coordinates of Q and Q'?

   3. Which segments would you measure to compare the y-coordinates of points P and P'?

d. 1. Describe the relationship between the coordinates of point Q and its image Q'.

   2. Describe the relationship between the coordinates of point P and its image P'.

   3. Are these relationships also true for each preimage and image in Exploration **1**?

e. What generalization might you make about the relationship between the coordinates of a point in the preimage and the coordinates of its image under a reflection in each of the following lines:

   1. the x-axis?

   2. the y-axis?

f. Many mathematical ideas are based on observed patterns. When conjectures based on patterns are stated in a general form and proved, they become accepted mathematical **theorems**.

   1. In Activity **2**, you made a conjecture about the relationship between the measures of the incoming and outgoing angles. Do your measurements in Exploration **2** support this conjecture?

   2. If so, could this conjecture now become a theorem?

Warm-Up

1. Determine the coordinates of the image of each point when reflected in the x-axis.

   a. (4,7)

   b. (−3,6)

   c. (a,b)

2. Determine the coordinates of the image of each point when reflected in the y-axis.

   a. (10,6)

   b. (−11,−4)

   c. (a,b)

3. On a coordinate grid, draw the shortest path from point $A(2,4)$ to point $B(7,2)$ that touches the x-axis.

Discussion 2

a. 1. Students should conjecture that $\overline{AB}$ is the perpendicular bisector of $\overline{PP'}$.

   2. Yes. Because $\overline{DP} \cong \overline{DP'}$ and $\angle PDA$ is a right angle, $\overline{AB}$ is the perpendicular bisector of $\overline{PP'}$.

b. Sample response: Because the shortest total distance occurred when S was at the same position as C, the path with the shortest total distance always passes through the reflection point on the mirror line.

c. 1. Because $m\angle QEB$ is 90°, the x-coordinates of Q and Q' are the same.

   2. Because $\overline{EQ}$ and $\overline{EQ'}$ are congruent, the y-coordinates of Q and Q' have the same absolute value, but are opposites.

   3. $\overline{DP}$ and $\overline{DP'}$

d. 1–2. The x-coordinates are the same, while the y-coordinates are opposites.

   3. Yes, because the mirror was placed along the x-axis.

e. 1. Under a reflection in the x-axis, the image of a point (x,y) has coordinates $(x,-y)$.

   2. Under a reflection in the y-axis, the image of a point (x,y) has coordinates $(-x,y)$.

f. 1. Student measurements should uphold the conjecture that the incoming and outgoing angles are congruent.

   2. Yes, this conjecture becomes a theorem only if proved in general for all cases. One approach might be to demonstrate that $\triangle PDC$ is similar to $\triangle QEC$, then show that $\angle PCD \cong \angle QCE$.

Warm-Up

1. a. (4,−7)

   b. (−3,−6)

   c. (a,−b)

2. a. (−10,6)

   b. (11,−4)

   c. (−a,b)

3. The shortest path between points A and B that touches the x-axis follows $\overline{AC}$ and $\overline{BC}$, where C is the point of intersection between the x-axis and $\overline{AB'}$ and B' is the reflection of B in the x-axis.

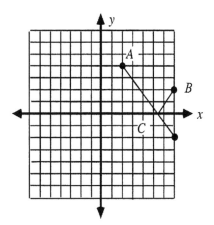

teacher note

A sheet of the waxed paper used to separate hamburger patties (patty paper) can be a helpful tool for identifying reflected images by paper folding.

Assignment

Problems suitable for use as assessment items are identified by an asterisk (*).

* **3.1 a–c.** Answers will vary. The following sample graph shows the points $A(4,5)$, $B(-1,-4)$, and $C(-6,2)$. The coordinates of the corresponding image points are $A'(-4,5)$, $B'(1,-4)$, and $C'(6,2)$.

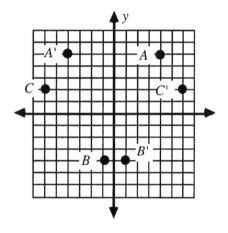

d. The coordinates of D' are $(-x,y)$.

3.2 a. In a plane, the shortest path between two points is always the line segment connecting the points.

b. Sample response: The lengths of the paths are equal. The distance from P to C is the same in both cases, and the distance from Q to C is the same as the distance from Q' to C. This can be seen by folding the graph paper along the line of reflection.

* **3.3 a–b.** Sample response:

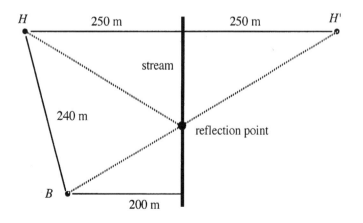

Assignment

3.1 a. Plot three points on a coordinate grid so that one point has all positive coordinates, one point has all negative coordinates, and one point has one positive and one negative coordinate. Label these points A, B, and C.

b. Plot the reflections of A, B and C in the y-axis. Label the image points A', B', and C', respectively.

c. List the coordinates of each point and its image.

d. Consider a point D with coordinates (x,y). If D is reflected in the y-axis, what are the coordinates of D'?

3.2 Use your graph paper from the exploration in Activity **2** to complete Parts **a** and **b** below.

a. Describe the shortest path from Q' to P.

b. How does the length of this path compare to the length of the path that light travels from Q to P? Explain your response.

3.3 A family wants to build the shortest possible trail from their house to the stream and then to the barn. The diagram below shows the distances between these locations.

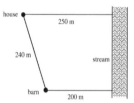

a. Make a scale drawing of this situation.

b. Use your drawing to determine where the trail should reach the stream to make the shortest trail from the house to the stream to the barn.

c. Explain how you used the properties of reflections to determine your solution.

* * * * *

---

c. Sample response: To find the shortest distance, you must reflect the house in a line that represents the bank of the stream, then connect the image of the house to the barn. The point where the segment intersects the stream is the point of reflection, where the incoming angle of the path equals the outgoing angle of the path. The path that connects the house to the point of reflection, then to the barn, represents the shortest path.

✳ ✳ ✳ ✳ ✳

3.4 The diagram below shows a square tile with its lower left-hand corner at the origin of an *xy*-coordinate system. Sketch a copy of this diagram on a sheet of graph paper.

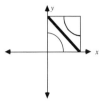

a. Sketch the image of the tile reflected in the *x*-axis.

b. Sketch the image of your response to Part **a** reflected in the *y*-axis.

3.5 The diagram below shows a section of an oil pipeline along with two nearby wells. To transport oil from the wells to the pipeline, the company plans to build a new pumping station somewhere on the line. If the company wants to minimize the amount of pipe needed to connect the two wells to the pipeline, where should it locate the pumping station?

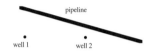

3.6 The diagram below shows the top of a pool table along with a cue ball.

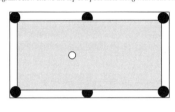

3.5 The point identified in the diagram below is the best location for the pumping station. This location provides the shortest total distance from the pumping station to both wells.

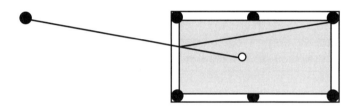

3.6 **a.** Answers may vary. The following diagram shows one possible shot. The paths of other shots may be determined by reflecting the corresponding pocket in a similar manner.

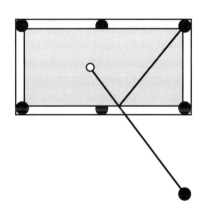

b. Sample response: The segment connecting the ball to the image of the pocket locates the point of reflection on the side rail. This is the point where the cue ball needs to be banked.

c. Another path to the same pocket may be determined by reflecting the pocket in a different side than the one in Part **a**. Sample response:

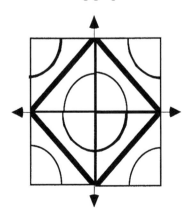

3.4 **a.** A reflection in the *x*-axis results in the graph below:

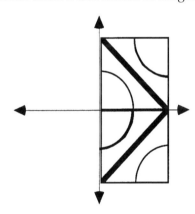

b. The reflection of the graph in Part **a** in the *y*-axis produces the following graph:

3.7 The diagram below shows the paths of four successful passes.

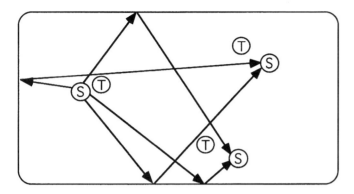

ACTIVITY
4

In this activity, students investigate double reflections using mirrors. **Note:** To continue their investigations, some students might wish to create a model of a double reflection using a geometry utility.

 teacher note

A brief assessment of the mathematical content in Activities **3** and **4**, for use at your discretion, appears in the Teacher Resources for this module.

Materials List

- straightedge (one per group)
- flat mirrors (two per group)
- tape (one roll per group)
- graph paper (one sheet per group)

Student Outcomes

After completing the following explorations and discussions, students should be able to:

✳ use correct notation for representing reflected and double-reflected points

✳ identify the path that light follows when reflected in two mirrors

✳ identify the coordinates of the image of a point reflected in both the *x*- and *y*-axes.

---

a. Trace a path that banks the cue ball off exactly one side and places it in a pocket.

b. Describe how you determined the path you chose in Part **a**.

c. Find another path to the same pocket, using a different side of the table to bank the ball.

3.7 In a hockey game between the Saints and the Tornadoes, six players are positioned as shown in the diagram below. Each circle that contains a letter S represents a member of the Saints; each circle that contains a T represents a member of the Tornadoes.

Draw all the paths that show a successful pass from the Saint on the left to one of the other two Saints. Each pass must reflect off one of the boards (sides). Explain why your pass is possible.

ACTIVITY
4

In the previous activities, you examined how light reflects off a single flat mirror. The kaleidoscope you built in the introduction, however, used two mirrors. In this situation, light reflects off one mirror, then the other. In the following exploration, you investigate the virtual images produced by light reflecting off two mirrors.

Exploration 1

a. On a sheet of graph paper, draw two perpendicular line segments and a point *Q*, as shown in Figure **1-13** on the next page.

---

mirror

.*Q*

mirror

FIGURE 1-13 Two perpendicular mirrors.

b. If hinged mirrors like those used in Activity **1** were placed along the line segments, how many images of point *Q* would you see in the mirrors? Record your prediction.

c. Use two hinged mirrors to test your prediction in Part **b**. Record how many images of point *Q* you actually observe.

d. To discover why this number of images occurs, use your diagram from Part **a** to complete Steps **1–6** below.

  1. Reflect *Q* in one of the line segments and label the image Q'_1.

  2. Reflect *Q* in the other line segment and label this image Q'_2.

  3. Place the hinged mirrors on the segments again. Observe that two of the virtual images of *Q* in the mirrors correspond to the two images of *Q* found in Steps **1** and **2**.

  4. Remove the hinged mirrors. Reflect Q'_1 in the other line segment and label its image *Q″* (read "Q double-prime").

  5. Repeat Step **4** using Q'_2 to locate Q''_2. What do you observe about the positions of *Q″* and Q''_2?

  6. Place the hinged mirrors back on the line segments and observe the virtual image that corresponds to *Q″*. **Note:** Save your diagram for use in Exploration **2**.

Discussion 1

a. How did the number of images you observed in Part **c** of Exploration **1** compare with your prediction in Part **b**?

b. Explain why the two mirrors in Exploration **1** produce three virtual images.

c. In Exploration **1**, you labeled the image of a single reflection *Q′*, and the image of a double reflection *Q″*. How would you label the image of a triple reflection?

d. How do your observations in Part **d** of Exploration **1** help explain the patterns you saw in the kaleidoscope?

Exploration 2

In this exploration, you use the properties of single reflections to investigate the path of light in a double reflection.

a. Add a point E to your diagram from Exploration **1**, as shown in Figure **1-14** below. In this diagram, point E represents the location of your eye.

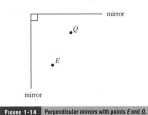

FIGURE 1-14 Perpendicular mirrors with points E and Q.

b. To find the path that light travels in a double reflection from Q to E, complete Steps **1–4** below.
1. Use a straightedge to connect E and Q''.
2. Label the point $\overline{EQ''}$ where intersects the mirror line segment as C_2.
3. Use a straightedge to connect C_2 and Q_1'.
4. Label the point where $\overline{C_2Q_1'}$ intersects the other mirror line segment as C_1.

c. Draw the path from Q to C_1, then to C_2, and finally to E. **Note:** Save your diagram for use in the assignment.

Discussion 2

a. What does the path drawn in Part **c** of Exploration **2** represent?
b. What do the points C_1 and C_2 represent?
c. Using light rays, explain why the virtual image that corresponds to Q'' appears where it does in the mirror.

Exploration 1

Students explore the double reflection of an object using hinged mirrors.

a–c. Students might predict that they will see two virtual images, one from each mirror. However, there are actually three images—two from single reflections and one from a double reflection of point Q.

d. Student diagrams should resemble the figure below. The order of reflection does not affect the position of Q''.

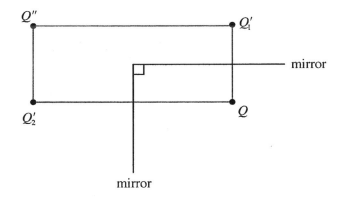

Note: Students should save their diagrams for use in Exploration **2.**

Discussion 1

a. Although most students will have predicted two virtual images, they should have seen three virtual images in the two mirrors.
b. Two of the virtual images are each produced by a single reflection in one of the two mirrors. The third virtual image is the result of a double reflection involving both mirrors.
c. The image of a triple reflection could be labeled Q'''.
d. Kaleidoscopes use two or more mirrors to produce many images and create elaborate designs.

Exploration 2

a–c. Students construct the path that light follows in a double reflection. Their final diagrams should resemble the one shown below:

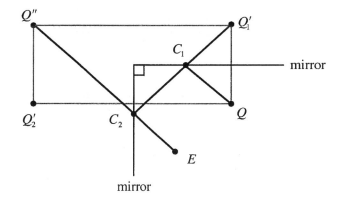

Discussion 2

a. The path represents light traveling in a double reflection from point Q to point E.
b. Points C_1 and C_2 represent the points of reflection in the two mirrors.
c. The virtual image appears where it does in the mirror because the light ray involved in the double reflection comes from that direction toward your eye (Q'', C_2, and E are all collinear).

Warm-Up

1. **a.** $P' = (2,5);\ P'' = (-2,5)$
   b. $P' = (4,-6);\ P'' = (-4,-6)$
   c. $P' = (-3,-1);\ P'' = (3,-1)$
   d. $P' = (a,-b);\ P'' = (-a,-b)$

2. **a.** The shortest path between points A and B that touches both the x-and y-axes follows $\overline{AC}$, $\overline{CD}$, and $\overline{BD}$, where C is the point of intersection between the x-axis and $\overline{DA'}$ and A' is the reflection of A in the x-axis, and where D is the point of intersection between the y-axis and $\overline{BA''}$ and A'' is the reflection of A' in the y-axis.

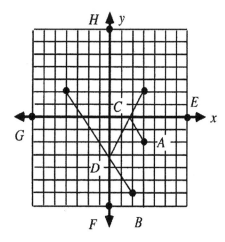

b. Sample response: The incoming angles, $\angle ACE$ and $\angle CDH$, measure approximately $32°$ and $58°$, respectively. The outgoing angles, $\angle DCG$ and $\angle BDF$, measure approximately $32°$ and $58°$, respectively. Incoming angle $\angle ACE$ and outgoing angle $\angle DCG$ are congruent, as are incoming angle $\angle CDH$ and $\angle BDF$. The angles $\angle ACE$ and $\angle CDH$ are both complements of and $\angle DCG$ and $\angle BDF$.

Assignment

Problems suitable for use as assessment items are identified by an asterisk (*).

4.1 Sample response:

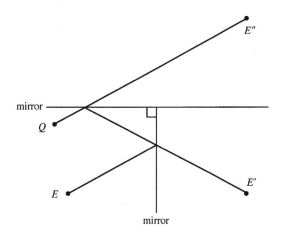

Warm-Up

1. For each point P below, determine the coordinates of P', a reflection of P in the x-axis, and the coordinates of P'', a reflection of P' in the y-axis.

   a. $(2,-5)$

   b. $(4,6)$

   c. $(-3,1)$

   d. (a,b)

2. **a.** On a coordinate grid, draw the shortest path from $A(3,-2)$ to $B(2,-6)$ that touches both the x- and y-axes.

   b. Determine the measures of the incoming and outgoing angles on the graph that you drew in Part **a.** Describe the relationships among the angles.

Assignment

4.1 The diagram below shows two perpendicular mirrors and the points Q and E. On a copy of this diagram, draw the path that light travels in a double reflection from Q to E.

4.2 Use the diagram of two perpendicular mirrors that you created in Exploration **2** to complete Parts **a–e** below.

a. Label the intersection of the two mirror line segments as point $Z(0,0)$ and graph two more points: $A(0,-4)$ and $B(4,0)$.

b. Use a protractor to measure $\angle ZC_2C_1$ to the nearest degree. Record the measurement on your graph paper and label the angle as either outgoing or incoming.

c. Explain how the measurements of the remaining angles can be determined by knowing only the measure of $\angle ZC_2C_1$.

d. Label the remaining three angles as incoming or outgoing and record their measures.

24   Module 1 ■ *Reflect on This*

4.2 a. Sample diagram: Q''

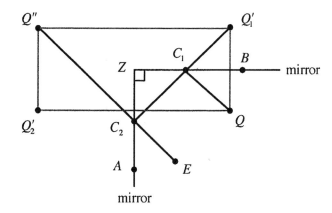

b. Answers will vary. Sample response: The measure of the incoming angle $\angle ZC_2C_1$, to the nearest degree, is $37°$.

c. Because $m\angle C_2ZC_1$ is $90°$ and the sum of the angles in $\triangle C_2ZC_1$ is $180°$, $\angle ZC_1C_2$ and $\angle ZC_2C_1$ are complements. For the sample response in Part **a**, $m\angle ZC_1C_2 = 90° - 37° = 53°$. The remaining two angles are congruent to their companion outgoing or incoming angles.

d. Sample response: Incoming angle $\angle BC_1Q$ and outgoing angle $\angle ZC_1C_2$ both measure $53°$; incoming angle $\angle ZC_2C_1$ and outgoing angle $\angle AC_2E$ both measure $37°$.

e. 1. Calculate the sum of the measures of the two incoming and two outgoing angles.

2. Use the sum of the four angles to make a conjecture about the path of a light ray in a double reflection or the path of a pool ball in a double bank shot.

4.3 To model a pair of mirrors, draw two perpendicular segments on a sheet of graph paper as in Exploration 2. Label the intersection of the two segments point $Z(0,0)$ and graph two more points: $A(0,-4)$ and $B(4,0)$. Find the path that light would travel from point $O(4,-1)$ to point $E(3,-7)$ if it reflected off both mirrors. Label all points, angles, and segments that correspond to those found in Exploration 2. Identify the incoming and outgoing angles and give their measures.

4.4 a. On a sheet of blank paper, use a protractor to draw two line segments representing mirrors hinged at 70°.

b. Label two points between the mirrors: point O, representing an object, and point E, representing the perspective of an eye.

c. Find the locations of the images of O. Label these points O' and O''.

d. Sketch the path of light from O to E in a double reflection.

e. Measure one of the incoming or outgoing angles and record this measurement on your drawing.

f. Determine the measures of the remaining three angles and record these measures on your drawing. Label all angles either as incoming or outgoing.

g. Calculate the sum of the measures of all four angles. Does this sum support the conjecture you made in Problem **4.2**?

4.5 A full-size pool table measures approximately 126 cm × 255 cm.

a. Make a scale drawing of a pool table, including the six pockets.

b. Mark the location of a ball somewhere on your scale drawing, then draw the path of a shot that requires the ball to strike at least two side rails before reaching a pocket.

c. Label the appropriate points (with measurements in centimeters), so that a pool player could:

1. locate the starting position of the ball on an actual pool table.

2. locate the point where the ball must hit the first side rail to make the shot.

d. If possible, test your calculations on a real pool table, and write an account of your test.

* * * * *

---

e. 1. The sum of the four angles is 180°.

2. When the two mirrors are hinged at 90°, the path of light in a double reflection—like the path of a pool ball banked off two sides—reverses its direction.

4.3 In the following diagram, the path of light follows $\overline{OC_1}$, $\overline{C_1C_2}$, and $\overline{C_2E}$. Incoming angle $\angle BC_1O$ is congruent to outgoing angle $\angle ZC_1C_2$; both angles measure 49° (to the nearest degree). Incoming angle $\angle C_1C_2Z$ is congruent to outgoing angle $\angle AC_2E$; both angles measure 41° (to the nearest degree).

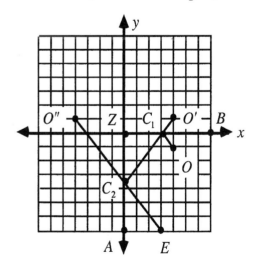

* 4.4 a–e. Responses will vary, depending on the locations of points O and E. Sample response:

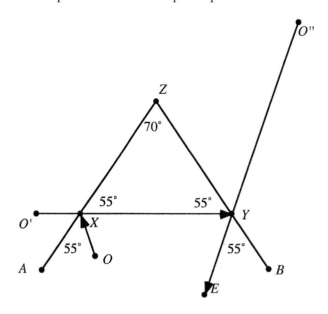

f. In the sample drawing above, $\angle YXZ$ and $\angle BYE$ are incoming angles; $\angle AXO$ and $\angle XYZ$ are outgoing angles.

g. The sum of the measures of the four angles is 220°. Unless students stipulate that the hinge angle must measure 90° in their responses to Problem **4.2**, this sum should contradict their conjectures.

* 4.5 By creating their scale drawings near the center of a sheet of graph paper, students can use paper folding to locate reflections. Sample response:

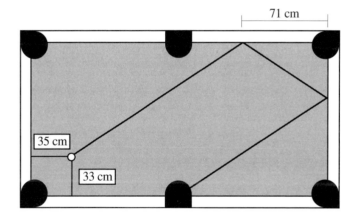

* * * * *

4.6 As shown in the diagram below, the outgoing angle for each wave is congruent to the incoming angle. The middle wave reflects back along its original path.

radio waves

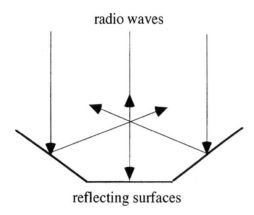

reflecting surfaces

4.7 a. The following diagram shows the only possible path.

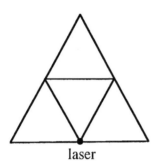

laser

b. The measure of each incoming and outgoing angle is 60°. The measure of each angle of incidence and angle of reflection is 30°.

c. The four small triangles are congruent equilateral triangles. They are similar to the original triangle.

4.6 Some large radio telescopes use several reflecting surfaces positioned in special ways. The diagram below shows three such surfaces in a radio telescope built in Arecibo, Puerto Rico, in 1963. On a copy of this diagram, draw the path of each reflected radio wave and explain why these paths occur.

radio waves

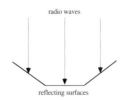

reflecting surfaces

4.7 The diagram below shows three hinged mirrors positioned in the shape of an equilateral triangular prism. A hole in the center of one mirror allows a laser beam to enter the prism.

laser

a. Draw a path for the laser beam that allows it to reflect off each of the other two mirrors exactly once and pass back through its starting point.

b. Determine the measures of every incoming and outgoing angle and the measures of every angle of incidence and angle of reflection.

c. Identify the shapes formed by the lines of reflection. How are these shapes related to the original triangle?

Summary Assessment

1. Most miniature golf courses have holes requiring a player to hit the ball off at least one wall to score a hole-in-one. An example is shown in the diagram below.

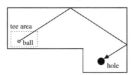

Design and draw some miniature golf holes according to the following three rules.

- The drawing must be to scale, with all dimensions indicated.
- Only line segments may be used for walls.
- A tee area must be provided.

As you design holes, sketch some possible paths for a hole-in-one. In your final drawing for each hole, however, do not reveal your winning strategy. Design one of each of the following types of holes.

a. A hole that looks simple, but where a hole-in-one is probably impossible.

b. A hole that looks difficult, but has a simple path for the ball.

c. A hole that has many possible paths.

d. A hole that requires a player to bank the ball off exactly three walls to get a hole-in-one.

2. To test your designs, trade drawings with a classmate. Try to sketch the path of a hole-in-one in each of your classmate's drawings.

3. After your designs have been tested, present one of them to the rest of the class. Use mathematical ideas and the language of this module to explain your design.

teacher note

An additional assessment, for use at your discretion, appears in the Teacher Resources for this module.

Summary Assessment

1. Some sample responses are shown below.
   a. This hole looks simple, but a hole-in-one is impossible.

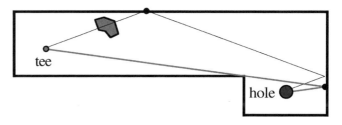

   b. This hole looks difficult, but actually has a simple path for a hole-in-one.

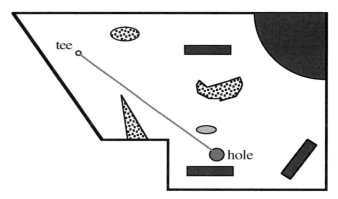

   c. This hole has at least three possible paths for a hole-in-one.

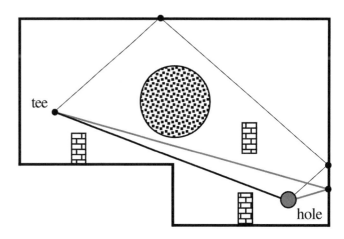

d. This hole requires a player to bank the ball off exactly three walls to get a hole-in-one.

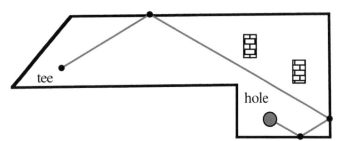

2. Students test each other's designs by trying to sketch the path of a hole-in-one.

3. Students may have used one or more of the following methods when creating their designs:
   - Determine the placement of the ball in the tee area. Choose a starting angle and direction for the shot. Given this angle and direction, determine the ball's path using incoming angles and outgoing angles. Place the hole in a location that aligns with the ball's path.
   - Determine the placement of the ball in the tee area and the placement of the hole. Using trial-and-error and incoming and outgoing angles, determine a path from the ball to the hole.
   - Determine the placement of the ball in the tee area and the placement of the hole. Using lines of reflection, images, preimages, and points of reflection, determine a path from the ball to the hole.

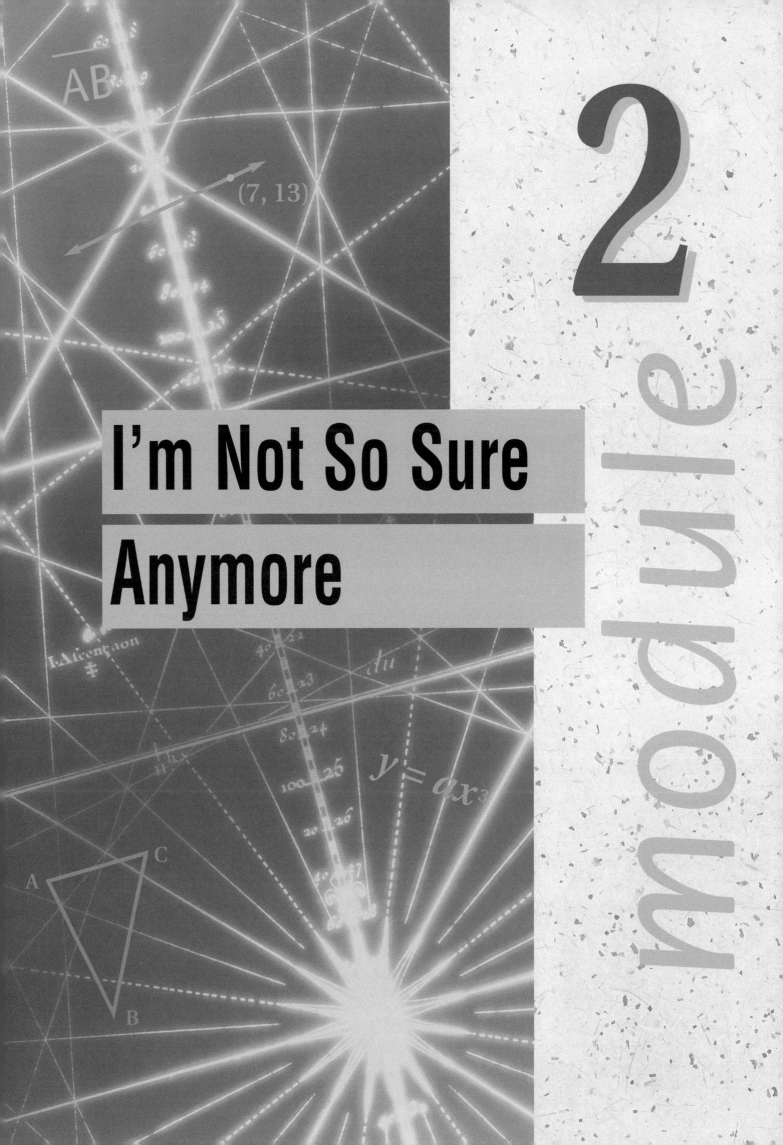

I'm Not So Sure Anymore

2 module

Overview

In this module, students simulate various simple lotteries and determine the probabilities of winning. These probabilities are then used to find expected values.

Introduction:	Students use use simulations to generate numbers and compile experimental probability.
Activity 1:	Students create sample spaces to determine theoretical probability and compare theoretical probability to experimental probability.
Activity 2:	Students extend data on a spreadsheet and use it to examine experimental and theoretical probabilities for experiments with a large number of outcomes.
Activity 3:	Students use the spreadsheet from Activity **2** to calculate expected winnings and determine whether or not a game is fair.

Objectives

In this module, students will:

✳ use a variety of methods for simulation (Introduction, 1, 2, 3)

✳ determine experimental probability (Introduction, 1, 3)

✳ find that the sum of the probabilities for all outcomes of an experiment is 1 (Introduction, 1, 2, 3)

✳ distinguish between experimental and theoretical probabilities (1)

✳ create sample spaces (1, 2, 3)

✳ determine theoretical probability using sample spaces (1, 2, 3)

✳ be introduced to the fundamental counting principle (2)

✳ identify and extend data patterns (2)

✳ calculate expected value (3)

✳ determine when a game is fair (3).

Prerequisites

For this module, students should know:

* ✳ how to determine percentages
* ✳ how to convert among percentages, decimals, and fractions
* ✳ how to find the probability of a single event
* ✳ how to use a spreadsheet
* ✳ how to use a random number generator on a spreadsheet or calculator
* ✳ the definition of a simulation.

 Flashbacks, for use at your discretion, appear in the Teacher Resources for this module. These brief problem sets provide a review of some prerequisite skills for each activity.

Planning Guide

Activity	Materials	Technology	Time Line
Introduction	■ numbered objects ■ container	■ random number generator	1 day
Activity 1	■ paper clips ■ spinner template ■ playing cards	■ random number generator	2 days
Activity 2	■ playing cards ■ sample space template	■ spreadsheet	2 days
Activity 3	■ sample space template	■ random number generator ■ spreadsheet	2 days
Assessment Activities	■ sample space template	■ none	3 days **Total: 10 days**

 teacher note

Blackline masters of the templates appear in the Teacher Resources for this module.

Introduction

The introduction is designed to engage students in the context of the module by examining various lottery games. (You might wish to show students some actual lottery tickets.)

teacher note

Some helpful resources include E. Packal's *The Mathematics of Games and Gambling* and two books by J. Paulos: *Innumeracy: Mathematical Illiteracy and its Consequences* and *Beyond Numeracy: Ruminations of a Numbers Man.*

Materials List

- six objects, each labeled with one of the digits from 1 to 6 (per group)
- container (one per group)

Technology

- random number generator

teacher note

Many forms of technology, including calculators and spreadsheets, have a built-in random number generator. Students should refer to the manual for specific instructions. Typically, this feature generates a number in the range (0,1).

Students may suggest using the first digit after the decimal point (ignoring 0, 7, 8, and 9) to obtain a random selection from 1 through 6.

As an alternative, students may multiply the random number by 6, resulting in a number in the range (0,6). It then might be possible to identify only the integer portion of the random number, resulting in a random integer in the range [0,5]. Adding 1 results in a random integer in the range [1,6].

Some calculators, such as Texas Instruments' TI-84 Plus, also include probability simulators.

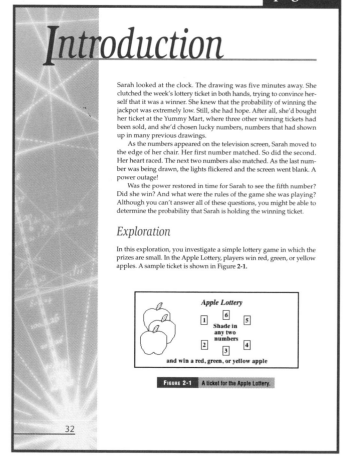

Introduction

Sarah looked at the clock. The drawing was five minutes away. She clutched the week's lottery ticket in both hands, trying to convince herself that it was a winner. She knew that the probability of winning the jackpot was extremely low. Still, she had hope. After all, she'd bought her ticket at the Yummy Mart, where three other winning tickets had been sold, and she'd chosen lucky numbers, numbers that had shown up in many previous drawings.

As the numbers appeared on the television screen, Sarah moved to the edge of her chair. Her first number matched. So did the second. Her heart raced. The next two numbers also matched. As the last number was being drawn, the lights flickered and the screen went blank. A power outage!

Was the power restored in time for Sarah to see the fifth number? Did she win? And what were the rules of the game she was playing? Although you can't answer all of these questions, you might be able to determine the probability that Sarah is holding the winning ticket.

Exploration

In this exploration, you investigate a simple lottery game in which the prizes are small. In the Apple Lottery, players win red, green, or yellow apples. A sample ticket is shown in Figure 2-1.

FIGURE 2-1 A ticket for the Apple Lottery.

Student Outcomes

After completing the following exploration and discussion, students should be able to:

* simulate a probability experiment

* determine experimental probability

* find that the sum of the probabilities for all the outcomes of an experiment is 1.

All lottery games have rules, often printed on the back of the ticket. Figure 2-2 shows the back of an Apple Lottery ticket.

How to Play
• Shade two different numbers from 1 to 6 on the front of the ticket.

How to Win
Apple Lottery officials randomly draw two different numbers from 1 to 6.
• Win a yellow apple by matching 2 numbers.
• Win a green apple by matching 1 number.
• Win a red apple by matching 0 numbers.

FIGURE 2-2 The back of an Apple Lottery ticket.

a. When numbers are chosen at random, there is no way to predict which numbers will be chosen. Suggest a method that Apple Lottery officials might use to draw two different numbers from 1 to 6 at random.

b. In the Apple Lottery, there are three different **events**—winning a red apple, winning a green apple, and winning a yellow apple.

Predict the number of each type of apple you would win if you played the Apple Lottery 1000 times. Record your predictions.

c. Pick two numbers from 1 to 6 that you would shade on an Apple Lottery ticket. Record these numbers.

d. Recall that a simulation is a model of a real-world occurrence. The results of a simulation are often used to make predictions.

Use the following steps to simulate the Apple Lottery officials drawing two numbers.

1. Place 6 objects in a container. Each object should be marked with a different number from 1 to 6.

2. Shake the container. Without looking, draw two of the numbered objects.

e. Compare the numbers drawn in Part **d** with the two numbers you picked in Part **c**. Record the type of apple won.

f. Repeat Parts **d** and **e** 24 more times.

Module 2 ■ *I'm Not So Sure Anymore* 33

mathematics note

One way of predicting the likelihood of an event is to perform many trials under controlled conditions. The results of these trials provide the **experimental** (or **empirical**) **probability** of the event occurring. The experimental probability of an event can be calculated using the following ratio:

$$\frac{\text{number of times event occurs}}{\text{total number of trials}}$$

For example, suppose that you counted 60 heads in 100 trials of a coin toss. The experimental probability of obtaining a head on any one toss is:

$$\frac{60}{100} = \frac{3}{5}$$

g. Using your results from Part **f**, determine the experimental probability of each of the following events:

1. winning a red apple

2. winning a yellow apple

3. winning a green apple

4. winning an apple of any color.

h. Combine your results from Part **f** with those of the rest of the class. Use the combined results to determine the experimental probability of each of the following events:

1. winning a red apple

2. winning a yellow apple

3. winning a green apple

4. winning an apple of any color.

i. 1. Predict how many apples of each color you would win in 1000 games of the Apple Lottery.

2. Compare your response to the prediction made in Part **b** of the exploration.

Discussion

a. Compare the experimental probabilities found in Parts **g** and **h** of the exploration. Which do you believe give better estimates of the true chances of winning? Explain your response.

34 Module 2 ■ *I'm Not So Sure Anymore*

Exploration

a. Sample response: Officials could mark 6 balls with a different number from 1 to 6, mix them in a container, then pick 2 balls out of the 6.

b. Predictions will vary. **Note:** After calculating the experimental probabilities for each event in Part **h,** students may revise their predictions.

c. Apple Lottery rules state that players must pick two different numbers. Students might find the exploration less confusing if they keep the same lottery ticket throughout the exploration; however, changing the choice of numbers will not affect their results.

d. To simulate two numbers drawn for the Apple Lottery, each group requires a container of six objects (each object labeled with one of the digits from 1 to 6) or a random number generator.

e–f. Students might want to organize their data in a table. Sample data:

Color of Apple	Number of Wins
red	11
yellow	2
green	12

g. The following experimental probabilities were calculated using the sample data given in Part **f:**
1. $11/25 = 44\%$ 2. $2/25 = 8\%$
3. $12/25 = 48\%$ 4. $25/25 = 100\% = 1$

h. You might wish to organize a table for the entire class. The following experimental probabilities were calculated using the sample data in the table below.

Color of Apple	Number of Wins
red	215
yellow	40
green	245

1. $215/500 = 43\%$ 2. $40/500 = 8\%$
3. $245/500 = 49\%$ 4. $245/500 = 49\%$

i. 1. Using the sample data given in Part **h,** some appropriate predictions are 430 red apples, 80 yellow apples, and 490 green apples.

2. The predictions based on experimental results might contradict the predictions made in Part **b.**

Discussion

a. Students should recognize that the combined data is likely to give more reliable experimental results. Sample response: The probabilities found in Part **h** should give a better estimate. Flipping a coin 4 times may result in 4 heads, but it seems very unlikely to flip a coin 400 times and see only heads.

Module 2 ■ *I'm Not So Sure Anymore* **29**

b. Sample response: The probability is 100% or 1 because you win an apple every time you play the game.

c. 1. Students may suggest rolling dice, drawing cards, using a random number table, or using a calculator or computer.

2. Answers will vary, depending on the responses given above. For example, rolling a pair of dice could result in 2 sixes.

3. The rules of the Apple Lottery require two different numbers. A simulation that can generate identical numbers would have to examine the second trial to be sure a duplicate number was not generated. If a duplicate is found, the simulation would have to continue generating random numbers until a different second number is identified.

4. Sample response: When using two dice, disregard a roll that results in a pair. Some might argue that this is not a good simulation. The only way to find out is to try it and see if you seem to get consistent empirical results.

d. Sample response: Technology can allow you to generate many trials quickly. Having the results of more trials can produce a better estimate of the true chances of winning.

Students list a sample space for an experiment and use it to determine theoretical probabilities. They employ technology to simulate a large number of trials, then calculate experimental probabilities from their data.

Material List

■ paper clips (one per student)

■ spinner template (one copy per student; a blackline master appears in the Teacher Resource for these materials)

■ playing cards (optional)

Technology

■ random number generator

Student Outcomes

After completing the following exploration and discussion, students should be able to:

✳ use a variety of methods for simulation

✳ determine experimental probability

b. Explain why the experimental probability of winning an apple in the Apple Lottery is 1.

c. 1. What other methods could you use to generate two random numbers for the Apple Lottery?

2. Do these methods guarantee that two different numbers will be generated?

3. What problem might occur when using a simulation that can generate identical numbers?

4. How could you modify the simulation to ensure that the two numbers are different?

d. What advantages might there be in using technology to simulate the Apple Lottery?

ACTIVITY 1

When using experimental probability to make predictions, the larger the number of trials you use, the better the estimate you get of the true likelihood of an event. In the following exploration, you use technology to help you simulate the results of many games of the Apple Lottery.

Exploration

a. Select two numbers from 1 to 6 for a new Apple Lottery ticket. Record these numbers.

b. When Apple Lottery officials draw two numbers, these might or might not match your numbers. The first column in Table **2-1** on the next page lists all the possible pairs of numbers in the Apple Lottery. This is the **sample space** for the lottery.

Make a copy of Table **2-1**. For each possible pair of numbers, record the number of matching digits and the color of the apple you would win with your ticket.

c. Simulate the Apple Lottery by completing the following steps.

1. Randomly generate the first number.

2. Randomly generate the second number.

3. If the second number is the same as the first, generate another number. Repeat until you obtain a number different from the first.

d. Use Table **2-1** to determine which apple you won.

Module 2 ■ *I'm Not So Sure Anymore* **35**

✳ find that the sum of the probabilities for all the outcomes of an experiment is 1

✳ create sample spaces

✳ use a sample space to determine theoretical probabilities.

Exploration

a. Students select two numbers according to Apple Lottery rules. They might find data collection easier if they keep the same numbers throughout the exploration.

b. The sample table at the top of the next page corresponds to the selection 3, 4.

Pair of Numbers	Number of Matching Digits	Color of Apple Won
1, 2	0	R
1, 3	1	G
1, 4	1	G
1, 5	0	R
1, 6	0	R
2, 3	1	G
2, 4	1	G
2, 5	0	R
2, 6	0	R
3, 4	2	Y
3, 5	1	G
3, 6	1	G
4, 5	1	G
4, 6	1	G
5, 6	0	R

TABLE 2-1 ■ Apple Lottery Sample Space

Pair of Numbers	Number of Matching Digits	Color of Apple Won
1, 2		
1, 3		
1, 4		
1, 5		
1, 6		
2, 3		
2, 4		
2, 5		
2, 6		
3, 4		
3, 5		
3, 6		
4, 5		
4, 6		
5, 6		

e. Repeat Parts **c** and **d** 99 more times, recording the number of times you won each color of apple.

f. Use the results of your 100 trials to determine the experimental probability of each of the following events:

1. winning a red apple

2. winning a yellow apple

3. winning a green apple

g. Combine your results from Part **f** with those of the rest of the class. Use this data to determine the probability of each of the following events:

1. winning a red apple

2. winning a yellow apple

3. winning a green apple

c–e. Students might want to organize their data in a table. Sample data:

Color of Apple	Number of Wins
red	45
yellow	6
green	49

f. The following experimental probabilities were calculated using the sample data given in Part **e:**

1. $45/100 = 45\%$

2. $6/100 = 6\%$

3. $49/100 = 49\%$

g. Students determine experimental probabilities using the class data.

h. The sample space for the Apple Lottery contains 15 possible outcomes.

1. 6/15 = 40%
2. 1/15 ≈ 6.7%
3. 8/15 ≈ 53.3%
4. 15/15 = 100% = 1

Discussion

a. Answers will vary. The sample data given in Part **e** results in experimental probabilities that are reasonably close to the theoretical probabilities.

b. The combined data should give experimental probabilities that more closely correspond to the theoretical probabilities. This comparison prepares students for discussion of the law of large numbers, which is explored in later modules.

c. The theoretical probabilities of winning each type of apple are not affected by the pair of numbers selected.

Warm-Up

1. Completed table:

Percentage	Decimal	Fraction
25%	0.25	1/4
12%	0.12	3/25
8%	0.08	2/25
150%	1.50	3/2
0.3%	0.003	3/1000
62.5%	0.625	5/8

2. Sample response: Experimental probability is based on the outcomes observed during an experiment. For example, if a coin is tossed 10 times and 7 heads result, the experimental probability of tossing a head is 7/10. Theoretical probability is based on the distribution of all the possible outcomes in the sample space. Since there is 1 head out of 2 equally likely outcomes on the toss of a coin, the theoretical probability of tossing a head is 1/2.

3. **a.** The sample space for tossing two coins is: HH, HT, TH, TT.

   b. The probability of obtaining two heads is 1/4. The probability of obtaining one head and one tail is 1/2. The probability of obtaining two tails is 1/4.

   c. 1

4. 16/48 = 1/3

---

mathematics note

The set of all possible outcomes for an experiment is the **sample space**.

An **event** is a subset of the sample space.

If each outcome in a sample space has the same chance of occurring, then the **theoretical probability** of an event can be calculated using the following ratio:

$$\frac{\text{number of outcomes in the event}}{\text{total number of outcomes in the sample space}}$$

For example, you can represent the sample space for tossing two fair coins as {HH, TH, HT, TT}, where H stands for head and T stands for tail. The event of getting one tail when tossing two coins consists of 2 outcomes: TH and HT. Because the total number of outcomes in the sample space is 4, the theoretical probability of getting one tail is:

$$\frac{2}{4} = \frac{1}{2}$$

h. Use the information in Table 2-1 to determine the theoretical probability of each of the following events:

1. winning a red apple
2. winning a yellow apple
3. winning a green apple
4. winning an apple of any color

Note: Save your results for use in Problem **3.1**.

Discussion

a. Compare the theoretical probabilities of the events in the Apple Lottery with the experimental probabilities you determined in Part **f** of the exploration.

b. Compare the experimental probabilities determined using the class results in Part **h** with their corresponding theoretical probabilities.

c. How does the pair of numbers you selected for your Apple Lottery ticket affect the theoretical probability of winning each type of apple?

Module 2 ■ *I'm Not So Sure Anymore* 37

Warm-Up

1. Complete the following table, expressing all fractions in their simplest form.

Percentage	Decimal	Fraction
		1/4
	0.12	
8%		
	1.5	
0.3%		
		5/8

2. Describe the differences between experimental probability and theoretical probability. Give an example of each.

3. **a.** What is the sample space for tossing two coins?

   b. Determine the theoretical probability of obtaining each possible outcome when tossing two coins.

   c. What is the sum of the probabilities in Part **b**?

4. A bag contains 20 red marbles, 16 green marbles, and 12 blue marbles. If you select one marble at random from the bag, what is the probability that the marble is green?

Assignment

1.1 Explain why picking a new ticket in the Apple Lottery does not change the theoretical probability of winning a particular type of apple.

1.2 Judging from the theoretical probabilities, how many apples of each color do you think you would win after playing the Apple Lottery 1000 times?

1.3 Time has expired at the divisional basketball championship. The game is tied and Charrette is at the foul line. During the season, she made 4 out of every 5 of her free throws.

One way to simulate this situation is to use a spinner, as shown in the diagram on the right.

a. What does one spin represent in this simulation?

b. Use a pencil and a paper clip to simulate the arrow in the spinner. On a copy of the diagram above, spin the paper clip to determine whether Charrette makes or misses the free throw. If the paper clip lands on a boundary segment, spin again.

38 Module 2 ■ *I'm Not So Sure Anymore*

> c. Record the results of 30 trials. Find the experimental probability of Charrette making the free throw.
>
> d. Compare the experimental and theoretical probabilities of Charrette making the free throw.
>
> 1.4 Describe the sample space for each of the following situations.
>
> a. At the end of the school year, a student receives a letter grade for a science class.
>
> b. Two ordinary dice are rolled and the numbers added. For example, if one die shows a 6 and the other shows a 2, the result is 8.
>
> 1.5 Camie has asked Alicia to play a game of cards. This game involves two piles of four cards each. The first pile contains the ace, king, queen, and jack of diamonds. The second pile contains the ace, king, queen, and jack of spades. The object of the game is to select a card from the first pile, then match it with a card from the second pile.
>
> a. Determine the sample space for this game.
>
> b. What is the theoretical probability of obtaining a winning combination of cards?
>
> c. Does this game seem fair? Explain your response.
>
> d. If all eight cards were shuffled together in one pile, would the sample space and theoretical probabilities remain the same? Explain your response.
>
> ✷ ✷ ✷ ✷ ✷
>
> 1.6 A football coach wants to know the probability of winning the coin toss in the next three games if the team captain calls heads each time.
>
> a. One player decides to use a simulation to predict the probability of this event. The table below shows the results of 250 trials of tossing three coins.
>
> | Three Heads | Two Heads | One Head | No Heads |
> |---|---|---|---|
> | 29 | 109 | 91 | 21 |
>
> Use these results to determine the experimental probability of getting three heads.
>
> b. Another player tells the coach that he can determine the probability of getting three heads using the following sample space:
>
> {HHH, HHT, HTH, THH, HTT, THT, TTH, TTT}
>
> Use this sample space to determine the theoretical probability of getting three heads.
>
> c. Do the results of the simulation agree with the theoretical probability? Explain your response.
>
> Module 2 ■ *I'm Not So Sure Anymore*   39

teacher note

Each student will require a paper clip and a copy of the spinner template to complete Problem **1.3**. A blackline master appears in the Teacher Resources for this module. Alternately, students may use technology to simulate the experiment.

Students might wish to use playing cards to help determine the sample space in Problem **1.5**.

Assignment

Problems suitable for use as assessment items are identified by an asterisk (*).

1.1 Changing tickets does not change the theoretical probabilities because the number of outcomes in the sample space and the number of times each event occurs remain the same. No matter what pair of numbers is chosen, 6 cells in Table **2-1** correspond to a red apple, 1 cell to a yellow apple, and 8 cells to a green apple.

1.2 Students should reason that 40% of the apples will be red, about 53% green, and about 7% yellow. By multiplying the theoretical probability for each apple by 1000, the predicted results are 400 red, 533 green, and 67 yellow.

1.3 a. A spin represents one free throw attempt.

b–d. The experimental results should be close to the theoretical probability of 80%.

* 1.4 a. The sample space is the five letter grades: {A, B, C, D, F}.

b. The sample space is {2, 3, 4, 5, 6, 7, 8, 9, 10, 11, 12}.

1.5 a. There are 16 outcomes in the sample space. In the following table, A represents an ace, K a king, Q a queen, J a jack, S a spade, and D a diamond.

AD, AS	AD, KS	AD, QS	AD, JS
KD, AS	KD, KS	KD, QS	KD, JS
QD, AS	QD, KS	QD, QS	QD, JS
JD, AS	JD, KS	JD, QS	JD, JS

b. Because there are 4 winning combinations, the theoretical probability is 4/16 = 25%.

c. Answers will vary. Sample response: This game does not seem fair because Alicia has less than a 50% chance of winning the game.

d. Sample response: No. If all eight cards were shuffled together, two diamonds or two spades could be drawn, which means that Camie has a lower chance of winning.

 ✳ ✳ ✳ ✳ ✳

1.6 a. The experimental probability of getting three heads is 29/250 = 11.6%.

b. The theoretical probability of getting three heads is 1/8 = 12.5%.

c. Students should observe that the experimental probability supports the theoretical probability.

1.7 a. The sample space is listed in the table below. The types of apples won correspond with the numbers 3, 4.

Pair of Numbers	Number of Matching Digits	Color of Apple Won
1, 2	0	R
1, 3	1	G
1, 4	1	G
1, 5	0	R
2, 3	1	G
2, 4	1	G
2, 5	0	R
3, 4	2	Y
3, 5	1	G
4, 5	1	G

b. The theoretical probability of winning a red apple is 3/10 = 30%, a yellow apple 1/10 = 10%, and a green apple 6/10 = 60%.

c. 1. Use technology to randomly generate two numbers from 1 to 5 and repeat this 100 times.

2. Sample data:

Color of Apple	Number of Wins
red	32
yellow	14
green	54

3. Using the sample data, the experimental probability of winning a red apple is 32/100 = 32%, a yellow apple 14/100 = 14%, and a green apple 54/100 = 54%.

d. Sample response: Yes, the experimental probability supports the theoretical probability. The values are very close.

e. Sample response: Theoretically, you would have a better chance of winning a yellow apple in the Apple Lottery in which players choose numbers from 1 to 5. In this version, the probability is 10%; it was less than 7% in the original version.

1.7 In another version of the Apple Lottery, players choose two different numbers from 1 to 5. After lottery officials randomly select two different numbers from 1 to 5, prizes are awarded as in the original Apple Lottery.

a. Determine the sample space for this version of the Apple Lottery.

b. What is the theoretical probability of winning a red apple? a yellow apple? a green apple?

c. Devise a way to simulate playing this game 100 times.

1. Describe your simulation.

2. Run the simulation 100 times and record the results.

3. Using this data, what is the experimental probability of winning a red apple? a yellow apple? a green apple?

d. Do the results of the simulation agree with the theoretical probabilities you calculated in Part b? Explain your response.

e. In which version of the Apple Lottery are you more likely to win a yellow apple? Explain your response.

Research Project

A new game called the Match Lottery has the same rules as the Apple Lottery, except that the second number drawn need not be different from the first. In the Match Lottery, for example, players may select the numbers 3, 3.

Write a report on the Match Lottery that includes the following:

a. a description of the sample space

b. an explanation of how the difference in rules affects its simulation

c. the results of at least 100 trials in which the lottery ticket chosen has two different numbers

d. the results of at least 100 trials in which the lottery ticket chosen has two identical numbers

e. the experimental probabilities of winning each prize

f. the theoretical probabilities of winning each prize

g. an explanation of whether or not the results of the simulations support the theoretical probabilities

h. an explanation of whether or not any tickets have a better chance of winning a yellow apple than other tickets.

Research Project

a. The sample space for the Match Lottery contains 36 outcomes, as shown in the following matrix:

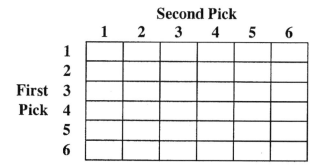

In Activity **1,** the theoretical probabilities for the Apple Lottery are calculated using a sample space of 15 outcomes. In that sample space, each possible outcome represents two ordered pairs and each has an equally likely chance of occurring. For example, the ordered pairs (1,2) and (2,1) are considered as the same outcome. However, it is also possible to consider the ordered pairs (1,2) and (2,1) as different outcomes, resulting in a sample space of 30 equally likely outcomes. This does not affect the theoretical probabilities for each event.

Because the Match Lottery allows pairs, this adds six more outcomes to the sample space: (1,1), (2,2), (3,3), (4,4), (5,5), and (6,6). If a sample space of 36 outcomes is not used, an outcome with two different numbers is more likely to occur than an outcome with two identical numbers. Therefore, ordered pairs such as (1,2) and (2,1) must be considered as different outcomes.

b. Since the Match Lottery does not require the two numbers chosen to be different, duplicate numbers are no longer a concern in simulating the game. If students use six numbered objects to simulate the lottery (as in the introduction), the first object drawn must be replaced and mixed with the others before the second object is drawn.

c. The table below shows the results of 100 trials using a ticket in which the numbers 1 and 2 were selected.

Color of Apple	Number of Wins
red	47
yellow	5
green	48

d. The following table shows the results of 100 trials using a ticket in which the numbers 1 and 1 were selected.

Color of Apple	Number of Wins
red	69
yellow	5
green	26

e. Using the sample data for a ticket in which two different numbers were selected, the experimental probability of winning a red apple is 47%, a yellow apple 5%, and a green apple 48%.

Using the sample data for a ticket in which two identical numbers were selected, the experimental probability of winning a red apple is 69%, a yellow apple 5%, and a green apple 26%.

f. Using a Match Lottery ticket in which the numbers 1 and 2 were selected, the apples won in any particular drawing can be indicated as follows (where Y, G, and R represent yellow, green, and red, respectively):

		Second Pick				
	1	**2**	**3**	**4**	**5**	**6**
1	G	Y	G	G	G	G
2	Y	G	G	G	G	G
First 3	G	G	R	R	R	R
Pick 4	G	G	R	R	R	R
5	G	G	R	R	R	R
6	G	G	R	R	R	R

When two different numbers are chosen, the theoretical probability of winning a red apple is $16/36 \approx 44\%$, a yellow apple $2/36 \approx 6\%$, and a green apple $18/36 \approx 50\%$.

Using a Match Lottery ticket in which the numbers 1 and 1 were selected, the apples won in any particular drawing can be indicated as follows:

		Second Pick				
	1	**2**	**3**	**4**	**5**	**6**
1	Y	G	G	G	G	G
2	G	R	R	R	R	R
First 3	G	R	R	R	R	R
Pick 4	G	R	R	R	R	R
5	G	R	R	R	R	R
6	G	R	R	R	R	R

When two identical numbers are chosen, the theoretical probability of winning a red apple is $25/36 \approx 69\%$, a yellow apple $1/36 \approx 3\%$, and a green apple $10/36 \approx 28\%$.

g. The sample results given in Parts c and d are reasonably close to the theoretical probabilities.

h. Based on the theoretical probabilities, a ticket with two different numbers is more likely to win a yellow apple than a ticket with two identical numbers.

ACTIVITY 2

In this activity, students use a spreadsheet to investigate the number of possible outcomes in large sample spaces.

Materials List

- playing cards (optional)
- sample space template (optional)

Technology

- spreadsheet

teacher note

In the following exploration, students discover a simple pattern that includes part of Pascal's triangle. Playing cards might be useful for keeping track of possible combinations.

Students must save their completed tables or receive a copy of the sample space template to begin the assignment. A blackline master of the template appears in the Teacher Resources for this module.

Student Outcomes

After completing the following exploration and discussion, students should be able to:

✳ use a variety of methods for simulation

✳ find that the sum of the probabilities for all outcomes of an experiment is 1

✳ create sample spaces

✳ determine theoretical probability using sample spaces

✳ make informal use of the fundamental counting principle

✳ identify and extend data patterns

✳ recognize and understand the small probabilities of winning many lottery games.

Exploration

a. Students enter the headings and first column of Table **2-2** in their spreadsheets.

ACTIVITY 2

To calculate the probability of winning a lottery, you must determine the number of outcomes in the sample space. Even though the sample space for the Apple Lottery is relatively small, other lotteries may have more than a million possible outcomes.

Exploration

By counting the number of outcomes in small sample spaces, you might observe some patterns that could help you determine the size of large sample spaces.

In one simple lottery, for example, players select 1 number from the set {1, 2, 3}. The sample space for this lottery contains 3 singles:

1	2	3

If players must select 2 different numbers from the set {1, 2, 3}, the sample space contains 3 pairs:

1, 2	1, 3	2, 3

If players must select 3 different numbers from this set, the sample space contains 1 triple:

1, 2, 3

The numbers of outcomes in these sample spaces are recorded in the third row of Table **2-2** below. (Because this lottery has only three available numbers, there are no quadruples or quintuples.)

TABLE 2-2 ■ *Size of Sample Space for Different Lotteries*

Numbers for the Lottery	No. of Singles	No. of Pairs	No. of Triples	No. of Quadruples	No. of Quintuples
{1}	1	0	0	0	0
{1, 2}	2	1	0	0	0
{1, 2, 3}	3	3	1	0	0
{1, 2, 3, 4}					
⋮	⋮	⋮	⋮	⋮	⋮
{1, 2, 3, . . . , 50}	50				

Module 2 ■ I'm Not So Sure Anymore 41

b. 1. There are 4 singles in the sample space:

1	2	3	4

2. There are 6 doubles in the sample space:

1, 2	1, 3	1, 4	2, 3	2, 4	3, 4

3. There are 4 triples in the sample space:

1, 2, 3	1, 2, 4	1, 3, 4	2, 3, 4

4. There is 1 quadruple in the sample space:

1, 2, 3, 4

c. The value in any cell of the spreadsheet can be determined by adding the value of the cell directly above it with the value of the cell up one row and to the left one column. For example, the number of triples in the sample space for the set {1, 2, 3, . . . , 50} is 19,600 because 18,424 + 1176 = 19,600.

 Note: A complete table appears in the sample space template included in the Teacher Resources for this module.

Numbers for the Lottery	No. of Singles	No. of Pairs	No. of Triples	No. of Quadruples	No. of Quintuples
{1}	1	0	0	0	0
{1, 2}	2	1	0	0	0
{1, 2, 3}	3	3	1	0	0
{1, 2, 3, 4}	4	6	4	1	0
{1, 2, 3, 4, 5}	5	10	10	5	1
{1, 2, 3, . . . , 6}	6	15	20	15	6
⋮	⋮	⋮	⋮	⋮	⋮
{1, 2, 3, . . . , 49}	49	1176	18,424	211,876	1,906,884
{1, 2, 3, . . . , 50}	50	1225	19,600	230,300	2,118,760

page 42

a. Create a spreadsheet with headings like those in Table **2-2**.

b. Consider a lottery in which players pick from the set {1, 2, 3, 4}. As you complete Steps **1–4**, record your responses in the spreadsheet.

1. If players select 1 number from the set, how many singles are there in the sample space?

2. If players select 2 different numbers from the set, how many pairs are there in the sample space?

3. If players select 3 different numbers from the set, how many triples are there in the sample space?

4. If players select 4 different numbers from the set, how many quadruples are there in the sample space?

c. Continue to determine the size of the sample spaces for other sets of lottery numbers. As you work, look for patterns that will allow you to quickly fill in all the cells of the spreadsheet.

Note: Save your completed table for use later in this module.

Discussion

a. What patterns do you observe in the spreadsheet?

b. How did you complete the spreadsheet?

c. What does the number in each cell represent?

d. How would you use the spreadsheet to determine the theoretical probability of winning a lottery in which 3 different numbers are picked from the set {1, 2, 3, . . . , 20}?

Warm-Up

1. What is the theoretical probability of rolling each of the following using a fair, six-sided die?

a. a three

b. a six

c. an even number

d. an even or an odd number

e. an even and an odd number

Discussion

a. Answers may vary. See response to Part **c** of the exploration.

b. Sample response: It is best to work through the first few cells in each column. This helps to see the patterns to generate formulas for the spreadsheet.

c. Each cell represents the size of the sample space for a lottery that draws *n*-tuples from a set of available numbers. In other words, each number in a cell represents the number of outcomes in a given sample space.

Note: In Level 1, students again use the fundamental counting principle in the module "Going in Circuits." It is formally developed in the Level 2 module, "Everyone Counts."

d. Sample response: By looking at the intersection of the column titled "number of triples" and the row titled {1, 2, 3, . . . , 20}, you can discover that there are 1140 outcomes in the sample space. If all three numbers must match, then there is only one way to win. The probability is $1/1140 \approx 0.09\%$.

Warm-Up

1. a. 1/6   b. 1/6   c. 1/2
    d. 1   e. 0
2. a. There are 36 possible outcomes.

1,1	2,1	3,1	4,1	5,1	6,1
1,2	2,2	3,2	4,2	5,2	6,2
1,3	2,3	3,3	4,3	5,3	6,3
1,4	2,4	3,4	4,4	5,4	6,4
1,5	2,5	3,5	4,5	5,5	6,5
1,6	2,6	3,6	4,6	5,6	6,6

3. 100% − 2% = 98%

teacher note

Students must have a copy of the sample space template or their spreadsheet from the exploration to begin the assignment.

Problem **2.3** again makes informal use of the fundamental counting principle. It must be completed to do Problem **2.4**.

Assignment

Problems suitable for use as assessment items are identified by an asterisk (*).

* **2.1** The number of quadruples is 91,390. This can be found in the intersection of the column titled "number of quadruples" and the row titled {1, 2, 3, . . . , 40}.

2.2 a. The probability is 1/10,626 ≈ 0.00009 ≈ 0.009%.
    b. The probability is 10/10,626 ≈ 0.0009 ≈ 0.09%.

2.3 a. The sample space contains 8 outcomes, as shown below.

(1,1)	(1,2)	(1,3)	(1,4)
(2,1)	(2,2)	(2,3)	(2,4)

    b. Because 4 possible white balls can be drawn for each of the 2 black balls, the size of the sample space is 2 • 4 = 8.

* **2.4 a.** The size of the sample space is 324,632.
    b. The size of the sample space is 35.
    c. Using the method from Problem **2.3,** the size of the sample space is 324,632 • 35 = 11,362,120.
    d. For any one ticket, the theoretical probability of matching the five white balls and one black ball is:

$$\frac{1}{11,362,120} = 0.000009\%$$

2.5 Answers will vary. If the class contains 30 students, then there are 142,506 different groups of 5.

✳ ✳ ✳ ✳ ✳

* **2.6** Sample response: I disagree with Josh. By extending the spreadsheet from the exploration, there are 38,760 possible ways to draw six numbers from the set {1, 2, 3, . . . , 20}. However, there are 43,758 possible ways to draw eight numbers from the set {1, 2, 3, . . . , 18}.

2.7 There are 45 ways to pick 2 gloves from a set of 10. Because there are only 5 different pairs, the probability of picking a matching pair is 5/45 ≈ 11%.

2.8 a. The size of the sample space is 1,221,759.
    b. The size of the sample space is 45.
    c. The size of the sample space is

$$45 • 1,221,759 = 54,979,155.$$

---

2. What is the sample space for rolling a pair of six-sided dice?

3. After analyzing its customer records, a rental-car company found that approximately 2% of its customers were involved in accidents. What is the probability that a customer chosen at random was not involved in an accident?

Assignment

2.1 Using your spreadsheet from the exploration, determine the number of quadruples you can select from 40 available numbers.

2.2 In one state lottery, players choose 4 different numbers from a set of 24. To win the jackpot, a player must match all 4 numbers.

    a. Use your spreadsheet to determine the probability of winning the jackpot with one ticket.

    b. What is the probability of winning the jackpot with 10 different tickets for the same drawing?

2.3 In the Double Pick Lottery, players pick a number from 1 to 4 from a white panel and a number from 1 to 2 on a black panel. Lottery officials randomly draw one ball from a container of four white balls and one ball from a container of two black balls. To win a prize, players must match the numbers on both the white and black balls.

A ticket for the Double Pick Lottery is shown below.

    a. List the sample space for this game and determine the number of possible outcomes.

    b. Describe how to determine the size of the sample space using the spreadsheet created in the exploration.

2.4 Another popular lottery game involves picking five numbers from 1 to 35 on a white panel and one number from 1 to 35 on a black panel. Lottery officials draw five balls from a container of 35 white balls and one ball from a container of 35 black balls. To win the lottery, players must match all five white balls and the black ball.

    a. Determine the size of the sample space when selecting five numbers from a set of 35.

    b. Determine the size of the sample space for selecting one number from a set of 35.

    c. Using the method you described in Problem **2.3b,** determine the size of the sample space for this game.

    d. Determine the theoretical probability of matching the five white balls and one black ball.

2.5 Determine the number of different groups of 5 that there are in your math class.

✳ ✳ ✳ ✳ ✳

2.6 In Lottery A, officials randomly draw six numbers from the set {1, 2, 3, . . . , 20}. In Lottery B, officials randomly draw eight numbers from the set {1, 2, 3, . . . , 18}.

Josh thinks that he is more likely to match all the numbers in Lottery B than in Lottery A because the set of available numbers is smaller. Do you agree with Josh? Explain your response.

2.7 A drawer contains an assortment of 5 different pairs of gloves (a total of 10 single gloves). If you randomly select two gloves from the drawer, what are your chances of getting a matching pair? Explain your response.

2.8 In one state lottery, players pick five numbers from the set {1, 2, 3, . . . , 45} and one number from the set {1, 2, 3, . . . , 45}.

    a. Determine the size of the sample space for randomly selecting five numbers from the set {1, 2, 3, . . . , 45}.

    b. Determine the size of the sample space for randomly selecting one number from the set {1, 2, 3, . . . , 45}.

    c. Determine the size of the sample space for making both selections in Parts **a** and **b.**

    d. Determine the theoretical probability that a player will pick the same six numbers as the lottery officials on a single ticket.

2.9 In another lottery game, officials randomly select four numbers from the set {1, 2, 3, . . . , 12} and a fifth number from a different set. The probability that a player will pick the same five numbers as lottery officials on a single ticket is 1/2970. How many numbers are there in the second set?

ACTIVITY 3

In many lotteries, the cost of playing is relatively small, even though the potential winnings could be very large. Typically, the probability of winning a large prize with any one ticket is low. Will playing the game many times increase your chances? In the following activity, you learn how much a lottery player can reasonably expect to win.

Exploration

The Apple Lottery has decided to change its prizes. In the new version of the game, players that match neither of the two numbers win nothing, players that match exactly one of the numbers receive $1.00, and players that match both of the numbers receive $3.00.

The cost of a New Apple Lottery ticket is $1.00. In the following exploration, you examine how much a player might expect to win at this game.

a. Create a spreadsheet with headings like those in Table 2-3 below.

TABLE 2-3 ■ Experimental Results for New Apple Lottery

Event	Prize	No. of Wins	Total Winnings
two matches	$3.00		
one match	$1.00		
no matches	$0.00		
	Sum	20	

b. Play the New Apple Lottery 20 times. Determine the number of times you won each prize and enter your results in the appropriate column of the spreadsheet.

c. Determine the total winnings for each row in the spreadsheet.

d. Find the sum of the winnings for all three events.

e. Calculate the mean amount won per game.

d. For any one ticket, the theoretical probability of matching all six numbers is:

$$\frac{1}{54,979,155} \approx 0.000002\%$$

2.9 Because the size of the sample space is 2970 and the number of quadruples that can be selected from the set {1, 2, 3, . . . , 12} is 495, the number of elements in the second set is 2970/495 = 6.

ACTIVITY 3

Students calculate the expected value for various games and determine if a game is fair.

teacher note

A brief assessment of the mathematical content in Activities 1–3, for use at your discretion, appears in the Teacher Resources for this module.

Materials List

■ sample space template (one per student; optional)

Technology

■ spreadsheet

teacher note

Students should retain their completed copies of Table **2-2** or a copy of the sample space template for use in the assignment. A blackline master of the template appears in the Teacher Resources for this module.

Student Outcomes

After completing the following exploration and discussion, students should be able to:

✷ use a variety of methods for simulation
✷ determine experimental probability
✷ find that the sum of the probabilities for all the outcomes of an experiment is 1
✷ create sample spaces
✷ determine theoretical probability using sample spaces
✷ calculate expected value
✷ determine if a game is fair or not.

Exploration

Students play the New Apple Lottery 20 times and record their results.

a–d. Sample data appears in the table below.

Event	Prize	No. of Wins	Total Winnings
two matches	$3.00	2	$6.00
one match	$1.00	8	$8.00
no matches	$0.00	10	$0.00
	Sum	20	$14.00

e. Using the sample data, the mean amount is $14/20 = $0.70.

f–g. The sum of the expected winnings is the same as the mean amount won per game. Sample table:

Event	Prize	Experimental Probability	Expected Winnings
two matches	$3.00	1/10	$0.30
one match	$1.00	2/5	$0.40
no matches	$0.00	1/2	$0.00
	Sum	1	$0.70

Discussion

a. Because 20 plays is a relatively small number of trials, the mean amount may vary considerably.

b. As shown below, the expressions for mean amount won per game and total expected winnings are equivalent:

$$\frac{2(\$3.00) + 8(\$1.00) + 10(\$0.00)}{20} = \frac{1}{10}(\$3.00) + \frac{2}{5}(\$1.00) + \frac{1}{2}(\$0.00)$$

c. Answers will vary. Sample response: Each game costs $1.00 to play and the mean amount won is $0.70, so you can expect a mean loss of $0.30 per game.

d. Sample response: To make the coin game a fair one, the cost of playing must equal the expected value. If a $2.00 prize were given for a match, then the expected value would be $1.00. Another possibility would be a $1.50 prize for a match and a $0.50 prize for no match.

e. Answers will vary. Using the sample data given in the exploration, the New Apple Lottery does not appear to be a fair game because the cost of playing ($1.00) does not equal the expected value ($0.70).

f. Sample response: Most lotteries are not fair games because they are designed to make a profit for their organizers.

Warm-Up

1. **a.** 2167.2
   b. 1500
   c. 5

---

f. Determine the experimental probability of winning each prize in the New Apple Lottery. Record these probabilities in a spreadsheet with headings like those in Table 2-4 below.

TABLE 2-4 ■ *Experimental Probabilities for New Apple Lottery*

Event	Prize	Experimental Probability	Expected Winnings
two matches	$3.00		
one match	$1.00		
no matches	$0.00		
	Sum		

g. 1. Multiply the value of each prize by its experimental probability and enter the product in the expected winnings column of Table 2-4.

2. Find the sum of the experimental probabilities and the sum of the expected winnings for the three events.

3. Compare the sum of the expected winnings to the mean amount won per game calculated in Part e.

Discussion

a. Compare the mean amount you won per game with others in the class.

b. Why does the sum of the expected winnings determined in Part g of the exploration equal the mean amount won per game?

c. On average, how much do you think you would win or lose by playing the New Apple Lottery?

---

mathematics note

The mean value of an experiment is the **expected value**. Expected value can be calculated by adding the products of the value of each event and its corresponding theoretical probability.

For example, consider a game in which players predict heads or tails, then flip a coin. If the prediction matches the result of the coin toss, the player wins $1.00. If the prediction does not match, the player wins $0.00. The products of the value of each event and its corresponding theoretical probability are shown in Figure 2-3.

Event	Value	Theoretical Probability	Product
match	$1.00	1/2	$0.50
no match	$0.00	1/2	$0.00
	Sum	1	$0.50

FIGURE 2-3   Expected value of a coin game.

Because the sum of the products is $0.50, the expected value of the game is $0.50.

A **fair game** is one in which the expected value equals the cost of playing. For example, if you paid $0.50 to play the coin game described above, the game would be mathematically fair.

d. If the coin game described in the mathematics note cost $1.00 to play, how might the prizes be changed to make it a fair game?

e. Judging from your experimental results, do you believe that the New Apple Lottery is a fair game? Explain your response.

f. Why do you think most lotteries are not fair games?

Warm-Up

1. **a.** What number is 72% of 3010?
   b. Sixteen percent of what number is 240?
   c. Fifteen is 300% of what number?
   d. Four-fifths of what number is 60?
   e. What number is 7/8 of 88?

2. The following table shows the probabilities of all the possible outcomes of an event. Use this information to calculate the expected value in this situation.

Outcome (x)	Probability P(x)
10	1/6
4	1/3
2	1/2

3. The theoretical probability of success in a certain event is 30%. Predict how many successes will occur in each of the following:

   a. 10 trials
   b. 40 trials
   c. *n* trials

Assignment

3.1 To determine if the New Apple Lottery is a fair game, you must analyze it using expected value.

   a. Create and complete a spreadsheet with headings like those in the table below.

Event	Value	Theoretical Probability	Product
two matches	$3.00		
one match	$1.00		
no matches	$0.00		
	Sum		

   b. Explain why the New Apple Lottery is not a fair game.
   c. Change the values of the prizes to make the lottery a fair game.
   d. Are there other prize values that make this a fair game? Explain your response. *Hint:* Use the spreadsheet to help you examine possible prize values.

d. 75
e. 77
2. The expected value is 4.
3. a. 3
   b. 12
   c. 0.3*n*

teacher note

Students should retain their completed copies of Table **2-2** or a copy of the sample space template for use in the assignment. A blackline master of the template appears in the Teacher Resources for this module.

For Problem **3.1,** students should refer to the sample space determined in Part **b** of the exploration in Activity **1.**

Assignment

Problems suitable for use as assessment items are identified by an asterisk (*).

* **3.1 a.** In the table below, dollar amounts are rounded to the nearest cent.

Event	Value	Experimental Probability	Product
two matches	$3.00	1/15	$0.20
one match	$1.00	8/15	$0.53
no matches	$0.00	6/15	$0.00
	Sum	1	$0.73

   b. Since the cost of playing ($1.00) does not equal the expected value ($0.73), this is not a fair game.

   c. The following table shows one possible payoff scheme.

Event	Value	Experimental Probability	Product
two matches	$3.00	1/15	$0.20
one match	$1.50	8/15	$0.80
no matches	$0.00	6/15	$0.00
	Sum	1	$1.00

   d. There are many other payoff schemes that make this a fair game (for example, a prize of $6.60 for matching both numbers, $1.05 for matching one number, and $0.00 for matching no numbers).

* 3.2 a. From the spreadsheet created in Activity **2,** there are 435,897 ways in which 5 numbers may be chosen from 37. The expected value can be calculated as follows:

$$\$20,000\left(\frac{1}{435,897}\right) + 200\left(\frac{160}{435,897}\right) + \$5\left(\frac{4960}{435,897}\right) \approx \$0.18$$

  b. Buying more tickets will not make this a fair game. For example, if a player buys 5 tickets, the cost to play would be $5.00. Each time the game is played, the expected value is approximately $0.18; therefore five plays would have an expected value of approximately $0.18 • 5 = $0.90. The cost of playing is still not equal to the expected value.

3.3 a. **1.** 1/20
     2. 1/20

  b. The expected value (in cents) can be calculated as follows:

$$1 \bullet \frac{1}{20} + 2 \bullet \frac{1}{20} + 3 \bullet \frac{1}{20} + \cdots + 20\,\frac{1}{20} = 10.5$$

  Because the expected value does not equal the cost to play, this is not a fair game. (It favors the player.)

3.4 a. 30 • 80% = 24 shots
     b. 500 • 80% = 400 shots
     c. 80% • n or 0.8n shots

3.5 a. Because there are 750 tickets, the probability that any one ticket will win is 1/750.

  b. The expected value can be calculated as follows:

$$\$300 \bullet \frac{1}{750} = \$0.40$$

  c. The expected value of $0.40 is not equal to the cost of a raffle ticket, so this is not a fair game.

3.2 In one state lottery, players select five numbers from 1 through 37. Tickets cost $1.00 each. The table below shows the values of the prizes in this lottery.

No. of Matches	Prize	Probability of Winning with One Ticket
5	$20,000.00	$\frac{1}{435,897}$
4	$200.00	$\frac{160}{435,897}$
3	$5.00	$\frac{4960}{435,897}$

  a. If a player buys one ticket, what is the expected value of the game? Describe how you determined your response.

  b. Can players make the lottery a fair game by buying more than one ticket? Explain your response.

3.3 In a carnival game, players pay 10 cents for one roll of a 20-sided die. Each side of the die shows a different number from 1 to 20. The number rolled is the value of the prize in cents.

  a. Find the theoretical probability of rolling each of the following:
     1. 20
     2. 15

  b. Use expected value to determine if this is a fair game.

3.4 A basketball player has an 80% chance of making a free throw. Determine the number of shots you would expect the player to make in:

  a. 30 attempts
  b. 500 attempts
  c. n attempts

3.5 Imagine that you have purchased one ticket for a benefit raffle. A total of 750 tickets have been sold at $2 each. From these tickets, one winner will be chosen at random. The prize is worth $300.

  a. Determine the probability that you will win the $300 prize.
  b. What is the expected value of this raffle for one ticket?
  c. Is the raffle a fair game? Explain your response.

3.6 A typical roulette wheel has 38 compartments, each of which has an equal chance of being selected during one spin of the wheel.

    a. If a player wins $30 for selecting the right compartment, what is the expected value of the game?

    b. For this to be a fair game, how much should it cost to play? Explain your response.

* * * * *

3.7 As part of its annual fund drive, the local hospital sells 400 raffle tickets for $5.00 each. From these tickets, one winner will be chosen at random to receive a prize of $100.00. If you buy one ticket, what is the expected value for the raffle? Explain your response.

3.8 In the Red and Blue Lottery, players choose four numbers from 1 to 20 on a red panel and one number from 1 to 20 on a blue panel. Tickets cost $1.00 each. The table below shows the probability of winning the two smaller prizes in the game.

No. of Matches	Prize	Probability of Winning with One Ticket
four red, one blue		$\frac{1}{96,900}$
three red, one blue	$200.00	$\frac{16}{24,225}$
two red, one blue	$5.00	$\frac{12}{1615}$

    a. Describe how to determine the probability of matching four numbers on the red panel and one number on the blue panel.

    b. If the expected value for one play is approximately $0.70, what is the value of the prize for matching four red numbers and one blue number?

    c. If the lottery commission sells 100,000 tickets for one game, how much money can it expect to make?

3.6 **a.** The expected value can be calculated as follows:

$$\$30 \cdot \frac{1}{38} \approx \$0.79$$

    b. Because the expected value of the game is approximately $0.79, the cost to play should also be $0.79.

✳ ✳ ✳ ✳ ✳

3.7 The probability of winning with one ticket is 1/400. The expected value is:

$$\$100 \cdot \frac{1}{400} = \$0.25$$

3.8 **a.** From the spreadsheet created in Activity **2,** there are 4845 ways in which four numbers may be chosen from 20. For each one of the 4845 ways to choose four red numbers, there are 20 possible blue numbers. This results in a sample space of 4845 • 20 = 96,900. Because only one choice will match, the probability is 1/96,900.

    b. Using the definition of expected value:

$$\$x \left(\frac{1}{96900} \right) + \$200 \left(\frac{16}{24,225} \right) + \$5 \left(\frac{12}{1615} \right) = \$0.70$$

Therefore, $x = \$51,430$.

    c. The expected earnings for the lottery equal the difference between the cost to play and the expected value for the player. For 100,000 tickets, the expected earnings are 100,000($1.00 − $0.70) = $30,000.

teacher note

You might wish to distribute copies of the sample space template (a completed version of Table **2-2)** for use in this assessment. A blackline master appears in the Teacher Resources for this module. An additional assessment, for use at your discretion, also appears in the Teacher Resources for this module.

Summary Assessment

Sample response: The Sample Lottery costs $1.00 for each ticket. Players pick three different numbers from 1 to 10. The prizes for 3, 2, 1, and 0 matches are $10, $5, $1, and $0, respectively.

From the spreadsheet made in Activity **2,** there are 120 different ways that 3 numbers can be chosen from 10. Therefore, the probability for matching all three different numbers is $1/120 \approx 0.83\%$. Using the spreadsheet again, the probability for matching two numbers is $1/45 \approx 2.22\%$, and the probability for matching one number is $1/10 = 10\%$.

The probability for no matches is what's left over:

$$100\% - 0.83\% - 2.22\% - 10\% \approx 87\%$$

The table below shows the theoretical probabilities for each prize and the expected value for the game.

Matches	Prize	Probability	Winnings
three	$10.00	0.0083	$0.08
two	$5.00	0.0222	$0.11
one	$1.00	0.1	$0.10
none	$0.00	0.8695	$0.00
	Total	1.0	$0.29

Because the expected value per play is $0.29, the expected revenue for the lottery is $0.71 per play. If 1 million people play the game, the expected revenue is $710,000.

Since 10% of lottery profits go to its creator, I expect to make 10% of $0.71 or a little more than 7 cents per play. This will amount to $71,000 for 1 million plays.

The following table shows the results of 1000 trials simulated using technology. (**Note:** Students are not required to run 1000 trials.)

Summary Assessment

Your state legislature has decided to start a new lottery. Earnings from the game will fund the construction of an amusement park. To attract an innovative and appealing design, the governor has agreed to pay 10% of all lottery profits to the creator of the new game.

Design a new lottery for your state. Your proposal to the state gaming commission should include:

- a description of how to play the lottery and the cost to play (you might wish to include a sketch of a sample lottery ticket)
- a list of prizes and a description of how each prize is won
- the theoretical probability of winning each prize
- the expected value of the lottery for one ticket and for 1 million tickets
- the amount you expect to earn for one ticket and for 1 million tickets
- a summary of the experimental results obtained from a simulation of your lottery.

Show all calculations and explain how your experimental results support the theoretical probabilities and expected values.

Module 2 ■ *I'm Not So Sure Anymore* 51

Matches	Prize	No. of Wins	Payoff
three	$10.00	5	$50.00
two	$5.00	26	$130.00
one	$1.00	119	$119.00
none	$0.00	850	$0.00
	Total	1000	$299.00

The total winnings of $299.00 are close to the expected value of 1000($0.29) = $290. The following table shows that the experimental probabilities are reasonably close to the theoretical probabilities.

Matches	Theoretical Probability	Experimental Probability
three	0.83%	0.5%
two	2.22%	2.6%
one	10.00%	11.9%
none	86.95%	85%

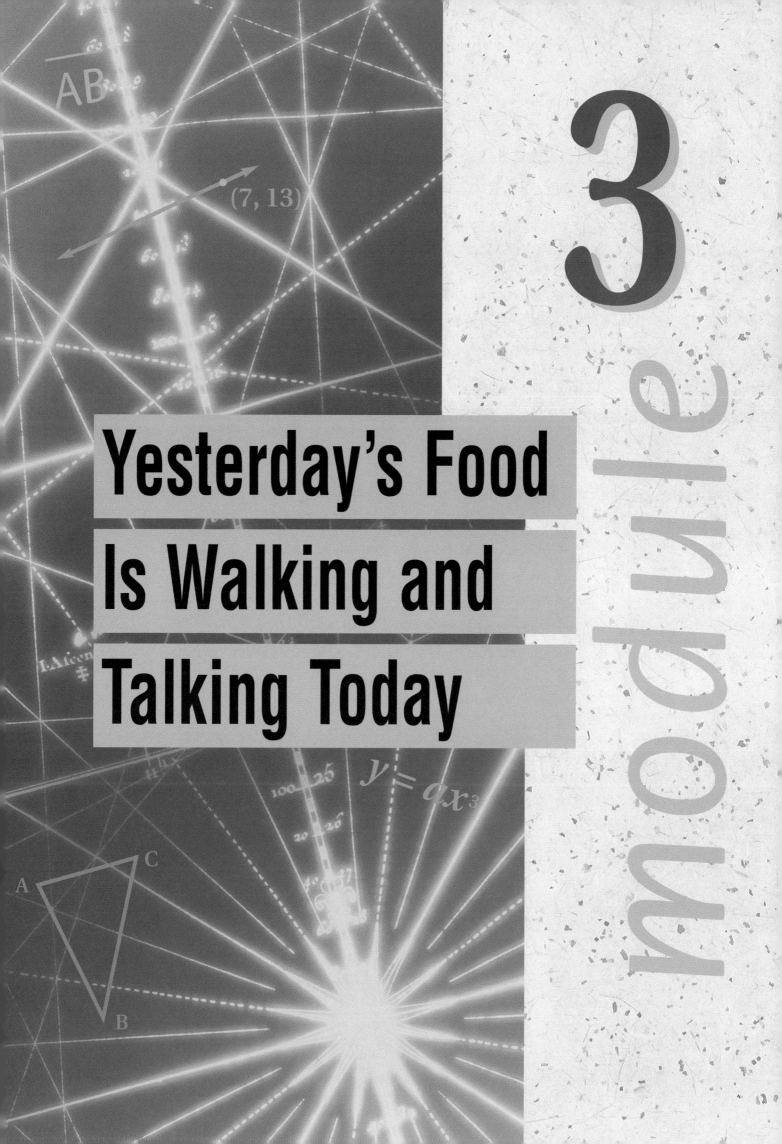

Yesterday's Food Is Walking and Talking Today

3

module

Overview

This module uses calorie intake and expenditure to extend students' understanding of linear relationships. By examining slope, y-intercept, and point of intersection, students gain experience analyzing graphs and solving equations.

Introduction: Students conduct a scientific experiment on the calorie content of food.

Activity 1:   Students use rates of kilocalorie usage to write linear equations of the form $y = mx$.

Activity 2:   Students investigate equations of the form $y = mx + b$.

Activity 3:   Students find the intersection of two equations and use the distributive property to transform equations in point-slope form to slope-intercept form.

Objectives

In this module, students will:

* interpret data from a table (Introduction)
* use a graphing utility to display data (1, 2)
* analyze scatterplots and line graphs (1, 2, 3)
* examine ratio as a measure of slope (1)
* examine slope as a rate (1, 2)
* write a linear equation given two data points (1)
* identify the domain and range of a linear relation (1)
* examine the slopes of parallel lines (2)
* write a linear equation given the slope and the y-intercept (2)
* write the equation of a line in point-slope form (2)
* use the distributive property to simplify linear expressions (3)
* graphically solve systems of linear equations (3)
* solve linear equations for y in terms of x (3).

Prerequisites

For this module, students should know:

✳ metric conversions

✳ how to express a rate

✳ how to plot and interpret points on a coordinate plane

✳ how to solve equations in one variable

✳ the principal subsets of the set of real numbers.

 Flashbacks, for use at your discretion, appear in the Teacher Resources for this module. These brief problem sets provide a review of some prerequisite skills for each activity.

Planning Guide

Activity	Materials	Technology	Time Line
Introduction	■ large can ■ small can ■ crucible (or tuna can) ■ metal rod ■ thermometer (°C) ■ 100–500 mL water ■ matches or lighter ■ paper clips ■ roasted mixed nuts ■ balance ■ safety goggles	■ spreadsheet ■ temperature probe ■ science interface device	1 day
Activity 1	■ none	■ graphing utility ■ spreadsheet ■ symbolic manipulator	3 days
Activity 2	■ none	■ graphing utility ■ spreadsheet ■ symbolic manipulator	3 days
Activity 3	■ none	■ graphing utility ■ symbolic manipulator	2 days
Assessment Activities	■ none	■ none	3 days **Total: 12 days**

 teacher note

In all activities, students use a graphing utility and spreadsheet to graph scatterplots and linear equations.

In the exploration in the introduction, you might wish to use a science interface device and temperature probe instead of a thermometer.

Introduction

In this introduction, students estimate the caloric value of food. The experiment is designed to engage students in the context of the module. Students burn several different kinds of nuts, measure the amount of heat produced, and convert their data into calories and kilocalories.

Materials List

- safety goggles (one pair per student)
- large can with both ends removed and vent holes added (one per group)
- small can with open top (one per group)
- 100–500 mL water at room temperature (per group)
- crucible (one per group; a tuna can or jar lid may be substituted)
- thermometer (one per group)
- balance (one per group)
- metal rod (one per group)
- matches or lighter (one per group)
- paper clip (one per group)
- roasted mixed nuts (enough for each group to burn several nuts)

Technology

- science interface device (optional)
- temperature probe (optional)
- spreadsheet (optional)

teacher note

Students must wear eye protection throughout the experiment. They also should be advised to avoid loose clothing, tie back long hair, and remove dangling jewelry.

You might wish to conduct this exploration as a demonstration.

Student Outcomes

After completing the following exploration and discussion, students should be able to:

✳ express calorie content of food as a ratio of calories per gram.

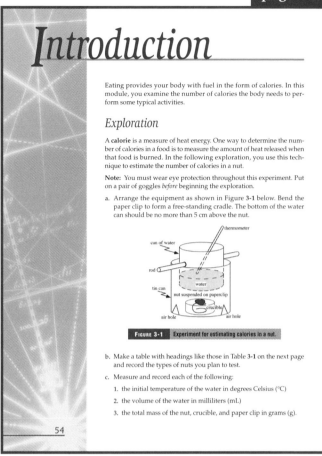

Introduction

Eating provides your body with fuel in the form of calories. In this module, you examine the number of calories the body needs to perform some typical activities.

Exploration

A **calorie** is a measure of heat energy. One way to determine the number of calories in a food is to measure the amount of heat released when that food is burned. In the following exploration, you use this technique to estimate the number of calories in a nut.

Note: You must wear eye protection throughout this experiment. Put on a pair of goggles *before* beginning the exploration.

a. Arrange the equipment as shown in Figure 3-1 below. Bend the paper clip to form a free-standing cradle. The bottom of the water can should be no more than 5 cm above the nut.

FIGURE 3-1 Experiment for estimating calories in a nut.

b. Make a table with headings like those in Table 3-1 on the next page and record the types of nuts you plan to test.

c. Measure and record each of the following:
   1. the initial temperature of the water in degrees Celsius (°C)
   2. the volume of the water in milliliters (mL)
   3. the total mass of the nut, crucible, and paper clip in grams (g).

54

Exploration

a. The experimental setup illustrated in Figure **3-1** is just one of many possible configurations. You might wish to consult a science teacher for suggestions on equipment. The paper clip should be bent to support the nut as it burns.

b. See sample data given in Parts **e–f** on the next page.

c. Beginning with water at room temperature and positioning the nut no more than 5 cm below the can of water yields better experimental results. Although it is important to measure the volume of water carefully, the quantity will vary from 100 mL to 500 mL, depending on the size of the can.

TABLE 3-1 ■ *Data for Calorie Experiment*

Type of Nut	Initial Temperature (°C)	Maximum Temperature (°C)	Initial Mass (g)	Final Mass (g)	Volume of Water (mL)

d. 1. Ignite the nut. As the nut burns, observe the change in water temperature.

2. Allow the nut to burn completely. Record the maximum temperature of the water.

e. Determine the total mass of the ash, crucible, and paper clip. The difference between this value and the mass measured in Part c is the change in mass (the number of grams that burned).

f. Repeat Parts c–e for several different types of nuts.

science note

A **calorie (cal)** is the amount of energy required to raise the temperature of one milliliter (1 mL) of water one degree Celsius (1°C).

A **kilocalorie (kcal)**, 1000 cal, is the amount of energy needed to raise the temperature of one liter (1 L) of water 1°C.

A **dietary calorie** (typically referred to as a Calorie with a capital C) is equal to 1 kcal. The calorie-per-gram rating on most food labels refers to dietary calories.

g. Create a table with headings like those in Table **3-2** below.

TABLE 3-2 ■ *Kilocalories in Different Kinds of Nuts*

Type of Nut	Change in Temperature (°C)	Change in Mass (g)	Volume of Water (mL)	Calories per Gram	Kcal per Gram

h. Use the data you recorded in Table **3-1** and the definitions described in the science note to complete Table **3-2**. In this case, the number of calories per gram in each type of nut can be calculated using the following formula:

$$\text{calories per gram} = \frac{\text{volume of water (mL)} \cdot \text{change in temperature (°C)}}{\text{change in mass (g)}}$$

Module 3 ■ *Yesterday's Food Is Walking and Talking Today* **55**

d. In the setup illustrated in Figure **3-1**, the nut can be ignited by moving the large and small cans, then replacing them after the nut has begun burning.

e–f. See sample data in Table **3-1** below.

g–h. See sample data in Table **3-2** below.

teacher note

The calorie content of food typically is determined using a bomb calorimeter. This device consists of a metal sphere in which food is placed along with pure oxygen. By submerging the calorimeter in water and igniting the contents electronically, the heat energy released can be measured precisely. Results are then adjusted according to the body's ability to metabolize each type of food.

Discussion

a. Experimental results can vary considerably. Most nuts contain close to 6 kcal/g.

b. One package of dry roasted peanuts reports 170 calories in a 28-g serving, or approximately 6.1 kcal/g.

TABLE 3-1 ■ *Data for Calorie Experiment*

Type of Nut	Initial Temperature (°C)	Maximum Temperature (°C)	Initial Mass (g)	Final Mass (g)	Volume of Water (mL)
brazil nut	23.0	25.0	24.66	24.62	100
peanut	24.0	30.0	20.58	20.49	100
almond	23.0	24.0	21.49	21.45	100
cashew	22.0	24.5	21.39	21.30	100

TABLE 3-2 ■ *Kilocalories in Different Kinds of Nuts*

Type of Nut	Change in Temperature (°C)	Change in Mass (g)	Volume of Water (mL)	Calories per Gram	Kcal per Gram
brazil nut	2.0	0.04	100	5000	5.0
peanut	6.0	0.09	100	6667	6.7
almond	1.0	0.04	100	2500	2.5
cashew	2.5	0.09	100	2778	2.8

c. Even though an incompletely burned nut will give off less heat, it also would lose less mass. The results should not be affected because the smaller loss of mass is accounted for when calculating kilocalories.

d. Using the experimental setup illustrated in Figure **3-1**, some heat is lost both while lighting the nut and during its burning. Experimental error may also be introduced in measuring the volume and temperature of the water and the mass of the nuts.

e. Sample response: The quantity of water has no bearing on the results since the calculations are adjusted accordingly.

ACTIVITY 1

Students calculate rates of kilocalorie usage for a variety of physical activities and use these rates to write equations of the form $y = mx$. Slope is defined as a rate and as the ratio of the change in vertical distance to the change in horizontal distance in the graph of a line. **Note:** Throughout this module, graphs of lines are used to model real-world relationships. Portions of a graph that lie outside the reasonable domain for the problem setting are represented as dashed lines.

Materials List

■ none

teacher note

A brief assessment of the mathematical content in Activity **1**, for use at your discretion, appears in the Teacher Resources for this module.

Discussion

a. Do all types of nuts appear to contain about the same number of kilocalories per gram?

b. Compare your results with the calorie-per-gram rating on a package of nuts.

c. If a nut failed to burn completely, would the experiment produce faulty data? Explain your response.

d. What types of experimental errors might have affected your data?

e. How would using a different quantity of water change the results of the experiment?

ACTIVITY 1

The human body uses calories at varying rates, depending on the level of activity. Calorie consumption also depends on a person's size, physical condition, and other factors. Table **3-3** shows the number of kilocalories used per minute during a variety of activities.

TABLE 3-3 ■ *Kilocalories Used Per Minute Per Kilogram of Body Mass*					
Activity	$\frac{\text{kcal}}{\text{min} \cdot \text{kg}}$	Activity	$\frac{\text{kcal}}{\text{min} \cdot \text{kg}}$	Activity	$\frac{\text{kcal}}{\text{min} \cdot \text{kg}}$
archery	0.065	drawing	0.036	painting	0.034
badminton	0.097	eating	0.023	racquetball	0.178
basketball	0.138	football	0.132	running	
card playing	0.025	golf	0.085	7.2 min/km	0.135
carpentry	0.052	gymnastics	0.066	5.6 min/km	0.193
circuit training		jumping rope	0.162	5.0 min/km	0.208
Universal	0.116	judo	0.195	3.7 min/km	0.252
Nautilus	0.092	lying at ease	0.022	sitting quietly	0.021
free weights	0.086	music playing		stock clerking	0.054
cycling		cello	0.041	swimming	
slow	0.064	drums	0.066	backstroke	0.169
medium	0.100	flute	0.035	crawl	0.156
fast	0.169	organ	0.053	table tennis	0.068
dancing		piano	0.040	typing	0.027
aerobic	0.135	trumpet	0.031	walking	0.080
normal	0.075	woodwind	0.032	writing	0.029

SOURCES: McArdle, et al., *Exercise Physiology*; Sharkey, *Physiology of Fitness*.

Technology

■ graphing utility

■ spreadsheet

Student Outcomes

After completing the following discussion, students should be able to:

✳ interpret data from tables

✳ solve simple linear equations.

teacher note

Student comprehension of Parts **d** and **e** of Discussion **1** are critical for the successful completion of this activity. You may wish to use this opportunity to demonstrate dimensional analysis. This process can be especially helpful when performing a multi-step conversion. For example, to convert volume measured in barrels (bbl) to cubic meters, students may "cancel" units as follows:

$$100\,\text{bbl} \cdot \frac{42\,\text{gal}}{1\,\text{bbl}} \cdot \frac{3.8\,\text{L}}{1\,\text{gal}} \cdot \frac{1000\,\text{mL}}{1\,\text{L}} \cdot \frac{1\,\text{cm}^3}{1\,\text{mL}} \cdot \frac{1\,\text{m}^3}{1 \cdot 10^6\,\text{cm}^3} = 15.96\,\text{m}^3$$

Discussion 1

a. What types of activities burn calories at a high rate?

b. What types of activities burn calories at a low rate?

c. When would your body burn no calories at all?

d. The units for the values in Table **3-3** are

$$\frac{\text{kcal}}{\text{min} \bullet \text{kg}}$$

Describe how these units can help you determine the number of kilocalories a 60-kg person burns while lying at ease for 30 min.

e. A 60-kg person playing basketball for x minutes burns 500 kcal. This can be represented by the equation $500 = 8.28x$.

   1. Both sides of this equation must have the same units: kilocalories. Explain why the expression $8.28x$ represents kilocalories.

   2. Describe how to determine x, the number of minutes spent playing basketball.

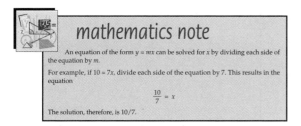

mathematics note

An equation of the form $y = mx$ can be solved for x by dividing each side of the equation by m.

For example, if $10 = 7x$, divide each side of the equation by 7. This results in the equation

$$\frac{10}{7} = x$$

The solution, therefore, is 10/7.

Exploration

a. Choose one activity from Table **3-3** that requires a high amount of energy, one that requires a moderate amount of energy, and one that requires a low amount of energy.

b. Create a table with headings like those Table **3-4** on the next page. Record the names of your chosen activities.

Discussion 1

a. As indicated in Table **3-3,** strenuous physical activities such as jumping rope, aerobic dancing, and swimming burn calories at a high rate.

b. As indicated in Table **3-3,** activities that require little physical exertion, such as lying at ease and sitting quietly, burn calories at a low rate.

c. The human body uses energy to maintain a constant temperature near 37°C (98.6°F), to circulate blood, and to perform other basic functions. The body ceases to burn calories only after death.

d. Sample response: Because you are looking for an answer in kilocalories, you must cancel minutes and kilograms by multiplying the table entry for lying at ease

$$0.22 \, \frac{\text{kcal}}{\text{min} \bullet \text{kg}}$$

by 30 min and 60 kg.

e. 1. Sample response: Using the appropriate entry from Table **3-3**, the energy usage for a 60-kg person playing basketball for x minutes can be represented by the following expression:

$$60 \text{ kg} \left(0.138 \, \frac{\text{kcal}}{\text{min} \bullet \text{kg}} \right) x \text{ min}$$

When this expression is multiplied, the units of kilograms and minutes cancel, leaving $8.28x$ kcal.

  2. To solve for x, divide both sides of the equation by 8.28:

$$500 = 8.28x$$
$$60.39 \approx x$$

Student Outcomes

After completing the following exploration and discussion, students should be able to:

✳ use a graphing utility to display data

✳ analyze scatterplots and line graphs

✳ describe ratio as a measure of slope

✳ describe slope as a rate

✳ write a linear equation given two data points

✳ identify the domain and range of a linear relation.

Exploration

Students create scatterplots and graph linear equations.

a–c. See the sample response in Table **3-4** below.

TABLE 3-4 ■ *Time Required to Burn Kilocalories for Three Activities*			
Energy Required	**High**	**Moderate**	**Low**
Activity	*Fast Cycling*	*Nautilus Circuit Training*	*Sitting Quietly*
Minutes to Burn 100 kcal	9.9	18.1	79.4
Minutes to Burn 200 kcal	19.7	36.2	158.7
Minutes to Burn 300 kcal	29.6	54.3	238.1
Minutes to Burn 400 kcal	39.4	72.5	317.5
Minutes to Burn 500 kcal	49.3	90.6	396.8

d. The following scatterplot uses the sample data given in Table **3-4.**

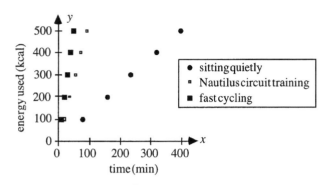

e. The table below lists equations for the sample activities given in Part **a.**

Activity	Equation
fast cycling	$y = 10.14x$
Nautilus circuit training	$y = 5.52x$
sitting quietly	$y = 1.26x$

f. Sample graph:

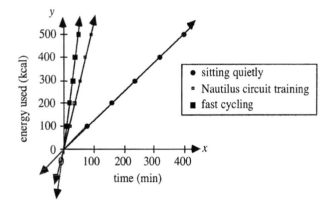

Discussion 2

a. The graphs all contain the origin.

b. High-energy activities have graphs that are closest to vertical.

c. Low-energy activities have graphs that are closest to horizontal.

d. 1. An 80-kg person uses 6 kcal of energy while playing cards for 3 min.

   2. In this situation, the rate is energy usage in kilocalories per minute.

e. 1. For the three sample equations given in Part **e** of the exploration, the slopes are 10.14, 5.52, and 1.26, respectively.

TABLE 3-4 ■ *Time Required to Burn Kilocalories for Three Activities*			
Energy Required	High	Moderate	Low
Activity			
Time to Burn 100 kcal			
Time to Burn 200 kcal			
Time to Burn 300 kcal			
Time to Burn 400 kcal			
Time to Burn 500 kcal			

c. For each activity you chose, calculate the time required for a 60-kg person to burn 100 kcal, 200 kcal, 300 kcal, 400 kcal, and 500 kcal. Record the answers in your table.

d. Graph a scatterplot of the data in Table **3-4** on a single set of axes. Represent time on the *x*-axis and energy used on the *y*-axis.

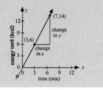

mathematics note

An equation of the form $y = mx$ represents a line that passes through the origin where *m* is the **slope** of the line. The slope is the ratio of the change in vertical distance to the change in horizontal distance between any two points on the line.

The slope of a line containing two points with coordinates (x_1, y_1) and (x_2, y_2) is

$$m = \frac{y_2 - y_1}{x_2 - x_1}$$

where $y_2 - y_1$ is the change in the vertical distance and $x_2 - x_1$ is the change in the horizontal distance. If $x_1 = x_2$, the line is vertical and has no slope.

For example, the graph in Figure **3-2** shows the energy used by a 80-kg person playing cards. This graph can be represented by an equation of the form $y = mx$, where *y* represents energy used in kilocalories and *x* represents time in minutes.

FIGURE 3-2 The slope of a line.

58   Module 3 ■ *Yesterday's Food Is Walking and Talking Today*

Using the points (7,14) and (3,6), the change in the vertical distance is 14 – 6; the change in the horizontal distance is 7 – 3. Therefore, the slope of the line is:

$$m = \frac{14 - 6}{7 - 3} = \frac{8}{4} = 2$$

Since the line passes through the origin and its slope is 2, the equation of the line is $y = 2x$.

e. For each activity in Table **3-4**, find an equation that expresses *y* in terms of *x*, where *y* represents energy used in kilocalories and *x* represents time in minutes.

f. Graph your equations from Part **e** on the same set of axes as the scatterplots from Part **d**.

Discussion 2

a. What common point is contained by all the graphs in Part **f** of the exploration?

b. What type of activities have graphs that are closest to vertical?

c. What type of activities have graphs that are closest to horizontal?

d. In Figure **3-2**, the line $y = 2x$ is used to represent the energy consumed over time by a 80-kg person playing cards.

   1. Describe what a vertical change of 6 and a horizontal change of 3 means in terms of playing cards.

   2. In this situation, the slope of the line $y = 2x$ is the measure of a rate. Describe this rate.

e. 1. Identify the slope of each equation you wrote in Part **e** of the exploration.

   2. Explain how the values in Table **3-4** can be used to determine the slope of each equation.

   3. Describe the rates represented by the slopes of these equations.

Module 3 ■ *Yesterday's Food Is Walking and Talking Today*   59

mathematics note

A **relation** between two variables is a set of ordered pairs of the form (x,y).

The **domain** of a relation is the set of first elements in the ordered pairs (the x-values). The **range** of a relation is the set of second elements in the ordered pairs (the y-values).

A **function** is a relation in which each element of the domain is paired with an element of the range and each element of the domain occurs in only one ordered pair. A function may be described by a rule or equation.

In mathematics, functions usually involve domains and ranges that are sets of real numbers. When a function is written without specifying the domain, you can assume that the domain comes from the set of real numbers. The range can be determined by finding the y-value that corresponds with each number in the domain.

For example, consider the function defined by the equation $y = 2x + 1$. In this case, the domain is the set of all real numbers. Each x-value is paired with only one y-value: a number that is 1 greater than twice the x-value. The range is also the set of all real numbers.

---

f. 1. What is the domain of the relation described by each equation you wrote in Part **e** of the exploration?

   2. What is the range of each relation?

g. 1. When the equation $y = 2x$ is used to represent the energy consumed over time by an 80-kg person playing cards, what values of the domain make sense?

   2. What values of the range correspond with these values of the domain?

Warm-Up

1. Use dimensional analysis to complete each of the following.

   a. _____ hr = 50 min = _____ sec

   b. 121 km = _____ m = _____ cm = _____ mm

   c. 60 mi/hr = _____ km/hr = _____ km/sec = _____ m/sec

   d. 2.4 L/hr = _____ mL/min

---

2. The slope of each equation can be calculated using any two values from a given column in Table **3-4.** For fast cycling, two points are 9.9 min for 100 kcal and 19.7 min for 200 kcal. The change in y (energy used) is $200 - 100 = 100$. The change in x (time) is $19.7 - 9.9 = 9.8$. Therefore, the slope is:

$$\frac{100 \text{ kcal}}{9.8 \text{ min}} \approx 10.2 \text{ kcal/min}$$

3. The slopes of the equations represent the rate of energy usage in kilocalories per minute.

f. 1. Each domain is the set of all real numbers.

   2. Each range is the set of all real numbers.

g. 1. Sample response: Because it is not possible to play cards for a negative number of minutes, only non-negative real numbers make sense.

   2. The corresponding range is the set of non-negative real numbers. **Note:** In Figure **3-2,** the unused part of the graph is indicated by a dotted line.

Warm-Up

1. All responses below are given to the correct number of significant digits.

   a. 0.83 hr; 3000 sec

   b. 121,000 m; 12,100,000 cm; 121,000,000 mm

   c. 97 km/hr; 350,000 km/sec; 350,000,000 m/sec

   d. 40 mL/min

2. **a.** $x = 3$ **b.** $y = 5$
    c. $x = -4$ **d.** $y = -14$
    e. $y = -17$ **f.** $y = 40$

3. **a.** $m = -3$

    b. $m = -17/3$

    c. $m = 0$

    d. The slope is undefined.

    e. $m = \dfrac{d - b}{c - a}$

4. **a.** $D = \{-3,1,2,4\}$; $R = \{3,6,7\}$; it is a function.
    b. $D = \{1,2,3\}$; $R = \{3,4,6,12\}$; it is not a function.

5. **a.** $m = 0$

    b. The slope is undefined.

---

teacher note

In Problem **1.9**, students write equations for horizontal and vertical lines.

Assignment

Problems suitable for use as assessment items are identified by an asterisk (*).

1.1 **a.** $(57 \text{ kg})(23 \text{ min})\left(0.178 \dfrac{\text{kcal}}{\text{min} \bullet \text{kg}}\right) \approx 230 \text{ kcal}$

    b. $(61 \text{ kg})(120 \text{ min})\left(0.132 \dfrac{\text{kcal}}{\text{min} \bullet \text{kg}}\right) \approx 970 \text{ kcal}$

    c. $y = (58 \text{ kg})(x \text{ min})\left(0.085 \dfrac{\text{kcal}}{\text{min} \bullet \text{kg}}\right)$ or $y \approx 4.9x$

    d. Both the domain and the range are the set of non-negative real numbers.

1.2 **a.** $\dfrac{300 \text{ kcal}}{(58 \text{ kg})\left(0.195 \dfrac{\text{kcal}}{\text{min} \bullet \text{kg}}\right)} \approx 27 \text{ min}$

    b. $\dfrac{320 \text{ kcal}}{(72 \text{ kg})\left(0.135 \dfrac{\text{kcal}}{\text{min} \bullet \text{kg}}\right)} \approx 33 \text{ min}$

    c. $y = (60 \text{ kg})(x \text{ min})\left(0.027 \dfrac{\text{kcal}}{\text{min} \bullet \text{kg}}\right)$

    or $y = 1.6x$; $x = \dfrac{y}{1.6}$

1.3 In Parts **a** and **b,** students may check their responses using proportional reasoning. For example,

$$\frac{500}{30} = \frac{x}{17}$$

a. Alexi uses about 280 kcal in 17 min of running. Sample graph:

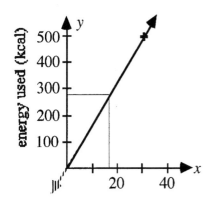

b. David uses about 20 kcal in 12 min of typing. Sample graph:

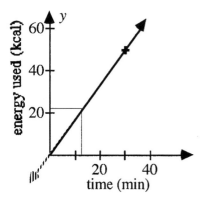

---

2. Solve each equation for the indicated variable.

    a. $4x = 12$ **b.** $-3y = -15$

    c. $-100 = 25x$ **d.** $y + 4 = -10$

    e. $y - 3 = -20$ **f.** $y/-4 = -10$

3. Find the slope of the line through each of the following pairs of points.

    a. (4,6) and (3,9)

    b. (−3,9) and (5,−8)

    c. (4,−6) and (3,−6)

    d. (5,−8) and (5,−7)

    e. (a,b) and (c,d)

4. List the domain and range for each relation below. Describe whether or not each relation is also a function.

    a. {(2,3), (−3,6), (4,7), (1,6)}

    b. {(−1,12), (3,4), (−1,3), (2,6)}

5. **a.** What is the slope of the line with the equation $y = -2$?

    b. What is the slope of the line with the equation $x = 4$?

Assignment

1.1 **a.** How many kilocalories does a 57-kg person use playing racquetball for 23 min?

    b. Tristin has a mass of 61 kg. If he plays football for 2 hr, how many kilocalories will he burn?

    c. Write an equation that describes the number of kilocalories expended by a 58-kg person while playing golf for x minutes.

    d. Identify the domain and range of the relation you described in Part c.

1.2 **a.** Sigrid has a mass of 58 kg. While practicing judo, she used 300 kcal of energy. How many minutes did she practice?

    b. Miguel has a mass of 72 kg. His breakfast contained 320 kcal. How long will it take Miguel to use these kilocalories at his aerobics class?

    c. A 60-kg person uses y kilocalories while typing. Write an equation that expresses the amount of time, x, spent typing.

1.3 **a.** While running for 30 min, Alexi burns 500 kcal. Draw and label a graph to represent this situation. Use the graph to estimate how many kilocalories Alexi had burned after 17 min of running.

   b. While typing for 30 min, David burns 50 kcal. Draw and label a graph to represent this situation. Use the graph to estimate how many kilocalories David had used after 12 min of typing.

   c. While swimming, Alexi burns 150 kcal in 12 min and David burns 300 kcal in 28 min. Draw one graph to represent this situation. Use the graph to determine who would burn more kilocalories in 1 hr of swimming. Explain your reasoning.

   d. Which quantity represents the range of the relations described in Parts **a–c**: the number of minutes or the number of kilocalories? Explain your response.

1.4 **a.** Determine the slope for each change in vertical and horizontal distance shown in the table below.

Change in Vertical Distance	Change in Horizontal Distance	Slope
8	4	
4	8	
–8	4	
3	–12	

   b. On a single set of axes, sketch the graphs of the lines that pass through the origin with the slopes in Part **a**.

1.5 Find the slope of the line through each of the following pairs of points.

   a. (3,7) and (12,3)

   b. (5,2) and (6,–4)

   c. (12,–8) and (10,4)

   d. (–7,–2) and (–3,2)

   e. $\left(\frac{9}{7}, \frac{2}{5}\right)$ and $\left(-\frac{5}{7}, -\frac{3}{5}\right)$

1.6 The slopes of the lines you graphed in the exploration describe rates of energy usage in kilocalories per minute. Give an example of a rate which corresponds with each of the following:

   a. a large positive value for slope

   b. a small positive value for slope

   c. a negative value for slope.

d. The range of each relation is the number of kilocalories, because the range is represented by the y values and the *y* values on the graph represent the number of kilocalories used.

1.4 **a.** A completed table is shown below.

   b. Sample graph:

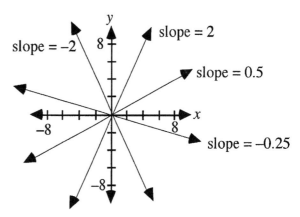

1.5 **a.** $\dfrac{3-7}{12-3} = -\dfrac{4}{9}$ **b.** $\dfrac{-4-2}{6-5} = -6$

   c. $\dfrac{4-(-8)}{10-12} = -6$ **d.** $\dfrac{2-(-2)}{-3-(-7)} = 1$

   e. $\dfrac{-\dfrac{3}{5} - \dfrac{2}{5}}{-\dfrac{5}{7} - \dfrac{9}{7}} = \dfrac{1}{2}$

1.6 **a.** In the exploration, the rate of energy use for a 60-kg person cycling fast is relatively large and positive (10.14 kcal/min). A speed of 100 km/hr is another example.

   b. In the exploration, the rate of energy use for a 60-kg person sitting quietly is relatively small and positive (1.26 kcal/min). A speed of 0.01 km/hr is another example.

   c. In Activity **2**, students investigate negative rates by considering the kilocalories held in reserve during exercise. For example, the rate of energy loss for a 60-kg person cycling fast is –10.14 kcal/min.

c. Sample response: The graph of Alexi's energy usage has a greater slope than the graph of David's energy usage. Because Alexi burns calories at a faster rate, he will burn more calories in 1 hr.

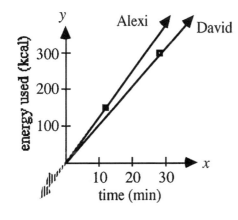

Change in Vertical Distance	Change in Horizontal Distance	Slope
8	4	2
4	8	0.5
–8	4	–2
3	–12	–0.25

1.7 **a.** The coordinates are $A(2,2)$, $B(4,4)$, and $C(8,8)$.

   b. **1.** The vertical change is 2, the horizontal change is 2, and the slope is 1.

   2. The vertical change is 4, the horizontal change is 4, and the slope is 1.

   3. The vertical change is 6, the horizontal change is 6, and the slope is 1.

   c. No. Slope is the ratio

$$\frac{\text{change in vertical distance}}{\text{change in horizontal distance}}$$

   This ratio remains constant for any two points on the line.

* **1.8** The following sample responses use painting as the activity.

   a. $y = (50 \text{ kg})(x \text{ min})\left(0.034 \ \dfrac{\text{kcal}}{\text{min} \cdot \text{kg}}\right)$ or $y = 1.7x$

   b. The following sample graph shows the energy used over time while a 50-kg person is painting.

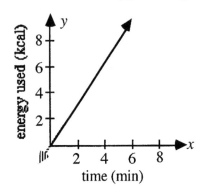

   c. In this setting, both the domain and the range are the set of non-negative real numbers. Values in the domain represent the number of minutes spent painting. Values in the range represent the number of kilocalories used.

   d. The slope of the line in Part **b** is about 1.7. In this situation, it represents the rate (in kilocalories per minute) at which a 50-kg person uses energy while painting.

   e. **1.** $y = 1.7(30) = 51 \text{ kcal}$
      2. $y = 1.7(100) = 170 \text{ kcal}$

   f. Using the sample responses given above, 30 min of painting results in an energy usage of 51 kcal, and 100 min of painting results in an energy usage of 170 kcal. The change in y (kilocalories) is 119, the change in x (time) is 70 min, and the ratio or slope is about 1.7.

1.7 Use the following graph to complete Parts **a–c**.

   a. List the coordinates of points A, B, and C.

   b. Find the change in vertical distance, the change in horizontal distance, and the slope (m) between:

   1. points A and B

   2. points B and C

   3. points A and C.

   c. Does the pair of points used to calculate the slope of a line affect the value of the slope? Explain your response.

1.8 **a.** Select one activity from Table **3-3**. Write an equation that describes the energy used over time by a 50-kg person performing this activity, where y represents energy in kilocalories and x represents time in minutes.

   b. Graph the equation.

   c. Identify the domain and range in this setting.

   d. Find the slope of the line and describe what it represents in this situation.

   e. Determine the number of kilocalories used when performing this activity for:

   1. 30 min

   2. 100 min

   f. Describe how the slope of the line can be determined from your responses in Part **e**.

1.9 **a.** Draw the graph of a horizontal line and label the coordinates of any two points on the line.

    b. Determine the slope of the line.

    c. Draw the graph of a vertical line and label the coordinates of any two points on the line.

    d. Determine the slope of the line.

mathematics note

A horizontal line has a slope of 0 and an equation of the form $y = c$. All the points on a horizontal line have the same y-coordinate, c.

A vertical line has no slope and an equation of the form $x = c$. All the points on a vertical line have the same x-coordinate, c.

    e. 1. Write the equation of the horizontal line in Part **a.**

        2. Identify the domain and range for this relation.

    f. 1. Write the equation of the vertical line in Part **c.**

        2. Identify the domain and range for this relation.

* * * * *

1.10 Sam's fast-food lunch contained 865 kcal. If his mass is 75 kg, how long would Sam have to jump rope to burn this amount of energy?

1.11 **a.** A sumo wrestler has a mass of 227 kg. Write an equation that describes the energy he uses over time while lying at ease. Let y represent number of kilocalories and x represent time in minutes.

    b. Sam's mass is 75 kg. Write an equation that describes the energy he uses over time while lying at ease. As in Part **a,** let y represent number of kilocalories and x represent time in minutes.

    c. Graph the two equations you wrote in Parts **a** and **b** on the same set of axes.

    d. Which line appears closer to vertical? What does this observation indicate in this setting?

---

* 1.9 **a–d.** Sample graph:

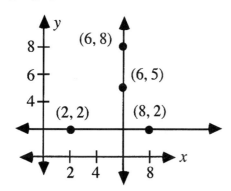

The slope of the horizontal line is:

$$\frac{2-2}{8-2} = \frac{0}{6} = 0$$

The slope of the vertical line is undefined:

$$\frac{8-5}{6-6} = \frac{3}{0}$$

e. Answers will vary.

  1. The equation of the sample horizontal line is $y = 2$.

  2. The domain is the set of all real numbers and the range is 2.

f. Answers will vary.

  1. The equation of the sample vertical line is $x = 6$.

  2. The domain is 6 and the range is the set of all real numbers.

* * * * *

1.10 While jumping rope, Sam burns kilocalories at the rate below:

$$\left(0.162 \, \frac{\text{kcal}}{\text{min} \cdot \text{kg}}\right)(75 \text{ kg}) \approx 12 \text{ kcal/min}$$

At this rate, the time to burn 865 kcal can be found as follows:

$$\frac{865 \text{ kcal}}{12 \, \frac{\text{kcal}}{\text{min}}} \approx 72 \text{ min}$$

1.11 **a.** $y = 227 \cdot 0.022 \cdot x$ or $y = 5x$

    b. $y = 75 \cdot 0.022 \cdot x$ or $y = 1.7x$

    c. Sample graph:

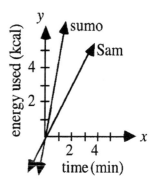

    d. The sumo wrestler's graph is closer to vertical. This means he uses energy at a faster rate than Sam.

1.12 a. $\dfrac{1220 \text{ m} - 1000 \text{ m}}{4 \text{ hr}} = 55 \text{ m/hr}$

b. $\dfrac{655{,}000 - 534{,}000}{1990 - 1980} = \dfrac{121{,}000 \text{ people}}{10 \text{ yr}}$

$= 12{,}100 \text{ people/yr}$

c. $\dfrac{\$32 - \$8}{1990 - 1950} = \dfrac{\$24}{40 \text{ yr}} = \$0.60/\text{yr}$

d. $\dfrac{1500 - 2400}{3 - 1} = \dfrac{-900 \text{ m}}{2 \text{ sec}} = -450 \text{ m/sec}$

e. Sample response: The domain is the times from 1 sec to 3 sec. The range is the altitudes from 2400 m to 1500 m.

ACTIVITY 2

This activity introduces students to the slope-intercept form of linear equations.

Materials List

■ none

Technology

■ spreadsheet

■ graphing utility

■ symbolic manipulator (optional)

teacher note

Table **3-5** gives only a sample listing of breakfast foods. You can obtain complete lists from the original sources.

Student Outcomes

After completing the following exploration and discussion, students should be able to:

✳ interpret data from a table

✳ use a graphing utility to display data

✳ describe slope as a rate

✳ describe the slopes of parallel lines

✳ write a linear equation given the slope and the *y*-intercept.

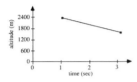

1.12 The slope of a line can be used to describe the average rate of change in one quantity with respect to another. For example, one familiar rate of change is speed, often expressed in kilometers per hour.

a. Rolando is climbing a mountain. At 10:00 A.M., he stood at an elevation of 1000 m. By 2:00 P.M., he had reached an elevation of 1220 m. Determine Rolando's average rate of change in elevation in meters per hour.

b. In 1980, the city of Tucson, Arizona, had a population of 534,000. By 1990, its population had grown to 655,000. Find Tucson's average rate of change in population in people per year.

c. In 1950, the price of a pair of jeans was about $8.00. By 1990, the price had risen to about $32.00. Find the average rate of change in the price of jeans in dollars per year.

d. The graph below shows the change in a parachutist's altitude (in meters) during an interval of 2 sec. Use the graph to estimate the parachutist's average rate of change in altitude in meters per second.

e. Identify the domain and range for the graph in Part **d.**

ACTIVITY 2

Many dietary specialists think of breakfast as the most important meal of the day. In this activity, you use linear equations to help plan an adequate breakfast for an active morning. Table **3-5** shows the number of kilocalories per serving in some typical breakfast foods.

TABLE 3-5 ■ Kilocalories Per Serving for Common Breakfast Foods

Food	kcal/item	Food	kcal/item
Toast, white	80	Croissant, egg, bacon, cheese	386
Toast, wheat	70	Biscuit, bacon, egg, cheese	483
Doughnut, plain	240	Biscuit with sausage	330
Cereal, with sugar	180	Cherry pie	260
Cereal, plain	120	Egg with muffin	340
Apple	60	English muffin with butter	186
Banana	80	Hotcakes with butter	500
Grapefruit	60	French toast	400
Orange juice	120	Fries	360
Egg, fried	120	Omelet	290
Egg, scrambled	80	Sausage, one patty	200
Egg, substitute	90	Milk, 2%	112
Milk, whole	160	Milk, chocolate	192
Yogurt, plain	120	Peanut butter and jam	500
Coffee	0	Soda pop	144

Sources: Gebhardt and Matthews, *Nutritive Value of Foods*; McArdle, et al., *Exercise Physiology*; Page and Raper, *Food and Your Weight*.

Exploration

a. Use the information in Tables **3-3** and **3-5** to design a breakfast that will supply a 62-kg person with the number of kilocalories necessary to play racquetball for 1 hr.

b. Make a table that shows the kilocalories remaining from the meal at the end of each 5-min interval of racquetball.

c. Create a scatterplot of the data from Part **b.** Let the time in minutes be the domain of the relation and the energy remaining be the range.

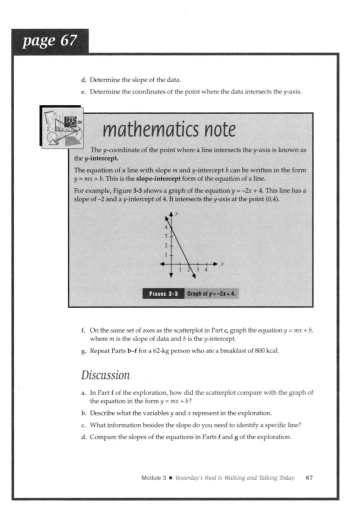

d. Determine the slope of the data.

e. Determine the coordinates of the point where the data intersects the *y*-axis.

mathematics note

The *y*-coordinate of the point where a line intersects the *y*-axis is known as the **y-intercept.**

The equation of a line with slope *m* and *y*-intercept *b* can be written in the form $y = mx + b$. This is the **slope-intercept** form of the equation of a line.

For example, Figure **3-3** shows a graph of the equation $y = -2x + 4$. This line has a slope of –2 and a *y*-intercept of 4. It intersects the *y*-axis at the point (0,4).

FIGURE 3-3 Graph of $y = -2x + 4$.

f. On the same set of axes as the scatterplot in Part **c**, graph the equation $y = mx + b$, where *m* is the slope of data and *b* is the *y*-intercept.

g. Repeat Parts **b–f** for a 62-kg person who ate a breakfast of 800 kcal.

Discussion

a. In Part **f** of the exploration, how did the scatterplot compare with the graph of the equation in the form $y = mx + b$?

b. Describe what the variables *y* and *x* represent in the exploration.

c. What information besides the slope do you need to identify a specific line?

d. Compare the slopes of the equations in Parts **f** and **g** of the exploration.

Exploration

a. The kilocalories needed for a 62-kg person to play racquetball for 1 hr can be found as follows:

$$\left(0.178 \frac{\text{kcal}}{\text{min} \cdot \text{kg}}\right)(60 \text{ min})(62 \text{ kg}) \approx 662 \text{ kcal}$$

An adequate breakfast might include a glass of 2% milk (112 kcal), an omelet (290 kcal), a glass of orange juice (120 kcal), and two pieces of wheat toast (140 kcal).

b–g. While playing racquetball, a 62-kg person burns approximately 55 kcal every 5 min. See the sample table below.

Both graphs have the same slope. Using the points (5,607) and (10,552), for example, the slope is:

$$\frac{607 - 552}{5 - 10} = -11$$

The graphs intersect the *y*-axis at 662 and 800, respectively.

The equation that models the energy remaining after a 662-kcal breakfast is $y = -11x + 662$. The equation that models the energy remaining after a 800-kcal breakfast is $y = -11x + 800$. The following graph shows both equations along with the respective scatterplots.

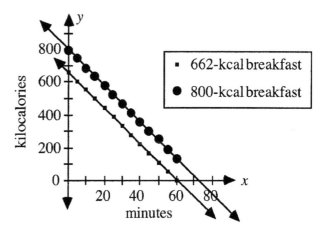

Discussion

a. Sample response: The graph of the equation goes through the points on the scatterplot.

b. In this situation, *y* represents the kilocalories remaining from breakfast as the person plays racquetball, while *x* represents the minutes that the person plays racquetball.

c. The two identifying characteristics of a line are slope and *y*-intercept.

d. The slopes of the equations are equal; therefore, the graphs of the equations are parallel.

Time (min)	Energy Remaining from 662-kcal Meal	Energy Remaining from 800-kcal Meal
0	662	800
5	607	745
10	552	690
⋮	⋮	⋮
55	57	195
60	2	140

e. When a linear equation is written in slope-intercept form, the slope is the coefficient of x, while the y-intercept is the constant. In the equation $y = 7x + 6$, for example, the slope is 7 and the y-intercept is 6.

f. Sample response: Given the slope m and the y-intercept b of a line, the general form of its equation is $y = mx + b$.

Warm-Up

1. **a.** $m = 3$, $b = 1$ **b.** $m = -2$, $b = 5$
   c. $m = 2/3$, $b = -5$ **d.** $m = -1$, $b = -3$
2. **a.** $y = 7x - 3$ **b.** $y = (1/4)x - 5$
   c. $y = -(2/5)x + 7$
3. **a.** Both lines have a slope of 3, so they are parallel.
   b. The two lines have different slopes, 1/4 and 3/4, so they are not parallel.
   c. Both lines have a slope of -2, so they are parallel.

teacher note

Students might find symbolic manipulators helpful in the assignment. In Problem **2.7**, students write an equation of a line in point-slope form.

Assignment

Problems suitable for use as assessment items are identified by an asterisk (*).

* 2.1 a. The kilocalories needed for a 50-kg person to dance aerobically for 1 hr can be found as follows:

$$\left(0.135\ \frac{\text{kcal}}{\text{min} \cdot \text{kg}}\right)(60\ \text{min})(50\ \text{kg}) = 405\ \text{kcal}$$

One possible breakfast includes wheat toast (70 kcal) and an egg with muffin (340 kcal) for a total of 410 kcal.

b. The corresponding equation for the sample breakfast in Part **a** is $y = -6.75x + 410$, where y represents the kilocalories remaining from the meal and x represents time in minutes.

c. $y = -6.75x + 600$

d. Sample graph:

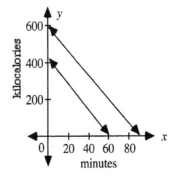

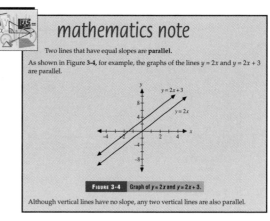

mathematics note

Two lines that have equal slopes are **parallel.**

As shown in Figure **3-4**, for example, the graphs of the lines $y = 2x$ and $y = 2x + 3$ are parallel.

FIGURE 3-4   Graph of $y = 2x$ and $y = 2x + 3$.

Although vertical lines have no slope, any two vertical lines are also parallel.

    e. Given the equation of a line in the form $y = mx + b$, describe how to determine its slope and y-intercept.

    f. Given the slope and y-intercept of a line, describe how to write an equation of the line.

Warm-Up

1. Identify the slope and y-intercept of each of the following lines.
      a. $y = 3x + 1$
      b. $y = -2x + 5$
      c. $y = (2/3)x - 5$
      d. $y = -1x - 3$

2. Write an equation in slope-intercept form for each of the following:
      a. the line with a slope of 7 and y-intercept of -3
      b. the line that crosses the y-axis at $(0,-5)$ and has a slope of 1/4
      c. the line with a slope of $-2/5$ and y-intercept of 7

---

   3. Identify each of the following pairs of lines as parallel or not parallel. Justify your responses.
     a. $y = 3x - 5$ and $y = 3x + 2$
     b. $y = 0.25x + 1$ and $y = 0.75x + 1$
     c. $2y = -4x + 6$ and $4y = -8x + 20$

Assignment

2.1 Imagine that a 50-kg person plans to dance aerobically for 1 hr.
   a. Use the information in Tables **3-3** and **3-5** to design a breakfast that will provide enough energy for this activity.
   b. Write an equation in slope-intercept form that describes the number of kilocalories remaining from the meal in Part **a** at the end of each minute of dancing.
   c. Write an equation in slope-intercept form that describes the number of kilocalories remaining from a 600-kcal meal at the end of each minute of dancing.
   d. Sketch the graphs of both equations on a single set of axes.

2.2 a. Identify the y-intercept of a nonvertical line that passes through the origin $(0,0)$.
   b. Write an equation for the line with a slope of 3 and a y-intercept of 4.
   c. Write an equation for the line that crosses the y-axis at $(0,5)$ and has a slope of -2.
   d. Write an equation for the line with a slope of 7/3 and a y-intercept of 2/5.
   e. Write an equation for the line that crosses the y-axis at $(0,-3)$ and has a slope of 2/5.

2.3 The following two equations were rewritten in slope-intercept form by solving for y in terms of x.

$$\begin{aligned} y - 5 &= 7x \\ y - 5 + 5 &= 7x + 5 \\ y &= 7x + 5 \end{aligned} \qquad \begin{aligned} y + 5x &= 7x \\ y + 5x + (-5x) &= 7x + (-5x) \\ y &= 7x + (-5x) \\ y &= 2x \end{aligned}$$

Use similar methods to solve each of the following equations for y.
   a. $y + 3 = 2x$ b. $y - 5 = 3x + 2$
   c. $y + 6x = 2x - 7$ d. $3x + 4y = 7$
   e. $2x - 3y = 6$

2.4 The following two equations were rewritten in slope-intercept form by multiplying both sides of each equation by the same quantity.

$$\frac{y}{3} = 4x \qquad\qquad 4y = 16x$$

$$3 \cdot \frac{y}{3} = 3 \cdot 4x \qquad \frac{1}{4} \cdot 4y = \frac{1}{4} \cdot 16x$$

$$y = 12x \qquad\qquad y = 4x$$

Use a similar method to solve each of the following equations for y.

a. $\dfrac{y}{-5} = 2x$

b. $7y = 4x$

c. $-2y = 8x$

2.5 As shown in the graph below, the points with coordinates (2,2), (6,4), and (x,y) are on the same line. In this case, the coordinates (x,y) represent any point on the line.

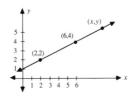

a. Calculate the slope of the line using the points (2,2) and (6,4).

b. Calculate the slope of the line using the points (2,2) and (x,y).

c. Write a mathematical equation that describes the relationship between the two slopes calculated in Parts **a** and **b**.

70   Module 3 ▪ *Yesterday's Food Is Walking and Talking Today*

2.6 As shown in the following graph, the points with coordinates (x,y), (x_1,y_1), and (x_2,y_2) are on the same line. In this case, the coordinates (x,y) represent any point on the line.

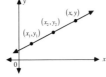

a. Write a representation for the slope of the line using the points (x_1,y_1), and (x_2,y_2).

b. Write a representation for the slope of the line using the points (x,y) and (x_1,y_1).

c. What relationship exists between the two representations you wrote in Parts **a** and **b**?

d. Write a mathematical equation that describes this relationship.

mathematics note

The equation of a line that passes through the point (x_1,y_1) and has a slope of m can be written in the form: $y - y_1 = m(x - x_1)$. This is the **point-slope form** of the equation of a line.

For example, the point-slope equation of a line that passes through the point (2,–4) and has slope of –7 is $y - (-4) = -7(x - 2)$.

2.7 a. Write an equation in point-slope form for each of the following lines.

1. The line that passes through (5,8) and has a slope of –3.

2. The line that passes through (2,10) and (12,5).

3. The line that passes through the origin and has a slope of 2/3.

4. The line that passes through (–6,4) and (–2,5).

b. Rewrite each equation from Part **a** in slope-intercept form.

＊ ＊ ＊ ＊ ＊

Module 3 ▪ *Yesterday's Food Is Walking and Talking Today*   71

2.2 **a.** 0

b. $y = 3x + 4$

c. $y = -2x + 5$

d. $y = \dfrac{7}{3}x + \dfrac{2}{5}$

e. $y = \dfrac{2}{5}x - 3$

2.3 **a.** $y = 2x - 3$

b. $y = 3x + 7$

c. $y = -4x - 7$

d. $y = -\dfrac{3}{4}x + \dfrac{7}{4}$

e. $y = \dfrac{2}{3}x - 2$

2.4 **a.** $y = -10x$

b. $y = \dfrac{4}{7}x$

c. $y = -4x$

2.5 **a.** $\dfrac{4-2}{6-2} = \dfrac{1}{2}$

b. $\dfrac{y-2}{x-2}$

c. $\dfrac{y-2}{x-2} = \dfrac{1}{2}$ or $y - 2 = \dfrac{1}{2}(x - 2)$

2.6 **a.** $\dfrac{y_2 - y_1}{x_2 - x_1}$

b. $\dfrac{y - y_1}{x - x_1}$

c. Sample response: These two expressions are equal because they both represent the slope of the same line.

d. $\dfrac{y - y_1}{x - x_1} = \dfrac{y_2 - y_1}{x_2 - x_1}$ or $y - y_1 = \dfrac{y_2 - y_1}{x_2 - x_1}(x - x_1)$

2.7 **a.** 1. $y - 8 = -3(x - 5)$

2. $y - 10 = -\dfrac{1}{2}(x - 2)$ or $y - 5 = -\dfrac{1}{2}(x - 12)$

3. $y - 0 = \dfrac{2}{3}(x - 0)$ or $y = \dfrac{2}{3}x$

4. $y - 4 = \dfrac{1}{4}(x - (-6))$ or $y - 5 = \dfrac{1}{4}(x - (-2))$

b. 1. $y = -3x + 23$

2. $y = -\dfrac{1}{2}x + 11$

3. $y = \dfrac{2}{3}x$

4. $y = \dfrac{1}{4}x + \dfrac{11}{2}$

＊ ＊ ＊ ＊ ＊

Module 3 ▪ *Yesterday's Food Is Walking and Talking Today*   **61**

2.8 a. linear   **b.** nonlinear
    c. nonlinear   **d.** nonlinear
    e. linear   **f.** nonlinear
    g. linear

2.9 a. 1. $m \approx 0.16$
      2. $m \approx 0.145$
   b. 1. $y - 8.2 = 0.16(x - 6.4)$ or $y - 7.5 = 0.16(x - 1.9)$
      2. $y - 0.120 = 0.145(x - 9.00)$
        or $y - (-0.460) = 0.145(x - 5.00)$
   c. 1. $y = 0.16x + 7.2$
      2. $y = 0.145x - 1.19$

ACTIVITY 3

Students find the intersection of two equations and use the distributive property to transform equations in point-slope form to slope-intercept form.

teacher note

A brief assessment of the mathematical content in Activities **2** and **3**, for use at your discretion, appears in the Teacher Resources for this module.

Materials List

■ none

Technology

■ graphing utility
■ symbolic manipulator (optional)

Student Outcomes

After completing the following exploration and discussion, students should be able to:

✳ analyze scatterplots and line graphs

✳ graphically solve systems of linear equations

✳ use the distributive property to simplify linear expressions.

2.8 Some equations do not represent lines. Using appropriate technology, graph the following equations and identify which ones are linear.
   a. $y = 2x + 3$
   b. $y = x^3 + 2$
   c. $y = 3x^2$
   d. $y = \dfrac{4}{x}$
   e. $y = -\dfrac{1}{3}x - 2$
   f. $y = \sqrt{x}$
   g. $y = 5x - 2$

2.9 Ordered pairs do not always involve integer values. Even when ordered pairs contain decimal values, however, the slope and equation of a line can still be found using the methods described in this activity.
   a. Find the slope of the line through each of the following pairs of points:
     1. (6.4,8.2) and (1.9,7.5)
     2. (9.00,0.12) and (5.00,–0.46)
   b. Write equations in point-slope form for the lines in Part **a**.
   c. Rewrite each equation from Part **b** in slope-intercept form.

ACTIVITY 3

In the previous activities, you examined nutritional information using a number of different methods, including graphs.

Exploration

After breakfast, Maurice and Janet enjoy a leisurely ride on their bicycles. As Janet rides, the number of kilocalories remaining from her meal can be described by the equation $y = -6x + 500$, where x represents time in minutes.
    Because Maurice is heavier than Janet, he uses more energy while cycling. The equation that describes the number of kilocalories remaining from his breakfast is $y = -9x + 710$.
   a. Describe what the slope and y-intercept of each equation represents in this situation.

Exploration

a. The slope of each equation represents the number of kilocalories burned per minute while cycling. The y-intercept represents the number of kilocalories in each person's breakfast.

b. Sample graph:

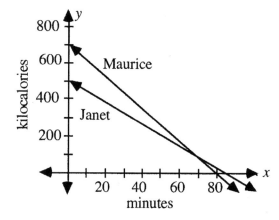

c. The point common to both lines is (70,80). Students should be able to estimate these coordinates from the graph or by using the intersection capabilities of a graphing utility.

d. Sample response: After 70 min of cycling, both Maurice and Janet have 80 kcal remaining from their breakfasts.

b. Graph both equations on the same set of axes.

c. Estimate the coordinates of the point common to both lines.

d. Describe what the coordinates of the common point represent in terms of kilocalories and time.

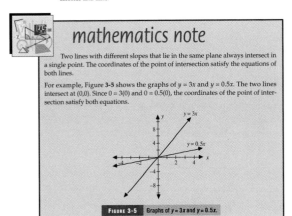

mathematics note

Two lines with different slopes that lie in the same plane always intersect in a single point. The coordinates of the point of intersection satisfy the equations of both lines.

For example, Figure **3-5** shows the graphs of $y = 3x$ and $y = 0.5x$. The two lines intersect at $(0,0)$. Since $0 = 3(0)$ and $0 = 0.5(0)$, the coordinates of the point of intersection satisfy both equations.

FIGURE 3-5 Graphs of $y = 3x$ and $y = 0.5x$.

Discussion

a. What information do the two equations in the exploration give about Janet and Maurice?

b. What would have to be true about these two equations if their graphs did not intersect?

c. Describe how to determine when Maurice and Janet had the same number of kilocalories remaining from breakfast.

d. What advantages are there to writing the equation of a line in slope-intercept form?

Discussion

a. The y-intercept of each equation represents the number of kilocalories in each person's breakfast. The slopes indicate the rates at which each person uses calories while cycling.

b. The equations would have to have the same slope.

c. The x-coordinate of the point of intersection indicates when Maurice and Janet had the same number of kilocalories remaining from breakfast.

d. Sample response: When an equation is written in slope-intercept form, it is easy to determine both the slope of the line and the point where the line intersects the y-axis.

e. Each equation can be written in slope-intercept form using the distributive property.
   1. $y = 5x - 20$
   2. $y = -3x - 6$
   3. $y = -7x + 35$

f. The following steps can be used to change an equation in point-slope form to an equation in slope-intercept form. Note that the y-intercept is represented by $-mx_1 + y_1$.

$$y - y_1 = m(x - x_1)$$
$$y - y_1 = mx - mx_1$$
$$y = mx - mx_1 + y_1$$

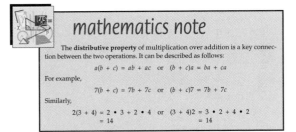

mathematics note

The **distributive property** of multiplication over addition is a key connection between the two operations. It can be described as follows:

$$a(b + c) = ab + ac \quad \text{or} \quad (b + c)a = ba + ca$$

For example,

$$7(b + c) = 7b + 7c \quad \text{or} \quad (b + c)7 = 7b + 7c$$

Similarly,

$$2(3 + 4) = 2 \cdot 3 + 2 \cdot 4 \quad \text{or} \quad (3 + 4)2 = 3 \cdot 2 + 4 \cdot 2$$
$$= 14 \qquad\qquad\qquad = 14$$

e. The following two equations were rewritten in slope-intercept form using the distributive property:

$y = 2(x + 3)$ $y = -5(x - 3)$
$y = 2 \cdot x + 2 \cdot 3$ $y = -5 \cdot x - (-5) \cdot 3$
$y = 2x + 6$ $y = -5x - (-15)$
                             $y = -5x + 15$

Use the distributive property to write each of the following equations in slope-intercept form:

1. $y = 5(x - 4)$
2. $y = -3(x + 2)$
3. $y = -7(x - 5)$

f. Using the distributive property, describe how to change an equation in point-slope form, $y - y_1 = m(x - x_1)$, to an equation in slope-intercept form, $y = mx + b$.

Warm-Up

1. Use the distributive property to expand each of the following expressions.
   a. $3(x - 2)$
   b. $0.5(x + 7)$
   c. $-2(x - 5)$
   d. $-\frac{5}{7}\left(x - \frac{2}{5}\right)$
   e. $1.6(x + 5.1)$
   f. $r(s - t)$

Warm-Up

1. a. $3x - 6$
   b. $0.5x + 3.5$
   c. $-2x + 10$
   d. $-\dfrac{5}{7}x + \dfrac{2}{7}$
   e. $1.6x + 8.16$
   f. $rs - rt$

2. The two expressions are equivalent because they both can be written as $4x + 12$ using the distributive property.

3. **a.** $m = 4/3$, $b = 8/3$

b. $m = -0.2$, $b = 0.3$

c. $m = 2$, $b = -19$

d. $m = 0.2$, $b = 6$

e. $m = s$, $b = r - st$

teacher note

In Problem **3.1**, students solve a linear equation for y in terms of x.

Assignment

Problems suitable for use as assessment items are identified by an asterisk (*).

3.1 **a.** $y = 2x - 3$

b. $y = 2x + 9$

c. $y = 16x - 13$

d. $y = 5x + 10$

e. $y = 3x + 2$

f. $y = 6x - 18$

3.2 **a.** The equation in slope-intercept form is

$$y = -16x + 620.$$

The slope represents Ricardo's rate of energy usage in kilocalories per minute.

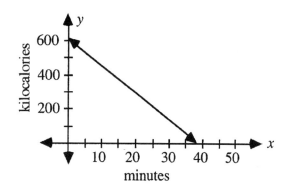

b. The equation in slope-intercept form is

$$y = 2x + 100.$$

page 75

2. Use the distributive property to determine if the expressions $4(x + 3)$ and $2(2x + 6)$ are equivalent.

3. Identify the slope and y-intercept of each of the following lines.

a. $y = (4/3)(x + 2)$ **b.** $y = -0.2(x - 1.9)$

c. $y + 7 = 2(x - 6)$ **d.** $y - 4 = 0.2(x + 10)$

e. $y - r = s(x - t)$

Assignment

3.1 It might require several steps to change some equations to slope-intercept form. For example, consider the following two equations:

$$y - 3 = 2(x - 5)$$
$$y - 3 = 2x - 10$$
$$y = 2x - 10 + 3$$
$$y = 2x - 7$$

$$\frac{y}{3} = x - 1$$
$$3\left(\frac{y}{3}\right) = 3(x - 1)$$
$$y = 3x - 3$$

Use similar methods to rewrite each of the following equations in slope-intercept form.

a. $y - 5 = 2(x - 4)$

b. $y + 2 = 2x + 11$

c. $y + 7 = 2(8x - 3)$

d. $\frac{y}{5} = x + 2$

e. $2y = 6x + 4$

f. $\frac{y}{3} = 2x - 6$

3.2 **a.** The equation $y - 700 = -16(x + 5)$, where x represents time in minutes, describes the number of kilocalories remaining from Ricardo's breakfast during a cross-country race. Write this equation in slope-intercept form and sketch its graph. What does the slope represent in this situation?

b. During the Olympic decathlon competition, Perry burned kilocalories at a rate described by the equation $y - 94 = 2(x + 3)$, where x represents time in minutes. Write this equation in slope-intercept form and sketch its graph. What does the y-intercept represent in this situation?

c. Kelly is spending a rainy summer afternoon reading a mystery novel. While reading, she uses kilocalories at a rate described by the equation $3y - 150 = 5(x - 12)$, where x represents time in minutes. What can you tell about Kelly's energy usage from this equation?

Module 3 ■ *Yesterday's Food Is Walking and Talking Today*   **75**

The y-intercept represents the number of kilocalories Perry had used before beginning the decathlon.

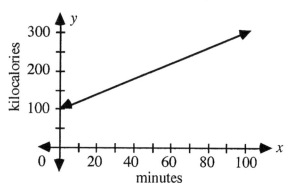

c. Sample response: In the form given, the equation yields little useful information. If rewritten in slope-intercept form

$$y = \frac{5}{3}x + 30$$

then you can tell that Kelly used 30 kcal of energy before beginning to read and is currently burning them at a rate of 5/3 kcal/min.

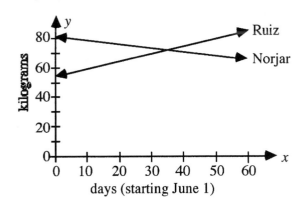

3.3 In Olympic competition, wrestlers must compete in specific classes according to their mass in kilograms. Two athletes, Norjar and Ruiz, plan to wrestle in the same class. On June 12, Norjar had a mass of 78 kg. By June 16, his mass had decreased to 77 kg. Ruiz's mass on June 14 was 62 kg. By June 18, it had risen to 64 kg.

a. Write the dates and masses for Norjar as two ordered pairs. What is the slope of the line containing these points?

b. Write an equation for the line describing Norjar's change in mass in slope-intercept form.

c. Determine an equation that describes Ruiz's change in mass.

d. Graph the two equations from Parts b and c on the same set of axes.

e. What does the point common to both lines represent in this situation?

f. What are the coordinates of this common point?

g. If the mass of each wrestler continues to change at its previous rate, on what date will their masses be equal?

h. What is the value of their masses on the date the masses are equal?

3.4 a. Determine the slope of the line that passes through the points (4,8) and (6,14).

b. Use the point (4,8) and the slope from Part a to write an equation of the line in point-slope form.

c. Use the point (6,14) and the slope from Part a to write an equation of the line in point-slope form.

d. Are the two equations you wrote in Parts b and c equivalent? Justify your response.

3.5 Imagine that you are the project director for the next space shuttle flight. For an experiment on energy usage in space, mission specialists Kimberly and Manuel must have the same mass on launch day. To reach this target mass, Manuel has increased his daily activities, while Kimberly has increased her consumption of calories. As project director, you have received the data in the table below.

Astronaut	Day 5	Day 10	Day 15	Day 20
Kimberly	no data	63.0 kg	64.5 kg	66.0 kg
Manuel	74.0 kg	no data	72.0 kg	71.0 kg

If the mass of both astronauts continues to change at the rate for the previous 16 days, on what day can the launch proceed?

f. If students represent dates as shown in the graph in Part **d,** then the coordinates are approximately (35,72).

g. Because there are 30 days in June, their masses are equal on July 5.

h. Their masses should be about 72 kg.

3.4 a. $\dfrac{8-14}{4-6} = 3$

b. $y - 8 = 3(x - 4)$

c. $y - 14 = 3(x - 6)$

d. The equations are equivalent. Both can be written as $y = 3x - 4$.

3.5 The equation for Kimberly's change in mass, where y represents mass in kilograms and x represents time in days, is:

$$y = \frac{3}{10}x + 60$$

The equation for Manuel's change in mass is:

$$y = -\frac{1}{5}x + 75$$

By finding the intersection of the graphs of these equations, students should determine that the launch can proceed on day 30.

* 3.3 a. Using ordered pairs, this information can be expressed as (12,78) and (16,77). The slope of the line through these points is

$$\frac{77-78}{16-12} = -\frac{1}{4}$$

b. $y = -\dfrac{1}{4}x + 81$

c. $y = \dfrac{1}{2}x + 55$

d. Sample graph:

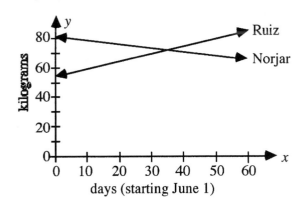

e. The point common to both lines shows when the masses of the two wrestlers are equal.

3.6 An acceptable alternate for Kimberly or Manuel must have a mass of 69 kg on day 30.

   a. The table below shows the equation for each potential alternate.

Britte	$y = 0x + 69$
Kwasi	$y = -\dfrac{7}{30}x + 76$
Sergei	$y = -\dfrac{9}{10}x + 96$
Yukawa	$y = \dfrac{13}{40}x + \dfrac{237}{4}$

   b. Because she does not have to gain or lose mass, Britte is the likely choice.

* 3.7   **a.** $y = 15x + 60$

   b. The coordinates of the point of intersection are approximately (3.8,117). This represents the time when Rolf and Tanya have used the same number of kilocalories. After 3.8 min, each person has used 117 kcal.

3.8   **a.** Students should find the points of intersection graphically.

    1. $(-2,-10)$

    2. $(-12,-21)$

    3. $\left(\dfrac{16}{3}, \dfrac{14}{3}\right)$

    4. $(5,4)$

   b. To verify each solution, students should substitute the coordinates of the point of intersection into both equations.

✱ ✱ ✱ ✱ ✱

3.9   **a.** $y = -x - 1$

   b. $y = -1$

   c. $y = \dfrac{1}{2}x$

3.10   **a.** $y = 150x$

   b. The slope of the line is 150. This indicates that Denali climbs at a constant rate of 150 m/hr.

   c. Denali will reach the top of the cliff in 2 hr.

3.11   **a.** $(7,4)$

   b. $\left(\dfrac{4}{3}, \dfrac{4}{3}\right)$

   c. $(5,-2)$

3.6 Four other astronauts also have been training for the launch described in Problem **3.5**. They are willing to change their caloric intake as necessary to substitute for Manuel or Kimberly. As project director, you must select one of them as an alternate. The table below shows the mass of each astronaut at some time during the previous 16 days.

Astronaut	Mass
Britte	69.0 kg on day 5
Kwasi	72.5 kg on day 15
Sergei	78.0 kg on day 20
Yukawa	62.5 kg on day 10

   a. Using the mass of Manuel and Kimberly and the launch day found in Problem **3.5**, write an equation for each potential alternate that describes the change in mass required to meet the mission restrictions.

   b. As project director, which astronaut would you select to serve as an alternate for this launch? Explain your decision.

3.7 Rolf and Tanya meet every morning to exercise. While warming up, Tanya uses 100 kcal of energy. She then burns 4.4 kcal/min during her walk. Rolf uses 60 kcal of energy during his warm-up and burns 15 kcal/min while running.

   a. The equation $y = 4.4x + 100$, where x represents time in minutes, describes Tanya's energy usage in kilocalories. Write an equation that describes Rolf's energy usage in kilocalories.

   b. Graph both equations in Part **a** on the same set of axes. Estimate the coordinates of the point of intersection and describe what these coordinates represent in this situation.

3.8   **a.** Find the coordinates of the point of intersection for each of the following pairs of equations.

    1. $y = 4x - 2$, $y = 2x - 6$

    2. $y = 3(x + 5)$, $y = x - 9$

    3. $y = \dfrac{1}{2}(x + 4)$, $y = 2(x - 3)$

    4. $(y - 2) = 2(x - 4)$, $(y - 5) = (x - 6)$

   b. Check each solution by verifying that the coordinates satisfy both equations.

✱ ✱ ✱ ✱ ✱

3.9 Write an equation in slope-intercept form for the line that passes through the given point with the given slope.

   a. (4,3), $m = -1$

   b. (3,–1), $m = 0$

   c. (–4,–2), $m = 1/2$

3.10 Denali is climbing a cliff 300 m high. After 30 min, she has moved 75 m up the cliff.

   a. Assuming that Denali continues to climb at a constant rate, write an equation that describes her distance from the bottom in meters in terms of time in hours.

   b. Identify the slope of the equation in Part **a** and describe what it represents in this situation.

   c. How long will it take Denali to reach the top of the cliff?

3.11 Find the coordinates of the point common to each pair of lines below.

   a. $\begin{cases} y = x - 3 \\ 4x + y = 32 \end{cases}$

   b. $\begin{cases} -3x + 6y = 4 \\ 2x + y = 4 \end{cases}$

   c. $\begin{cases} 3x + y = 13 \\ 2x - 4y = 18 \end{cases}$

Summary Assessment

Rick has a mass of 66 kg. Before sitting down at his desk, he always eats breakfast and completes a morning workout. After eating a large breakfast, Rick exercises by running at the fast rate of 3.7 min/km. After eating a moderate breakfast, he exercises by bicycling at a slow rate.

For Rick, a large breakfast consists of hotcakes with butter, an omelet, a cup of 2% milk, and a glass of orange juice. This provides a total of 1022 kcal. A moderate breakfast consists of an omelet, a cup of 2% milk, and a glass of orange juice, for a total of 522 kcal.

1. On a single set of axes, create a graph of each of the following:

    a. the kilocalories remaining from the large breakfast while Rick runs at the fast rate of 3.7 min/km

    b. the kilocalories remaining from the moderate breakfast while Rick bicycles at a slow rate

2. a. Estimate the coordinates of the intersection of the two lines in Problem 1.

    b. Describe what these coordinates represent in this situation.

3. After a certain number of minutes of running or biking, Rick will have the same number of kilocalories remaining from either breakfast. Determine how long Rick can perform his job as a writer using these remaining kilocalories.

4. The graph below shows Rick's energy usage in kilocalories while running fast and cycling slowly.

    a. Use the concepts of slope and rate to explain which line represents energy used while cycling and which line represents energy used while running.

    b. Describe how the graph can be used to approximate the slope of each line.

    c. Identify the domain and range of the relations that describe Rick's energy usage during both activities.

teacher note

To complete the summary assessment, students will need access to the information given in Table **3-3**.

An additional assessment, for use at your discretion, appears in the Teacher Resources for this module.

Summary Assessment

1. Rick burns 16.6 kcal/min while running and 4.2 kcal/min while cycling.
    a. The equation for kilocalories remaining while running after a large breakfast is $y = -16.6x + 1022$.
    b. The equation for kilocalories remaining while cycling after a moderate breakfast is $y = -4.2x + 522$.

Sample graph:

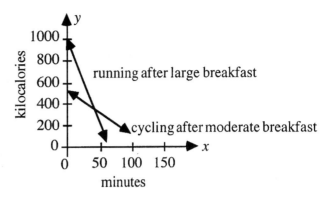

2. a. The approximate coordinates of the intersection are (40,350).
    b. Sample response: After approximately 40 min of running, there will be about 350 kilocalories remaining from Rick's large breakfast. The same number of kilocalories will remain from the moderate breakfast after he cycles for 40 min.
3. While writing, Rick burns kilocalories at 1.9 kcal/min. Because he has 350 kcal left from breakfast, it will take

$$\frac{350 \text{ kcal}}{1.9 \text{ kcal/min}} \approx 184 \text{ min}$$

to use the remaining kilocalories.
4. a. Rick burns kilocalories at a faster rate while running. The line which is closer to vertical has a larger slope; therefore it represents the faster rate of kilocalorie usage while running. The line with the smaller slope represents the energy used while cycling.
    b. The slope of each line can be determined by estimating the ratio of vertical change to horizontal change. The line that represents energy used while running has a vertical change of approximately 32 kcal for a horizontal change of 2 min. The slope is approximately 32/2 or 16 kcal/min. The line that represents energy use while cycling has a vertical change of approximately 8 kcal for a horizontal change of 2 min. The slope is approximately 4 kcal/min.
    c. The domain and range for both activities are the non-negative real numbers.

5. a. The slope of the line is:

$$\frac{270-590}{60-20} = \frac{-320}{40} = -8$$

Two possible equations in point-slope form are $y - 590 = -8(x - 20)$ and $y - 270 = -8(x - 60)$.

b. In slope-intercept form, the equation of the line is $y = -8x + 750$. This shows that Rick had a 750-kcal breakfast.

c. Because the slope of the line is –8, Rick is using 8 kcal/min while exercising. Since Rick weighs 66 kg, the rate per kilogram of body mass can be found as follows

$$\frac{8 \text{ kcal/min}}{66 \text{ kg}} \approx 0.12 \frac{\text{kcal}}{\text{min} \cdot \text{kg}}$$

One activity from Table **3-3** that uses kilocalories close to this rate is circuit training on a Universal gym, which burns

$$0.116 \frac{\text{kcal}}{\text{min} \cdot \text{kg}}$$

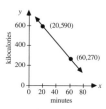
5. The following graph shows the number of kilocalories remaining after an entirely different breakfast and exercise routine for Rick.

a. Write an equation in point-slope form that describes the kilocalories remaining from breakfast as Rick exercises.

b. Rewrite the equation in Part **a** so that it shows the number of kilocalories in Rick's breakfast.

c. Identify an exercise that would result in this rate of energy use for Rick.

A New Look
at Boxing

4

Overview

In this module, students explore three-dimensional solids constructed from two-dimensional templates. Students construct and measure interior and exterior angles of regular polygons, determine which polygons tessellate a plane, and calculate surface areas of polygons and prisms. Students also work with percentages and ratios while calculating the material wasted in the production of templates.

Introduction: Students distinguish between prisms and non-prisms.

Activity 1:   Students create nets and templates and calculate their surface area.

Activity 2:   Students measure exterior and interior angles of regular polygons and determine which polygons tessellate a plane.

Activity 3:   Students develop and apply a formula for the area of a regular polygon.

Objectives

In this module, students will:

* identify prisms (Introduction)
* distinguish between a net and a template (1)
* find the area of regular polygons (1, 2, 3)
* use nets to find the surface area of solids (1, 3)
* calculate the waste created by a template and a shape that encloses it (1, 3)
* determine interior and exterior angle measures for regular polygons (2)
* determine which regular polygons can tessellate a plane (2)
* tessellate a plane with various polygons (2, 3)
* construct regular polygons inscribed in a circle using central angles (3)
* identify and use the apothem to determine the area of a regular polygon (3)
* derive a formula for the area of regular polygons (3).

Prerequisites

For this module, students should know:

* the names of polygons
* how to name angles, rays, segments, and lines
* the definitions of a parallelogram, rectangle, square, triangle, and trapezoid
* the definition of a regular polygon

* how to find the area of a square, rectangle, triangle, and trapezoid
* how to make a scale drawing
* how to use a geometry utility
* how to use a spreadsheet
* how to find percent increase and decrease
* how to use metric measurements.

 Flashbacks, for use at your discretion, appear in the Teacher Resources for this module. These brief problem sets provide a review of some prerequisite skills for each activity.

Planning Guide

Activity	Materials	Technology	Time Line
Introduction/Activity **1**	■ scissors ■ rulers ■ tape or glue sticks ■ grid paper template ■ rectangular boxes (such as cracker boxes)	■ none	2 days
Activity **2**	■ scissors ■ pentagon template ■ polygon template ■ grid paper template ■ construction paper or light cardboard	■ spreadsheet	3 days
Activity **3**	■ rulers ■ protractors ■ box template	■ geometry utility ■ spreadsheet	3 days
Assessment Activities	■ scissors ■ rulers ■ tape or glue sticks ■ grid paper template ■ construction paper or light cardboard	■ geometry utility	3 days **Total: 11 days**

 teacher note

Each student or group must have a box before beginning the exploration in Activity **1**. Ordinary cereal boxes will work, but smaller boxes (such as cracker boxes) may be easier to manage.

Two helpful references are Britton and Seymour's *Introduction to Tessellations* and Grünbaum and Shephard's *Tilings and Patterns*.

Blackline masters for the templates appear in the Teacher Resources for this module.

Introduction

Students review the definition of a prism and discuss several examples.

Student Outcomes

After completing the following discussion, students should be able to:

✳ distinguish between prisms and non-prisms.

Discussion

a. A cereal box can be considered a prism because it is formed by two congruent polygons in parallel planes—the top and bottom of the box. The front, back, and sides of the cereal box are parallelograms which can be formed by joining the corresponding vertices of the top and bottom.

Because the front and back are two congruent polygons in parallel planes, they also could be considered as the bases of the prism. The same reasoning can be used to designate the two sides of this box as bases.

b. The two triangular faces are the bases of the prism.

c. Many familiar objects are prisms, including compact disc boxes, briefcases, refrigerators, and some television sets.

d. A tennis-ball container is a cylinder, not a prism. The top and bottom of the can are congruent and lie in parallel planes, but these bases are circles instead of polygons. Therefore, there are no vertices that can be connected to form parallelograms.

ACTIVITY 1

Students use rectangular boxes to explore templates, nets, and surface area. They draw templates and nets, explore shapes that enclose templates, and calculate percentage waste.

teacher note

A brief assessment of the mathematical content in Activity **1**, for use at your discretion, appears in the Teacher Resources for this module.

Introduction

Gloria watches the clock: tick, tick, tick. Time always seems to drag when she's waiting for lunch. Finally, the bell rings. It's pizza time!

Friends, pop, breadsticks, and pizzas make Little Cheesers the most popular lunchtime hangout at Gloria's school. There's only one problem: time flies when she's having fun, and lunch is only 30 minutes long. As she heads for the door, Gloria asks for a box. She still has one slice of pizza left. On the way back to school, Gloria finishes her meal. Without a second thought, she tosses the box into the trash.

The cashier used a full-size box for Gloria's leftovers. A box big enough to hold a whole pizza might not be the best container for a single slice. If the box had been the right shape and size, less material would have been wasted. In this module, you will look at some different properties of boxes and explore how much material it takes to make them.

mathematics note

A **prism** is a three-dimensional figure determined by two congruent polygons in parallel planes whose corresponding vertices are connected by segments. The two congruent and parallel faces are the prism's **bases**. The parallelograms formed by joining the corresponding vertices of the bases are the prism's **lateral faces.**

For example, Figure **4-1a** shows a cereal box that, like many pizza boxes, is a prism with rectangular faces. Figure **4-1b** shows a box for a candy bar in the shape of a triangular prism.

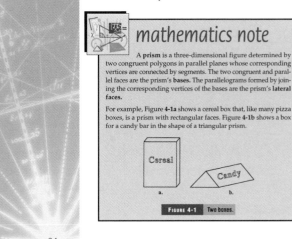

FIGURE 4-1 Two boxes.

84

Discussion

a. Explain why a cereal box is a prism.

b. Which faces of the prism in Figure **4-1b** are the bases?

c. Describe several examples of other objects that are prisms.

d. Is a tennis-ball container a prism? Explain your response.

ACTIVITY 1

The cardboard for the cereal box in Figure **4-1** was cut from a pattern. What does this pattern look like? In this activity, you examine a box and the pattern used to create it.

Exploration

Use a box similar to the cereal box in Figure **4-1** to complete the following steps.

a. Estimate the total area, in square centimeters, of all the sides of the box.

b. On a sheet of grid paper, make a scale drawing of the pattern you think the manufacturer used to create the box. Use dotted line segments to indicate folds. Cut out your paper pattern and fold it into a box.

c. Without tearing the cardboard, take the box apart and lay it flat. The box probably was constructed using glued tabs.

A pattern with tabs is a **template.** A pattern without tabs is a **net.** Figure **4-2** shows both a net and a template for a cube.

 net   template

FIGURE 4-2 Cube net and template.

d. Find the area of the net for the box. Compare this area to the estimate you made in Part **a.**

e. Imagine that the template for the box was cut from a rectangle of cardboard. Record the dimensions of the smallest rectangle that will enclose the template.

Module 4 ■ *A New Look at Boxing*   **85**

Discussion

a. Does your folded box from Part **b** of the exploration resemble the original box?

b. How does your paper pattern from Part **b** of the exploration compare to the template for the box?

c. Without making any calculations, compare the area of the net to the area of the template.

d. Why might a box manufacturer be interested in the smallest rectangle that will enclose a template?

e. How do the areas of the net and the template compare to the actual surface area of the box?

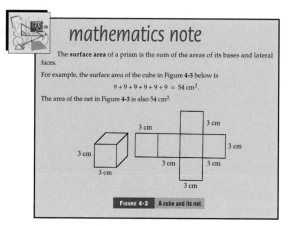

mathematics note

The **surface area** of a prism is the sum of the areas of its bases and lateral faces.

For example, the surface area of the cube in Figure **4-3** below is

$$9 + 9 + 9 + 9 + 9 + 9 = 54 \text{ cm}^2.$$

The area of the net in Figure **4-3** is also 54 cm².

FIGURE 4-3   A cube and its net.

f. Are all containers prisms? Use examples to support your answer.

Exploration

a. Encourage students to discover their own methods of determining the surface area of the box (without tearing apart the box). Sample response: The dimensions of the box are 30 cm × 19 cm × 8 cm. Its surface area is approximately 1900 cm².

b. The following sample sketch (not drawn to scale) shows a template for a typical cereal box. Students may or may not draw the tabs.

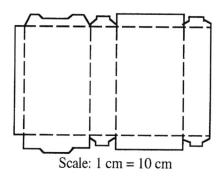

Scale: 1 cm = 10 cm

c–d. The area of the net should be close to the estimate of the surface area made in Part **a.**

e. Answers will vary depending on the template.

Discussion

a. The folded paper patterns should resemble the original boxes.

b. The paper patterns should be similar to the templates (or nets, if students did not draw tabs).

c. The area of the template is greater than the area of the net.

d. Sample response: Most manufacturers try to minimize waste and its associated costs.

e. The area of the net is the surface area of the box, but the area of the template is greater than the surface area of the box.

f. Sample response: All containers are not prisms. A can of tomato paste, for example, is a cylinder.

Materials List

■ scissors (one pair per student)

■ rulers (one per student)

■ tape or glue sticks (one per group)

■ grid paper (several sheets per group)

■ rectangular boxes (one per group)

Student Outcomes

After completing the following exploration and discussion, students should be able to:

✳ create scale drawings of nets

✳ use scale drawings to calculate surface area of prisms

✳ distinguish between nets and templates

✳ determine the smallest rectangle that will enclose a template (in the context of waste in manufacturing).

Warm-Up

1. **a.** triangular prism
    b. rectangular prism
    c. This object is not a prism because its bases are not polygons.
2. **a.** 127.5 cm² **b.** 765 cm² **c.** 45 cm²

teacher note

In Problem **1.2**, students calculate the percentage of material wasted in the production of a template.

Assignment

Problems suitable for use as assessment items are identified by an asterisk (*).

1.1 a. The diagram below shows the corresponding net.

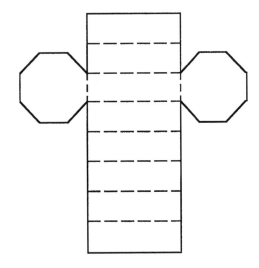

b. Sample sketches:

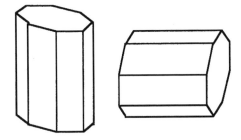

* **1.2** Answers will vary. The following sample responses were calculated using a box 30 cm × 19 cm × 8 cm.
    a. The dimensions of the smallest rectangle are 60 cm × 38 cm. Its area is approximately 2280 cm².
    b. The area of the template is approximately 2166 cm².
    c. Since the area of the rectangle minus the area of the template equals the amount wasted,

    $$2280 \text{ cm}^2 - 2166 \text{ cm}^2 = 114 \text{ cm}^2.$$

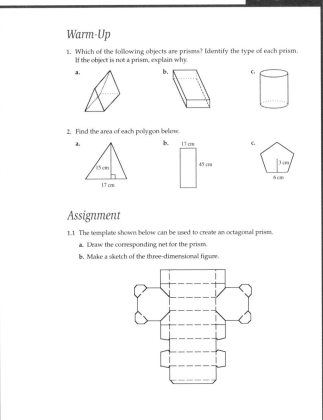

Warm-Up

1. Which of the following objects are prisms? Identify the type of each prism. If the object is not a prism, explain why.

   a.   b.   c.

2. Find the area of each polygon below.

   a. 15 cm, 17 cm   b. 17 cm, 45 cm   c. 3 cm, 6 cm

Assignment

1.1 The template shown below can be used to create an octagonal prism.

   a. Draw the corresponding net for the prism.

   b. Make a sketch of the three-dimensional figure.

Module 4 ■ *A New Look at Boxing*   87

The percentage wasted can be calculated as follows:

$$\frac{114 \text{ cm}^2}{2280 \text{ cm}^2} \cdot 100 \approx 5\%$$

d. Assuming that the dimensions of a roll of cardboard are multiples of the dimensions of the smallest rectangle that encloses the template, the cost of the waste can be calculated as follows:

$$\frac{114 \text{ cm}^2}{1 \text{ box}} \cdot \frac{1 \text{ m}^2}{(100 \text{ cm})^2} \cdot \frac{\$0.14}{1 \text{ m}^2} \cdot 500{,}000 \text{ boxes} \approx \$800.00$$

1.3 a–b. Sample sketch:

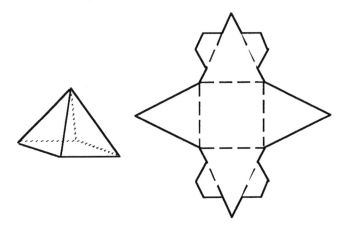

c. Sample response: This container is not a prism because it does not have two congruent faces in parallel planes.

1.2 In Part **e** of the exploration, you recorded the dimensions of the smallest rectangle that would enclose the template for the box.

   a. Find the area of this rectangle in square centimeters (cm²).

   b. Find the area of the template.

   c. When the template is cut from the rectangle in Part **a**, what percentage of the cardboard is wasted?

   d. Imagine that a box manufacturer makes 500,000 boxes by cutting templates from cardboard rectangles. If cardboard costs 14 cents per square meter, what is the cost of the wasted cardboard? Describe any assumptions you make in solving this problem.

1.3 a. Make a sketch of a container that is not a prism but has faces that are polygons.

   b. Draw a possible template for this container.

   c. Explain why this container is not a prism.

1.4 A sugar company would like to sell packages of 100 sugar cubes. Each cube is approximately 1 cm on a side.

   a. Draw a net for a container which could be used to package 100 sugar cubes.

   b. Explain how you could position several copies of your net so that the containers could be produced efficiently.

* * * * *

1.5 You are in charge of repainting the red background on all the stop signs in a large city. Before you can order paint, you must determine the area of a stop sign. Draw a regular octagon and describe how to find its area.

1.6 Gold bullion is often molded into blocks. The diagram on the right shows a type of block for which the cross section is an isosceles trapezoid. The trapezoid has a height of 4 cm and bases of 10 and 16 cm.

   a. Draw a net that could be used to create a model of the block.

   b. Use the net to find the surface area of the block.

Determining the shape that encloses the template helps minimize waste in box construction. But there's more. How will those shapes fit together? For example, a box template might be enclosed by a rectangle. To improve efficiency, a manufacturer

---

* * * * *

1.5 Answers may vary. Several possible methods are described below.

   ■ Lay a grid over the octagon, and count the grid squares within the octagonal region. Add half the boundary squares to this total.

   ■ Cut the octagon into triangles from one vertex, then determine the sum of the areas of the triangles.

   ■ Cut the octagon into triangles from the center, then determine the sum of the areas of the triangles.

   ■ Cut the octagon into triangles and rectangles using a tic-tac-toe pattern, then determine the sum of the areas of those polygons.

1.6 a. Sample drawing:

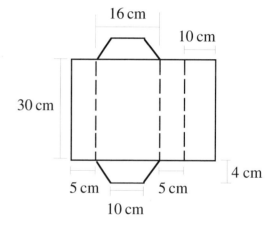

   b. The surface area of the block is 1184 cm².

In this activity, students investigate tessellations and determine which regular polygons tessellate the plane. Students also examine figures which are not regular that tessellate the plane.

Materials List

   ■ polygon template (six copies per student)
   ■ pentagon template (one copy per student)
   ■ grid paper template (one copy per student)
   ■ scissors (one pair per student)
   ■ construction paper or light cardboard (optional)

Technology

   ■ spreadsheet
   ■ geometry utility (optional)

1.4 a. The dimensions of the corresponding box for the sample net shown below are 5 cm × 5 cm × 4 cm.

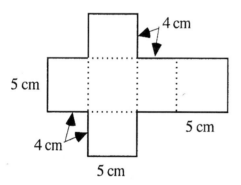

   b. Sample response: Positioning several nets as shown in the following diagram could reduce the amount of wasted cardboard.

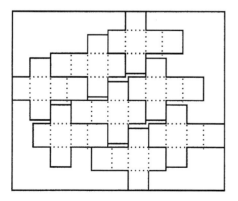

teacher note

In Part **a** of the exploration, six copies of the polygon template are necessary to supply each student (or group) with an appropriate number of polygons: 18 triangles, 15 squares, 4 pentagons, 10 hexagons, 8 octagons, and 6 dodecagons.

As an alternative, you may photocopy the template onto heavyweight paper (such as 90# stock). Each student may then use one copy of each polygon to trace shapes on paper and explore tessellations. A blackline master of the template appears in the Teacher Resources for this module.

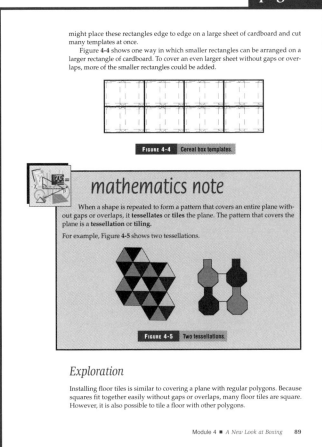

might place these rectangles edge to edge on a large sheet of cardboard and cut many templates at once.

Figure **4-4** shows one way in which smaller rectangles can be arranged on a larger rectangle of cardboard. To cover an even larger sheet without gaps or overlaps, more of the smaller rectangles could be added.

FIGURE 4-4 Cereal box templates.

mathematics note

When a shape is repeated to form a pattern that covers an entire plane without gaps or overlaps, it **tessellates** or **tiles** the plane. The pattern that covers the plane is a **tessellation** or **tiling**.

For example, Figure **4-5** shows two tessellations.

FIGURE 4-5 Two tessellations.

Exploration

Installing floor tiles is similar to covering a plane with regular polygons. Because squares fit together easily without gaps or overlaps, many floor tiles are square. However, it is also possible to tile a floor with other polygons.

Module 4 ■ *A New Look at Boxing*   89

Student Outcomes

After completing the following exploration and discussion, students should be able to:

✴ determine, through observation, which regular polygons tessellate a plane

✴ determine, by examining interior angle measures, which regular polygons tessellate a plane

✴ determine the sum of the exterior angle measures of a regular polygon

✴ relate the sum of the interior angle measures to the number of sides in a regular polygon

✴ relate the measure of an interior or exterior angle to the number of sides in a regular polygon.

Exploration

a. Regular triangles, squares, and hexagons will tile a plane. Students may record their drawings by tracing around templates. They might realize that the sum of the angle measures around any vertex of a tiling is 360°.

b. 1. The sum of the measures of the exterior angles of the triangle is 360°.

    2. The measure of each exterior angle of the triangle is 120°.

    3. The measure of an interior angle of an equilateral triangle is 60°.

    4. The number of equilateral triangles that could fit at one vertex is 6.

c. See the sample spreadsheet in the table below.

No. of Sides in Polygon	Measure of Exterior Angle (x)	Measure of Interior Angle (m)	No. of Polygons that "Fit" at One Vertex ($360°/m$)
3	120°	60°	6
4	90°	90°	4
5	72°	108°	≈ 3.33
6	60°	120°	3
7	≈ 51.43°	≈ 128.57°	2.8
8	45°	135°	≈ 2.67
9	40°	140°	≈ 2.57
10	36°	144°	2.5
11	≈ 32.73°	≈ 147.27°	≈ 2.44
12	30°	150°	2.4

a. Cut out templates of all the regular polygons, other than squares, with up to 12 sides. Determine which of these regular polygons can tile a plane. Use drawings to record your results.

b. On a sheet of paper, extend the sides of an equilateral triangle to form three equal exterior angles. In Figure 4-6 below, ∠1, ∠2, and ∠3 are the exterior angles and ∠4, ∠5, and ∠6 are the interior angles.

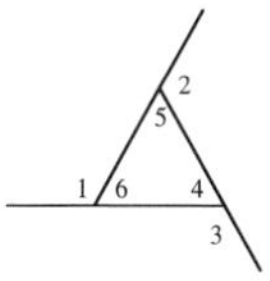

FIGURE 4-6 An equilateral triangle with exterior angles.

1. Without measuring, determine the sum of the measures of the exterior angles. *Hint:* Start at the vertex of ∠1 as shown in Figure 4-6 and visualize walking around the polygon (triangle) until you return to the starting point facing in the same direction. How many degrees did you turn during the walk?

2. Record the measure of a single exterior angle in a spreadsheet with headings like those in Table 4-1 below.

3. Use your response to Step 2 to determine the measure of an interior angle of the regular polygon and record the result in Table 4-1.

4. Determine the number of these regular polygons that would "fit" at one vertex and record the result in Table 4-1.

TABLE 4-1 ■ *Measures of Angles of Regular Polygons*

No. of Sides in Polygon	Measure of Exterior Angle (x)	Measure of Interior Angle (m)	No. of Polygons that "Fit" at One Vertex (360°/m)
3			
4			
⋮			

c. Repeat Part b for all regular polygons with up to 12 sides.

90   Module 4 ■ *A New Look at Boxing*

Discussion

a. How can you use Table 4-1 to determine which regular polygons tessellate a plane?

b. Identify the regular polygons that tessellate a plane. Explain your answer.

c. Will the method of finding the sum of the measures of the exterior angles described in Part b of the exploration work for any regular polygon? Explain your response.

d. What is the sum of the measures of the exterior angles of any regular polygon?

e. What is the measure of an exterior angle of a regular polygon with *n* sides?

f. What is the measure of an interior angle of a regular polygon with *n* sides?

g. If you knew the number of degrees in an interior angle of a regular polygon, how could you determine the number of sides in the polygon?

Warm-Up

1. Determine the sum of the measures of the exterior angles for a regular polygon with:

a. 3 sides

b. 6 sides

c. *n* sides

2. Determine the measure of an exterior angle for a regular polygon with:

a. 5 sides

b. 9 sides

c. *n* sides

3. Determine the measure of an interior angle for a regular polygon with:

a. 5 sides

b. 9 sides

c. *n* sides

Assignment

2.1 Consider a regular polygon with 24 sides.

a. Find the measure of an interior angle of the polygon.

b. Find the sum of the measures of the interior angles of the polygon.

Module 4 ■ *A New Look at Boxing*   91

Discussion

a. Sample response: The right-hand column of the table shows how many of the polygons could fit at one vertex. If this value is a natural number, this means that the polygons could fit with no gaps or overlaps.

b. Triangles, squares, and hexagons are the only regular polygons that tessellate a plane. The sum of the angle measures around any vertex of a tiling of these regular polygons is 360°.

c. The notion of "walking around" the exterior angles may be extended to any regular polygon.

d. The sum of the measures of the exterior angles of any regular polygon is 360°.

e. The measure of an exterior angle of a polygon with n sides is $(360/n)°$.

f. The measure of an interior angle of a polygon with n sides is $180° - (360/n)°$.

g. Sample response: Set the measure of the interior angle equal to $180° - (360/n)°$ and solve the equation for n, the number of sides.

Warm-Up

1. a. 360°
   b. 360°
   c. 360°
2. a. 72°
   b. 40°
   c. $(360/n)°$
3. a. 108°
   b. 140°
   c. $180° - (360/n)°$

teacher note

To complete Problem **2.6**, each student will need one sheet of grid paper. To complete Problem **2.7**, each student will need one copy of the pentagon template. Blackline masters appear in the Teacher Resources for this module.

Assignment

Problems suitable for use as assessment items are identified by an asterisk (*).

2.1 a. $180° - (360/24)° = 165°$
    b. $(24)165° = 3960°$

2.2 $180° - (360/102)° = 176\frac{8}{17}° \approx 176.47°$

2.3 At least three regular polygons must fit around a point to form a tessellation. For any regular polygon with more than six sides, the sum of the measures of three interior angles will always be more than 360°. Therefore, there are no regular polygons with more than six sides that tessellate the plane.

* 2.4 Answers will vary. Sample response: One tiling is made of triangles placed on a flat surface. Each triangle has three sides of equal length. The pattern is created by placing these identical triangles side by side so that there are no gaps or overlaps. Each triangle is immediately adjacent to three other triangles and a total of six triangles meet at any one vertex.

2.5 $\dfrac{400\text{ cm}}{35.5\text{ cm}} \approx 11; \dfrac{6000\text{ m}}{0.224\text{ m}} \approx 26,785; 11 \bullet 26,785 \approx 294,635$

2.6 a. Sample response:

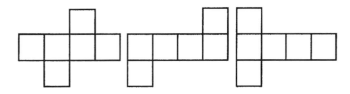

b. Sample response:

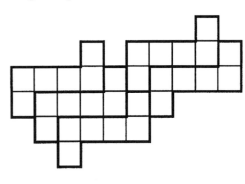

* * * * *

2.7 a. The diagram below shows one way in which this pentagon can tessellate the plane. This is often referred to as a "Cairo tessellation" because such tiles were used on the streets of Cairo, Egypt.

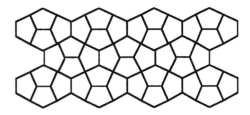

b. Sample design:

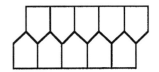

2.2 Find the measure of an interior angle of a regular polygon with 102 sides.

2.3 Is there a regular polygon with more than six sides that will tile a plane? Explain your response.

2.4 Describe one of your tilings from Part **a** of the exploration so that someone unfamiliar with regular polygons and tessellations could reconstruct the pattern.

2.5 A box manufacturer wishes to cut templates from a roll of cardboard 400 cm wide and 6000 m long. The dimensions of the smallest rectangle that will enclose the template are 22.4 cm by 35.5 cm. How many templates can be cut from one roll?

2.6 **a.** The net shown below is just one of several possible nets of a cube. Draw three different cube nets.

b. On a sheet of grid paper, find a cube net that tessellates a plane. Use at least six copies of the net to show that the pattern may be extended in all directions.

* * * * *

2.7 Although a regular pentagon will not tile the plane, there are pentagons that do form tessellations. The pentagon in the following diagram is equilateral but not equiangular.

a. Trace this pentagon and determine whether it will tessellate the plane.

b. Design a pentagon different from the one above that tessellates the plane.

2.8 Do you think that all quadrilaterals will tessellate a plane? Explain your response.

2.8 Yes. The sum of the measures of the interior angles of any quadrilateral is 360°. By placing the four different vertices of a quadrilateral at a vertex of the tiling, the sum of the measures at that vertex is 360°. This guarantees the quadrilateral can be used to tile the plane.

2.9 a. The interior angles measure 157.5°, while the exterior angles measure 22.5°.

b. The sum of the measures of the interior angles is 2520°, while the sum of the measures of the exterior angles is 360°.

c. The polygon contains 36 sides. This can be found by solving the following equation for n.

$$180 - \frac{360}{n} = 170$$

2.9 **a.** Find the measures of an interior angle and an exterior angle of a 16-sided regular polygon.

b. Calculate the sum of the interior angles and the sum of the exterior angles of a 16-sided regular polygon.

c. If the measure of an interior angle of a regular polygon is 170°, how many sides does the polygon contain?

Research Project

Regular polygons can be arranged in many interesting patterns.

a. Find at least six ways in which a combination of regular polygons will tessellate a plane. In each tiling, use at least two different regular polygons.

b. Make a careful drawing of each of your patterns.

c. Describe each pattern in a few sentences.

d. Find at least two examples of tilings that use polygons other than squares and rectangles in your home or community.

Not all prisms have rectangular bases. Some have bases that are triangular. Others, such as the octagonal prisms shown in Figure **4-7**, have bases that are regular polygons.

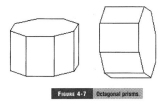

FIGURE 4-7 Octagonal prisms.

In this activity, you use your knowledge of the area of triangles and squares to develop a method for finding the area of regular polygons with five or more sides.

Module 4 ■ *A New Look at Boxing* 93

Research Project

The research project allows students to continue their explorations of tiling patterns to include combinations of polygons. For example, the tiling shown below is formed by a combination of squares and octagons.

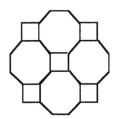

Note: See Grünbaum and Shephard's *Tiling and Patterns* for a complete discussion of the tilings of regular polygons.

In this activity, students use a geometry utility to construct regular polygons and complete a table of the apothems, side lengths, and areas. They then use a spreadsheet to help discover a formula for the area of a regular polygon.

teacher note

A brief assessment of the mathematical content in Activities **2** and **3**, for use at your discretion, appears in the Teacher Resources for this module.

Materials List

■ ruler (one per student)

■ protractor (one per student)

■ box template (one per student)

Technology

■ geometry utility

■ spreadsheet

teacher note

You might wish to demonstrate the construction of a regular pentagon by following the steps described in Part **a** of the exploration. Students should recall how to find the central angle of a polygon from the Level 1 module "Reflect on This." The measure of each central angle should be 72°.

Student Outcomes

After completing the following exploration and discussion, students should be able to:

✻ construct regular polygons inscribed in circles with a geometry utility

✻ divide regular polygons into congruent triangles

✻ relate the number of sides in a regular polygon to the number of congruent triangles it contains

✻ identify and measure the apothem

✻ use congruent triangles to find the area of a regular polygon

✻ identify a formula for calculating the area of a regular polygon using the apothem and perimeter.

Exploration

a. Students should recognize how constructing a circle helps them draw the regular polygon.

b–e. See sample Table **4-2** below.

f. Sample response: The area determined by the geometry utility is about the same as the area calculated using triangles.

g. Students repeat Parts **a–f**, using 7 points to create a regular heptagon and 10 points to create a regular decagon.

h. Sample response: The formula for the area of a regular n-gon is Area = $0.5 \bullet a \bullet s \bullet n$, where a represents the length of the apothem, s represents the length of a side, and n represents the number of triangles.

Discussion

a. Sample response: As a polygon's number of sides increases, it begins to look more like a circle.

b. Sample response: As the measure of the central angle decreases, the polygon begins to look more like a circle.

c. The two areas should be approximately equal.

d. Sample response: Yes, this equation is equivalent to the formula because the number of sides is equal to the number of triangles.

Exploration

a. Use a geometry utility to construct a regular pentagon by completing the following steps.

  1. Construct a circle. Place five points on the circle. Use segments to connect the center of the circle to each of the five points. Each angle formed by two adjacent radii is a **central angle**.

  2. Drag the points on the circle until the measures of all the central angles are equal.

  3. Connect the points on the circle to form a regular pentagon.

b. Create a table with headings like those in Table **4-2** below.

TABLE 4-2 ■ Triangles in Regular Polygons

Polygon	No. of Triangles	Apothem (a)	Length of Side (s)	Area of Polygon
pentagon	5			
heptagon				
decagon				
n-gon				

c. Measure the perpendicular distance from the center of the polygon to one side. This distance is the length of the **apothem**. In Figure **4-8**, for example, $\overline{AG}$ is the apothem. Record this measure in the appropriate column in Table **4-2**.

FIGURE 4-8 Constructing a regular pentagon.

d. Measure the length of one side of the polygon. Record this length in the appropriate column of Table **4-2**.

TABLE 4-2 ■ *Triangles in Regular Polygons*

Polygon	No. of Triangles	Apothem (a)	Length of Side (s)	Area of Polygon
pentagon	5	5.0 cm	7.2 cm	90.0 cm²
heptagon	7	4.0 cm	3.8 cm	53.2 cm²
decagon	10	6.0 cm	3.9 cm	117 cm²
n-gon	n	a	s	$\frac{1}{2} a \bullet s \bullet n$

e. 1. Your construction of a polygon contains congruent triangles. Create a formula using the length of the apothem to find the area of one of these triangles.

   2. Use the area of one congruent triangle to find the total area of the polygon. Record this area in the appropriate column of Table **4-2**.

f. Use the geometry utility to find the area of the polygon. Compare this value to the one you determined in Part **e**.

g. Repeat Parts **a–f** for a regular heptagon and a regular decagon.

h. Create a formula for finding the area of a regular *n*-gon. Enter it in the appropriate cell of Table **4-2**.

Discussion

a. As the number of sides of a polygon increases, what happens to the shape of the polygon?

b. How does the measure of the central angle of a polygon affect the shape of the polygon?

c. How do the areas of the polygons found using your formula compare to the areas of the same polygons found using the geometry utility?

d. The area of a regular polygon with *n* sides, apothem *a*, and side length *s* can be described by the following equation:

$$\text{Area} = \left(\frac{1}{2}as\right)n$$

Is this equation equivalent to the formula you developed in Part **h** of the exploration? Explain your response.

Warm-Up

1. Draw an appropriately labeled diagram for each of the following.

   a. $\overline{AB}$ **b.** ray *RS*

   c. line *r*   **d.** ∠*TAL*

   e. obtuse ∠*FUN*   **f.** acute ∠*SUN*

2. **a.** Name the sides of ∠*SUN* from Part **f** of Problem **1**.

   b. Name the vertex of ∠*SUN*.

   c. List two other ways of naming ∠*SUN*.

---

teacher note

To complete Problem **3.4,** each student will need one copy of the box template. A blackline master appears in the Teacher Resources for this module.

Warm-Up

1. **a.**

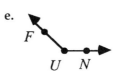

A   B

   b.

R   S

   c.

r

   d. A   L

T

   e.

F

U   N

   f.   S

U   N

2. **a.** ray *US* and ray *UN*

   b. point *U*

   c. ∠*NUS*   or   ∠*U*

3. **a.** 72°
   b. 40°
   c. $(360/n)°$
4. They are perpendicular.
5. **a.** 84 cm
   b. 144 cm
   c. $12n$ cm
6. The perimeter of the polygon.

Assignment

Problems suitable for use as assessment items are identified by an asterisk (*).

3.1 The side length of the hexagon and the perpendicular distance from the center point to a side (the apothem) are the only measurements needed.

3.2 Students should recognize that the perimeter of a regular polygon equals the number of sides multiplied by the side length. This should lead them to the following equation, where a represents the apothem and P represents the perimeter:

$$A = \frac{1}{2}aP$$

3.3 The area of the net is approximately 820 cm². This box is similar to a container in which cupcake papers are sold.

* 3.4 a. The area of the template is approximately 46 cm². The area of the shape that encloses the template is approximately 49 cm².

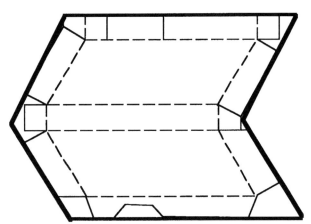

3. Determine the measure of the central angle for a regular polygon with:
   a. 5 sides
   b. 9 sides
   c. n sides

4. What is the geometric relationship between the apothem and a side of a regular polygon?

5. Determine the perimeter of a regular polygon with a side length of 12 cm and each of the following numbers of sides:
   a. 7
   b. 12
   c. n

6. The formula for the area A of a regular polygon is:

$$A = \frac{1}{2}a \cdot s \cdot n$$

What does the expression $s \cdot n$ represent?

Assignment

3.1 The floor of Greg's new hot tub is shaped like a regular hexagon. He wants to install a tile floor. What measurements should he make?

3.2 Write a formula for finding the area of a regular polygon in terms of the apothem and the perimeter.

3.3 Use the net below to find the surface area of the corresponding hexagonal box.

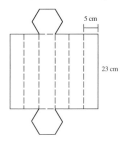

b. Sample tessellation:

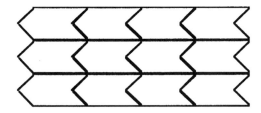

c. The percentage of cardboard wasted can be calculated as follows:

$$\frac{49 \text{ cm}^2 - 46 \text{ cm}^2}{49 \text{ cm}^2} \approx 0.06 = 6\%$$

✳ ✳ ✳ ✳ ✳

3.4 A product engineer has created the template below for a cardboard box.

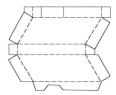

To hold down production costs, you must design a shape that encloses the template and minimizes waste. Prepare a presentation for the product engineer that includes:

a. the area of the template and the area of the shape

b. a sketch of the tessellation of the shape

c. the percentage of cardboard wasted when the template is cut from the shape.

* * * * *

3.5 Find a box that is not a rectangular prism. Carefully unfold the box and lay its template flat.

a. Draw the smallest shape that encloses the template and also tessellates a plane.

b. Sketch the tessellation of the shape.

c. Find the area of the shape from Part a.

d. Calculate the percentage of cardboard wasted when the template is cut from the shape.

3.6 A soccer ball can be modeled with 12 regular pentagons and 20 regular hexagons, each with a side length of approximately 4.5 cm. Find the approximate surface area of a soccer ball. *Hint:* You might need to draw a sample hexagon and pentagon and measure their apothems.

3.5 Answers will vary. The following sample response uses a container shaped like a pyramid.
   a. Sample response:

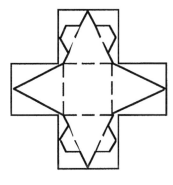

b. Sample tessellation:

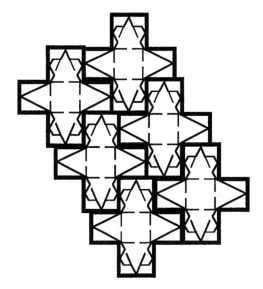

c. The area of the sample template shown in Part **a** is 7.1 cm². The area of the shape that encloses it is 11.1 cm².

d. The percentage of cardboard wasted can be calculated as follows:

$$\frac{11.1 \text{ cm}^2 - 7.1 \text{ cm}^2}{11.1 \text{ cm}^2} \approx 0.36 = 36\%$$

3.6 The length of the apothem of the hexagon is approximately 3.9 cm. The area of each hexagon is

$$0.5 \bullet 3.9 \text{ cm} \bullet 6 \bullet 4.5 \text{ cm} \approx 53 \text{ cm}^2.$$

The length of the apothem of the pentagon is approximately 3.1 cm. The area of each pentagon is

$$0.5 \bullet 3.1 \text{ cm} \bullet 5 \bullet 4.5 \text{ cm} \approx 35 \text{ cm}^2.$$

The total surface area of the soccer ball is approximately

$$12 \bullet 35 \text{ cm}^2 + 20 \bullet 53 \text{ cm}^2 = 1480 \text{ cm}^2.$$

teacher note

An additional assessment, for use at your discretion, appears in the Teacher Resources for this module.

Summary Assessment

Answers will vary, depending on the design of the template. Students should select a written or verbal format that includes all of the following information.

1. Sample template:

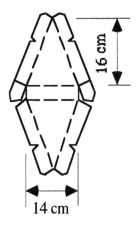

16 cm

14 cm

2. The area of the sample template above is approximately 454 cm^2.

3. The shape that encloses the sample template is shown below.

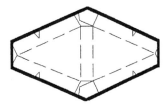

4. This shape can tessellate the plane as follows:

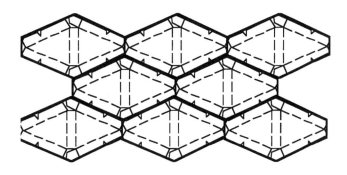

Summary Assessment

You have been asked to design and build an efficient box for one slice of pizza. The specifications and costs are listed below.

- A whole pizza has a diameter of 30 cm. Each pizza is cut into 8 equal slices.
- Cardboard costs 22 cents per square meter.
- The template must assemble into a closed container.
- The shape enclosing the template should both tessellate the plane and minimize waste.

Prepare a report describing your container, including the following:

1. a template
2. the area of the template
3. the shape that encloses the template and tessellates a plane
4. a sketch of the tessellation
5. the cost to make one template
6. the percentage of cardboard wasted in making one template
7. an attractive advertising logo sketched on a template
8. a model of the container.

5. The area of the shape is 468 cm^2. The cost of the cardboard required to make one template is:

$$\frac{468 \text{ cm}^2}{1 \text{ box}} \cdot \frac{1 \text{ m}^2}{10{,}000 \text{ cm}^2} \cdot \frac{\$0.22}{1 \text{ m}^2} \approx \frac{\$0.01}{1 \text{ box}}$$

6. The percentage of cardboard wasted can be calculated as follows:

$$\frac{(468 - 454) \text{ cm}^2}{468 \text{ cm}^2} \approx 0.03 = 3\%$$

7. Logos will vary.

8. Students should provide models of their containers.

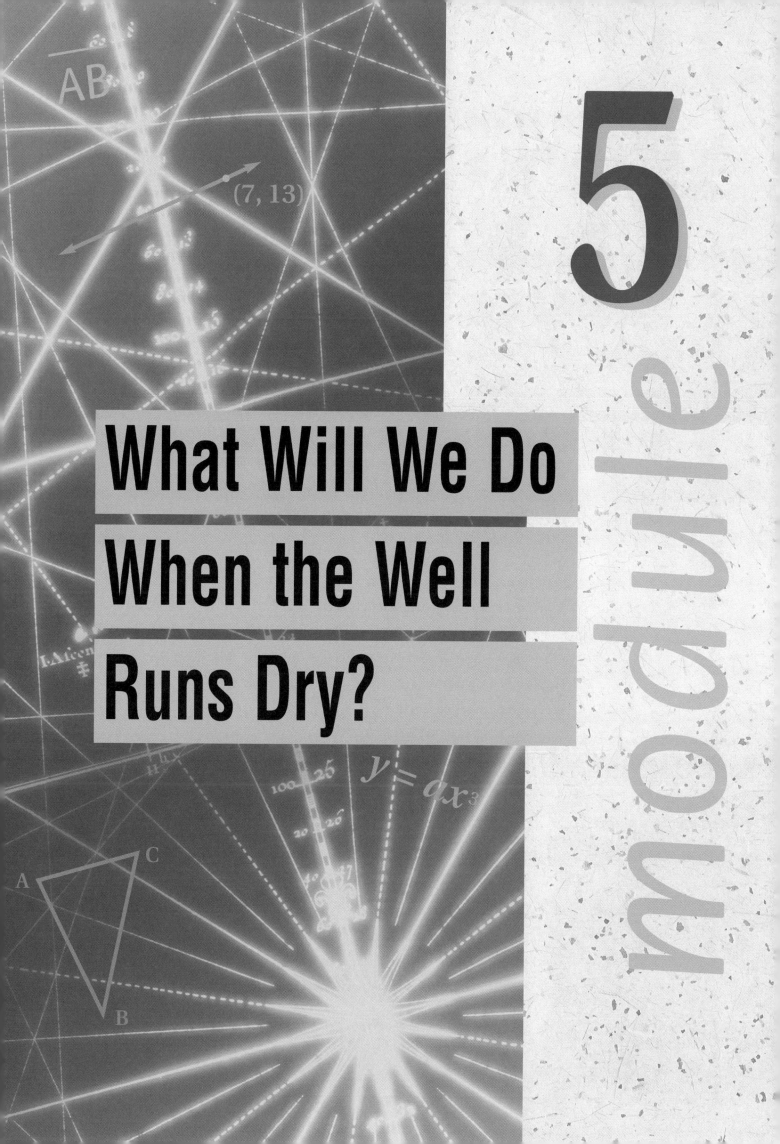

What Will We Do When the Well Runs Dry?

Overview

In this module, students examine personal water use and continue their investigation of linear equations. Students use their collected data to explore volume, rate of change, slope, linear modeling, and residuals.

Introduction:	Students consider the value of clean water and ways to measure volume of daily water usage.
Activity 1:	Students calculate volumes of prisms with polygonal bases and estimate volumes of solids with irregular bases.
Activity 2:	Students calculate rate of flow, write linear equations as mathematical models, and interpret slope as a rate.
Activity 3:	Students examine residuals and use them to evaluate the fit of a linear model. Students then use their models to make predictions.

Objectives

In this module, students will:

* determine the volumes of triangular, rectangular, and trapezoidal prisms using appropriate units (1)
* approximate areas of irregular figures (1)
* approximate the volume of three-dimensional solids with irregular bases (1)
* investigate the relationships among cubic centimeters, cubic decimeters, and liters (1)
* collect and tabulate data (2)
* convert rates to different units (2)
* construct and interpret graphs (2, 3)
* develop and use linear models (2, 3)
* determine rates of change using slope (2, 3)
* examine residuals and use them to evaluate models (3).

Prerequisites

For this module, students should know:

* the definition of a polygon
* units of metric measurement for length
* how to calculate the area of rectangles, triangles, and trapezoids
* how to draw the net of a three-dimensional solid

* how to find the slope of a line
* how to write linear equations given two data points
* how to write a linear equation in the form $y = mx + b$
* how to use graphing utilities and spreadsheets
* the definition of absolute value
* how to write numbers in scientific notation
* how to express ratios as percentages.

 Flashbacks, for use at your discretion, appear in the Teacher Resources for this module. These brief problem sets provide a review of some prerequisite skills for each activity.

Planning Guide

Activity	Materials	Technology	Time Line
Introduction/Activity **1**	▪ metric rulers ▪ cardboard ▪ scissors ▪ tape ▪ 1-L containers ▪ centimeter graph paper ▪ rice ▪ large cans or buckets	▪ none	3 days
Activity **2**	▪ metric rulers ▪ straightedges ▪ cardboard ▪ scissors ▪ tape ▪ 1-L containers ▪ centimeter graph paper ▪ rice ▪ stopwatches or timers ▪ large cans or buckets	▪ none	3 days
Activity **3**	▪ centimeter graph paper ▪ straightedges	▪ graphing utility ▪ spreadsheet (optional	2 days
Assessment Activities	▪ none	▪ none	3 days **Total: 11 days**

 teacher note

In Activities **1** and **2**, students will require sheets of light, strong cardboard (such as tagboard) to construct models. Manila file folders also work well.

Plastic soda bottles with the necks removed may be substituted for the 1-L containers. Buckets should hold at least 4 L.

A blackline master for 1-cm grid paper appears in the Teacher Resources for this module.

Introduction

The introduction is designed to relate national and global water resource issues to potential problems in the local area.

Student Outcomes

After completing the following exploration and discussion, students should be able to:

✳ relate the resource of clean water to their daily lives

✳ consider ways to measure volume of personal water usage.

Discussion

a. Some students might argue that water would become even more expensive if population growth exceeds our ability to produce drinkable water, or if worldwide standards of living place higher demands on water.

 Other students might respond that the price of water could remain stable if cost-effective ways are developed to conserve existing water supplies or to desalinate sea water.

b. Answers will vary, depending on the region and on different perceptions of the term *shortage.* If a local shortage does exist, encourage students to discuss possible causes for this situation.

c. 1. Some possible causes are drought, waste, water pollution, deforestation, and the paving of water recharge areas.

 2. Answers will vary. Some causes might be reversed, while others might be controlled or lessened.

d. 1. Students will determine their average daily use in the research project in Activity **3.** In 1990, the average U.S. citizen used approximately 420 L of water per day.

 2. Answers will vary. Some students might suggest monitoring a household water meter, then dividing household use by the number of family members.

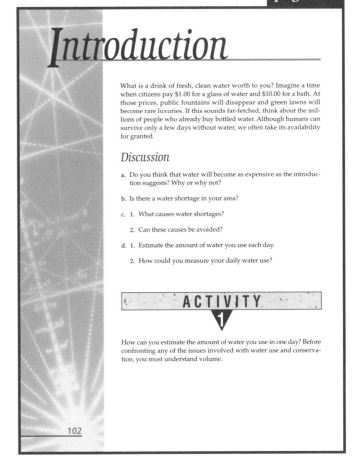

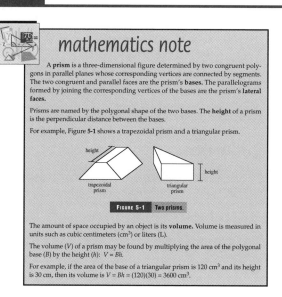

mathematics note

A **prism** is a three-dimensional figure determined by two congruent polygons in parallel planes whose corresponding vertices are connected by segments. The two congruent and parallel faces are the prism's **bases.** The parallelograms formed by joining the corresponding vertices of the bases are the prism's **lateral faces.**

Prisms are named by the polygonal shape of the two bases. The **height** of a prism is the perpendicular distance between the bases.

For example, Figure **5-1** shows a trapezoidal prism and a triangular prism.

trapezoidal
prism

triangular
prism

FIGURE 5-1 Two prisms.

The amount of space occupied by an object is its **volume.** Volume is measured in units such as cubic centimeters (cm³) or liters (L).

The volume (V) of a prism may be found by multiplying the area of the polygonal base (B) by the height (h): $V = Bh$.

For example, if the area of the base of a triangular prism is 120 cm³ and its height is 30 cm, then its volume is $V = Bh = (120)(30) = 3600$ cm³.

Exploration 1

In this exploration, you determine the volume of a cube.

a. On a sheet of cardboard, draw a net for a cube with 10 cm × 10 cm faces.

b. Cut out, fold, and tape the net to form a cube.

c. Calculate the volume of the cube in each of the following units:

  1. cubic centimeters (cm³)

  2. cubic decimeters (dm³).

d. Determine a relationship between cubic centimeters and cubic decimeters.

e. Estimate the number of liters (L) of water that the cube will hold.

Module 5 ■ *What Will We Do When the Well Runs Dry?* **103**

ACTIVITY

1

In this activity, students estimate and calculate the volume of prisms and other three-dimensional solids.

teacher note

A brief assessment of the mathematical content in Activity **1**, for use at your discretion, appears in the Teacher Resources for this module.

Materials List

- metric rulers (one per group)
- cardboard (approximately 50 cm × 30 cm per group)
- scissors (one pair per group)
- tape (one roll per group)
- 1-L containers (one per group)
- rice (at least 1 kg per group)
- centimeter graph paper (at least two sheets per group)
- large cans or buckets (one per group)

teacher note

You might wish to point out the lateral faces, bases, edges, and heights of various prisms in your classroom. In this module, students examine only right prisms; therefore, the heights are the same as the lengths of the edges. In an oblique prism, the height is not the same as the length of an edge.

Student Outcomes

After completing the following exploration and discussion, students should be able to:

✳ create a cubic decimeter from a net

✳ determine the relationship between cubic centimeters and cubic decimeters

✳ determine the relationship between cubic decimeters and liters.

Exploration 1

Using cubic centimeters and cubic decimeters, students develop a sense of the volume equivalent to a liter.

a–b. Students construct cubes with an edge length of 10 cm.

c. 1. 1000 cm³

   2. 1 dm³

d. 1000 cm³ = 1 dm³

e. Estimates will vary. The volume of the cube is 1 L.

f. Students check their estimates from Part **e** by pouring rice into their cubes.

g. 1. $1\,\mathrm{L} = 1000\,\mathrm{cm}^3$
   2. $1\,\mathrm{L} = 1\,\mathrm{dm}^3$

Discussion 1

a. 1. The cube created in the exploration is a prism because it is a three-dimensional figure formed by two parallel and congruent polygons (squares) and the parallelograms (squares) formed by connecting the corresponding vertices of these polygons.
   2. The bases and the lateral faces of a cube are indistinguishable because all six are congruent squares. Any two parallel faces may be designated as the bases; the remaining four faces may then be identified as lateral faces.

b. 1. Every prism has two bases.
   2. Every prism with an n-gon as its bases has n lateral faces. For example, the bases of a cube have 4 sides; therefore it has 4 lateral faces.
   3. Every prism with an n-gon as its bases has n lateral edges. For example, the bases of a cube have 4 sides; therefore it has 4 lateral edges.
   4. Every prism with an n-gon as its bases has a total of $3n$ edges. For example, the bases of a cube have 4 sides; therefore it has a total of 12 edges.

c. 1. $1\,\mathrm{dm}^3 = 1000\,\mathrm{cm}^3$
   2. $1\,\mathrm{L} = 1000\,\mathrm{cm}^3$
   3. $1\,\mathrm{L} = 1\,\mathrm{dm}^3$

Student Outcomes

After completing the following exploration and discussion, students should be able to:

✳ calculate volumes of prisms with polygonal bases

✳ estimate areas of closed, irregular planar figures

✳ estimate volumes of three-dimensional solids with irregular bases.

Exploration 2

In this exploration, students investigate a method for finding the volume of objects that are not prisms. **Note:** In Part **c**, each group should construct just one three-dimensional model.

a. Students may draw circles, ellipses, or other figures consisting of curves.

b. If students use 1-cm grid paper, the area of each square is $1\,\mathrm{cm}^2$. Therefore, the sum of Steps **2** and **3** approximates the area of the figure in square centimeters.

c. Students use cardboard to construct three-dimensional solids 10 cm high.

f. Because it would not be practical to pour water into your cardboard cube, check your estimate by completing Steps 1–3 below.
   1. Open one face of the cube.
   2. Fill the cube with rice. **Note:** Make sure that the edges of the cube are securely taped. To prevent spills, you may place the cube inside a bucket while pouring rice.
   3. Use a 1-L container to measure the amount of rice in the cube.
g. Determine a relationship between liters and each of the following units:
   1. cubic centimeters
   2. cubic decimeters.

Discussion 1

a. 1. Is the cube you created in Exploration 1 a prism? Why or why not?
   2. How can you distinguish between the bases of a cube and its lateral faces?
b. 1. How many bases does a prism have?
   2. How many lateral faces does a prism have?
   3. How many lateral edges are there in a prism?
   4. What is the total number of edges in a prism?
c. Describe the relationship between each of the following:
   1. a cubic centimeter and a cubic decimeter
   2. a liter and a cubic centimeter
   3. a liter and a cubic decimeter.

Exploration 2

In Exploration **1**, you estimated, then calculated, the volume of a prism. In many communities, however, water supplies are stored in reservoirs that do not have polygonal bases. In this exploration, you examine a method for estimating the volume of objects that are not prisms.

a. On a 10 cm × 10 cm sheet of graph paper, draw a closed geometric figure that is not a polygon, such as the one shown in Figure **5-2** below.

FIGURE 5-2 A closed figure.

b. To estimate the area of the figure, complete Steps 1–4 below.
   1. Determine the area of each square on the graph paper.
   2. Count the number of whole squares in the figure.
   3. Count the number of partial squares in the figure and divide this number by 2.
   4. Find the sum of your answers to Steps **2** and **3**. Multiply this sum by the area of one square determined in Step **1**.
c. Using bases shaped like your geometric figure from Part **a**, make a three-dimensional solid 10 cm high, such as the one shown in Figure **5-3**. Tape the edges of the solid as securely as possible.

FIGURE 5-3 A three-dimensional solid.

d. Use the estimated area of the figure found in Part **b** to estimate the volume of the solid in each of the following units:
   1. cubic centimeters
   2. liters.
e. Check your estimate from Part **d** by opening your solid, filling it with rice, then measuring the amount of rice in the solid. **Note:** To prevent spills, you may place the solid inside a bucket while pouring rice.

Discussion 2

a. In Part **b** of Exploration 2, you estimated the area of a figure by counting squares. What other methods could you use to determine the area of a figure that is not a polygon?
b. 1. How did you determine the volume of the solid in Part **d** of Exploration 2?
   2. How did this value compare to the amount of rice that filled the solid?

c. Describe how you could calculate the volume of a prism with bases shaped like each of the following:

1. triangles, rectangles, or trapezoids

2. polygons other than triangles, rectangles, or trapezoids.

Warm-Up

1. Convert each of the following measurements:

   a. 2 L = _____ cm³   b. 500 cm³ = _____ dm³

   c. 257 dm³ = _____ L   d. 75 cm³ = _____ L

   e. 4.5 L = _____ dm³   f. x dm³ = _____ cm³

2. Use the pentagonal prism in the diagram below to identify these parts:

   a. the bases

   b. a lateral face

   c. a lateral edge.

3. Determine the number of each of the following in a hexagonal prism:

   a. bases   b. lateral faces

   c. lateral edges   d. total edges.

Assignment

1.1 José has a bathtub that holds 250 L of water. Thaddeus has a tub that has inside measurements of 5 dm × 3 dm × 15 dm. Which tub holds more water? Justify your response.

1.2 A forced-air heating duct has dimensions 2 m × 6 dm × 50 cm.

   a. Make a scale drawing of this duct in centimeters.

   b. Determine its volume in cubic centimeters.

1.3 Determine the volume of each of the following objects:

   a. a water trough

   13 cm   10 cm
   120 cm

---

c. 1. Sample response: Calculate the volume by multiplying the area of the base by the height of the prism. To calculate the area of the base, use the standard formula for the area of the polygon.

   2. Sample response:, Calculate the volume by multiplying the area of the base by the height of the prism, regardless of the shape of the base. To determine the area of the base, divide the polygon into triangles, rectangles, or trapezoids, find the areas of these using the standard area formulas, then add them.

Warm-Up

1. a. 2000 cm³
   b. 0.5 dm³
   c. 257 L
   d. 0.075 L
   e. 4.5 dm³
   f. $x/1000$ cm³
2. a. pentagon $ABCDE$ and pentagon $VWXYZ$
   b. $AVZE, AVWB, EZYD, BWXC,$ or $CXYD$
   c. $\overline{AV}, \overline{BW}, \overline{CX}, \overline{DY},$ or $\overline{EZ}$
3. a. 2
   b. 6
   c. 6
   d. 18

Assignment

Problems suitable for use as assessment items are identified by an asterisk (*).

1.1 Calculate the volume of Thaddeus's tub as follows: (5 dm)(3 dm)(15 dm) = 225 dm³ = 225 L. The volume of José's tub is 250 L; therefore it holds more.

1.2 a. Sample drawing:

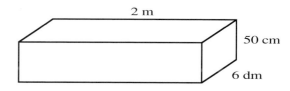

   2 m   50 cm   6 dm

   b. (200 cm)(60 cm)(50 cm) = 600,000 cm³

* 1.3 a. Considering the water trough as a rectangular prism, the volume is:

$$(120 \text{ cm})(13 \text{ cm})(10 \text{ cm}) = 15{,}600 \text{ cm}^3 = 15.6 \text{ L}$$

---

d. 1. To calculate the volume of the solid in cubic centimeters, students should multiply the estimated area from Part **b** by 10 cm.

   2. To calculate the volume in liters, students should divide the volume in cubic centimeters (found in Step **1** above) by 1000.

e. Students use rice to verify their estimates from Part **d**.

Discussion 2

a. Answers may vary. Sample response: Find the area by estimating the average length and average width of the figure, then finding the product of the two.

b. 1. Sample response: We multiplied the estimated area by the height of 10 cm to find the volume in cubic centimeters, then divided this value by 1000 to find the equivalent volume in liters.

   2. Answers will vary, depending on the accuracy of the estimates of base area.

b. Considering the toilet tank as a trapezoidal prism, the volume is:

$$(0.5)(42 + 40)(25)(15) = 15{,}375 \text{ cm}^3 = 15.375 \text{ L}.$$

* **1.4 a.** To estimate the volume, students first should determine the approximate surface area of the lake, then multiply by the average depth of 15 m. Some students might suggest tracing the lake onto centimeter graph paper (because the scale is 1 cm to 1 km), then counting the number of squares. Others might estimate the average length and width of the lake, then find the product of these two.

Using the latter method, the volume of the lake is approximately

$$(6500 \text{ m})(5700 \text{ m})(15 \text{ m}) \approx 5.6 \cdot 10^8 \text{ m}^3$$

$$= 5.6 \cdot 10^{11} \text{ L}.$$

b. Answers will vary, depending on the estimate of the lake's volume. The volume of water used by the Canadian town each day is

$$(50{,}000)(380) = 1.9 \cdot 10^7 \text{ L}.$$

Using the estimate from Part **a,** the time that the water will last can be calculated as follows:

$$\frac{5.6 \cdot 10^{11}}{1.9 \cdot 10^7} \approx 29{,}000 \text{ days} \approx 79 \text{ yr}$$

✳ ✳ ✳ ✳ ✳

1.5 a. Sample drawing:

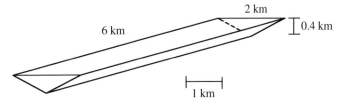

b. The shape of the reservoir is a triangular prism. Using decimeters, the area of the base is

$$(0.5)(4000)(20{,}000) = 4 \cdot 10^7 \text{ dm}^2.$$

Using the formula for the volume of a prism,

$$(4 \cdot 10^7 \text{ dm}^2)(6 \cdot 10^4 \text{ dm}) = 2.4 \cdot 10^{12} \text{ dm}^3$$

or $2.4 \cdot 10^{12}$ L.

c. The volume of water used by the city each day is $(6{,}000{,}000)(420) = 2.52 \cdot 10^9$ L. Therefore, the time that the water will last can be calculated as follows:

$$\frac{2.4 \cdot 10^{12}}{2.52 \cdot 10^9} \approx 950 \text{ days} \approx 2.6 \text{ yr}$$

b. a toilet tank.

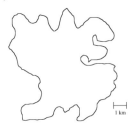

1.4 A Canadian town of 50,000 draws its water from the lake pictured below. The average depth of the lake is 15 m.

a. Estimate the volume of water in the lake and describe how you determined your estimate.

b. The average person in this town uses 380 L of water per day. If the lake is not replenished, how long will the water last?

✳ ✳ ✳ ✳ ✳

1.5 The municipal reservoir for a U.S. city of 6 million people lies in a V-shaped valley. One end of the reservoir is dammed, and the other is faced by a steep rock wall. The body of water itself is 6 km long, 2 km wide, and has an average depth of 400 m.

a. Make a scale drawing of this reservoir in kilometers.

b. Determine its volume in liters.

c. The average person in this city uses 420 L of water per day. Assuming that the reservoir is not refilled, how long can it supply the city with water?

Module 5 ■ *What Will We Do When the Well Runs Dry?*   **107**

1.6 Cubic centimeters generally are used to measure the volume of solid materials. Health professionals also use these units to measure liquid volumes. In this setting, 1 cm^3 is referred to as 1 cc. What is the relationship between cubic centimeters and milliliters?

1.7 The following diagram shows the dimensions of a swimming pool with rectangular ends. How many liters of water does this pool hold?

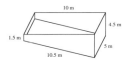

1.8 Construction companies often measure volume using cubic yards. How many cubic yards of concrete are needed to pave a driveway with the following dimensions: 20 ft × 15 ft × 6 in.?

1.9 The diagram below shows a small fish pond.

Determine the volume of the pond in each of the following units:

a. cubic meters   b. liters.

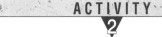
ACTIVITY 2

How much water does a leaky faucet waste? How long does it take to fill a bathtub? How long would it take a broken water main to flood a basement? The answers to these questions depend partly on the water's rate of flow. In this activity, you

1.6 Because 1000 cm^3 = 1 L, 1 cm^3 = 0.001 L. Since 1 mL also represents 0.001 L, 1 cm^3 = 1 mL.

* 1.7 Considering the pool as a trapezoidal prism, its volume is: (0.5)(1.5 m + 4.5 m)(10 m)(5 m) = 150 m^3 or 150,000 L.

1.8 Considering the driveway as a rectangular prism, its volume is (20 ft)(15 ft)(0.5 ft) = 150 ft^3. Since 27 ft^3 = 1 yd^3, 150 ft^3 ≈ 5.6 yd^3.

*1.9 Answers will vary. Sample response: By tracing the outline of the pond on a 1-cm square grid, the surface area is estimated to be approximately 12 m^2. The volume of the pond is roughly (12 m^2)(4 m) = 48 m^3 = 48,000 L.

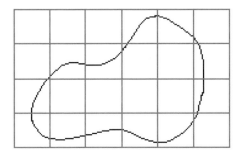

ACTIVITY 2

In this activity, students explore rate of flow and make connections between rates and the slopes of linear models.

Materials List

- 1-L containers (one per group)
- metric rulers (one per group)
- scissors (one pair per group)
- cardboard (three sheets, approximately 50 cm × 30 cm, per group)
- tape (one roll per group)
- rice (approximately 2 kg per group)
- stopwatches or timers (one per group)
- buckets (one per group)
- centimeter graph paper (several sheets per student)
- straightedges (one per student)

teacher note

In this activity, rice is used to simulate water. Any dry material that flows freely and does not pose a hazard to electronic equipment may be substituted.

In the exploration, students model the flow of rice through a funnel with a linear function. In reality, the change in pressure due to the decreasing depth of the rice results in data that is not truly linear. (Water flow depending on pressure is a classic differential equations problem.) However, given the depth of the funnels used, a linear model is acceptable for this activity.

If water is available in your classroom (and the dangers of spills can be minimized), you may modify the exploration accordingly. For example, students may measure the time required for a plastic jug of water to empty through openings of three different sizes—0.5 cm, 1.0 cm, and 2.0 cm—by drilling holes of those diameters in three different lids.

Student Outcomes

After completing the following exploration and discussion, students should be able to:

✴ calculate rate of flow

✴ convert flow rates to different units, including liters per second, liters per minute, and liters per hour

✴ create scatterplots and suggest linear models

✴ use linear models to make predictions

✴ write linear equations in the form $y = mx + b$

✴ relate slopes to rates of change.

Exploration

This exploration requires students to work in groups of at least two: one student to hold the funnel and another to start the timer. You might wish to demonstrate Parts **a** and **b** before students begin work.

a–d. Sample data:

Funnel Opening (cm)	Time for Trial 1	Time for Trial 2	Time for Trial 3
2	27.0	27.0	24.0
3	6.0	6.0	6.0
4	3.0	3.0	3.0

e. Answers will vary. Using the sample data in Table **5-1**, the average time for the 2-cm funnel is 26.0 sec, the average for the 3-cm funnel is 6.0 sec, and the average for the 4-cm funnel is 3.0 sec.

use graphs to relate the rate of flow to the slope of a line. This activity extends the notions of lines found in "Yesterday's Food is Walking and Talking Today" to model a rate of flow.

Exploration

In this exploration, you measure the rate at which water flows through a funnel. **Note:** To prevent damage to papers, books, and electronic equipment, rice is used to simulate water.

a. Use cardboard to make a sturdy funnel with a volume of at least 2 L and an opening at the narrow end approximately 2 cm in diameter.

b. 1. Hold the funnel over a bucket and place one hand under the narrow end to block the flow of rice. Pour 2.0 L of rice into the funnel.

   2. Simultaneously remove your hand from the narrow end of the funnel and start a timer. Determine the time (to the nearest 0.1 sec) required for the funnel to empty completely. Record the time in a table with headings like those in Table 5-1 below.

TABLE 5-1 ■ *Time Data*

Funnel Opening (cm)	Time for Trial 1	Time for Trial 2	Time for Trial 3
2			
3			
4			

c. Repeat Part **b** for two more trials.

d. To complete Table **5-1**, repeat Parts **a–c** using funnels with openings of 3 cm and 4 cm.

mathematics note

A **rate** compares the change in one quantity to the change in another quantity.

For example, the rate of flowing water compares a change in volume to a change in time. A rate of flow of 20 liters per minute may be written as 20 L/min.

e. Calculate the average time (to the nearest 0.1 sec) required for each size of funnel to empty.

Module 5 ■ *What Will We Do When the Well Runs Dry?* 109

f. Use these average times to determine the rate at which rice flowed from each funnel in the following units.

   1. liters per second

   2. liters per minute

   3. liters per hour.

g. Use the rates from Part **f** to predict the volume (to the nearest 0.1 L) that could flow through each funnel in 1 min, 2 min, 5 min, and 10 min. Record your predictions in a table with headings like those in Table **5-2**.

Time (min)	Volume (L) 2-cm Funnel	3 cm Funnel	4-cm Funnel
1			
2			
5			
10			

TABLE 5-2 ■ *Time vs. Volume Data*

h. 1. Make a scatterplot of the predictions in Table **5-2** for the 2-cm funnel. Let *x* represent the time in minutes and *y* represent the volume in liters.

   2. Find a line that fits the points as closely as possible. Draw the line on the same set of axes as the scatterplot.

   3. Determine the slope of the line.

i. Use your line to estimate the volume that could flow through the funnel in 7 min and in 12 min. **Note:** Save your work in this exploration for use in the assignment.

Discussion

a. Compare the data you collected in Table **5-1** with that of others in the class. What might have caused the differences you observe?

b. What relationship did you observe between the size of the funnel opening and the rate of flow?

c. Do you think that the rates determined in Part **f** of the exploration are reliable? Explain your response.

d. Describe the relationship between the rate of flow and the slope of the line that you found in Part **h** of the exploration.

e. If a leaky faucet drips once every second and each drip has a volume of 0.50 mL, what volume of water will leak from the faucet in 1 day?

110   Module 5 ■ *What Will We Do When the Well Runs Dry?*

---

f. Answers will vary. The following sample responses show the rate of flow for the 2-cm funnel.

   1. $2.0 \text{ L}/26.0 \text{ sec} \approx 0.08 \text{ L/sec}$

   2. Because there are 60 sec in 1 min,
   $$\left(\frac{2.0 \text{ L}}{26.0 \text{ sec}}\right)\left(\frac{60 \text{ sec}}{1 \text{ min}}\right) \approx 4.6 \text{ L/min}$$

   3. Because there are 60 min in 1 hr,
   $$\left(\frac{2.0 \text{ L}}{26.0 \text{ sec}}\right)\left(\frac{60 \text{ sec}}{1 \text{ min}}\right)\left(\frac{60 \text{ min}}{1 \text{ hr}}\right) \approx 280 \text{ L/hr}$$

g. Answers will vary. The predictions in the table below were made using the sample data given on the previous page.

h. 1–2. Sample scatterplot:

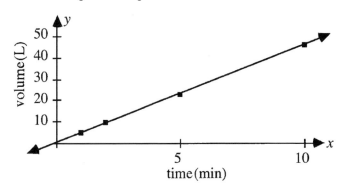

   3. The slope of the line on the sample graph above can be calculated as follows:
   $$\frac{46 - 0}{10 - 0} = \frac{23}{5} = 4.6$$

i. Students should use the graph of the line to make their predictions. The sample responses below correspond to the graph shown in Part **h**.

   1. 32 L

   2. 55 L

Discussion

a. Some possible causes for the variations in experimental data include errors in measurement, differences in the shape of the funnel opening, and differences in timing.

b. Sample response: As the size of the funnel opening increases, so does the rate of flow.

c. Answers will vary. As the sample data shows fairly consistent results, this suggests that the average rate is a reliable measurement.

d. Sample response: The rate of flow and the slope are the same. As the rate increases, the slope of the line increases.

e. The volume of water may be calculated as follows:
$$\left(\frac{0.50 \text{ mL}}{1 \text{ sec}}\right)\left(\frac{60 \text{ sec}}{1 \text{ min}}\right)\left(\frac{60 \text{ min}}{1 \text{ hr}}\right)\left(\frac{24 \text{ hr}}{1 \text{ day}}\right) \approx 43{,}000 \text{ mL/day}$$
$$= 43 \text{ L/day}$$

Time (min)	Volume (L)		
	2-cm Funnel	3-cm Funnel	4-cm Funnel
1	4.6	20	40
2	9.2	40	80
5	23	100	200
10	46	200	400

Warm-Up

1. **a.** $m = 3$
   b. $m = -5/13$
   c. $m = 0$
   d. The slope is undefined.
2. $m = 2/3$; $b = -7$
3. $y = -1.2x + 2$
4. **a.** $y = x + 4$
   b. $y = -(1/3)x - 2$
5. **a.** $y = -6x + 16$
   b. $y = (1/7)x - 23/7$
   c. $y = (2/3)x + 8$
   d. $y = -(4/3)x + 61/3$
   e. $y = -5x + 6$
   f. $y = -4$

Assignment

Problems suitable for use as assessment items are identified by an asterisk (*).

2.1 **a. 1.** The y-intercept is 0.

   2. Sample response: It represents the volume of rice that has passed through the funnel after 0 min.

   b. One equation for the line is $y = 4.6x + 0$.

   c. Using the sample equation given in Part **b**, the predicted values are $(4.6)(7) = 32.2$ L and $(4.6)(12) = 55.2$ L.

   d. The predicted values found using the graph of the line should be very close to those found using its equation.

* 2.2 The following responses use the sample data given in the exploration.

   a. An equation for the line in the sample graph below is $y = 20x + 0$.

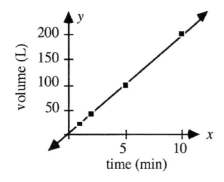

page 111

Warm-Up

1. Find the slope of the line that contains each of the following pairs of points:
   a. (5,2) and (7,8)
   b. (10,8) and (–3,13)
   c. (–2,5) and (6,5)
   d. (–1,–4) and (–1,5)

2. Create a graph of the line $y = (2/3)x - 7$. Identify its slope and y-intercept.

3. Graph a line with a slope of –6/5 and a y-intercept of 2. Write its equation in the form $y = mx + b$.

4. Write the equation of each line shown below:

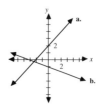

5. Write the equation of each line described below in the form $y = mx + b$.
   a. the line with slope –6 that passes through the point (3,–2)
   b. the line with slope 1/7 that passes through the point (–5,–4)
   c. the line that passes through the points (–6,4) and (3,10)
   d. the line that passes through the points (7,11) and (–2,23)
   e. the line that passes through the points (0,6) and (1,1)
   f. the horizontal line passing through the point (2,–4)

Module 5 ■ *What Will We Do When the Well Runs Dry?*   111

page 112

Assignment

2.1 Use your line from Part **h** of the exploration to complete the following.
   a. 1. Identify the y-intercept of the line.
   2. What does the y-intercept represent in terms of the exploration?
   b. Write an equation of the line in the form $y = mx + b$, where y represents volume in liters and x represents time in minutes.
   c. Use your equation to predict the volume that could flow through the funnel in 7 min and in 12 min.
   d. Compare these predictions with the ones you made in Part **i** of the exploration.

2.2 **a. 1.** Make a scatterplot of the data in Table **5-2** for the 3-cm funnel.
   2. Find a line that fits the data as closely as possible. Draw the line on the same set of axes as the scatterplot.
   3. Write an equation of the line in the form $y = mx + b$, where y represents volume in liters and x represents time in minutes.
   b. Repeat Part **a** for the data for the 4-cm funnel.

2.3 Graph the equations found in Problem **2.1b** and Problem **2.2a** and **b** on the same coordinate system. Describe any similarities or differences you observe and explain why they occur in terms of the exploration.

2.4 The table below shows the average time required to empty a 2.0-L water bottle using openings of different sizes.

Bottle Opening (cm)	Time to Empty (sec)
0.6	78.0
1.3	18.0
2.5	5.0

   a. Use this data to determine the rate at which water flowed through each opening in the following units.
   1. liters per second
   2. liters per minute
   3. liters per hour.
   b. Write an equation of the form $y = mx + b$ to describe the flow of water through each opening, where y represents volume in liters and x represents time in minutes.

* * * * *

112   Module 5 ■ *What Will We Do When the Well Runs Dry?*

2.5 The All School Club is a service organization at Larry's school. When Larry became president of the club, he decided to start a membership drive. The campaign hopes to sign 4 new members per week. After 10 weeks, this should bring the club's total membership to 375 students. The following table shows the membership during the first five weeks of the campaign.

Week	Total Membership
1	335
2	339
3	343
4	347
5	351

a. 1. Draw a scatterplot of this data. Let x represent the week and y represent the total membership.

2. Draw a line that fits the data as closely as possible.

b. 1. Is the slope of the line positive or negative?

2. What does the slope indicate in terms of the membership drive?

c. 1. Identify the y-intercept of the line.

2. What does the y-intercept represent in terms of the membership drive?

2.6 Crickets make chirping sounds by rubbing their wings together. For some crickets, the relationship between the number of chirps per minute and the air temperature is very close to a line. When the air temperature is 20°C, these crickets chirp 124 times per minute. When the temperature is 26.6°C, they chirp 172 times per minute.

a. Graph this information on a scatterplot. Let x represent the temperature in degrees Celsius and y represent the number of chirps per minute.

b. Draw a line that fits the data as closely as possible.

c. Identify the y-intercept of this line.

d. Determine the slope of the line.

e. Write an equation of the line in the form $y = mx + b$.

f. Predict the temperature at which these crickets make 150 chirps per minute.

b. An equation for the line in the sample graph below is $y = 40x + 0$.

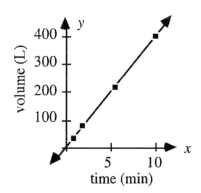

* 2.3 Sample response: The volume of rice that has passed through each funnel after 0 min is 0, so all three lines have y-intercepts of 0. The slope of the line for the 4-cm funnel is much steeper than the others. This is because the rate of flow through the 4-cm funnel is faster than the rates for either of the other two funnels. The bigger the opening, the faster the flow rate and the steeper the line.

2.4 a. The rate of flow through the 0.6-cm opening is:

$$\frac{2.0\,\text{L}}{78.0\,\text{sec}} \approx 0.03\,\text{L/sec} \approx 1.5\,\text{L/min} \approx 92\,\text{L/hr}$$

The rate of flow through the 1.3-cm opening is:

$$\frac{2.0\,\text{L}}{18.0\,\text{sec}} \approx 0.11\,\text{L/sec} \approx 6.7\,\text{L/min} \approx 400\,\text{L/hr}$$

The rate of flow through the 2.5-cm opening is:

$$\frac{2.0\,\text{L}}{5.0\,\text{sec}} = 0.40\,\text{L/sec} = 24\,\text{L/min} = 1440\,\text{L/hr}$$

b. The equation for the amount of water flowing through the 0.6-cm opening is $y = 1.5x$.

The equation for the amount of water flowing through the 1.3-cm opening is $y = 6.7x$.

The equation for the amount of water flowing through the 2.5-cm opening is $y = 24x$.

✳ ✳ ✳ ✳ ✳

2.5 a. Sample graph:

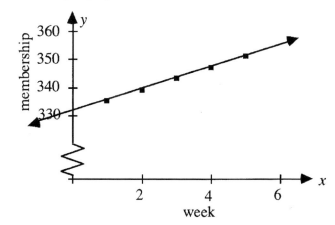

b. 1. The slope of the line is positive.
   2. The positive slope indicates that the membership is increasing.

c. 1. Answers may vary. For the sample line given in Part **a**, the y-intercept is 331.
   2. The y-intercept represents the number of students in the All School Club when the membership drive began.

* 2.6 a–b. Sample graph:

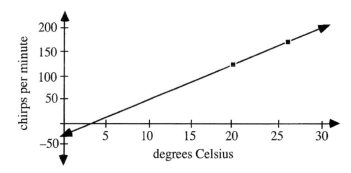

c. For the sample graph given in Part **a** above, the y-intercept is approximately –22.

d. For the sample graph, the slope is approximately 7.3.

e. An equation for the line given in Part **a** is $y = 7.3x - 22$.

f. The predicted temperature is approximately 24°C.

teacher note

The board foot is a unit of volume. One board foot represents the volume of wood in a board with dimensions 1 in. × 12 in. × 12 in., or 144 in.³. For finished lumber, the actual dimensions are slightly smaller than the nominal dimensions.

2.7 **a.** Sample graph:

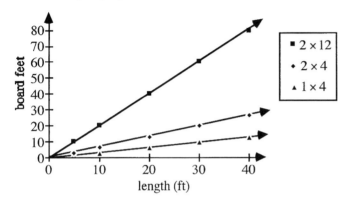

b. Sample response: It is a linear relationship. As the length of a board increases, the number of board feet it contains also increases. This is shown by the positive association of the scatterplots.

c. See sample graph in Part **a** above.

d. The equation for 2 × 12 lumber is $y = 2x$, where y represents number of board feet and x represents length in feet. The equation for 2 × 4 lumber is $y = (2/3)x$. The equation for 1 × 4 lumber is $y = (1/3)x$.

e. Answers will vary. Sample response: A 2 × 12 that measures 0.5 ft long is equal to 1 board foot. This can be found by tracing the graph of the equation for a 2 × 12 until the number of board feet equals 1. This occurs at a length of 0.5 ft.

It is also possible to substitute 1 for y in the equation $y = 2x$ and solve for x. This also results in a board 0.5 ft long.

In this activity, students use residuals to determine how closely a line models a set of data points.

2.7 Lumber typically is sold in units called board feet. The table below shows the number of board feet contained in lengths of three common dimensions of lumber: 1 × 4, 2 × 4 and 2 × 12. (A 2 × 4 is approximately 2 in. thick and 4 in. wide.)

Dimensions	Length				
	5 ft	10 ft	20 ft	30 ft	40 ft
1 × 4	$1\frac{2}{3}$	$3\frac{1}{3}$	$6\frac{2}{3}$	10	$13\frac{1}{3}$
2 × 4	$3\frac{1}{3}$	$6\frac{2}{3}$	$13\frac{1}{3}$	20	$26\frac{2}{3}$
2 × 12	10	20	40	60	80

a. On a single coordinate system, create a scatterplot that shows the number of board feet in a piece of lumber versus its length for each of the following dimensions:

1. 1 × 4

2. 2 × 4

3. 2 × 12.

b. Describe the relationship between the length of a piece of lumber and the number of board feet it contains.

c. Draw a line that fits each scatterplot as closely as possible.

d. Write an equation for each line from Part **c** in the form $y = mx + b$.

e. Find the dimensions, including the length, of a piece of lumber that contains 1 board foot. Describe how you determined your response.

ACTIVITY 3

An aquifer is a water-filled layer of sand or gravel—a sort of underground deposit of water. The High Plains Aquifer, which underlies parts of eight states, is one of the largest known. It contains as much water as Lake Huron: about 4.24 quadrillion liters. For this reason, some geologists call it the "sixth Great Lake."

The geographical boundaries of the aquifer are shown in Figure 5-4 on the next page.

This region accounts for nearly 15% of the grain, 25% of the cotton, and almost 40% of the beef produced in the United States. Much of this production is due at least in part to the availability of water from the High Plains Aquifer.

FIGURE 5-4 The High Plains Aquifer.

SOURCE: Dugan and Schild, *Water-Level Changes in the High Plains Aquifer.*

Although rain and snow help to replenish the aquifer, scientists predict that in some areas, it may be depleted in less than 100 years. To prevent this, many farmers are planting crops that require less water, while others are irrigating in ways that conserve the resource. Without irrigation, however, acres of productive farms would return to the original prairie.

Exploration

To monitor changes in the aquifer, researchers drilled wells in Chase County, Nebraska. They measured the distance from the surface of the ground to the water. As shown in Figure 5-5, high-water readings were taken in June, and low-water readings were taken in September.

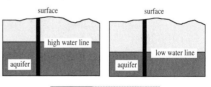

FIGURE 5-5 High and low water lines.

Table **5-3** below shows the distances from the surface to the high and low water lines from 1964 to 1978. The information in Table **5-3** seems to indicate that some sort of change is occurring in the aquifer. In this exploration, you determine whether or not this data can be reasonably modeled by a line.

TABLE 5-3 ■ Distance from Surface to Water Line (in meters)

Year	High	Low	Year	High	Low
1964	17.1	18.1	1972	19.7	21.3
1965	17.2	18.1	1973	19.8	22.3
1966	17.1	18.2	1974	20.1	22.9
1967	17.4	18.2	1975	20.6	23.8
1968	17.7	19.4	1976	21.3	26.0
1969	18.1	19.8	1977	22.3	26.5
1970	18.9	20.7	1978	22.7	27.6
1971	19.4	21.3			

SOURCE: Dugan and Schild, *Water-Level Changes in the High Plains Aquifer.*

a. Enter the distances to the high-water level in a spreadsheet with headings like those in Table **5-4.** Note that the first column is headed "Years after 1964." This means that 1964 corresponds with 0, 1965 corresponds with 1, and so on.

TABLE 5-4 ■ Distances to High Water Level after 1964

Years after 1964	Distance (m)
0	17.1
1	17.2
⋮	⋮
14	22.7

b. Create a scatterplot of the data from Part **a.** Let *y* represent the distance and *x* represent the number of years after 1964.

c. Mathematical models often use graphs or equations to describe relationships that arise in real-world situations. A mathematical model that consists of a line or its equation is a **linear model.**

   1. Draw a linear model that fits the data from Part **a** as closely as possible.

   2. Find the equation of the line.

 teacher note

In this module, students are introduced only to the sum of the absolute value of the residuals as a method for evaluating fit. In later modules, students investigate the principle of least squares and other curve-fitting techniques.

A brief assessment of the mathematical content in Activities **2** and **3,** for use at your discretion, appears in the Teacher Resources for this module.

Materials List

■ straightedges (one per group)
■ centimeter graph paper (several sheets per group)

Technology

■ graphing utility
■ spreadsheet (optional)

Student Outcomes

After completing the following exploration and discussion, students should be able to:

✳ define and calculate a residual

✳ examine residuals for a given data set and use them to evaluate the fit of a linear model

✳ interpret the real-world significance of the slope of a linear model.

Exploration

In this exploration, students find a linear model for the distances to the high-water levels of the High Plains Aquifer, and use residuals to compare the data set to the model.

a. See completed spreadsheet in Part **d** on the next page.
b. Sample graph:

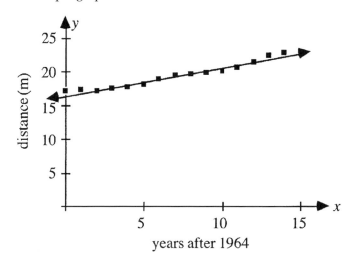

c. Students draw a line that closely models the data, such as the one shown in Part **b** above. The equation of this line is $y = 0.4x + 17$.

d–f. The predicted values in the table at the bottom of the page were made using the equation $y = 0.4x + 17$.

g. Using the sample responses given in Parts **d–f,** the average distance from each data point to the model is $8.2/15 \approx 0.55$.

Discussion

a. Sample response: The line does not fit the data exactly because it does not go through all the data points. An exact fit would have all residuals of 0.

b. Sample response: If the average distance from each data point to the model is small when compared to the spread of the data, then the model could be considered a reasonable one.

c. Sample response: This appears to be a good model because the sum of the absolute values of the residuals is only 8.2. Because there are 15 data points, this is only about 0.5 m per data point, which is small compared to the distances in the data.

d. Sample response: No. There could be a point 100 units from the line on one side and another point 100 units on the other side. The two corresponding residuals would be 100 and −100. Their sum would be 0, but the line would not fit the data exactly. **Note:** In general, the horizontal line $y = a$, where a is the mean of the y-values in the data, results in a sum of the residuals of 0.

d. 1. Add a third column to your spreadsheet with the heading "Predicted Distance."

2. Use the equation from Part **c** to predict the distance to the high-water level for each year in Table **5-3.**

3. Enter these predicted values in the appropriate column of the spreadsheet.

mathematics note

Figure **5-6** shows that a linear model might not fit every data point exactly. However, even when a line does not fit every point, it still can provide a reasonable model of the data.

A **residual** is the difference between an observed value and the predicted value. In Figure **5-6,** the residual for each data point is the difference between the y-coordinate of the data point and the corresponding y-value of the model. Because data points may be located above or below the line, the values of residuals may be positive or negative.

The **absolute value of a residual** is a measure of the distance from the data point to the linear model. In general, the smaller the sum of the absolute values of the residuals, the more closely a line approximates the data.

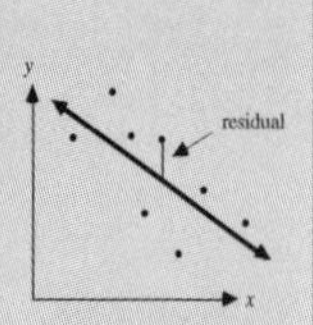

FIGURE 5-6
A linear model.

e. 1. Add a fourth column to your spreadsheet with the heading "Residuals."

2. Using your predicted distances from Part **d,** find and enter the residual for each data point.

3. Determine the sum of the residuals.

f. 1. Add a fifth column to your spreadsheet with the heading "Absolute Value of the Residuals."

2. Calculate and record the absolute value of each residual.

3. Determine the sum of the absolute values of the residuals.

g. Divide the sum of the absolute values of the residuals by the number of data points. This is the average distance from each data point to the model.

Year after 1964	Actual Distance	Predicted Distance	Residual	Absolute Value of Residual
0	17.1	17.0	−0.1	0.1
1	17.2	17.4	0.2	0.2
2	17.1	17.8	0.7	0.7
3	17.4	18.2	0.8	0.8
4	17.7	18.6	0.9	0.9
5	18.1	19.0	0.9	0.9
6	18.9	19.4	0.5	0.5
7	19.4	19.8	0.4	0.4
8	19.7	20.2	0.5	0.5
9	19.8	20.6	0.8	0.8
10	20.1	21.0	0.9	0.9
11	20.6	21.4	0.8	0.8
12	21.3	21.8	0.5	0.5
13	22.3	22.2	−0.1	0.1
14	22.7	22.6	−0.1	0.1
		Sum	7.6	8.2

Discussion

a. Does the line you drew in Part **c** of the exploration fit the data exactly? Explain your response.

b. How could you use the average distance from each data point to the model to determine if a model fits reasonably well?

c. Does your line appear to be a good model for the data?

d. If the sum of the absolute values of the residuals is 0, then a linear model fits the data perfectly. Is this also true for the sum of the residuals? Use an example to justify your response.

e. Describe the slope of your linear model. What might this slope indicate about the aquifer in Chase County?

f. Do you think that water-level data has been recorded for enough years to support your response to Part **e** of the discussion? Why or why not?

g. What practices might be implemented to ensure that future generations can continue to draw water from the High Plains Aquifer?

h. Is there an aquifer in your area? If so, where would you go to find more information about it?

Warm-Up

1. **a.** Complete the data table below for the line $y = 2x + 5$.

x	y
–5	
	0
0	
	15
15	

b. Describe how you can identify the line's x- and y-intercepts using the completed table in Part **a**.

2. **a.** On a coordinate grid, plot the points $A(1,4)$, $B(6,6)$, and $C(8,9)$.

b. One line that approximates these points is $y = 0.7x + 3$. Graph this line.

c. Determine the residuals for A, B, and C.

---

e. Sample response: The slope of the line is positive, indicating that the distance from the surface to the water is increasing with time. This means that the level of the aquifer is dropping.

f. Table **5-3** contains data for 15 years. Although this may seem like a long time to most students, it might not be long enough to describe a long-term trend in water levels. Natural climatic variations and drought cycles often occur over periods of many years.

g. Students may suggest modifying irrigation techniques, planting drought-tolerant crops, reducing personal water use, or controlling population growth.

h. Answers will vary by region. You may consult the local department of natural resources or water quality bureau for more information.

Warm-Up

1. **a.** Data table for the line $y = 2x + 5$:

x	y
–5	–5
–2.5	0
0	5
5	15
15	35

b. Sample response: The x-intercept is the value of x when $y = 0$. The y-intercept is the value of y when $x = 0$.

2. **a–b.** Sample graph:

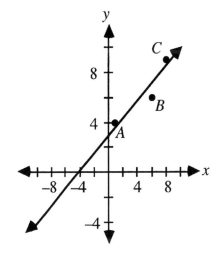

c. The residual for A is 0.3, for B is –1.2, and for C is 0.4.

Assignment

Problems suitable for use as assessment items are identified by an asterisk (*).

3.1 a–b. Sample graph:

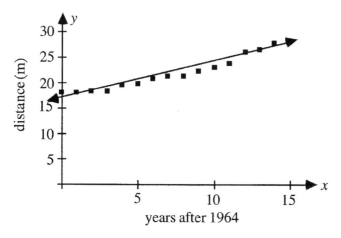

years after 1964

c. Answers will vary. An equation for the sample line in Part **a** is $y = 0.7x + 17$. The slope was calculated using the points (1,18.1) and (13,26.5) as follows:

$$m = \frac{26.5 - 18.1}{13 - 1} = \frac{8.3}{12} \approx 0.7$$

The y-intercept of 17 was approximated from the graph.

d–e. The predicted values in the table below were made using the equation $y = 0.7x + 17$.

Assignment

3.1 **a.** Create a scatterplot like the one in the exploration for the distances to the low water levels in Table **5-3**.

b. Draw a line that closely approximates the data.

c. Write an equation of the line in the form $y = mx + b$. Describe the method you used to find this equation.

d. Use your equation to predict the distances to the low-water levels of the aquifer from 1964 to 1978.

e. 1. Find the residual of each point in the scatterplot.

  2. Calculate the sum of the absolute values of the residuals.

f. Explain whether or not your line is a good model for the data.

3.2 Imagine that you have a leaky pipe under the kitchen sink. To catch the water, you place a coffee can under the leak.

The following table shows the time that the can has been in place and the total mass of the can and water.

Time (min)	Total Mass (g)
5	160
10	350
15	470
20	570
25	790

If y represents the total mass in grams and x represents the time in minutes, which of the following equations more closely approximates this data? Support your choice by determining the sum of the absolute values of the residuals for each model.

$$y = 30x + 16$$
$$y = 33x + 15$$

Module 5 ■ *What Will We Do When the Well Runs Dry?*　119

Year after 1964	Actual Distance	Predicted Distance	Residual	Absolute Value of Residual
0	18.1	17.0	−1.1	1.1
1	18.1	17.7	−0.4	0.4
2	18.2	18.4	0.2	0.2
3	18.2	19.1	0.9	0.9
4	19.4	19.8	0.4	0.4
5	19.8	20.5	0.7	0.7
6	20.7	21.2	0.5	0.5
7	21.3	21.9	0.6	0.6
8	21.3	22.6	1.3	1.3
9	22.3	23.3	1.0	1.0
10	22.9	24.0	1.1	1.1
11	23.8	24.7	0.9	0.9
12	26.0	25.4	−0.6	0.6
13	26.5	26.1	−0.4	0.4
14	27.6	26.8	−0.8	0.8
			Sum	10.9

3.3 When an inflated balloon is placed in a freezer, its volume decreases as the air inside it grows colder. When the balloon is removed from the freezer, its volume increases as it warms.

The table below shows some data comparing the temperature of the air in the balloon to its volume.

Temperature (°C)	Volume (mL)
10	500
20	520
30	531
40	558

a. Make a scatterplot of this data. Let y represent the volume in milliliters and x represent the temperature in degrees Celsius.

b. Draw a line that closely approximates the data.

c. Write an equation of the line in Part **b** in slope-intercept form.

d. 1. Find the sum of the absolute values of the residuals.

2. Describe what the calculation from Part **d1** means in relationship to the linear model.

e. Predict the volume of the balloon at an air temperature of 100°C.

＊ ＊ ＊ ＊ ＊

3.4 Jason is raising hamsters to sell to pet stores. As shown in the following table, he has 64 hamsters after 5 months.

Month (x)	Hamsters (y)
1	2
2	6
3	18
4	35
5	64

The local pet supplier buys hamsters only in lots of 200. To predict when he will have enough hamsters to sell, Jason decides to create a graph of the data in the table.

a. Make a scatterplot of Jason's data.

b. Draw a line that approximates the data.

c. Write an equation of the line in slope-intercept form.

Residuals for $y = 33x + 15$

Time (min)	Mass (g)	Predicted Value (g)	Absolute Value of Residual
5	160	180	20
10	350	345	5
15	470	510	40
20	570	675	105
25	790	840	50
		Sum	220

＊ **3.3 a–b.** Sample graph:

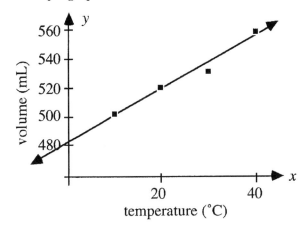

c. Answers will vary. An equation for the sample line shown in Part **a** is $y = 1.93x + 48.1$.

d. 1. Using the equation given in Part **c**, the sum of the absolute values of the residuals is 8.8.

2. The relatively small sum indicates that this linear model provides a good fit for the data.

e. Using the equation given in Part **c**, the predicted volume of the balloon is 674 mL.

＊ ＊ ＊ ＊ ＊

3.4 **a–b.** Sample graph:

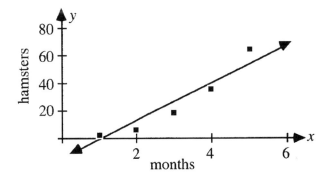

c. Answers will vary. An equation for the sample line shown in Part **a** is $y = 11.7x - 9.7$.

---

f. Answers will vary. The sample line is a good model because the sum of the absolute values of the residuals is only 10.9. Because there are 15 data points, this is only about 0.7 m per data point. The value of 0.7 is small compared to any value in the data, so the error in the model is small.

＊ **3.2** The equation $y = 30x + 16$ is the better model because it produces the smaller sum of the absolute values of the residuals, as shown in the following tables.

Residuals for $y = 30x + 16$

Time (min)	Mass (g)	Predicted Value (g)	Absolute Value of Residual
5	160	166	6
10	350	316	34
15	470	466	4
20	570	616	46
25	790	766	24
		Sum	114

d. Using the equation given in Part **c,** the sum of the absolute values of the residuals is 32.4.

e. Sample response: No. The scatterplot appears to be curved, not linear. The large sum of the absolute values of the residuals also indicates that the model may not be a good fit.

3.5 a. Sample graph:

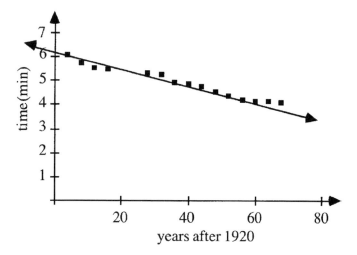

b. An equation of the sample line shown in Part **a** is $y = -0.03x + 6.1$.

c. Sample response: The sum of the absolute value of the residuals is about 1.8. The model appears to fit the data well because the average distance from the line to each data point is only 0.12 min, while the spread in the data is 1.98 min.

d. Using the sample equation from Part **b:**

$$-0.03(80) + 6.1 = 3.7 \text{ min}$$

This is 0.4 min less than the actual winning time.

e. Sample response: The time predicted for the year 2080 is $-0.03(160) + 6.1 = 1.3$ min. This does not seem realistic. Judging from the scatterplot, the change in recent winning times seems to be decreasing from one Olympics to the next. Using the line as a model, the predicted winning time will eventually be 0.

3.6 a. In the following sample responses, the predicted values were calculated using the equation $y = 0.4x + 17$.

1. $\left| \dfrac{17 - 17.1}{17.1} \right| \approx 0.5\%$

2. $\left| \dfrac{19.4 - 18.9}{18.9} \right| \approx 2.6\%$

3. $\left| \dfrac{21.4 - 20.6}{20.6} \right| \approx 3.9\%$

d. Find the sum of the absolute values of the residuals.

e. Do you think Jason should use a linear model to predict when he will have 200 hamsters? If so, predict the time. If not, explain why not.

3.5 Over the past 80 years, Olympic swimmers have lowered the winning time in the women's 400-meter freestyle by more than 2 min. The table below shows the winning times in each race from 1924 to 1988, rounded to the nearest 0.01 min.

Year	Time	Year	Time	Year	Time
1924	6.04	1952	5.20	1972	4.32
1928	5.71	1956	4.91	1976	4.17
1932	5.48	1960	4.84	1980	4.15
1936	5.44	1964	4.72	1984	4.12
1948	5.30	1968	4.53	1988	4.06

a. 1. Graph this information on a scatterplot. Let x represent the number of years after 1920 and y represent time in minutes.

 2. Draw a line that fits the data as closely as possible.

b. Write an equation of the line in the form $y = mx + b$.

c. Determine how well your model fits the data.

d. Use your model to predict the winning time in the 400-meter freestyle in 2000.

 Brooke Bennett's actual winning time was 4:05.80, or approximately 4.10 min. How does this compare to your prediction?

e. Use your model to predict the winning time in the 400-meter freestyle in 2080. Do you think this prediction is realistic? Explain your response.

3.6 Another way to determine how well a linear model fits a specific data point is to use **percent error**. The percent error is the absolute value of the difference between the estimated value and the measured value, divided by the measured value, and expressed as a percentage:

$$\text{percent error} = \left| \frac{\text{estimated} - \text{measured}}{\text{measured}} \right| \cdot 100$$

For example, if a data point has coordinates (10,24) and the corresponding point on the linear model has coordinates (10,21), then the percent error can be calculated as follows:

$$\left| \frac{21 - 24}{24} \right| \cdot 100 = 12.5\%$$

If the measured value is 0, then percent error cannot be calculated.

a. Using the predicted distances to the high water levels from Part **d** of the exploration, find the percent error for your model for each of the following years:

 1. 1964

 2. 1970

 3. 1975.

b. The equation $y = 0.7x + 17$ is one possible model for the distances to the low water levels in Table **5-3.** Find the percent error for this model for each of the following years:

 1. 1965

 2. 1970

 3. 1975.

c. Do you think that percent error would be a good measure of fit for a set of data? Why or why not?

Research Project

On average, each resident of the United States uses about 420 L of water per day. How does your daily water use compare to this value? In the following research project, you analyze your own personal water use.

 Create a table with headings like the one below. To complete the table, you will need to develop some innovative ways to measure water use. For example, how can you determine the volume of water used in a shower or bath? And how much water does it take to flush a toilet?

Use	Rate of Use	No. of Uses or Time Used	Daily Volume
washing machine			
dishwasher			
bathroom sink			
kitchen sink			
toilet			
shower or bath			
other			
other			
		Total	

 Your report should include a description of the methods you used to determine each measurement, a comparison of your daily water usage to the national average, and a discussion of any differences you observe.

Summary Assessment

1. The diagram below shows four farms that share irrigation water from the same reservoir. The average depth of the reservoir is 8.0 m. Each farmer has 2 center-pivot irrigation sprinklers. Each sprinkler can pump more than 4000 L of water per minute.

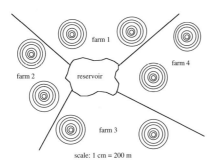

scale: 1 cm = 200 m

a. During the 3-month growing season, the farmers plan to irrigate their fields for 16 hours a day, every day. Assuming that the reservoir is not refilled during the growing season, do they have enough water for their plan? Justify your response, showing all calculations.

b. If the farmers do not modify their plan, for how many days can the reservoir supply them with water?

c. What is the maximum number of hours per day the farmers can operate the sprinklers and still irrigate for the full 3 months?

b. Students should find the predicted values for each year using the equation $y = 0.7x + 17$.

1. $\left| \dfrac{17.7 - 18.1}{18.1} \right| \approx 2.2\%$

2. $\left| \dfrac{21.2 - 20.7}{20.7} \right| \approx 2.4\%$

3. $\left| \dfrac{24.7 - 23.8}{23.8} \right| \approx 3.8\%$

c. Some students might argue that because percent error varies from point to point, it is not a good measure of fit for an entire set of data. Others might claim that it is a good measure of fit if all the percent errors are small or the largest percent error for the data is small.

Research Project

The information in the sample table at the bottom of the page was compiled by an actual SIMMS IM class. In this example, student water usage was close to the national average. **Note:** In areas where residential water use is metered, students can determine their daily consumption by reading the meter. By examining household water bills, they also can determine the daily cost of this water.

teacher note

An additional assessment, for use at your discretion, appears in the Teacher Resources for this module.

Summary Assessment

1. a. Sample response: The farmers do not have enough water for their plan. The approximate area of the reservoir is 240,000 m² The average depth is 8.0 m; therefore its volume is:

   $(240{,}000 \text{ m}^2)(8.0 \text{ m}) = 1.9 \cdot 10^6 \text{ m}^3$ or $1.9 \cdot 10^9$ L.

   Because the farmers have a total of 8 sprinklers, the daily volume of water used can be calculated as follows:

   $(8)\left(\dfrac{4000 \text{ L}}{\text{min}} \right)\left(\dfrac{60 \text{ min}}{\text{hr}} \right)\left(\dfrac{16 \text{ hr}}{\text{day}} \right) \approx 3.1 \cdot 10^7 \text{ L/day}$

   Therefore, the total volume of water needed for 90 days is $(90)(3.1 \cdot 10^7) = 2.8 \cdot 10^9$ L. This exceeds the volume of the reservoir.

   b. Sample response: The reservoir can supply the farmers with enough water for approximately 61 days. This can be calculated as follows:

   $\dfrac{1.9 \cdot 10^9 \text{ L}}{3.1 \cdot 10^7 \text{ L/day}} \approx 61 \text{ days}$

Use	Rate of Use	No. of Uses or Time Used	Daily Volume
washing machine	7 L/min	3 min	21 L
dishwasher	8 L/wash	1 wash	8 L
bathroom sink	8 L/min	2 min	16 L
kitchen sink	8 L/min	20 min	160 L
toilet	15 L/flush	5 flushes	75 L
shower or bath	16 L/min	8 min	128 L
		Total	408 L

c. Sample response: The volume of water available per day can be calculated as follows:

$$\frac{1.9 \bullet 10^9 \, \text{L}}{90 \, \text{days}} \approx 2.1 \bullet 10^7 \, \text{L/day}$$

The maximum number of hours per day is therefore:

$$\frac{2.1 \bullet 10^7 \, \text{L}}{8\left(\dfrac{4000 \, \text{L}}{\text{min}}\right)\left(\dfrac{60 \, \text{min}}{\text{hr}}\right)} \approx 10 \, \text{hr}$$

2. a–b. Sample graph:

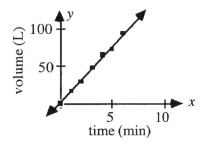

c. Answers may vary. Using the data points (6,94) and (0,0), one possible equation is $y = 15.7x$.

d. 1. 15.7 L/min
   2. 0.26 L/sec
   3. 942 L/hr

e. The rate of flow in liters per minute is the slope of the line.

f. The following responses were calculated using the sample equation given in Part **c**.
   1. $(15.7)(15) \approx 236$ L
   2. $(120)(15.7) \approx 1880$ L

g. The predicted values in the following table were calculated using the equation $y = 15.7x$.

Time (min)	Actual Volume (L)	Predicted Volume (g)	Absolute Value of Residual
0	0	0	0
1	15	15.7	0.7
2	29	31.4	2.4
3	48	47.1	0.9
4	65	62.8	2.2
5	73	78.5	5.5
6	94	94.2	0.2
		Sum	11.9

3. Sample response: The sum of the absolute value of the residuals is a measure of how well the line fits the data. Since the sum seems relatively small, this model appears to be a good fit.

2. The table below shows the volume of water flowing from a garden hose over time.

Time (min)	Volume (L)
0.00	0.0
1.00	15.0
2.00	29.0
3.00	48.0
4.00	65.0
5.00	73.0
6.00	94.0

a. Draw a scatterplot of the data. Let y represent volume in liters and x represent time in minutes.

b. Draw a line on the scatterplot that closely models the data points.

c. Write an equation for the line in the form $y = mx + b$.

d. Determine the average rate of flow in each of the following units:
   1. liters per minute
   2. liters per second
   3. liters per hour.

e. How is the rate of flow in liters per minute related to the graph in Part **b**? Include mathematical terms and concepts in your response.

f. Assuming that the rate of flow remains constant, determine the volume of water which will flow from the hose in:
   1. 15 min
   2. 2 hr.

g. 1. Find the absolute value of the residual for each data point.
   2. Determine the sum of the absolute values of the residuals.
   3. Describe what this sum tells you about your model.

h. Another possible model for this data is the line $y = 14x + 2$. Compare the sum of the absolute values of the residuals found using this equation to the sum you calculated in Part **g**. Use the comparison to determine which equation is the better model.

h. The following table shows the predicted values calculated using the equation $y = 14x + 2$. Based on the sum of the absolute values of the residuals, the equation $y = 15.7x$ is the better model.

Time (min)	Actual Volume (L)	Predicted Volume (g)	Absolute Value of Residual
0	0	2	2
1	15	16	1
2	29	30	1
3	48	44	4
4	65	58	7
5	73	72	1
6	94	86	8
		Sum	24

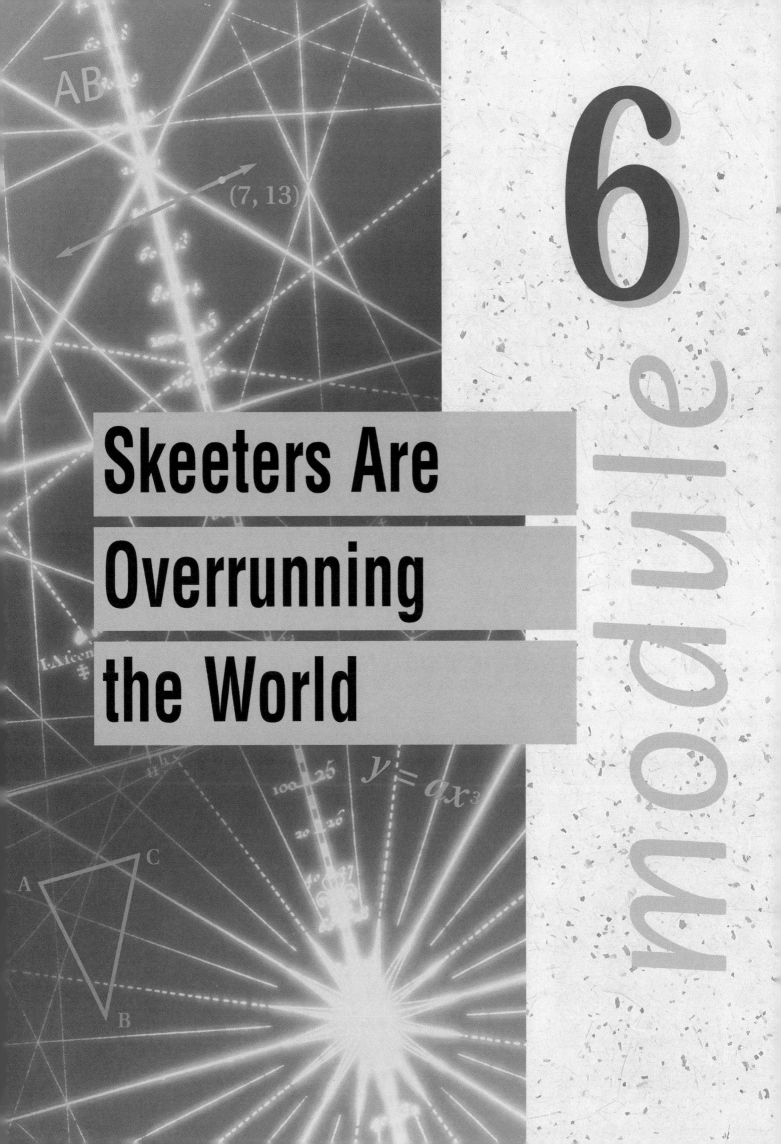

Skeeters Are Overrunning the World

6

module

Overview

In this module, students look at how the size of a population increases or decreases over time. Students use population models to simulate different growth rates and study the effects of those rates on population size. These models and the mathematics behind them are used to predict future population changes.

For the purposes of this module, a *population* is a collection of individuals of the same species in a given area. A few examples of such populations are grizzly bears in the Greater Yellowstone ecosystem, humpback whales in the Pacific Ocean, or humans on Earth. Scientists study a variety of population characteristics, including changes in age distribution, ratios of males to females, and total size.

Introduction: Students generate data for an exponential curve, graph the data, and look for patterns.

Activity 1:   Students learn function notation, determine growth rates, and investigate equations of the form $y = b^x$.

Activity 2:   Students use the previously generated data to continue their explorations of growth rate.

Activity 3:   Students investigate equations of the form $y = ab^x$.

Activity 4:   Students apply exponential functions to real-world contexts.

Objectives

In this module, students will:

✳ recognize nonlinear patterns (Introduction, 1)

✳ make predictions based on a nonlinear graph (Introduction, 1)

✳ model data with exponential curves (Introduction, 1, 2, 3, 4)

✳ create graphs of exponential curves to model data with different initial populations and growth rates (1)

✳ determine the independent and dependent variables for a function (1)

✳ graph and interpret an exponential function in the form $y = 1 \cdot b^x$ (1, 2)

✳ develop mathematical models for population growth (1, 2, 3)

✳ define a function using function notation (2)

✳ identify and determine a constant growth rate (2)

✳ explore the relationship between b and r in exponential equations of the form $y = 1 \cdot b^x$, where $b = 1 + r$ (2, 3)

✳ calculate average growth rate (2, 3)

✳ examine how the initial population affects population growth (3, 4)

✳ write exponential equations of the form $y = ab^x$ (3, 4)

✳ graph and interpret exponential functions of the form $y = ab^x$ (3, 4)

✳ apply exponential functions to real-world contexts (4).

Prerequisites

For this module, students should know:

✳ how to interpret exponential notation

✳ how to use a spreadsheet

✳ how to graph data on an xy-coordinate system

✳ how to calculate percent change

✳ how to evaluate an equation

✳ how to convert percentages to decimals.

 Flashbacks, for use at your discretion, appear in the Teacher Resources for this module. These brief problem sets provide a review of some prerequisite skills for each activity.

Planning Guide

Activity	Materials	Technology	Time Line
Introduction	■ graph paper ■ multicolored candies or disks with distinctive mark on one side ■ boxes with lids ■ overhead transparency with 1-cm grid (optional) ■ markers for overhead transparencies (optional)	■ none	2 days
Activity 1	■ graph paper ■ multicolored candies or disks with a distinctive mark on one side ■ boxes with lids ■ colored pencils (optional)	■ spreadsheet	3 days
Activity 2	■ none	■ spreadsheet	2 days
Activity 3	■ none	■ spreadsheet	2 days
Activity 4	■ none	■ spreadsheet ■ graphing utility	2 days
Assessment Activities	■ graph paper	■ spreadsheet	3 days **Total: 14 days**

teacher note

The activities in this module are based on the following five-step modeling process:

- ■ creating a simplified model of a given situation
- ■ translating the model into mathematics
- ■ using mathematics to solve a problem
- ■ relating the results of the mathematical manipulations to the simplified model and the given situation
- ■ revising the model as necessary and repeating the process.

Introduction

Students discuss populations and population growth. They engage in data collection and organization, then look for patterns and make predictions.

Materials List

- multicolored candies or disks with a mark on one side (approximately 500 per group)
- container with a large, flat bottom and a lid (one per group)
- graph paper (several sheets per group)
- overhead transparency with 1-cm grid (optional; one per group)
- overhead transparency pens (optional)

teacher note

The multicolored candies or disks are referred to as Skeeters in this module. In the following exploration, students require only a single color of Skeeters. In Activity **1,** students will need five different colors. Round, flattened candies such as Skittles™ work well. You also may use beans that have been marked on one side, or any other objects with two distinct sides that will not stack up when shaken.

If you use Skittles, you might wish to re-mark the yellow ones, as the "S" can be difficult to see. If you do not use Skittles, you should change the colors of the Skeeters described in the exploration in Activity **1** to fit the colors of your manipulatives.

Pizza boxes work well for containers. Local pizza parlors may donate boxes for educational use or provide them at a minimal cost.

Student Outcomes

After completing the following discussions and exploration, students should be able to:

✳ recognize nonlinear patterns in data

✳ make predictions based on their interpretations of a graph

✳ use a mathematical model for population growth

✳ make predictions based on their mathematical models.

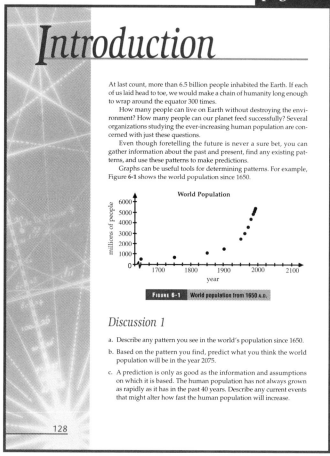

Introduction

At last count, more than 6.5 billion people inhabited the Earth. If each of us laid head to toe, we would make a chain of humanity long enough to wrap around the equator 300 times.

How many people can live on Earth without destroying the environment? How many people can our planet feed successfully? Several organizations studying the ever-increasing human population are concerned with just these questions.

Even though foretelling the future is never a sure bet, you can gather information about the past and present, find any existing patterns, and use these patterns to make predictions.

Graphs can be useful tools for determining patterns. For example, Figure 6-1 shows the world population since 1650.

World Population

FIGURE 6-1 World population from 1650 A.D.

Discussion 1

a. Describe any pattern you see in the world's population since 1650.

b. Based on the pattern you find, predict what you think the world population will be in the year 2075.

c. A prediction is only as good as the information and assumptions on which it is based. The human population has not always grown as rapidly as it has in the past 40 years. Describe any current events that might alter how fast the human population will increase.

128

Discussion 1

a. Students should observe that population numbers are increasing with time. Students also might notice that the pattern is nonlinear.

b. Answers will vary. Sample response: If the population continues to rise as in the past 40 years, there will be about 14 billion people in 2075.

c. Students might identify a variety of causes for the change in the rate of growth. Improved nutrition and medical care could increase the rate of survival. On the other hand, the population can be limited by the availability of land, food, water, and energy; or the death rate could increase due to diseases such as AIDS, famine, and pollution.

Exploration

Statistics like those shown in Figure **6-1**, along with an appropriate mathematical model, allow researchers to make forecasts about population trends. For example, scientists at the United Nations predict a world population of at least 8.2 billion by the year 2020.

Simulations are experiments that researchers often use to help predict real-world situations. They gather the results of the simulations and analyze them. Then they compare this data with known information about the actual population. If the results seem questionable, the simulation may be revised. This modeling process can be summarized by the following five steps:

- creating a model
- translating the model into mathematics
- using the mathematics
- relating the results to the real-world situation
- revising the model.

In the following exploration, you investigate this modeling process using a population of Skeeters.

a. Obtain a large, flat container with a lid, a sack of Skeeters, and several sheets of graph paper.

b. Before beginning the simulation, read Steps **1–7** below and predict the number of Skeeters in the box after 20 shakes.

   1. Place two Skeeters in your container. This is the initial population.

   2. After closing the lid, shake the container.

   3. Open the lid and count the number of Skeeters with the marked side up.

   4. Skeeters reproduce asexually (by themselves). Reproduction is triggered when the marked side of a Skeeter is exposed to light. Add one Skeeter to the container for each mark counted.

   5. Record the total number of Skeeters now in the container. This is the end of one "shake."

     The end of each shake represents the end of one time period. The number of Skeeters present at the end of a shake is the total population at that time. (Remember that at shake 0, the number of Skeeters was 2.)

   6. Design a method of recording and organizing your data.

   7. Repeat Parts **2–5** for 15 shakes.

teacher note

In Part **c** of the exploration, students create scatterplots of their data. In the following discussion, they are asked to compare their scatterplots with those of their classmates. To make this comparison easier, the class should agree on appropriate scaling of their graphs.

To facilitate discussion, you might wish to provide each group with an overhead transparency of a 1-cm grid. If students select the same origin and axes, then comparisons can be made easily using an overhead projector.

Exploration

In this exploration, Skeeters provide a physical representation of a real-world population. The simulation produces data to help model population growth.

teacher note

In Part **b** of the exploration, you might wish to ask one group to demonstrate the process for the class, paying particular attention to orderly data gathering.

a–b. Students should record an initial prediction before beginning the simulation. They will compare this estimate to the prediction made in Part **d.**

Sample response: The number of Skeeters will increase with each shake. I predict that there will be 200 after 20 shakes.

The following table shows sample data for 15 shakes.

Shake	Population	Shake	Population
0	2	8	40
1	3	9	61
2	4	10	87
3	6	11	114
4	7	12	164
5	12	13	225
6	17	14	308
7	26	15	424

c. 1. Sample scatterplot:

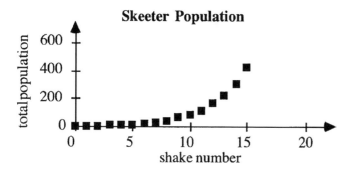

Skeeter Population

2. Students should notice a nonlinear, curved pattern.
d. 1. Sample response: The total population after shake 20 will be approximately 1300.
   2. Answers will vary. One possible strategy involves estimating the volume of a single Skeeter, then multiplying this value by the predicted population.

      Sample response: Our box would be overcrowded. At shake 15 during the exploration, the bottom of the box was already full. Any additional Skeeters would begin to stack on top of one another.

   3. Due to the randomness of Skeeter reproduction, students may get substantially different results. Using the sample data given above, the total population after shake 15 was 424. If this pattern continued, the total population after shake 16 would be approximately 636, and after shake 17 approximately 954.

Discussion 2

a. Students should notice that their scatterplots have the same general, nonlinear shape. Some graphs might increase more rapidly than others.
b. Sample response: The population increases after each shake. Each subsequent shake adds a greater number of Skeeters than the previous shake.
c. 1. Students should observe that the population size remains relatively unchanged for small shake numbers, but increases rapidly as the shake number (or time) increases.
   2. Students should note that these graphs do not seem to be linear, as they get steeper as the number of shakes increases. Some may describe the shape of this pattern as like the letter *J*, the side of a mixing bowl, or a skateboard ramp.
d. 1. This pattern of growth may sometimes be observed in populations of bacteria or—for a relatively short period of time—in other animals and plants that rapidly colonize a new habitat.
   2. Students might point out several limitations in using this model to simulate natural populations. For example, Skeeters reproduce asexually, whereas most animals and plants reproduce sexually. The simulation also does not account for predator-prey relationships, deaths, or environmental changes. In

c. 1. Create a scatterplot to display the data you recorded. Represent the shake number on the *x*-axis and the total population on the *y*-axis. Select a scale for each axis that will allow you to make predictions for shake numbers through 20.
   2. Describe any patterns you see in your data.
d. 1. Use the pattern described in Part **c** to predict the number of Skeeters after shake 20.
   2. Is your box large enough to hold this population? Explain your response.
   3. Predict how many shakes it would take for the Skeeter population to reach 1000. Describe how you reached your prediction.

Discussion 2

a. Discuss any similarities or differences you observe between your scatterplot and those of your classmates.
b. How did the number of Skeeters in your population change during the exploration?
c. 1. Consider your scatterplot as describing the change in the population of Skeeters over time. Use this idea to explain the shape of the graph.
   2. How do the graphs obtained in the exploration compare to the linear graphs explored in previous modules?
d. 1. What other types of living creatures might show the same pattern of population growth as the Skeeters?
   2. What limitations might this simulation have in modeling a real-world population?

ACTIVITY

Genetics and environment can cause differences in appearance and behavior within any population. In this activity, you investigate some Skeeter populations with different growth characteristics.

Exploration

In this exploration, each color of Skeeter has its own growth characteristics and initial population. Table **6-1** on the next page shows a list of these characteristics for each color.

130   Module 6 ■ *Skeeters Are Overrunning the World*

other words, the simulation is too simplified to model most populations very well.

ACTIVITY

Students use equations of the form $y = 1 \cdot b^x$, where y represents total population and x represents the shake number, to model Skeeters data. In this equation, b represents the factor by which the population is changing.

Materials List

■ multicolored candies or disks (approximately 500 per group)
■ container with a large, flat bottom and a lid (one per group)
■ graph paper (several sheets per group)
■ colored pencils to match Skeeter colors (optional; one set per group)

Technology

■ spreadsheet

TABLE 6-1 ■ *Skeeter Growth Characteristics*		
Color	**Growth Characteristics**	**Initial Population**
green	For every green Skeeter with or without a mark showing, add 2 green Skeeters.	1 green
yellow	For every yellow Skeeter with or without a mark showing, add 1 yellow Skeeter.	1 yellow
orange	For every orange Skeeter with a mark showing, add 1 orange Skeeter.	1 orange
red	For every red Skeeter with a mark showing, add 1 red Skeeter.	2 red
purple	For every purple Skeeter with a mark showing, add 1 purple Skeeter.	5 purple

a. Consider the information given in Table **6-1**.

    1. Predict what will happen to the population of green Skeeters for the first 3 shakes.

    2. Predict which population will be largest after 10 shakes.

b. Obtain a large, flat container with a lid, a sack of Skeeters of different colors, and a sheet of graph paper. Place the initial population of each color of Skeeters (indicated in Table **6-1**) in the box.

c. Place the lid on the container and shake it.

d. At the end of each shake, use the growth characteristics from Table **6-1** to add the appropriate number of Skeeters of each color.

e. Record the total number of Skeeters of each color at the end of each shake. (Record the initial population as the number at shake 0.)

f. Repeat Parts **c–e** for 10 shakes.

g. After 10 shakes, graph the data for each Skeeter population on the same coordinate system, using different colors to indicate the different populations.

    Note: Save your data for the orange, red, and purple populations for Activities **2** and **3**.

Discussion

a. Describe the relationship between the numbers of yellow Skeeters at the end of two consecutive shakes.

b. 1. Describe the relationship between the number of yellow Skeeters at the end of a shake and the shake number.

    2. Restate this relationship as a mathematical equation.

teacher note

Students may use technology to record and graph their data. If students make paper-and-pencil graphs in Part **g** of the exploration, they might want colored pencils to indicate the different populations.

Students should save their tables and graphs for use later in this activity, and in Activities **2** and **3**.

Student Outcomes

After completing the following exploration and discussion, students should be able to:

✳ perform a simulation for a mathematical model of population growth

✳ record the data generated by the simulation

✳ create a scatterplot of the data

✳ use the vertical line test to determine if a graph does not represent a function

✳ use function notation

✳ determine the growth rate of a population from one time period to the next

✳ differentiate between independent and dependent variables.

Exploration

Students might run out of yellow or green Skeeters before completing 10 shakes. However, the doubling and tripling patterns should be clear before this occurs.

a. 1. After three shakes, the green Skeeter population will be 27.

    2. After 10 shakes, the green Skeeter population will be the largest.

b–f. Sample data:

Shake	Green	Yellow	Orange	Red	Purple
0	1	1	1	2	5
1	3	2	1	4	7
2	9	4	2	6	11
3	27	8	3	6	20
4	81	16	4	7	28
5	243	32	5	10	41
6	729	64	7	13	60
7	2187	128	10	20	102
8	6561	256	14	26	153
9	19,683	512	22	36	226
10	59,049	1024	31	53	346

g. Sample graph:

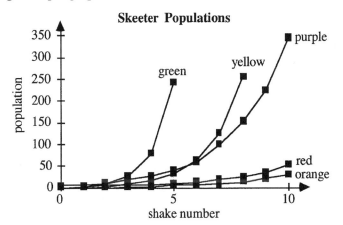

Skeeter Populations

Discussion

a. Students should notice that the population doubles from shake to shake or that the new population is always equal to the previous population multiplied by 2.

b. 1. Sample response: total number = $2^{\text{shake number}}$

    2. This relationship can be expressed as $y = 2^x$, where y represents the number of Skeeters at the end of the shake and x represents the shake number.

c. The equation from Part **b** can be used to describe the population of yellow Skeeters after any shake. To help verify that the equation works, students may evaluate it for the values of x from 0 to 10. The corresponding values for y should match the population numbers obtained in the exploration.

d. The values for shake number represent the domain; the values for population represent the range.

e. Sample response: The relationship between shake number and population is a function for every color because, in each set of data, the shake number is different in each ordered pair.

f. Sample response: Graph **2** does not represent a function because some values of x are paired with two values of y. It does not pass the vertical line test.

g. All of the graphs should pass the vertical line test.

h. 1. Sample response: This notation represents the population of green Skeeters after shake number 4.

2. Sample response: The population of yellow Skeeters after shake number s could be represented as $y(s)$, the population of red Skeeters as $r(s)$, the population of orange Skeeters as $o(s)$, and the population of purple Skeeters as $p(s)$.

i. The growth rate is constant for the yellow and green Skeeter populations. For the other colors, the growth rate changes slightly from shake to shake.

c. Does your equation from Part **b** describe the population of yellow Skeeters after any shake? Explain your response.

d. In the relations you graphed in Part **g** of the exploration, which values represent the domain and which values represent the range?

e. Recall that a **function** is a relation for which each element of the domain corresponds to exactly one element of the range. In other words, a set of ordered pairs (x,y) is a function if every value of x is paired with a value of y and every value of x occurs in only one ordered pair.

For which colors of Skeeters is the relationship between shake number and population a function?

f. A **vertical line test** can be used to determine when a graph does *not* represent a function. If it is possible to draw a vertical line that intersects a graph at more than one point, then this graph is not the graph of a function.

Which of the graphs below does not represent a function? Use the definition of a function to support your response.

1.   2.

g. Do any of the graphs you created in Part **g** of the exploration fail the vertical line test?

mathematics note

Discussing several different functions at the same time can be confusing if they all contain the notation "$y =$." In **function notation**, a symbol or letter is used to name the function. This letter is followed by a set of parentheses containing the variable representing the domain, an equals sign (=), and the rule for the function.

For example, the function $y = 2x + 4$ can be written as $f(x) = 2x + 4$ (pronounced "f of x equals two x plus four"). Similarly, the function $y = -3x + 2$ can be written as $g(x) = -3x + 2$. In these examples, the letters f and g designate two different functions. The variable x inside the parentheses indicates that it represents the domain in both functions. Finally, $2x + 4$ and $-3x + 2$ are the rules for the functions.

132   Module 6 ■ *Skeeters Are Overrunning the World*

To evaluate a function for a given number, use that number to replace the variable inside the parentheses. For example, consider the function $f(x) = 2x + 4$. The notation $f(-5)$, pronounced "f of negative five," indicates the value of function f when $x = -5$. Substituting for x in the rule of the function:

$$f(-5) = 2(-5) + 4$$
$$= -10 + 4$$
$$= -6$$

Because $f(-5) = -6$, the ordered pair $(-5,-6)$ is a point on the graph of the function f.

h. Use the notation $g(s)$ to describe the population of green Skeeters after shake number s.

1. Given this notation, what does $g(4)$ mean?

2. How could you use function notation to describe the other populations of Skeeters in the exploration?

mathematics note

The **growth rate** of a population from one time period to the next is the percent increase or decrease in the population between the two time periods.

For example, Table **6-2** shows the population of wild horses on an island over three years.

TABLE 6-2 ■ *A Horse Population*

Year	Total Population
1992	15
1993	18
1994	24

The growth rate of the horse population from 1993 to 1994 is:

$$\frac{24 - 18}{18} \approx 0.33 = 33\% \text{ per year}$$

i. Is the growth rate constant from shake to shake for each population of Skeeters in the exploration? Explain your response.

Module 6 ■ *Skeeters Are Overrunning the World*   133

Warm-Up

1. Determine the percent increase in each of the following populations:
   a. initial population = 250; current population = 325
   b. initial population = 25,000; current population = 40,000

2. Write each the following using exponential notation.
   a. $3 \cdot 3 \cdot 3 \cdot 3 \cdot 3$
   b. $7 \cdot 7 \cdot 7$
   c. $15 \cdot 15 \cdot 15 \cdot 15$

3. Write each of the following in expanded form.
   a. 5^7
   b. 2^5
   c. 11^3

4. Evaluate each of the following functions for the given value of x.
   a. $f(x) = 3 - 12x$; $x = 2$
   b. $h(x) = 2^x - 1$; $x = 3$
   c. $k(x) = 2x + 4$; $x = 7$

Assignment

1.1 a. Complete the following table for the yellow Skeeter population.

Shake Number	Total Population	Expanded Notation	Exponential Notation
0	1	$1 \cdot 1$	$1 \cdot 2^0$
1	2	$1 \cdot 2$	$1 \cdot 2^1$
2	4	$1 \cdot 2 \cdot 2$	$1 \cdot 2^2$
⋮	⋮	⋮	⋮
10			

b. Using function notation, write an equation that relates shake number to the total population after that shake.

c. Is the equation you wrote in Part b a function? Explain your response.

d. 1. Describe how to predict the total population of yellow Skeeters for shake numbers greater than 10.

134   Module 6 ■ *Skeeters Are Overrunning the World*

Warm-Up

1. a. 30%
   b. 60%
2. a. 3^5
   b. 7^3
   c. 15^4
3. a. $5 \cdot 5$
   b. $2 \cdot 2 \cdot 2 \cdot 2 \cdot 2$
   c. $11 \cdot 11 \cdot 11$
4. a. $f(2) = -21$
   b. $h(3) = 7$
   c. $k(7) = 18$

Assignment

Problems suitable for use as assessment items are identified by an asterisk (*).

1.1 a. See sample table below.
   b. Sample response: $y(s) = 1 \cdot 2^s$, where $y(s)$ represents the population of yellow Skeeters after shake number s.
   c. Sample response: Yes. Each shake number is the first term in an ordered pair and occurs only once in the set of all ordered pairs.
   d. 1. Sample response: Substitute the shake number for s in the equation $y(s) = 1 \cdot 2^s$.

Shake Number	Total Population	Expanded Notation	Exponential Notation
0	1	$1 \cdot 1$	$1 \cdot 2^0$
1	2	$1 \cdot 2$	$1 \cdot 2^1$
2	4	$1 \cdot 2 \cdot 2$	$1 \cdot 2^2$
3	8	$1 \cdot 2 \cdot 2 \cdot 2$	$1 \cdot 2^3$
⋮	⋮	⋮	⋮
s	2^s		$1 \cdot 2^s$

2. Students might need some instruction on the use of the exponential function on their calculators: $2^{20} = 1,048,576$.

e. 1. 2

2. Students might recognize this number as the base of the exponent in the equation from Part **b.**

f. 100% per shake

1.2 a. See sample table below.

Sample equation: $g(s) = 1 \bullet 3^s$, where $g(s)$ represents the population of green Skeeters after shake number s.

b. Since $2^{24} = 16,777,216$, one possible response is 15 ($3^{15} = 14,348,907$).

c. 1. 3

2. Students may recognize this as the base of the exponent in the equation from Part **a.**

d. 200% per shake

* 1.3 a. Sample response: In both equations, the shake number is the exponent. The bases, however, are different.

b. Since the population total depends on the shake number, it is the dependent variable.

c. The equation for Problem **1.1b** is $y = 1 \bullet 2^x$; the equation for Problem **1.2a** is $y = 1 \bullet 3^x$.

---

2. Predict the total population of yellow Skeeters for shake 20.

e. 1. By what factor is the population of yellow Skeeters increased after each shake?

2. Explain how this factor relates to the equation you wrote in Part **b.**

f. What is the growth rate for the population of yellow Skeeters?

1.2 Create a table like the one in Problem **1.1** for your data for the green Skeeter population.

a. Use the table to determine how the shake number relates to the total population after that shake. Using function notation, write an equation for finding the population based on the shake number.

b. Predict the shake number at which the population of green Skeeters will be close to the population of yellow Skeeters at shake 24.

c. 1. By what factor is the population of green Skeeters increased after each shake?

2. Explain how this factor relates to the equation you wrote in Part **a.**

d. What is the growth rate for the green Skeeter population?

mathematics note

When the values for a variable depend on the outcome of another variable, that variable is **dependent.**

When the values for a variable do not depend on the outcome of another variable, that variable is **independent.**

In a savings account, for example, the amount of time for which money remains in the account determines the amount of interest earned. In this situation, time is the independent variable, while interest earned is the dependent variable.

When drawing a graph, the values for the independent variable are plotted along the horizontal axis. The values for the dependent variable are plotted along the vertical axis.

1.3 a. Compare the equations you wrote in Problems **1.1b** and **1.2a.** Describe any similarities or differences you observe.

b. Which quantity represents the dependent variable in these equations, the population or the shake number? Explain your response.

c. Rewrite each equation in terms of a dependent variable (y) and an independent variable (x).

Module 6 ■ *Skeeters Are Overrunning the World* **135**

Shake Number	Total Population	Expanded Notation	Exponential Notation
0	1	$1 \bullet 1$	$1 \bullet 3^0$
1	3	$1 \bullet 3$	$1 \bullet 3^1$
2	9	$1 \bullet 3 \bullet 3$	$1 \bullet 3^2$
3	27	$1 \bullet 3 \bullet 3 \bullet 3$	$1 \bullet 3^3$
⋮	⋮	⋮	⋮
s	3^s		$1 \bullet 3^s$

1.4 Consider some Skeeters whose population growth can be modeled by the equation $y = 1 \cdot 5^x$, where y represents the total population after a shake and x represents the shake number.

    a. Use this equation to predict the population after 10 shakes.

    b. How does the population after each shake compare to the population before the shake?

* * * * *

1.5 In January of 1990, Maridee deposited $5000 in a savings account. At the end of each year, the interest earned was added to the account. The following table shows the account balance, after interest was added, during the five years from 1990 to 1994.

Year	Account Balance
1990	$5000.00
1991	$5250.00
1992	$5512.50
1993	$5788.13
1994	$6077.53

    a. Create a scatterplot of the information in the table.

    b. What is the growth rate in the account per year?

    c. Use the growth rate determined in Part **b** to calculate the account balance at the end of 1995.

    d. In what year will the account balance have doubled Maridee's original deposit?

1.6 One type of Skeeter produces 3 offspring after every shake, whether the marked side is showing or not.

    a. Using an initial population of 1 of these Skeeters, create a table that shows the shake number and total population for the first 6 shakes.

    b. Write an equation in the form $y = 1 \cdot b^x$ that models the growth in this population.

    c. Determine the total population after 10 shakes.

    d. Does this population have a constant growth rate? If so, calculate this growth rate. If not, determine the growth rates between consecutive shakes for the first 6 shakes.

1.4 a. After 10 shakes, the population is $5^{10} = 9,765,625$.

    b. The population after each shake is 5 times the population before the shake.

✳ ✳ ✳ ✳ ✳

1.5 a. Sample scatterplot:

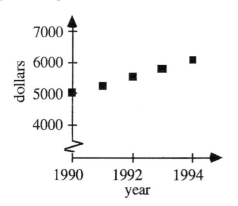

    b. In this setting, the annual growth rate is the annual interest rate. It can be calculated as follows:

$$\frac{5250.00 - 5000.00}{5000} = 0.05 = 5\%$$

  c. In 1995, the balance is

$$(\$6077.53 \cdot 0.05) + \$6077.53 \approx \$6381.41.$$

    d. Students should use technology to determine an estimate. After the interest is deposited in the 15th year, the account balance will be $10,394.64. This is the first time that the balance is at least double the original deposit.

1.6 a. Sample table:

Shake	Population
0	1
1	4
2	16
3	64
4	256
5	1024
6	4096

  b. $y = 1 \cdot 4^x$

  c. $y = 1 \cdot 4^{10} = 1,048,576$

  d. The constant growth rate for this population is 300% per shake.

ACTIVITY 2

Students determine a method for calculating the growth rates of the orange, red, and purple Skeeter populations. At this point in the module, it is unlikely that they will know a way to describe growth other than a simple doubling or tripling from shake to shake. In the assignment, students examine a growth rate of 50% (or 0.5) for the orange Skeeter population.

teacher note

A brief assessment of the mathematical content in Activities **1** and **2**, for use at your discretion, appears in the Teacher Resources for this module.

Materials List

■ none

Technology

■ spreadsheet

Student Outcomes

After completing the following discussions and exploration, students should be able to:

✳ write and interpret an exponential function of the form $f(x) = 1 \cdot b^x$

✳ describe the relationship between b and r in an exponential equation of the form $y = 1 \cdot b^x$, where $b = 1 + r$

✳ determine the value of b given r, and the value of r given b.

Discussion 1

a. Sample response: You would expect 50% of the population, or 5 Skeeters, to land with a mark showing.
b. If the coin is fair, the probabilities are the same: 50%.
c. The expected growth rate is 50% or 0.5 per shake.

ACTIVITY 2

In Activity **1** you looked at Skeeter populations that doubled or tripled after each shake. What happens if the ratio of consecutive populations is not an integer value?

Discussion 1

a. Recall the orange Skeeter population from Activity **1**. After each shake, only the Skeeters with the marked side showing produced offspring. If you shook a box containing 10 of these Skeeters, how many would you expect to land with the marked side up?

b. How does the probability of a Skeeter landing with the marked side up compare with the probability of a tossed coin landing heads up?

c. What growth rate would you expect to find between consecutive shakes of the orange Skeeter population?

d. One possible model for the population growth of green Skeeters is $g(s) = 1 \cdot b^s$, where $b = 1 + r$. In this model, r represents the growth rate expressed as a decimal. Explain why $b = 1 + r$.

Exploration

In this exploration, you determine a growth rate for the orange Skeeter population.

a. 1. Create a spreadsheet with headings like those in Table 6-3 below.

TABLE 6-3 ■ Orange Skeeter Population and Growth Rate

Shake	Expected Population	Actual Population	Actual Growth Rate (from Previous Shake)
0	1	1	
⋮	⋮	⋮	
10			

2. Use the growth rate determined in Part **c** of Discussion **1** to calculate the expected population after each shake. Record this in the appropriate column of the table.

3. Enter the actual data for the orange Skeeter population obtained in Activity **1** in the appropriate column of the spreadsheet.

4. Use the spreadsheet to calculate the actual growth rates between consecutive shakes. Record these values in the appropriate column.

d. Sample response: The present population is equal to the previous population plus the increase in population. The value of b is equal to $1 + r$ because 1 represents 100% of the initial population and r represents the growth rate written as a decimal.

Exploration

a. See sample spreadsheet below.

Shake	Expected Population	Actual Population	Actual Growth Rate (from Previous Shake)
0	1.0	1	
1	1.5	1	0
2	2.3	2	100%
3	3.4	3	50%
4	5.1	4	33%
5	7.6	5	25%
6	11.4	7	40%
7	17.1	10	43%
8	25.6	14	40%
9	38.4	22	58%
10	57.7	31	41%

b. On the same set of axes, create scatterplots of the expected data and the actual data for the orange Skeeter population.

c. 1. Use the growth rate from Part c of Discussion 1 to write an equation that describes the expected population after *x* shakes.

   2. Sketch a graph of the equation on the same set of axes as the scatterplots from Part b.

Discussion 2

a. In Part b of the exploration, how does the graph of the actual data compare with the graph of the expected data?

b. How well does the equation from Part c of the exploration model the actual data for the orange Skeeter population?

Warm-Up

1. For each annual growth rate below, determine the value of *b* in the corresponding equation of the form $y = 1 \cdot b^x$.

   a. 20%

   b. 50%

   c. 3%

   d. 100%

   e. 125%

   f. 10.5%

2. For each of the following values of *b* in an equation of the form $y = 1 \cdot b^x$, determine the growth rate per time period.

   a. 1.2

   b. 2.4

   c. 1.07

   d. 1 + 0.33

   e. 1.259

   f. 1.002

3. Given the initial values and annual growth rates below, determine the values for each of the next five years. Round all values to the nearest tenth.

   a. initial value = 10; growth rate = 20%

   b. initial value = 3000; growth rate = 5%

Warm-Up

1. a. 1.2
   b. 1.5
   c. 1.03
   d. 2
   e. 2.25
   f. 1.105
2. a. 20%
   b. 140%
   c. 7%
   d. 33%
   e. 25.9%
   f. 0.2%
3. a. 12, 14.4, 17.3, 20.7, 24.9
   b. 3150, 3307.5, 3472.9, 3646.5, 3828.8

b. Sample graph:

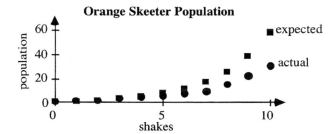

Orange Skeeter Population

c. 1. $y = 1 \cdot 1.5^x$

   2. The graph of the equation contains all of the expected population values. See Part **b** for the graph of the line.

Discussion 2

a. Sample response: The graph of the actual data is close to the graph of the expected data. However, the expected data contains fractional values. This cannot occur with actual Skeeters.

b. Answers will vary, depending on individual sets of data. The equation should model the data reasonably well.

teacher note

Students may complete the following assignment problems using a spreadsheet or table. They are not expected to write equations of the form $y = ab^x$ at this point in the module. They will investigate such equations in Activity 3.

Assignment

Problems suitable for use as assessment items are identified by an asterisk (*).

* 2.1 a. Sample response: At the end of the first shake, you would expect to add 0.5(20) = 10 Skeeters. The expected total population would be 20 + 10 = 30.

   b. Sample response: At the end of the second shake, you would expect to add 0.5(30) = 15 Skeeters. The expected total population would be 30 + 15 = 45.

   c. $0.5p$

   d. 50% or 0.5 per shake

2.2 Sample response: Yes. As long as each Skeeter has the opportunity to be tossed, the probability of a mark appearing is 1/2.

2.3 a. Sample response:

Year	Population
1990	27,000,000
1991	27,945,000
1992	28,923,075
1993	29,935,383
1994	30,983,121
1995	32,067,530
1996	33,189,894
1997	34,351,540
1998	35,553,844
1999	36,798,229
2000	38,086,167

Assignment

2.1 Imagine that you have a container of 20 Skeeters. After shaking the container, you add one Skeeter for every Skeeter with its marked side up.

   a. How many Skeeters would you expect to add at the end of the first shake? What would you expect the total population to be after the first shake?

   b. How many Skeeters would you expect to add at the end of the second shake? What would you expect the total population to be after the second shake?

   c. If you had p Skeeters before a shake, how many would you expect to add after the shake?

   d. What is the growth rate for this population?

2.2 When Skeeters are shaken in a container, is the probability of a Skeeter landing marked side up always 1/2? Explain your response.

2.3 In 1990, the population of Tanzania was approximately 27,000,000 people. The expected growth rate is 3.5% per year.

   a. Calculate the expected population in each of the 10 years after 1990.

   b. Make a scatterplot of the expected population data from Part a.

   c. How do you think the expected values for Tanzania's population will compare with the actual values? Explain your response.

* * * * *

2.4 Chauncy's parents have decided to offer him a weekly allowance. During the first year, he will receive $10 per week. In each of the following years, they have given him the choice of either a $7 raise or a 40% increase in his weekly allowance.

   If Chauncy plans on living at home for the next 5 years, which proposed increase should he choose? Explain your response.

2.5 In each year between 1990 and 1995, Sue earned a gross salary of $30,000. In 1990, she paid $4338 in federal income taxes. In 1991, she paid $3905 in federal income taxes.

   a. Calculate the growth rate in Sue's federal income taxes between 1990 and 1991.

   b. Use this rate to predict the taxes Sue can expect to pay in 1995.

   c. Describe some possible limitations in using this model to predict Sue's taxes.

b. Sample graph:

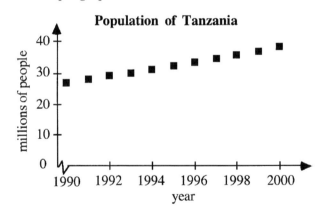

Population of Tanzania

c. Sample response: If the actual growth rate remains constant at about 3.5% per year, the expected values will give a reasonable approximation of the actual population. If the growth rate changes dramatically, the expected values may be very different.

* * * * *

2.4 Answers will vary. Sample response: Chauncy will receive more money over the 5-year period if he chooses the $7 raise. If he chooses the 40% increase, then he will receive more money only in the last 2 years. This can be seen in the table below.

Year	$7 Raise	40% Increase
0	$10.00	$10.00
1	$17.00	$14.00
2	$24.00	$19.60
3	$31.00	$27.44
4	$38.00	$38.42
5	$45.00	$53.78
Total (52 weeks/year)	$8,580.00	$8488.48

2.5 a. The annual growth rate can be calculated as follows:

$$\frac{3905 - 4338}{4338} \approx -0.10 = -10\%$$

b. Students may approach this problem by representing each year's tax as $p - 0.1p$, where p represents the previous year's tax. If the growth rate remains the same, Sue's taxes should be $2561.55.

c. Sample response: The growth rate for taxes is usually not constant. It depends on several factors, including inflation and legislation.

teacher note

To complete this activity, students will need their data from the orange, red, and purple Skeeter populations from the exploration in Activity **1**. Displaying the data both as a table and as a graph provides students with an opportunity to observe patterns involving growth rate and initial population.

ACTIVITY 3

In this activity, students examine how initial population affects population growth.

Materials List

■ none

Technology

■ spreadsheet

Student Outcomes

After completing the following discussions and exploration, students should be able to:

✱ graph and interpret an exponential equation in the form $y = a \bullet b^x$.

Discussion 1

a. Although the growth rates are the same for all three populations, the total populations after 10 shakes should be quite different. Students should recognize that initial population size affects total population. Encourage them to use tables and graphs to justify their observations.

b. Students may recognize that higher initial populations lead to very large population differences at low shake numbers.

Exploration

a–b. **Note:** Students might need instructions on using spreadsheet formula commands. You might wish to ask them to suggest the mathematical operations needed to create each cell from the preceding cell.

ACTIVITY 3

How does the initial population size influence future Skeeter populations? In this activity, you use technology to model the growth of three Skeeter populations from Activity **1**.

Discussion 1

a. Compare your data for the orange, red, and purple Skeeter populations from Activity **1**. Explain any similarities or differences you see.

b. What effect, if any, does the initial population appear to have on the growth of each population?

Exploration

In this exploration, you observe how initial population can affect population growth.

a. Create a spreadsheet with headings like those in Table **6-4** below. Use initial populations of 1 orange Skeeter, 2 red Skeeters, and 5 purple Skeeters.

TABLE 6-4 ■ *Three Skeeter Populations*			
Shake No.	Orange	Red	Purple
0	1	2	5
⋮	⋮	⋮	⋮

b. Using an expected growth rate of 0.5 Skeeters per shake, generate a table of values for each population for 20 shakes.

c. On the same set of axes, create a scatterplot of the expected data for each population for the first 5 shakes.

d. On another set of axes, create a scatterplot of the expected data for each population for 20 shakes.

Discussion 2

a. How do the growth rates you observed in the red, purple, and orange Skeeter populations in Activity **1** compare to the expected growth rate of 0.5?

In the following sample spreadsheet, all numbers were rounded to the nearest 0.01.

Shake	Orange	Red	Purple
0	1.00	2.00	5.00
1	1.50	3.00	7.50
2	2.25	4.50	11.25
3	3.38	6.75	16.88
4	5.06	10.13	25.31
5	7.59	15.19	37.97
6	11.39	22.78	56.95
7	17.09	34.17	85.43
8	25.63	51.26	128.15
9	38.44	76.89	192.22
10	57.67	115.33	288.33
11	86.50	173.00	432.49
12	129.75	259.49	648.73
13	194.62	389.24	973.10
14	291.93	583.86	1459.65
15	437.89	875.79	2189.47
16	656.84	1313.68	3284.20
17	985.26	1970.52	4926.31
18	1477.90	2955.78	7389.46
19	2216.84	4433.68	11084.19
20	3325.26	6650.52	16626.29

> b. Compare the population data you collected in Activity **1** with the expected data generated by the spreadsheet. What similarities or differences do you see?
>
> c. 1. In Part **c** of the exploration, what similarities or differences do you see in the scatterplots for the three populations?
>
>   2. Is it possible to determine the initial size of each population by looking at the graph?
>
> d. Describe the mathematical operations used to calculate the population of purple Skeeters in your spreadsheet.
>
> e. If a current population (p) of Skeeters has a growth rate of r, explain why the equation for the total population (T) after the next shake can be expressed as $T = p(1 + r)$.
>
> f. 1. If the population before a given shake is $p(1 + r)$, what expression can be used to describe the total population after that shake?
>
>   2. Describe a relationship between initial population (p), growth rate (r), shake number (n), and total population (T) after that shake number.
>
> ### Warm-Up
>
> 1. Given the following equations in the form $T = p(1 + r)^n$, identify the initial population and the growth rate.
>
>   a. $y = 4 \cdot 3^x$
>
>   b. $y = 100(1.23)^x$
>
>   c. $y = 1500(1.008)^x$
>
> 2. Given the following initial values and annual growth rates, write an exponential equation to describe the pattern of growth.
>
>   a. initial value = 5; growth rate = 100%
>
>   b. initial value = 4000; growth rate = 5.15%
>
>   c. initial value = 25; growth rate = 40%
>
> ### Assignment
>
> 3.1 How closely does the relationship found in Part **f** of Discussion **2** model the data collected in Activity **1** for the orange and red Skeeter populations? Explain your response.
>
> Module 6 ■ *Skeeters Are Overrunning the World*   141

c. Sample graph:

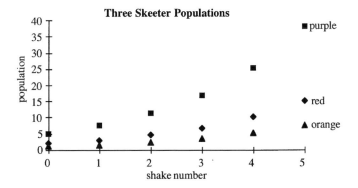

d. Sample graph:

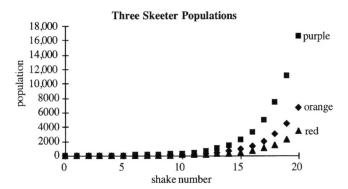

Discussion 2

a. The actual growth rates for the three populations are not constant. However, they tend to be close to 0.5 from shake to shake.

b. Students should notice that the expected data generated by technology gives decimal fractions of Skeeters. The data from the exploration in Activity **1** consists of discrete, whole-number values. The general patterns in corresponding sets of data should be reasonably close.

c. 1. Sample response: All three graphs rise to the right, showing a positive relationship between total population and shake number. Some graphs rise "faster" than others and each one intersects the y-axis at a different point.

   2. The initial size of each population is the y-intercept.

d. Sample response: To calculate the population after the first shake, add the value of the previous cell to 50% of that value. From there, fill down the column.

teacher note

Students should understand the following responses to Parts **e** and **f** of Discussion **2** before beginning the assignment.

e. The total population equals the initial population plus the increase in population. This can be expressed as $T = p + pr$. Using the distributive property, this expression can be rewritten as $T = p(1 + r)$.

f. 1. $[p(1 + r)](1 + r) = p(1 + r)^2$

   2. In general, students should recognize the following relationship:

$$T = p(1 + r)^n$$

   where T is the total population, p is initial population, r is growth rate, and n is the shake number.

Warm-Up

1. a. initial population = 4; growth rate = 200%

   b. initial population = 100; growth rate = 23%

   c. initial population = 1500; growth rate = 0.8%

2. a. $y = 5(2)^x$ b. $y = 4000(1.0515)^x$

   c. $y = 25(1.4)^x$

Assignment

Problems suitable for use as assessment items are identified by an asterisk (*).

3.1 Since the actual populations consist only of whole numbers, the relationship found in Part **f** of Discussion **2** will not fit the data exactly. It should, however, describe the general trend in both populations.

3.2 **a.** The variable y would represent the total population; a would represent the initial population; b would represent $1 + r$; x would represent the shake number.

  b. Changing the initial population changes the value of a in the equation and changes the y-intercept in its graph.

  c. Students should graph $y = 4(1 + 1.5)^x$. This problem gives students the opportunity to enter an exponential equation in a graphing utility. They might need help selecting the appropriate intervals for the domain and range.

3.3 Sample response: The population increases by 50% each time the box is shaken. Fifty percent of a small number is small, but 50% of a large number is large.

* 3.4 Students should substitute the appropriate values into the general form of an exponential equation: $2{,}734{,}375 = 7b^8$. Because $2{,}734{,}375/7 = 390{,}625$, $b^8 = 390{,}625$. Through guess-and-check, $5^8 = 390{,}625$. Students also may use a symbolic manipulator to solve the equation $2{,}734{,}375 = 7b^8$. Because $b = 5$, $r = 5 - 1 = 4 = 400\%$ per shake.

3.5 **a.** The domain is all non-negative integers. The range is a subset of the positive integers. Some integers are not part of the range because there are no integer values for x that satisfy $3 \cdot 2^x = y$. For example, there is no integer value for x that satisfies $3 \cdot 2^x = 5$.

  b. This is a function because every x-value is paired with a y-value and every x-value occurs in only one ordered pair.

3.6 **a.** Students might need to experiment to find appropriate intervals for the domain and range. Because $y_1 = 10 \cdot 1.5^8 = 256.3$ and $y_2 = 1 \cdot 2^8 = 256$, both equations are approximately equal to 256 when $x = 8$. Sample graph:

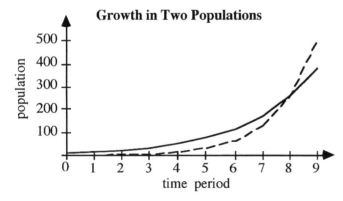

Growth in Two Populations

  b. When $x = 0$, $y_1 = 10 \cdot 1.5^0 = 10$ and $y_2 = 1 \cdot 2^0 = 1$. These values represent the initial population sizes.
  Note: Students might need to review the mathematical meaning of b^0 when b is not 0.

3.2 One equation that can be used to determine the total Skeeter population (T) given an initial population p, a growth rate r, and a shake number n, is
$$T = p(1 + r)^n$$
This is one example of an **exponential equation**. The general form of an exponential equation is $y = a \cdot b^x$.

  a. What would each variable in the general form of an exponential equation represent in terms of a Skeeter population?

  b. What effect would a change in the initial population have on the equation?

  c. Use appropriate technology to create a graph that shows the growth of a Skeeter population with an initial size of 4 and a growth rate of 150% per shake.

3.3 A constant growth rate of 0.5 per shake produces little change in population size from one shake to the next when the shake number is small, but results in greater increases in the size of each successive population after many shakes. Explain why this is so.

mathematics note

The exponential equation $y = a \cdot b^x$ can be used to describe a pattern of **exponential growth**. If this equation describes population growth, a represents the size of the initial population. The value of b is the sum of two percentages: 100 (representing the initial population) and r (representing the growth rate). The independent variable x represents a time period.

Considering a population of Skeeters, for example, the independent variable x represents the shake number at which the population is counted. The dependent variable y represents the total population. A population of Skeeters with an initial population of 6 and a growth rate of 0.5% per shake can be modeled by the equation $y = 6 \cdot 1.005^x$.

3.4 Two of your classmates have used a spreadsheet to model the growth of a population of Skeeters. The initial population was 7. After shake 8, the total population was 2,734,375. What growth rate did they use? *Hint:* Substitute the appropriate values into an equation of the form $y = a \cdot b^x$ to find b; then use this value to determine the growth rate.

3.5 **a.** The relation $y = 3 \cdot 2^x$ models the growth in a population of Skeeters. Describe the values of the domain and range in this setting.

  b. Is this relation a function? Explain your response.

3.6 **a.** The two equations below represent two different populations of Skeeters. Graph both equations on the same set of axes. When will these populations be approximately the same size?
  1. $y = 10 \cdot 1.5^x$
  2. $y = 1 \cdot 2^x$

  b. Find the size of each population when $x = 0$. What do these values represent?

3.7 The table below shows the population of Skeeters in a container after each of 5 shakes. Write an equation which could be used to describe this data. (Your equation may not describe the data exactly.)

Shake Number	Population Total
0	2
1	7
2	25
3	86
4	300
5	1050

* * * * *

3.8 The following table shows the growth in a savings account with an initial deposit of $4000.

Year	Account Balance
1990	$4000.00
1991	$4160.00
1992	$4326.40
1993	$4498.50
1994	$4679.40

  a. Write an equation in the form $y = a \cdot b^x$ to describe this data.

  b. Using your equation, what is the value of y when $x = 0$?

  c. What is the value of x when the initial deposit of $4000 has doubled?

3.9 In 1987, Vincent Van Gogh's painting *Irises* was auctioned for $53.9 million. Assume that the painting's value grew exponentially since 1889. If the painting initially sold for $50, by what percentage did its value increase each year?

Research Project

Imagine your own population of creatures with a growth rate and initial population different from those used in the explorations.

a. Use a spreadsheet to simulate the growth in this population for at least 10 time periods. Display your simulated data in both a table and a graph.

b. Find an equation that models the growth in the population over time.

c. Write a story about your population. Include a description of the growth rate and explain the consequences this rate will have on the population over time.

In 1991, the world's human population was approximately 5.3 billion. This total was increasing by about 250,000 per day, or 3 people every second. At this rate, over 1 billion people will have been added to the Earth's population by the end of the decade.

As a citizen of Earth and the United States, you have some questions to consider when making future personal and political decisions. What is the growth rate of the world population? How does this rate compare with the growth rate of the U.S. population? Is a growth rate of zero desirable? If so, how can zero population growth be obtained?

Exploration

Table 6-5 shows the population of the United States at 10-year intervals from 1790 to 1990.

TABLE 6-5 ■ U.S. Population from 1790 to 1990					
Year of Census	Number of People	Year of Census	Number of People	Year of Census	Number of People
1790	3,929,214	1860	31,443,321	1930	122,775,046
1800	5,308,483	1870	39,818,449	1940	131,669,275
1810	7,239,881	1880	50,155,783	1950	150,697,361
1820	9,638,453	1890	62,947,714	1960	179,323,175
1830	12,866,020	1900	75,994,575	1970	203,302,031
1840	17,069,453	1910	91,972,266	1980	226,545,805
1850	23,191,876	1920	105,710,620	1990	248,709,873

Source: U.S. Bureau of the Census.

144   Module 6 ■ Skeeters Are Overrunning the World

* 3.7 Sample equation: $y = 2 \cdot (1 + 2.5)^x = 2 \cdot 3.5^x$. **Note:** The population totals in the table have been rounded to the nearest whole number.

✴ ✴ ✴ ✴ ✴

3.8 **a.** $y = 4000(1.04)^x$
b. When $x = 0$, $y = \$4000$ (the initial deposit).
c. Students should use technology or trial-and-error to find an approximate value for x in the equation $8000 = 4000(1.04)^x$. Because $x \approx 17.67$, the value of the account will double in the year 2008.

3.9 To estimate the growth rate, students should use technology to solve the equation $53.9 \cdot 10^6 = 50(b)^{98}$ for b. The value of b is approximately 1.15 and because $b = 1 + r$, the value of r is approximately 0.15. Therefore, the painting's value increased by approximately 15% over 98 years.

Research Project

Responses will vary. As part of the research project, students should include a story about the population, a description of its growth rate, and an explanation of the consequences of the chosen growth rate over time.

ACTIVITY 4

In this activity, students examine the change in the U.S. population from 1790 to 1990. Students also examine the effects of a zero growth rate on a population.

teacher note

A brief assessment of the mathematical content in Activities **3** and **4**, for use at your discretion, appears in the Teacher Resources for this module.

Materials List

■ none

Technology

■ spreadsheet
■ graphing utility

Student Outcomes

After completing the following exploration and discussion, students should be able to:

✴ model real-world data using exponential functions of the form $f(x) = a \cdot b^x$.

Exploration

The following exploration is recommended for small groups. Students may use a spreadsheet to calculate the growth rates between census counts. **Note:** Each student will need a copy of the calculated growth rates for the assignment.

a. Students might see a variety of patterns in this data. For example, they may note that growth slowed during times of war, during the Great Depression of the 1930s, and during the latter half of this century.

b. See the sample spreadsheet below.

Discussion

a. Students may mention a range of possible explanations, including historical events such as the Civil War, World War II, and the Great Depression, and social trends such as the change from a rural to an urban society, advancements in medical science, or the decline in the number of children per family.

b. Students may choose the mean, median, or mode as a representative growth rate—or they may choose something entirely different. Students should be able to justify their choices using the data provided.

c. The death rate is 0.05.

d. In this case, $y = a \cdot b^x = 65 \cdot (1 - 0.05)^x = 65 \cdot 0.95^x$, where $a = 65$ represents the initial population and $b = 1 + r = 0.95$ or 95%.

e. The population decreases.

Warm-Up

1. $\$10,000(1.17)^{10} \approx \$48,068.28$
2. $\$14,000(0.79)^7 \approx \$2688.55$

a. Identify any patterns you see in the data in Table **6-5**.

b. In the previous activities, you calculated growth rates for Skeeter populations between consecutive shakes. Use a similar technique to calculate the growth rates for the U.S. population for each 10-year period.

Discussion

a. What historical events might have affected U.S. population growth during the past 200 years?

b. How would you find a representative growth rate for the U.S. population for the 200-year period from 1790 to 1990?

c. If a population with a growth rate of 0 has a birth rate of 0.05 per year, what is the death rate?

d. Consider a population with a growth rate of –0.05 per year and an initial population of 65. What equation could you use to model this population?

e. How does a negative growth rate affect the total population over time?

Warm-Up

1. Jurek invested $10,000 in an account that promised 17% annual growth. If the company's predictions are true, what would the value of this investment be in 10 years?

2. In 2004, Marissa bought a new car for $14,000. In the past, the value of this car has decreased at an average rate of 21% per year. If this trend continues, what will her car be worth in 7 years?

Assignment

4.1 You can make predictions about the future by describing the patterns found in the U.S. population data and displaying these patterns in graphs or equations.

a. Predict what the U.S. population would have been in 1990 if the growth rate had remained unchanged since 1790. Compare this number to the actual population in 1990.

b. Describe how you could use either the data in Table **6-5** or an exponential equation to predict the U.S. population in the year 2040.

c. If the future growth rate remains the same as it was from 1980 to 1990, predict the U.S. population in the year 2040.

Module 6 ■ *Skeeters Are Overrunning the World*   145

Census Date	Population	Growth Rate	Census Date	Population	Growth Rate
1790	3,929,214		1900	75,994,575	0.21
1800	5,308,483	0.35	1910	91,972,266	0.21
1810	7,239,881	0.36	1920	105,710,620	0.15
1820	9,638,453	0.33	1930	122,775,046	0.16
1830	12,866,020	0.33	1940	131,669,275	0.07
1840	17,069,453	0.33	1950	150,697,361	0.14
1850	23,191,876	0.36	1960	179,323,175	0.19
1860	31,443,321	0.36	1970	203,302,031	0.13
1870	39,818,449	0.27	1980	226,545,805	0.11
1880	50,155,783	0.26	1990	248,709,873	0.10
1890	62,947,714	0.26			

teacher note

You may remind students that because the data in Table **6-5** is given in ten-year increments (the interval of the national census), the exponent x in a corresponding equation of the form $y = a \cdot b^x$ represents the number of decades.

4.2 **a.** Select a growth rate that produces a decreasing population in each successive 10-year period.

   b. Use this growth rate and the U.S. population in 1990 to predict the U.S. population in 2040.

   c. What conditions might cause a population to decrease?

4.3 From 1920 to 1930, the U.S. population grew by approximately 16%.

   a. Use this growth rate to estimate the U.S. population in 1940 and 1950.

   b. Compare your estimates with the actual values for the U.S. population given in Table 6-5.

4.4 The following table shows the predicted growth rates, per year, in the populations of three urban areas. Use this data to predict the population of each city in the year 2023. What do you notice about the predicted populations for these cities?

City	2003 Population	Annual Growth Rate
New York	18,300,000	0.66%
Shanghai	12,800,000	–0.12%
Lagos	10,100,000	4.51%

SOURCE: United Nations Department of Economic and Social Affairs.

4.5 How does a growth rate of 0 affect total population numbers over time?

✶ ✶ ✶ ✶ ✶

4.6 In 1930, the U.S. national debt totaled $16,185,000,000. By 1940, it had risen to $42,968,000,000.

   a. Calculate the percent increase in the national debt over the decade from 1930 to 1940.

   b. What would the national debt have been in 1990 if the growth rate from 1930 to 1940 had remained unchanged?

   c. Since 1930, there have been periods of increase and decrease in the growth rate of the national debt. The actual debt in 1990 was about $3,233,000,000,000.

   1. In 1980, the national debt was $907,700,000,000. Calculate its growth rate from 1980 to 1990.

   2. What would the national debt have been in 2000 if the growth rate from 1980 to 1990 had remained unchanged? How does this figure compare with the actual debt in 2000 of $5.7 trillion?

Assignment

Problems suitable for use as assessment items are identified by an asterisk (*).

4.1 This problem is designed to help students develop an understanding of the consequences of unchecked population growth.

   a. The period from 1790 to 1990 represents 20 ten-year intervals. Using a growth rate of 35% per decade, $3,929,214 \cdot 1.35^{20} \approx 1,588,000,000$. This prediction is almost 6.4 times greater than the actual population in 1990 (248,709,863).

   b. Sample response: It is possible to make a rough estimate of the population for the year 2040 by using technology to create a scatterplot of the data, extending the trend of the last five points in the scatterplot, then using the trace function to estimate the population size.

   Given the appropriate initial population and growth rate, an exponential equation provides a quick way to predict population sizes.

   c. Using a growth rate of 10% per decade, the predicted population is

$$248,709,873 \cdot 1.10^5 \approx 400,550,000.$$

4.2 **a.** Sample response: –5% per decade.

   b. Because the period from 1990 to 2040 represents 5 ten-year intervals,

$$248,709,873 \cdot (1 - 0.05)^5 \approx 192,446,959.$$

   c. Sample response: Circumstances that could cause a population to decrease include famine, natural disasters, diseases, or increased emphasis on birth control.

4.3 **a.** The predicted population in 1940 can be calculated as follows:

$$122,775,046 \cdot 1.16^1 \approx 142,419,000$$

   Likewise, the predicted population in 1950 is:

$$122,775,046 \cdot 1.16^2 \approx 165,206,000$$

   b. The predicted populations are somewhat larger than the actual populations.

* 4.4 The following table shows the predicted population for each city.

New York	$18,300,000 \cdot 1.0066^{20} \approx 20,900,000$
Shanghai	$12,800,000 \cdot 0.9988^{20} \approx 12,500,000$
Lagos	$10,100,000 \cdot 1.0451^{20} \approx 24,400,000$

Sample response: In 20 years, the population of Lagos will surpass that of New York due to the difference in growth rates. The predicted decrease in population size for Shanghai shows the effect of a negative growth rate.

4.5 Sample response: The size of a population with a growth rate of 0 does not change over time. Using an equation of the form $y = a \cdot b^x$ to model the population, $b = 1 + r$, where r is the growth rate. If $r = 0$, then $b = 1$, and $1^x = 1$ for any positive value of x.

✶ ✶ ✶ ✶ ✶

4.6 **a.** The growth rate is approximately 165% per decade:

$$\frac{42,968,000,000 - 16,185,000,000}{16,185,000,000} \approx 1.65$$

   b. Since there are 5 ten-year periods from 1940 to 1990, the predicted debt is

$$42,968,000,000 \cdot (1 + 1.65)^5$$

   or about $5.6 trillion.

   c. 1. The growth rate is approximately 256%:

$$\frac{3.233 - 0.9077}{0.9077} \approx 2.56$$

   2. Since there is 1 ten-year period from 1990 to 2000, the predicted debt is $3.233(1 + 2.56)^1$ or about $11.51 trillion. This is approximately twice the actual value.

4.7 **a.** The growth rate is approximately 1.2% per year. At this rate, the student population will be about 1017 in 5 years. Therefore, the addition to the high school will be required before this time.

b. In 20 years, the student population will be approximately 1216 and overcrowding will again be a problem.

4.7 The enrollment at Eagle Canyon High School has been increasing steadily in the past few years. The present high school building is designed for a maximum of 1000 students. Within the next 5 years, the school board wants to build an addition that will increase the high school's capacity by 200 students.

a. Last year's enrollment at Eagle Canyon High was 947 students. This year's enrollment is 958 students. If this annual growth rate remains unchanged, will the new addition be needed within 5 years? Explain your response.

b. Assume that the growth rate in the student population remains unchanged. Even with the completion of the high school addition, will the school still have enough capacity for the next 20 years? Explain your response.

Summary Assessment

The table below contains data on the population, growth rate, land area, and population density for four nations. Use this information to complete Problems 1–4.

Nation	2000 Population	Annual Growth Rate	Land Area (km²)	Density (people/km²)
Canada	31,278,000	1.0%	8,968,000	3.5
China	1,268,853,000	0.7%	9,327,000	136.0
Hungary	10,137,000	–0.3%	92,000	110.2
India	1,002,708,000	1.6%	2,972,000	337.4

Source: U.S. Bureau of the Census.

1. For each nation listed in the table, write an exponential equation that describes its population growth.

2. Assuming that the given growth rates remain unchanged, predict the years in which the 2000 populations of Canada and Hungary will have doubled.

3. Although India has a smaller population than China, it is growing at a faster rate.

   a. Determine the year in which India's population will surpass that of China.

   b. What will India's population density be at that time?

4. If these four nations continue to grow at their current rates until 2040, which nation will show the greatest change in population density? Support your conclusion with figures and graphs.

teacher note

An additional assessment, for use at your discretion, appears in the Teacher Resources for this module.

Summary Assessment

1. The table below shows a sample equation for each nation.

Country	Growth Equation
Canada	$y = 31{,}278{,}000 \cdot 1.010^x$
China	$y = 1{,}268{,}853{,}000 \cdot 1.007^x$
Hungary	$y = 10{,}137{,}000 \cdot 0.997^x$
India	$y = 1{,}002{,}708{,}000 \cdot 1.016^x$

2. Using the sample equation given for Canada, the year in which the 2000 population will have doubled can be found by substituting as shown below, then solving for x.

$$2(31{,}278{,}000) = 31{,}278{,}000(1.010)^x$$
$$2 = 1(1.010)^x$$

Because $x \approx 67$ years, the corresponding year is

$$2000 + 67 = 2067.$$

Because the growth rate for Hungary's population is negative, its population is decreasing and should not be expected to double in the future. (If this negative rate remains constant, Hungary's population would reach one-half of its 2000 level in about 231 years.)

3. a. Students may use a spreadsheet or graphing utility to approach this problem, or use a symbolic manipulator to determine what value of x makes the following equation true:

$$1{,}268{,}853{,}000(1.007)^x = 1{,}002{,}708{,}000(1.016)^x$$

Because $x \approx 26$ years, India's population is predicted to surpass that of China in 2026.

   b. India's predicted population can be found as follows:

$$y = 1{,}002{,}708{,}000(1.016)^{26}$$
$$\approx 1{,}514{,}994{,}000$$

This results in a population density of about 509 people/km².

4. The table below shows the predicted population and density for each nation. India is predicted to experience the biggest change in density—an increase of approximately 89%.

Nation	2040 Population	Land Area (km²)	Density (people/km²)
Canada	46,568,000	8,968,000	5.2
China	1,677,220,000	9,327,000	179.8
Hungary	8,989,000	92,000	97.7
India	1,892,007,000	2,972,000	636.6

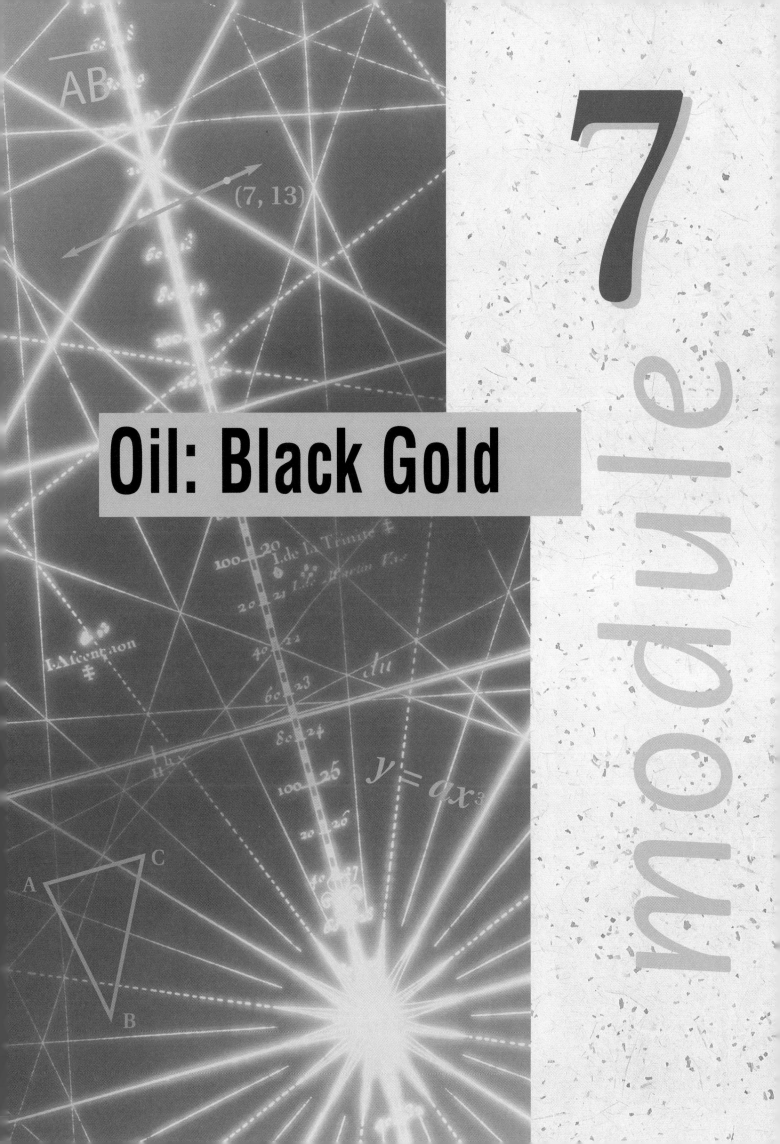

Oil: Black Gold

Overview

This module uses the context of oil spills to extend students' understanding of indirect and direct proportions, area, volume, and mathematical modeling.

Introduction: Students investigate how water and oil interact.

Activity 1:   Students review the concepts of area and volume and estimate areas of irregular shapes.

Activity 2:   Students use direct proportions to model oil spills on land.

Activity 3:   As an introduction to inverse proportions, students examine the relationship between the volume of a cylinder or prism and the area of its base.

Objectives

In this module students will:

✳ determine the volume of cylinders and prisms (Introduction, 1, 2, 3)

✳ determine the area of irregularly shaped figures (1, 2)

✳ develop mathematical models of real-world events (1, 2, 3)

✳ develop and graph direct and inverse proportions (2, 3)

✳ use mathematical models to make predictions about data sets (2, 3).

Prerequisites

For this module, students should know:

✳ how to calculate the areas of circles, triangles, rectangles, trapezoids, and regular polygons

✳ how to determine the equation of a line

✳ how to report calculations to a designated place value

✳ how to write numbers in scientific notation

✳ how to use dimensional analysis

✳ how to compare quantities using ratios

✳ how to interpret linear equations written in slope-intercept form.

 Flashbacks, for use at your discretion, appear in the Teacher Resources for this module. These brief problem sets provide a review of some prerequisite skills for each activity.

Planning Guide

Activity	Materials	Technology	Time Line
Introduction	■ water ■ used motor oil ■ medicine droppers ■ paper towels ■ shallow containers at least 15 cm in diameter ■ liquid detergent (optional)	■ none	3 days
Activity 1	■ centimeter grid paper ■ metric rulers ■ soft-drink cans	■ none	2 days
Activity 2	■ water ■ used motor oil ■ medicine droppers ■ paper towels ■ metric rulers ■ waxed paper ■ toilet tissue	■ spreadsheet ■ graphing utility	2 days
Activity 3	■ water ■ metric rulers ■ cylindrical containers ■ 200-mL beakers	■ spreadsheet	2 days
Assessment Activities	■ none	■ none	3 days **Total: 10 days**

teacher note

Many of the calculations in this module use measured quantities, so sample responses may be reported using significant digits. These responses might differ substantially from those rounded to a specific place value. If you use significant digits in your classroom, you might wish to consult with colleagues in the science department at your school.

You also might wish to discuss the proper disposal of oil-contaminated water and oil-soaked paper.

Introduction

Students investigate how water and oil interact. They experiment, make observations, test hypotheses, and communicate information to their classmates.

Materials List

- water
- used motor oil or clean oil with some red food coloring in it (several drops per group)
- shallow container at least 15 cm in diameter (one per group)
- medicine droppers (one per group)
- paper towels (for cleanup)
- liquid detergent (optional; several drops per group)

teacher note

The National Oceanic and Atmospheric Administration maintains the helpful website, "Oil Spills in History" (response.restoration.noaa.gov/faqs/history.html). The Prince William Sound Regional Citizens' Advisory Council (www.pwsrcac.org) provides a good source of information about the *Exxon Valdez* spill.

Student Outcomes

After completing the following discussions and exploration, students should be able to:

✳ describe relatively large volumes in more familiar terms

✳ describe the geometric characteristics (size, shape, and surface area) of an oil slick

✳ identify some of the properties and effects of an oil spill

✳ relate the mathematics in this module to the context of oil and the handling of petroleum products.

Discussion 1

a. Answers will vary. One gallon contains about 3.8 L, and 1000 L is equivalent to 1 m^3. If the dimensions of the room were 6 m × 9 m × 2.5 m, for example, this amount of oil would fill the room 304 times.

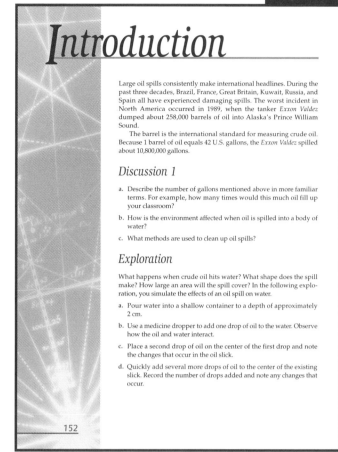

page 152

Introduction

Large oil spills consistently make international headlines. During the past three decades, Brazil, France, Great Britain, Kuwait, Russia, and Spain all have experienced damaging spills. The worst incident in North America occurred in 1989, when the tanker *Exxon Valdez* dumped about 258,000 barrels of oil into Alaska's Prince William Sound.

The barrel is the international standard for measuring crude oil. Because 1 barrel of oil equals 42 U.S. gallons, the *Exxon Valdez* spilled about 10,800,000 gallons.

Discussion 1

a. Describe the number of gallons mentioned above in more familiar terms. For example, how many times would this much oil fill up your classroom?

b. How is the environment affected when oil is spilled into a body of water?

c. What methods are used to clean up oil spills?

Exploration

What happens when crude oil hits water? What shape does the spill make? How large an area will the spill cover? In the following exploration, you simulate the effects of an oil spill on water.

a. Pour water into a shallow container to a depth of approximately 2 cm.

b. Use a medicine dropper to add one drop of oil to the water. Observe how the oil and water interact.

c. Place a second drop of oil on the center of the first drop and note the changes that occur in the oil slick.

d. Quickly add several more drops of oil to the center of the existing slick. Record the number of drops added and note any changes that occur.

152

b. Sample response: Both plants and animals that live in the water might be killed or injured. Birds whose feathers become fouled with oil often die of hypothermia. When oil reaches the coastline, it also can harm plant and animal life on shore.

c. When oil spills occur on water, workers typically attempt to contain it with floating booms or rings. When practical, a skimmer is used to draw off a layer of oil and water. The oil then is separated from this mixture. In most cases, less than 20% of spilled oil is recovered, usually much less. A substantial fraction of the oil (30%) or more evaporates.

In some cases, the oil is burned off. Dispersants also can be used to break the slick into smaller particles. These particles tend to sink and biodegrade. The more recently developed process of bioremediation involves the use of microorganisms to "eat" the oil.

On land, oil penetrates the soil and does not disperse as widely as it does on water. The cleanup generally consists of removing the contaminated earth, then using a variety of methods to separate the oil from the earth.

Discussion 2

a. In Part **b** of the exploration, how is the volume of oil in the drop related to the volume of oil in the slick?

b. Describe the geometric properties of the oil slick after the additional drops of oil were added.

c. How thick do you think the oil slick is?

d. How could you estimate the area covered by the surface of the oil slick?

e. When an oil spill occurs in the real world, what natural factors might affect the shape of the slick?

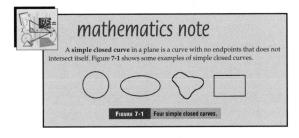

To reduce oil's harmful effects on the environment, clean-up efforts typically begin as soon as possible after a spill. Clean-up crews need to know both the area of the surface covered by the spill and the volume of oil, to help plan their work. Because precise answers are seldom available, they use working approximations. To make such approximations, the edges of oil slicks can be modeled using **simple closed curves**.

mathematics note

A **simple closed curve** in a plane is a curve with no endpoints that does not intersect itself. Figure **7-1** shows some examples of simple closed curves.

FIGURE 7-1 Four simple closed curves.

---

teacher note

As an extension to this exploration, you may allow students to add a few drops of liquid detergent to the oil after completing Part **d.** The two liquids repel each other dramatically. This extension allows students to simulate one phase in the cleanup of an oil spill.

Exploration

a. To clean accidental spills, students should have paper towels nearby.

b. Sample response: After adding one drop of oil to the water, the water and oil do not mix. The oil disperses quickly on the water's surface into a somewhat circular shape.

c. Sample response: When a second drop of oil is placed directly on top of the first one, the oil doesn't disperse nearly as quickly as the first drop did. The circular oil slick becomes larger.

d. Sample response: When several drops of oil are added at once to the existing oil slick, the area of the slick gets even larger, and it takes longer for the oil to disperse.

Discussion 2

a. They are the same. The shape changes but the volume does not.

b. Students probably will note that the surface of the oil slick is roughly circular or elliptical. The actual shape of the slick is a lens, thicker near the center and thinner near the edges. **Note:** In the remainder of this module, students use cylinders to model the shapes of oil slicks.

c. Answers will vary. Milgram, et al., describe "thin" layers of oil as about 0.05 cm deep and "thick" layers as about 0.4 cm deep. Highly refined oil on a calm body of water can spread to a very thin film, about $2.5 \cdot 10^{-3}$ thick.

d. Sample response: Because the oil slick is somewhat circular, estimate its radius and use this value to calculate the area.

e. The physical properties of the oil itself can greatly influence the spread of a slick. For example, heavy crude spreads more slowly than gasoline. Some environmental factors that affect the spread of a slick are wind, salinity, temperature, wave action, and shorelines.

In this activity, students review the concepts of area and volume and estimate areas of irregular shapes.

teacher note

A brief assessment of the mathematical content in Activity **1,** for use at your discretion, appears in the Teacher Resources for this module.

Materials List

- metric rulers (one per student)
- centimeter grid paper (one sheet per student)
- soft-drink can (one per student)

Student Outcomes

After completing the following exploration and discussion, students should be able to:

✳ estimate the area of an irregular shape by at least two different methods

✳ estimate the surface area and volume of an irregular solid

✳ convert among various units of measure when calculating area and volume.

Exploration

a. 1. In this case, each square on a centimeter grid represents 100 m². The area of slick A is approximately 1300 m². The area of slick B is approximately 1400 m².

2. The volume of oil in slick A is 1300 m² • 0.001 m = 1.3 m³. The volume of oil in slick B is 1400 m² • 0.001 m = 1.4 m³.

b. 1–3. Sample response: Slick A has a mean radius of about 2.0 cm. Slick B has a mean radius of about 1.9 cm.

4. Using the sample responses given above, the area of slick A is about $\pi(20 \text{ m})^2 \approx 1300$ m². The area of slick B is approximately $\pi(19 \text{ m})^2 \approx 1100$ m².

5. Using the sample responses given above, the volume of oil in slick A is 1300 m² • 0.001 m = 1.3 m³. The volume of oil in slick B is 1100 m² • 0.001 m = 1.1 m³.

Discussion

a. Sample response: There are about as many partially covered squares that are more than half covered as there are squares that are less than half covered. Counting all partially covered squares, then dividing by 2, gives a reasonable estimate for the area of the partially covered squares.

b. Sample response: To get a more accurate estimate of the area, you could use a grid with smaller squares.

c. Response teams can estimate the area of the surface covered by the slick using aerial mapping techniques or mathematical models involving volume, time, and surface tension.

d. 1. In the sample responses given in the exploration, the two estimates for slick A are the same, but the two estimates for slick B differ by 300 m².

2. Sample response: The larger estimate should be used to make sure that clean-up crews are prepared to encounter at least that much oil.

Exploration

Figure 7-2 shows the shapes of two oil slicks. In the following exploration, you investigate two different methods for estimating the area and volume of these slicks.

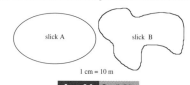

slick A   slick B

1 cm = 10 m

FIGURE 7-2   Two oil slicks.

a. In the module "What Will We Do When the Well Runs Dry," you estimated the area of irregular shapes by counting squares on a sheet of graph paper.

1. Use this method and a centimeter grid to estimate the area of each slick in Figure 7-2.

2. The oil in each slick is 1 mm deep. Use the formula for the volume of a cylinder to determine the volume of each slick.

mathematics note

A **cylinder** is a three-dimensional solid with bases that are congruent, simple closed curves (nonpolygons) in parallel planes. For example, Figure 7-3 shows three different cylinders.

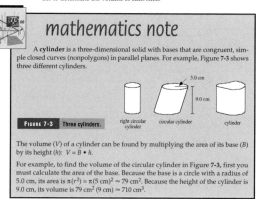

FIGURE 7-3   Three cylinders.   right circular cylinder   circular cylinder   cylinder

The volume (V) of a cylinder can be found by multiplying the area of its base (B) by its height (h): $V = B \cdot h$.

For example, to find the volume of the circular cylinder in Figure 7-3, first you must calculate the area of the base. Because the base is a circle with a radius of 5.0 cm, its area is $\pi(r^2) = \pi(5 \text{ cm})^2 \approx 79 \text{ cm}^2$. Because the height of the cylinder is 9.0 cm, its volume is 79 cm² (9 cm) ≈ 710 cm³.

154   Module 7 ■ *Oil: Black Gold*

---

b. Another method for estimating the area of irregular shapes uses the formula for the area of a circle with a radius r, $A = \pi r^2$. Complete Steps **1–5** below for both slicks in Figure 7-2.

1. Locate a point at the approximate center of the slick.

2. Measure the distance from the center to several random points on the edge of the slick.

3. Find the mean of the distances from Step 2. This mean is the approximate radius of a circle with comparable area.

4. Use the mean radius found in Step 3 and the formula for the area of a circle to estimate the area of the slick.

5. Assuming that the oil is 1 mm deep, determine the volume of the slick.

Discussion

a. When using a grid to estimate area, why do you divide the number of partially covered squares by 2?

b. How could you modify the grid used in Part **a** of the exploration to obtain more accurate estimates of area?

c. How might an environmental engineer find the area covered by the surface of an oil spill?

d. 1. Compare the two estimates you obtained for the volume of each slick.

2. If you were in charge of cleaning up slick B, which estimate would you use?

Warm-Up

1. Find the area of each of the following figures and describe how you determined your responses.

a.

3 cm   3 cm
3 cm   2.1 cm   3 cm
3 cm

b.

☐ = 1 mm²

c.

9.2 m
10.2 m   9.0 m   3.7 m
9.9 m

Module 7 ■ *Oil: Black Gold*   **155**

2. The formula for the volume of a prism or a cylinder is $V = B \cdot h$, where V is the volume, B is the area of the base, and h is the height.

Write an equation for the volume of each figure below, including the correct formula for the area of the base. Use your equations to calculate the volume of each figure.

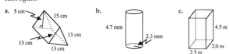

a. 5 cm 15 cm 13 cm 13 cm 13 cm **b.** 4.7 mm 2.3 mm **c.** 4.5 m 2.5 m 2.0 m

Assignment

1.1 **a.** Determine the volume of each fuel tank below in cubic centimeters.

1. This truck fuel tank is a rectangular prism.

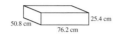

25.4 cm 50.8 cm 76.2 cm

2. This boat fuel tank is a triangular prism in which the bases are right triangles.

9.8 cm 48.5 cm 80.5 cm

b. How many liters of fuel will each tank hold?
Note: 1 cm^3 = 1 mL; 1 m^3 = 1000 L.

1.2 Paper usually is purchased in reams. One ream contains 500 sheets of paper and is about 5.2 cm thick. Considering this information, find the volume of one sheet of letter-size paper in cubic centimeters. **Note:** The dimensions of a sheet of letter-size paper are approximately 21.5 cm by 27.9 cm.

1.3 The tank on the oil truck in the figure below is a circular cylinder. Determine the volume of the tank.

1.94 m 12.19 m

156 Module 7 ▪ *Oil: Black Gold*

Warm-Up

1. **a.** The area of a regular polygon with n sides, apothem a, and side length s is:

$$A = \left(\frac{1}{2}as\right)n$$

$$= \left(\frac{1}{2} \cdot 2.1 \cdot 3\right)5$$

$$= 15.75 \text{ cm}^2$$

b. By counting squares, the area is approximately 34 mm^2.

c. The area of a trapezoid with height h and base lengths b_1 and b_2 is:

$$A = \frac{1}{2}(b_1 + b_2)h$$

$$= \frac{1}{2}(3.7 + 10.2)9.0$$

$$= 62.55 \text{ m}^2$$

2. **a.** $0.5(5)(13)(15) = 487.5 \text{ cm}^3$
   b. $\pi(2)(3^2)(4.7) \approx 78.1 \text{ mm}^3$
   c. $2.5(2.0)(4.5) = 22.5 \text{ m}^3$

teacher note

You might wish to remind students to pay close attention to the units in each problem.

To complete Problem **1.9**, each student or group will need an ordinary soft-drink can.

Assignment

Problems suitable for use as assessment items are identified by an asterisk (*).

1.1 **a.** **1.** $50.8(76.2)(25.4) \approx 98{,}322.4 \text{ cm}^3$ (or 98,300 cm^3 to three significant digits)
   2. $0.5(48.5)(9.8)(80.5) \approx 19{,}130.8 \text{ cm}^3$ (or 19,000 cm^3 to two significant digits)

b. **1.** Sample response:

$$\frac{98{,}300 \text{ cm}^3}{1} \cdot \frac{1 \text{ m}^3}{1{,}000{,}000 \text{ cm}^3} \cdot \frac{1000 \text{ L}}{1 \text{ m}^3} = 98.3 \text{ L}$$

2. Sample response:

$$\frac{19{,}000 \text{ cm}^3}{1} \cdot \frac{1 \text{ m}^3}{1{,}000{,}000 \text{ cm}^3} \cdot \frac{1000 \text{ L}}{1 \text{ m}^3} = 19 \text{ L}$$

1.2 The volume of one sheet can be found as follows:

$$\frac{21.5 \text{ cm} \cdot 27.9 \text{ cm} \cdot 5.2 \text{ cm}}{500} \approx 6.2 \text{ cm}^3$$

1.3 $\pi \cdot (1.94/2)^2 \cdot 12.19 \approx 36.0 \text{ m}^3$

1.4 a. The oil slick could be described as a right circular cylinder.

b. The area covered by the slick is $\pi \cdot (405\text{ m})^2 \approx$ 515,000 m^2. Because $V = B \cdot h$, the volume can be calculated as follows:

$$515{,}000 \cdot 2.5 \cdot 10^{-5}\text{ m} \approx 13\text{ m}^3$$

Because 1 m^3 = 1000 L, the volume of the spill is approximately 13,000 L.

1.5 a. There are 42 gal in 1 bbl and 3.8 L in 1 gal; therefore:

$$1\text{ bbl} \cdot \left(\frac{42\text{ gal}}{1\text{ bbl}}\right) \cdot \left(\frac{3.8\text{ L}}{1\text{ gal}}\right) \approx 160\text{ L}$$

Converting to cubic meters,

$$160\text{ L} \cdot \frac{1\text{ m}^3}{1000\text{ L}} = 0.16\text{ m}^3$$

Because $V = B \cdot h$, the area of the base can be calculated as follows:

$$0.16 = B(2.5 \cdot 10^{-3})$$

$$6400\text{ m}^2 = B$$

b. Students should realize that the spill probably will not reach the estimated size because some of the oil will evaporate over time, and that some will disperse as wave action breaks the slick into smaller droplets.

* 1.6 a. Sample response: There are 29 full squares and 25 partially covered squares. After dividing the number of partially covered squares by 2 and adding this to the number of full squares, the total is 41.5 squares. Each square on the grid represents an area of 1 km^2. This gives an approximate area of 41.5 km^2. **Note:** Students also may use the mean radius to estimate area.

b. Using a cylinder to model the shape of the slick:

$$V = \left(41.5\text{ km}^2 \cdot \frac{1 \cdot 10^{10}\text{ cm}^2}{1\text{ km}^2}\right)(0.05\text{ cm})$$

$$\approx 2 \cdot 10^{10}\text{ cm}^3$$

This can be converted to barrels as follows:

$$(2 \cdot 10^{10}\text{ cm}^3)\left(\frac{1\text{ mL}}{1\text{ cm}^3}\right)\left(\frac{1\text{ L}}{1000\text{ mL}}\right)\left(\frac{1\text{ gal}}{3.8\text{ L}}\right)\left(\frac{1\text{ bbl}}{42\text{ gal}}\right)$$

$$= 1.253 \cdot 10^5\text{ bbl}$$

1.7 a. Students may convert gallons to cubic kilometers as follows:

$$(1.9 \cdot 10^7\text{ gal})\left(\frac{3.8\text{ L}}{1\text{ gal}}\right)\left(\frac{1000\text{ mL}}{1\text{ L}}\right)\left(\frac{1\text{ cm}^3}{1\text{ mL}}\right)\left(\frac{1\text{ km}^3}{1 \cdot 10^{15}\text{ cm}^3}\right)$$

$$\approx 7.2 \cdot 10^{-5}\text{ km}^3$$

1.4 Imagine that some highly refined oil is spilled into a calm body of water. Under these conditions, the oil can spread to a very thin film, approximately $2.5 \cdot 10^{-3}$ cm thick.

    a. What type of three-dimensional figure could be used to describe the oil slick?

    b. The mean radius of the slick is 405 m. Determine the volume of oil in the spill in liters.

1.5 a. Estimate the area that would be covered by a spill of 1 barrel of highly refined oil in a calm body of water. (There are approximately 3.8 L in 1 gal.) Describe how you determined your estimate.

    b. Do you think that an actual spill of 1 barrel of oil will spread as much as you estimated in Part **a**? Why or why not?

1.6 The following diagram shows an aerial view of an oil slick. The grid superimposed on the photograph has squares that measure 1 km on each side.

    a. Estimate the area covered by the slick.

    b. Determine the volume of oil involved in the spill if the slick is 0.05 cm thick. Record your answer in barrels. (There are 42 gal in 1 bbl.)

1.7 In December, 1989, an explosion on an Iranian supertanker spilled 19 million gallons of crude oil into the Atlantic Ocean. The oil slick covered an area of about 260 km^2.

    a. Approximately how thick was this oil slick?

    b. How does the thickness of this spill compare to the thickness of a spill of highly refined oil?

* * * * *

Since $V = B \cdot h$ the thickness of the spill can be found as follows:

$$\frac{7.2 \cdot 10^{-5}\text{ km}^3}{260\text{ km}^2} = 2.8 \cdot 10^{-7}\text{ km}$$

This is equivalent to 0.028 cm.

b. As mentioned in Problem **1.4**, highly refined oil can spread to a thickness of approximately $2.5 \cdot 10^{-3}$ cm under ideal conditions. This spill is about 10 times thicker.

✳ ✳ ✳ ✳ ✳

1.8 The federal government assures wheat farmers of a certain base price per bushel if they farm a limited acreage. To determine if a farmer is in compliance, regulators take an aerial photograph of the farm. The diagram below shows an aerial view of a wheat field with a pond. This farm has been allotted a maximum of 200 acres of wheat. (One acre is approximately 4047 m².) Is this farmer in compliance?

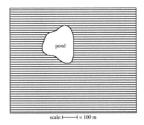

scale:├────┤ = 100 m

1.9 Use an ordinary soft-drink can to complete Parts **a–c** below.

    a. Measure the height and diameter of the can.

    b. Use these measurements to find the volume of the can in cubic centimeters.

    c. Convert the volume of the can in cubic centimeters to milliliters. How does this value compare to the volume printed on the can?

ACTIVITY 2

A **simulation** of a real-world event involves creating a similar, but more simplified, model. In the introduction, for example, you simulated an oil spill on the ocean using a few drops of oil in a pan of water. In this activity, you simulate oil spills on land by placing drops of oil on sheets of paper.

Exploration

In this exploration, you simulate spills involving eight different volumes of oil. **Note:** Save your data, observations, and calculations for the assignment in this activity.

1.8 Sample response: The dimensions of the field are 840 m by 1030 m. The area of the land, including the pond, is 865,200 m². The pond has a mean radius of approximately 135 m. The area of the pond is approximately 57,300 m². The area of the field without the pond is 807,900 m². This equals about 200 acres; therefore the farmer appears to be in compliance.

1.9 a. Sample response: The diameter is 6.6 cm and the height is 11.7 cm.

    b. $V = \pi \bullet r^2 \bullet h = \pi \bullet (3.3\,\text{cm})^2 \bullet 11.7\,\text{cm} \approx 400\,\text{cm}^3$

    c. Sample response: Since $1\,\text{cm}^3 = 1\,\text{mL}$, the volume of the can is about 400 mL. The volume printed on the can is 355 mL. The difference occurs because the printed volume measures the liquid in the can. The can is not filled exactly to the top and is not truly cylindrical (it has indentations in the top and bottom).

ACTIVITY 2

In this activity, students simulate oil spills on land. The ratio of the number of drops of oil to the resulting surface area of the spill is used to introduce direct proportions.

Materials List

- used motor oil
- paper towels
- medicine dropper (one per group)
- toilet tissue (eight sheets per group)
- metric rulers (one per group)
- waxed paper (eight sheets per group)
- tape

Technology

- graphing utility
- spreadsheet

teacher note

Plan for the disposal of oil-soaked paper before beginning the exploration. Used motor oil is recommended because its spread is easy to observe. Cooking oil or mineral oil also will work but are more difficult to observe.

The experiment requires a smooth, level, nonabsorbent surface. Place each sheet of toilet paper on a sheet of waxed paper to improve the experimental results and simplify cleanup. Tape down the sheets of waxed paper to prevent movement.

Student Outcomes

After completing the following exploration and discussion, students should be able to:

✳ identify direct proportions

✳ use direct proportions as mathematical models.

Exploration

This exploration works best in small groups. Students should find a direct proportion between the number of drops of oil and the area of the spill. (Because each drop represents a fixed volume, the values found for the constant of proportionality depend on the thickness of the paper and the time allowed for the oil to spread. The following sample responses are based on an observation time of 20 min.)

a–c. To obtain accurate data, students must keep each sheet level and motionless until the oil is absorbed. To ensure that enough time is allowed for 8 drops of oil to spread (about 15 min), students should start with sheet 8.

d. Sample response: More oil dropped on the paper produces larger shapes. Most of the time the oil spreads in a circular or elliptical fashion. **Note:** Uneven or tilted work surfaces, wrinkles in the paper, patterns in the paper, and the orientation of fibers within the paper may contribute to the formation of irregular shapes.

e. Students should use the method developed in Activity **1** to find the mean radius.

f. 1. Sample data:

Drops	Radius (cm)	Area (cm^2)
0	0	0
1	1.5	7.0
2	2.0	13
3	2.7	23
4	3.2	32
5	3.5	38
6	3.5	38
7	3.7	43
8	4.0	50

2. Sample scatterplot:

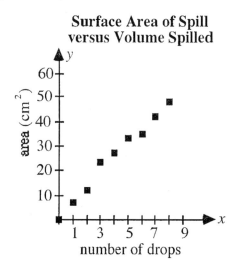

Surface Area of Spill versus Volume Spilled

a. Obtain a small amount of oil, a medicine dropper, a ruler, eight sheets of absorbent paper, and some paper towels.

b. Spread the eight sheets of absorbent paper on a flat, nonabsorbent surface. Arrange the sheets so that they do not touch each other. Number the sheets from 1 through 8 and place a pencil dot in the middle of each sheet. Be careful not to fold or wrinkle the paper.

c. Carefully place 8 drops of oil on the pencil dot on sheet 8. Make the size of each drop as consistent as possible.

Continue creating oil spills of different volumes by placing 7 drops on sheet 7, 6 drops on sheet 6, and so on.

d. Without disturbing the sheets of paper, observe each spill and record your observations. Describe the general relationship between the volume of oil (number of drops) and the shape and area of the spill.

e. Determine the mean radius of each spill to the nearest 0.1 cm. Start with sheet 1 and continue in numerical order to sheet 8.

f. 1. Determine the area covered by each spill and record these values in Table **7-1** below.

TABLE 7-1 ■ Volume and Area of Oil Spills	
Volume (drops)	Area (cm^2)
0	0
1	
2	
⋮	
8	

2. Create a scatterplot of the data in Table **7-1**. Represent the area covered by the spill on the *y*-axis and the volume of oil in drops on the *x*-axis.

3. Determine the equation of a line that reasonably approximates the data. The line should have the same *y*-intercept as the scatterplot.

g. Use your equation to predict the area of an oil spill with each of the following volumes:

1. 0.04 drops
2. 0.5 drops
3. 2.5 drops
4. 25 drops ($\approx$ 1 mL)
5. 25,000 drops ($\approx$ 1 L)

h. For each spill in Table **7-1**, calculate and record the ratio of the area covered to the volume (number of drops).

i. Dispose of the oil-soaked paper as directed by your teacher.

3. Answers will vary. Students might use a string or piece of dry spaghetti attached to the graph at the origin to try and hit the most points. For the sample data, either $y = 6x$ or $y = 7x$ provide reasonable models.

g. The following sample predictions were made using the equation $y = 7.0x$, where *y* represents the area in square centimeters and *x* represents the number of drops.

1. approximately 0.3 cm^2
2. approximately 4 cm^2
3. approximately 18 cm^2
4. approximately 180 cm^2
5. approximately 180,000 cm^2

Discussion

a. What observations did you make concerning the spread of the oil, the shape of the spill, and the area covered by the spill?

b. What problems did you encounter in measuring the area covered by the oil spills?

c. 1. How does the precision of your measurement of the mean radius affect the accuracy of the calculated area?

   2. What implications does your response have for measuring actual oil spills?

d. 1. Describe the area you predicted for an oil spill of 1 L (approximately 25,000 drops) in Part **g** of the exploration.

   2. Do you think that this prediction is realistic? Explain your response.

e. Is it reasonable to assume that 0 drops of oil produce an oil spill with a surface area of 0 cm²? Explain your response.

f. 1. Describe any pattern you observed in the ratios of surface area to volume determined in Part **h** of the exploration.

   2. What method might you use to find a single number *m* to represent all these ratios?

   3. If this value of *m* were used to write an equation $y = mx$, what would each variable represent in terms of the oil spills?

   4. How does this equation compare to the one you found in Part **f** of the exploration?

   5. Could this equation be used to accurately predict the area of an oil spill of 500 bbl on the ground? If not, how could you change the model to improve the prediction?

mathematics note

One quantity is **directly proportional** to another when the ratio of the two quantities is constant (the same). The constant is the **constant of proportionality** and the ratio is a **direct proportion**.

A direct proportion can be described by a linear equation of the form $y = mx$, where *m* is the constant of proportionality. The graph of a direct proportion always contains the origin because $y = 0$ whenever $x = 0$.

h. The following table shows the ratios, to the nearest whole number, for the sample data given in Part **f.**

Drops	Area (cm²)	Ratio
0	0	
1	7	7
2	13	7
3	23	8
4	32	8
5	38	8
6	38	6
7	43	6
8	50	6

Discussion

a. Students report their observations. You might wish to remind students that, in this exploration, the volume of each spill after the oil hits the paper is modeled by a cylinder whose height is the thickness of the paper. The volume of this cylinder is a combination of oil and the volume of paper fibers.

b. Sample response: The shapes were not exactly circles, and it was hard to determine the outer edges of the spill. Reading the ruler as it was suspended above the spill was also difficult.

c. 1. The accuracy of the area is restricted by the number of significant digits in the measurements.

   2. Sample response: Because measuring even small spills is difficult, the reported areas should be considered as estimates only.

d. 1. Sample response: The predicted area was approximately 180,000 cm², or about 18 m².

   2. Sample response: Probably not. By the time 1 L of oil could spread on such a large sheet of paper, some of it would have evaporated.

e. Sample response: Yes, it is reasonable because when no oil is dropped, no spill is created.

f. 1. In the sample data given in Part **f** of the exploration, all the ratios are either 6, 7, or 8.

   2. The mean of the ratios provides a reasonable representative value.

   3. The variable *y* represents the area covered by the spill in square centimeters; *x* represents the volume of oil in drops. The ratio of the area to the volume is *m*.

   4. Students should observe that the values of *m* in both equations are close.

   5. Sample response: No. In the experiment, a small amount of oil was spread very thin on a flat surface. Oil would soak deeper into soil and cover less surface area. You could adjust the model by collecting data for an experiment on soil with larger amounts of oil.

g. **1.** As the values of x increase, the values of y increase.
  2. As the values of x increase, the values of y decrease.

h. Sample response: Yes. A scatterplot of area versus volume appears to form a linear pattern with the origin included in the graph.

i. Because the line contains the origin, the slope of the line is:

$$m = \frac{q - 0}{p - 0} = \frac{q}{p}$$

Warm-Up

1. **a.** Direct proportion.
  b. Not a direct proportion.
  c. Direct proportion.
2. **a.** Direct proportion; the constant of proportionality is 0.75.
  b. Not a direct proportion.
  c. Direct proportion; the constant of proportionality is 10.
  d. Direct proportion; the constant of proportionality is $-3/2$.
  e. Not a direct proportion.
  f. Not a direct proportion.

Assignment

Problems suitable for use as assessment items are identified by an asterisk (*).

2.1 **a.** In this data set, x and y are directly proportional. The ratio of x to y is constant $(1/3)$ and the graph of a line modeling the data would pass through the origin.
  b. In this data set, x and y are not directly proportional. The ratio of x to y is not constant.
  c. In this data set, x and y are not directly proportional. Although the graph contains the origin, the ratio of x to y is not constant.
2.2 **a.** This graph does not represent a direct proportion. Although it does seem to show a set of data with a linear pattern, the graph does not pass through the origin.
  b. This graph does not show data with a constant ratio between x and y, so it cannot represent a direct proportion.
  c. This graph represents a direct proportion. The data appears to show a constant ratio between x and y and includes the origin. It could be described by an equation of the form $y = mx$.
  d. This graph does not represent a direct proportion. Although it does seem to show a set of data with a linear pattern, the graph does not show data with a constant ratio between x and y and does not pass through the origin.

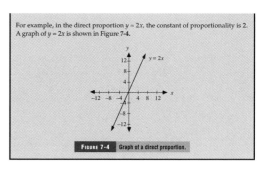

For example, in the direct proportion $y = 2x$, the constant of proportionality is 2. A graph of $y = 2x$ is shown in Figure 7-4.

FIGURE 7-4 Graph of a direct proportion.

g. Given the direct proportion $y = mx$, describe how the values of y change as:
  1. the values of x increase when $m > 0$
  2. the values of x increase when $m < 0$

h. Are an oil spill's area and volume directly proportional? Explain your response.

i. If you know any point with coordinates (p,q) on the graph of a direct proportion, what is the slope of the line?

Warm-Up

1. Determine which of the following graphs, if any, depict direct proportions.

2. Determine which of the following equations, if any, are direct proportions. If an equation represents a direct proportion, identify the constant of proportion.

  a. $y = 0.75x$ **b.** $y = 4x - 7$
  c. $y = 10x$ **d.** $y = -(3/2)x$
  e. $y = x^2$ **f.** $y = 2/x$

Assignment

2.1 Determine if x and y are directly proportional in each of the following relationships. Defend your responses.

a.

x	1	3	4	6	25
y	3	9	12	18	75

b.

x	1	3	4	6	25
y	8	14	17	23	80

c.

x	0	3	4	5	7
y	0	10	17	26	50

2.2 Which of the scatterplots below, if any, appear to represent direct proportions? Defend your responses.

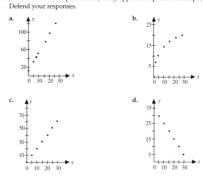

2.3 **a.** Graph each of the following equations of direct proportions on the same coordinate system, with $0 \le x \le 10$. Compare the graphs.

  1. $y = 0.5x$ **2.** $y = 5x$
  3. $y = 1x$ **4.** $y = -0.25x$
  5. $y = 1.75x$ **6.** $y = -3.5x$

b. In your own words, describe the characteristics of the graph of a direct proportion.

2.4 Use your data from the exploration to answer the following questions.

    a. Is the mean radius of an oil spill directly proportional to the volume of the spill?

    b. Is the square of the mean radius directly proportional to the volume?

2.5 When oil is spilled on a sheet of absorbent paper, the spill can be modeled by a cylinder. In this situation, the base of the cylinder is the shape of the spill, while the height of the cylinder is the thickness of the paper.

The volume of a cylinder is determined by multiplying the area of the base by the height. Is the volume of the spill directly proportional to the area covered by the spill? Explain your response.

✽ ✽ ✽ ✽ ✽

2.6 In a circle, the circumference (C) is directly proportional to the diameter (d). The constant of proportionality is π.

    a. Write an equation for this direct proportion.

    b. Is the relationship for each of the following a direct proportion? If so, write an equation for the proportion and identify the constant of proportionality. If not, explain why not.

        1. the circumference of a circle and its radius

        2. the area of a circle and its radius.

2.7 The relationship between temperature measured in degrees Fahrenheit (F) and temperature measured in degrees Celsius (C) is:

$$C = \frac{5}{9}F - \frac{160}{9}$$

Explain why this relationship is not a direct proportion.

2.8 Hailstones are formed when raindrops are caught in updrafts and carried into high clouds containing very cold air. The radius of a hailstone is directly proportional to the amount of time it remains in the high cloud.

    a. After remaining in a high cloud for 10 sec, a hailstone has a radius of about 1.3 cm. What was the radius of the hailstone after 1 sec?

    b. Write an equation for this direct proportion.

    c. How long would a hailstone have to remain in high clouds to reach a radius greater than 2.5 cm?

2.3 a. Students should use a graphing utility to complete this problem.

    b. Sample response: The graphs of direct proportions are all straight lines with different slopes. They all pass through the origin and have slopes that are the constants of proportionality.

2.4 a. The following graph uses the sample data given in Part **f** of the exploration. It does not show a direct proportion. (The radius increases in proportion to the square root of the volume.)

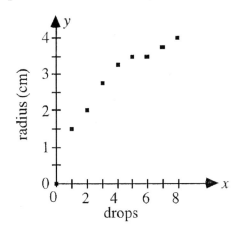

b. The following graph uses the sample data given in Part **f** of the exploration. This appears to be a direct proportion.

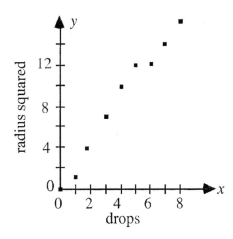

* 2.5 Sample response: Yes. The equation $V = Bh$ can be rewritten as $V = hB$. This equation is in the form of $y = mx$, a direct proportion in which the constant of proportionality is h, the thickness of the paper.

✽ ✽ ✽ ✽ ✽

2.6 a. $C = \pi \bullet d$

    b. 1. This is a direct proportion. The relationship can be described by the equation $C = 2\pi \bullet r$, where the constant of proportionality is $2\pi \approx 6.28$.

       2. This is not a direct proportion. The relationship can be described by the equation $A = \pi \bullet r^2$, which is not of the form $y = mx$. Its graph is not a line.

2.7 Sample response: This is not a direct proportion because the equation is not of the form $y = mx$ and the graph does not contain the origin.

2.8 a. 0.13 cm

    b. One equation for this relationship is $r = 0.13t$, where r represents the radius in centimeters and t represents time in seconds.

    c. The hailstone would have to remain in high clouds more than 19 sec.

$$
\begin{aligned}
r &= 0.13t \\
2.5 &= 0.13t \\
2.5/0.13 &= t \\
19 &\approx t
\end{aligned}
$$

2.9 a. $18,699 − $9948 = $8751

    b. Assuming that the relationship is a direct proportion, the yearly increases are equal.

       1. $875.10

       2. One equation for this relationship is $I = 875.1t$, where I represents the increase and t represents the number of years after 1980.

c. 1. $875.10 • 14 + $9948 = $22,199.40

2. One equation for this relationship is $P = 875.1t + 9948$, where P represents the per capita income and t represents the number of years after 1980.

3. Sample response: This is not a direct proportion because the equation is not of the form $y = mx$ and the graph does not contain the origin.

d. Sample response: The model may not be accurate because there are many factors in the economy that cause increases in income to vary from year to year.

ACTIVITY 3

In this activity, students investigate the relationship between the volume of cylinders and prisms and the area of the base. The concept of inverse proportion also is developed in this context.

Materials List

- containers in the shape of right cylinders (at least eight different sizes)
- metric rulers (one per group)
- 200-mL beaker (one per group)
- water (200 mL per group)

teacher note

To generate a sufficient amount of data, students require at least eight containers with different base areas, including one with a relatively large diameter and one with a relatively small diameter. To show students that the relationship is the same regardless of the shape of the base, you might wish to include some prisms in your collection of containers.

A brief assessment of the mathematical content in Activities **2** and **3,** for use at your discretion, appears in the Teacher Resources for this module.

Technology

- graphing utility
- spreadsheet

2.9 In 1980, per capita personal income in the United States was $9948. Ten years later, per capita income rose to $18,699.

a. What was the total increase in per capita personal income from 1980 to 1990?

b. Assume that the yearly increases in per capita income and the number of years after 1980 are directly proportional.

1. What was the yearly increase in per capita personal income between 1980 and 1990?

2. Write an equation for the direct proportion between yearly increases in per capita income and number of years after 1980.

c. 1. Predict the per capita personal income in 1994.

2. Write an equation that could be used to model the per capita income for any year after 1980.

3. Does this equation define a direct proportion? Explain your response.

d. The actual per capita personal income in 1994 was $21,846. What limitations might the model in Part c have for predicting per capita personal income?

ACTIVITY 3

As soon as a quantity of oil is spilled, it starts to spread. If not contained, the resulting slick can cover a very large area. As the oil continues to spread, the depth of the slick decreases. In the following exploration, you investigate the relationship between the depth of a spill and the area it covers.

Exploration

When liquid is poured into a cylindrical container, the surface of the liquid takes the same shape as the base of the container. In this exploration, you use a fixed amount of water to represent the volume of an oil spill. The spread of the spill is simulated by pouring the water into several containers with different base areas. **Note:** Save your work, including the spreadsheet, for use in the assignment.

a. Obtain a cylindrical container from your teacher. Determine and record its base area (B) in square centimeters.

b. Pour 200 mL of water into the container. Measure and record the height (h) of the water in centimeters.

c. Calculate $B • h$, where B is the base area and h is the height of the water in the container. Label the product with the appropriate units and record the result.

164   Module 7 ■ *Oil: Black Gold*

Student Outcomes

After completing the following exploration and discussion, students should be able to:

✳ identify the relationship between the volume of a cylinder or prism and the area of its base

✳ identify an inverse proportion

✳ use inverse proportions as mathematical models.

Exploration

This exploration is designed for work in groups. To save time, each group is instructed to measure one container, then combine their data with the rest of the class. As an alternative to this procedure, you may prepare eight stations and allow students to take turns measuring each container.

a. Students should measure the diameter of each cylinder to the nearest 0.1 cm.

b. Students also should measure heights to the nearest 0.1 cm.

d. 1. Collect the class data for the different containers.

2. Enter the data in a spreadsheet.

3. Sort the data so that the base areas appear in ascending order (from least to greatest).

e. Create a scatterplot of the height of the water versus the base area.

Discussion

a. 1. What should be true of each value for $B \cdot h$ calculated in Part **c** of the exploration?

2. Do the class values support this conclusion? Explain your response.

b. Describe the graph obtained in Part **e** of the exploration.

c. Consider a right circular cylinder and a right triangular prism with the same base areas. Each contains an equal volume of water. Does the height of the water depend on the shapes of the bases?

d. 1. In the exploration, what happened to the height of the water as it was poured into containers with larger base areas?

2. Is the height directly proportional to the area of the base? Explain your response.

e. Do you think that examining the heights of liquid in a series of containers with increasing base areas provides a good model of the spread of an oil spill? Explain your response.

Warm-Up

1. Identify each of the following data sets as directly proportional, inversely proportional, or neither.

a.

x	3	–10	–2	2.5	20
y	1.67	–0.5	–2.5	0.2	0.25

b.

x	–3	6	15	–21	12
y	–2	4	10	–14	8

c.

x	8	–12	–2	–3	4
y	–1/2	–4/3	–1	–7/3	0

d.

x	6	12	4	–3	24
y	2	1	3	–4	0.5

Module 7 ■ *Oil: Black Gold*   165

Discussion

a. 1. Sample response: Each entry in the column should be close to 200 cm³. **Note:** Students should recall that 1 cm³ = 1 mL.

2. Experimental values will be influenced by rounding errors and the accuracy of measuring tools. In most cases, the volume should be reasonably close to 200 cm³.

b. Sample response: The graph shows a curved pattern. As the area of the base increases, the height approaches 0; as the area of the base approaches 0, the height becomes very large.

c. Given equal volumes of water, the height of the water depends only on the area of the base.

d. 1. The height decreases as the area of the base increases. The height increases as the area of the base decreases.

2. Since the ratio of the two quantities is not constant, they are not directly proportional.

e. Models can be used to describe and make predictions. The sequence of containers models an oil spill in the sense that as oil spreads, the height of the spill decreases and the surface area of the spill increases. As with most models, however, there are limitations to its precision.

Warm-Up

1. a. inversely proportional
   b. directly proportional
   c. neither
   d. inversely proportional

c–d. See the sample data table below.

e. The graph on the right was created using the sample data given in Part **d.**

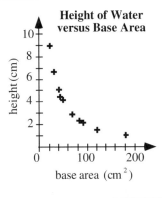

Height of Water versus Base Area

height (cm) vs base area (cm²)

Base Area (cm²)	Height of Water (cm)	Volume (cm³)
21	9.0	190
30	6.7	200
39	5.1	200
42	4.5	190
49	4.2	210
67	2.9	190
83	2.4	200
90	2.2	200
120	1.6	190
180	1.1	200

2. **a.** inverse proportion
   b. direct proportion
   c. direct proportion
   d. inverse proportion
   e. inverse proportion

Assignment

Problems suitable for use as assessment items are identified by an asterisk (*).

3.1 a. $200 = Bh$

   b. $h = 200/B$

   c. Sample graph:

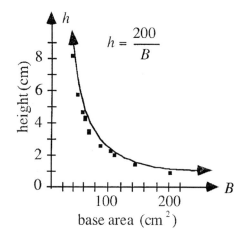

   d. Students should realize that the equation describes the exact relationship between base area and the height of the water. The scatterplot gives only an approximate relationship, since it is based on measurements. These measurements introduce error in the model.

   e. Because h represents height, its value must be a positive number. **Note:** In real-world interpretations of graphs, negative domain values frequently are excluded because they have no meaning.

3.2 a. $B = 200/h$

   b. 1. $B = 200/(2.5 \cdot 10^{-3}) = 80{,}000 \text{ cm}^2 = 8.0 \text{ m}^2$

      2. $d = 2\sqrt{8.0/\pi} \approx 3.2 \text{ m}$

* 3.3 a. $100 = Bh$ or $B = 100/h$

   b. Students may make the conversion as follows:

$$100 \text{ bbl} \cdot \frac{160 \text{ L}}{1 \text{ bbl}} \cdot \frac{1000 \text{ cm}^3}{1 \text{ L}} = 1.6 \cdot 10^7 \text{ cm}^3$$

   c. $B = (1.6 \cdot 10^7)/h$

   d. Students should substitute as follows:

$$B = \frac{1.6 \cdot 10^7 \text{ cm}^3}{2.5 \cdot 10^{-3} \text{ cm}} = 6.4 \cdot 10^9 \text{ cm}^2 = 0.64 \text{ km}^2$$

   e. $d = 2\sqrt{0.64/\pi} \approx 0.90 \text{ km}$

2. Identify each of the following situations as involving a direct proportion, an inverse proportion, or neither.

   a. the number of children at a party and the average amount each will receive from a piñata full of treats

   b. the number of people at a barbecue and the kilograms of hamburger needed

   c. the number of miles hiked and the number of calories expended

   d. the number of people in a family and the number of slices each receives from one pizza shared equally

   e. the number of raffle tickets sold and the probability of winning the grand prize.

Assignment

3.1 In the exploration, you poured 200 mL of water into containers with different base areas.

   a. Let B represent the base area of a container and h represent the height of water in the container. Write an equation that describes the relationship of B and h to 200 mL.

   b. Solve this equation for h.

   c. Graph the equation on the same set of axes as the scatterplot from Part **e** of the exploration.

   d. Which appears to be the better model of the experiment in the exploration—the scatterplot or the graph of the equation? Defend your choice.

   e. Why can there be no negative values for h?

3.2 **a.** Solve the equation you wrote in Problem **3.1a** for B.

   b. 1. Predict the area covered by an oil spill of 200 mL if it spreads to a thickness of $2.5 \cdot 10^{-3}$ cm.

      2. If the spill is circular, what is its diameter?

3.3 Consider a spill of 100 bbl of highly refined oil on a calm body of water.

   a. Write an equation that models this spill in terms of B, h, and 100 bbl.

   b. How many cubic centimeters of oil are there in 100 bbl? (There are approximately 160 L in 1 bbl; 1 cm³ contains 1 mL.)

   c. Rewrite your equation in Part **a** by replacing 100 bbl with its equivalent in cubic centimeters.

   d. Determine the area (in square kilometers) covered by a 100-bbl spill that spreads to a thickness of $2.5 \cdot 10^{-3}$ cm.

   e. If the spill is circular, what is its diameter?

3.4 **a.** Solve the following equation for y: $20 = x \cdot y$.

b. Choose at least five different values for x. Find the corresponding y-values and organize these results in a table.

c. As the values of x increase, what happens to the corresponding values of y? Is this consistent with what you observed in the exploration? Explain your response.

mathematics note

One quantity is **inversely proportional** to another when the product of the two quantities is constant. An inverse proportion can be described by an equation of the form $xy = k$, where k is the **constant of proportionality**. The equation of an inverse proportion can also be written in the form $y = k/x$.

For example, the inverse proportion $xy = 2$ can be written as $y = 2/x$. The graph of $y = 2/x$ is shown in Figure 7-5.

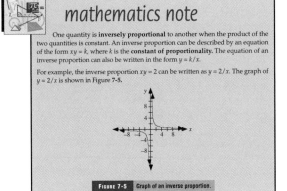

FIGURE 7-5 Graph of an inverse proportion.

3.5 **a.** Solve each of the following inverse proportions for y in terms of x and identify the constants of proportionality.

1. $x \cdot y = 20$ 2. $x \cdot y = 10$
3. $y \cdot x = 5$ 4. $0.5 = y \cdot x$

b. Using a graphing utility, graph the equations from Part **a** on the same set of axes, where $-10 \le x \le 10$. What appears to be true about each of the graphs?

c. 1. As the x-values approach 0, what happens to the corresponding y-values?

2. As the x-values increase from 100 to 1000 to 10,000, what happens to the corresponding y-values?

3.4 **a.** $y = 20/x$

b. Sample response:

x	y
2	10
4	5
5	4
20	1
40	0.5

c. As x increases, y decreases. As x decreases, y increases. This is consistent with the results from the exploration.

3.5 **a.** **1.** $y = 20/x$, $k = 20$
2. $y = 10/x$, $k = 10$
3. $y = 5/x$, $k = 5$
4. $y = 0.5/x$, $k = 0.5$

b. Sample response: Each graph is similar in shape and none pass through the origin.

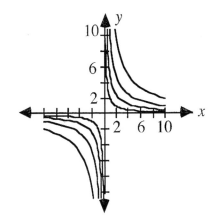

c. **1.** Sample response: If x is positive and close to 0, the y-values assume very large positive values. If x is negative and close to 0, the y-values assume very small negative values.

2. The y-values are positive and approach 0.

3. The *y*-values are negative and approach 0

d. Sample response: As the constant of proportionality decreases, the graph shifts toward the origin; as the constant increases the graph shifts away from the origin.

e. The constant of proportionality represents the volume of water.

3.6 a. Sample response: The graph of an inverse proportion is curved and does not contain the origin. The graph of a direct proportion is a line that passes through the origin.

b. Sample response: In an inverse proportion, the product of the two variables is constant. In a direct proportion, the quotient is constant.

3.7 a. Sample graph:

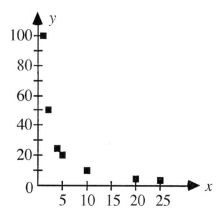

b. The *y*-values become small.

c. The *y*-values become large.

d. Sample response: This data represents an inverse proportion. The graph fits the pattern and the two variables multiplied together produce a constant.

e. $xy = 100$, $k = 100$

f. Sample response: I must travel 100 km. The chart of values represents my speed in kilometers per hour and the time in hours it takes to travel that distance.

3. As the *x*-values decrease from –100 to –1000 to –10,000, what happens to the corresponding *y*-values?

d. How does the constant of proportionality affect the graph?

e. What does the constant of proportionality represent in the equation you wrote in Problem **3.1**?

＊ ＊ ＊ ＊ ＊

3.6 a. Compare the shapes of the graphs of a direct proportion and an inverse proportion.

b. Compare the equations of a direct proportion and an inverse proportion.

3.7 Consider the set of ordered pairs shown in the following table.

x	y
1	100
2	50
4	25
5	20
10	10
20	5
25	4

a. Create a scatterplot of this data.

b. As the values of *x* become large, what happens to the values of *y*?

c. As the values of *x* become small, what happens to the values of *y*?

d. Is the relationship between *x* and *y* a direct proportion, an inverse proportion, or neither? Justify your conclusion.

e. Write an equation that describes this relationship and identify the constant of proportionality, if one exists.

f. Describe a real-world situation that might generate these ordered pairs.

3.8 At 0°C, 32.0 g of oxygen gas occupies a volume of 22.4 L with a pressure of 1.0 atmosphere (atm). As the volume is decreased at constant temperature, the pressure changes as shown in the following table.

Volume (L)	Pressure (atm)
22.4	1.00
17.1	1.31
11.2	2.00
5.60	4.00
2.24	10.0

a. Create a scatterplot of the data.

b. At constant temperature, are pressure and volume directly proportional or inversely proportional? Explain your response.

c. 1. Write an equation that describes the relationship and identify the constant of proportionality.

   2. Graph this equation on the same set of axes as the scatterplot from Part **a**.

d. Predict the pressure on 32.0 g of oxygen gas when the volume is 20.5 L.

3.9 Wavelength and frequency are two characteristics of waves. **Wavelength** is the distance between two consecutive peaks or troughs in a wave. **Frequency** is the number of wavelengths that pass a given point in a certain amount of time.

The standard unit of frequency is the **hertz (Hz)**. One hertz is equal to 1 cycle per second. For example, the diagram below shows a wave with a frequency of 4 cycles per second, or 4 Hz.

The table below shows the wavelengths and frequencies of some different forms of electromagnetic radiation.

Electromagnetic Radiation	Wavelength (m)	Frequency (Hz)
gamma rays	$1.0 \cdot 10^{-12}$	$3.0 \cdot 10^{20}$
X rays	$1.0 \cdot 10^{-10}$	$3.0 \cdot 10^{18}$
red light	$7.0 \cdot 10^{-7}$	$4.29 \cdot 10^{14}$
microwaves	$1.0 \cdot 10^{-2}$	$3.0 \cdot 10^{10}$
radio waves	$1.0 \cdot 10^{2}$	$3.0 \cdot 10^{6}$

a. Is the relationship between wavelength and frequency a direct proportion or an inverse proportion? Explain your response.

b. Write an equation that describes this relationship.

c. Identify the constant of proportionality.

d. Violet light has a wavelength of about $4.0 \cdot 10^{-7}$ m. Use your equation from Part **b** to determine the frequency of violet light.

3.8 **a.** See sample graph in Part **c** below.

b. Sample response: Pressure and volume are inversely proportional. When multiplied together, they produce a constant.

c. 1. $y = 22.4/x$, $k = 22.4$

   2. Sample graph:

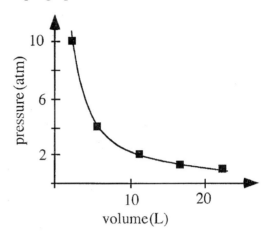

d. Students should substitute as follows:

$$y = 22.4/x$$
$$= 22.4/20.5$$
$$\approx 1.09 \text{ atm}$$

3.9 **a.** Sample response: The data is inversely proportional because as the wavelength increases, the frequency decreases.

b. $y = (3.0 \cdot 10^{8})/x$

c. The constant of proportionality is $3.0 \cdot 10^{8}$. **Note:** This is the speed of light in meters per second. The equation given in Part **b** is often written as $c = \lambda \cdot v$, where c represents the speed of light.

d. Students should substitute as follows:

$$y = \frac{3.0 \cdot 10^{8}}{4.0 \cdot 10^{-7}}$$

$$= 7.5 \cdot 10^{14} \text{ Hz}$$

teacher note

An additional assessment, for use at your discretion, appears in the Teacher Resources for this module.

Summary Assessment

1. To estimate the volume of oil spilled, students first must estimate the area covered by the slick. The mean radius of the slick in the diagram is about 2.8 cm. Using the given scale, this corresponds to an actual mean radius of 56 km. The area of the oil slick is approximately 9900 km².

   Using a cylinder to model the shape of the spill,

   $$V = Bh$$
   $$= 9900 \text{ km}^2 (2.5 \cdot 10^{-8} \text{ km})$$
   $$\approx 2.5 \cdot 10^{-4} \text{ km}^3$$

   Students may convert this value to gallons as follows:

   $$(2.5 \cdot 10^{-4} \text{ km}^3)\left(\frac{1 \cdot 10^{15} \text{ cm}^3}{1 \text{ km}^3}\right)\left(\frac{1 \text{ mL}}{1 \text{ cm}^3}\right)\left(\frac{1 \text{ L}}{1000 \text{ mL}}\right)\left(\frac{1 \text{ gal}}{3.8 \text{ L}}\right)$$
   $$= 6.6 \cdot 10^7 \text{ gal}$$

   Note: This is close to the volume of oil spilled in the 1978 grounding of the *Amoco Cadiz* off the coast of France.

2. **a.** Sample table:

Area of Slick (km²)	Volume of Spill (gal)
5000	33,000,000
7500	50,000,000
10,000	67,000,000
25,000	170,000,000

   b. The volume of the slick is directly proportional to the area. Sample graph:

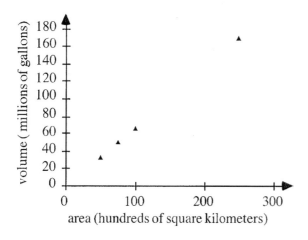

---

1. The diagram below shows the shape of an oil slick that spread to a thickness of 2.5 • 10⁻³ cm.

20 km

   Estimate the volume of oil in the spill in gallons.

2. a. Assuming that the spilled oil spreads to a thickness of 2.5 • 10⁻³, complete the following table.

Area of Slick (km²)	Volume of Spill (gal)
5000	
7500	
10,000	
25,000	

   b. Determine the type of relationship formed by the data collected in the table. Create a graph that displays this relationship.

   c. Find an equation that models the graph from Part **b**.

   d. Use this equation to predict the number of gallons of oil that would create a slick of 71,000 km².

---

c. One equation that fits the data is $y = 6700x$, where y represents volume in gallons and x represents area in square kilometers.

d. Using the equation from Part **c**:

$$y = 6700x$$
$$= 6700(71{,}000 \text{ km}^2)$$
$$\approx 4.8 \cdot 10^8 \text{ gal}$$

3. Assuming constant pressure, the time required to fill an oil tank is inversely proportional to the square of the diameter of the hose used to fill it. The table below shows the diameters of four hoses and the corresponding times to fill the tank.

Diameter (cm)	Square of Diameter	Time (min)
2		36
3		16
4		9
6		4

a. Complete the column for the squares of the diameters.

b. Create a scatterplot of the time versus the square of the diameter.

c. Find an equation that represents this inverse proportion.

d. Predict how long it would take to fill the tank using a hose with a diameter of 10 cm.

e. Predict the diameter of a pipe that could fill the tank in 30 min.

Module 7 ■ *Oil: Black Gold*   171

3. **a.** A completed table is shown below.

Diameter (cm)	Square of Diameter	Time (min)
2	4	36
3	9	16
4	16	9
6	36	4

b. Sample graph:

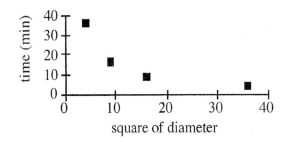

c. One possible equation is $x \bullet y = 144$, where y represents the time in minutes and x represents the square of the diameter of the pipe.

d. Students should substitute as follows:

$$10^2 \bullet y = 144$$
$$100 \bullet y = 144$$
$$y = 1.44 \text{ min}$$

e. Students should substitute as follows:

$$x \bullet 30 = 144$$
$$x = 144/30$$
$$x = 4.8$$

Because x represents the square of the diameter, $d = \sqrt{4.8} \approx 2.2$ cm. **Note:** Time is inversely proportional to the area of the base, which is itself directly proportional to the square of the diameter.

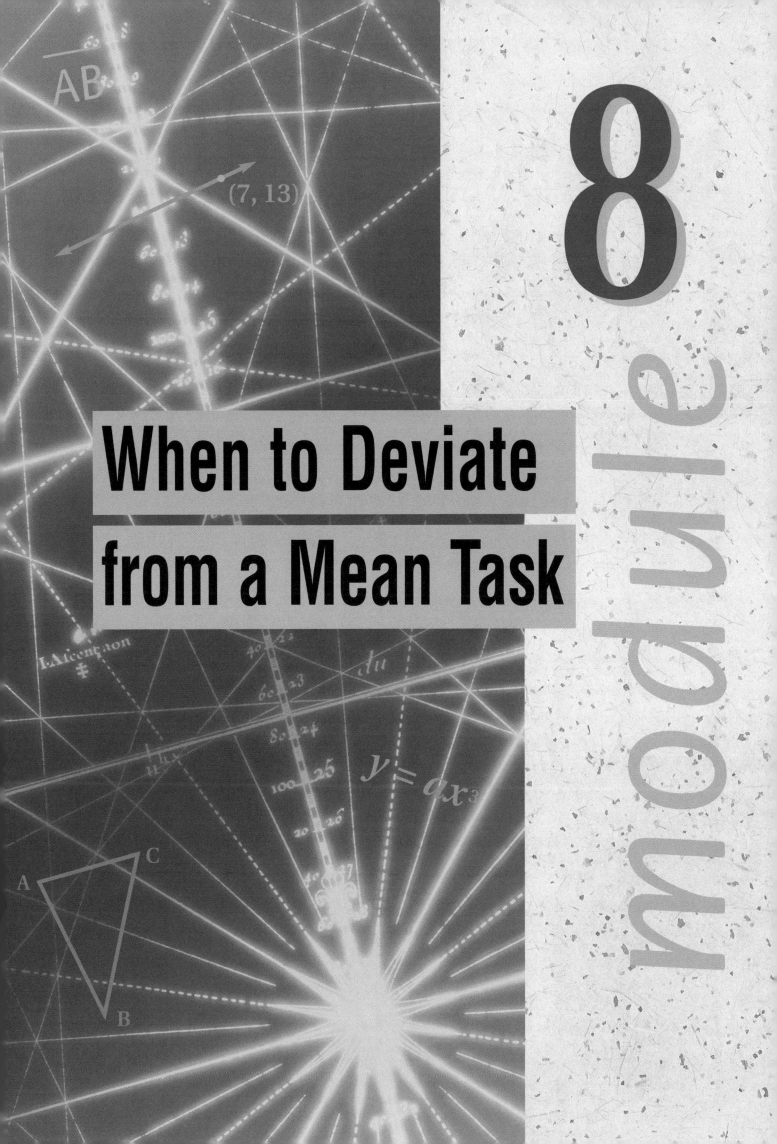

When to Deviate from a Mean Task

8

module

Overview

This module examines the statistics of a single variable. Students review and extend their knowledge of frequency tables, histograms, pie charts, stem-and-leaf plots, box-and-whisker plots, and measures of central tendency (mean, median, mode). Mean absolute deviation and standard deviation are introduced as measures of spread. Several problems address the potential use of statistics to mislead consumers.

Activity 1:	Students review frequency tables, histograms, and pie charts (circle graphs).
Activity 2:	Students review stem-and-leaf plots, range, and measures of central tendency.
Activity 3:	Students determine quartiles and create box-and-whisker plots.
Activity 4:	Students determine mean absolute deviation and use this measure of spread to interpret and analyze data.
Activity 5:	Students determine standard deviation and compare it to mean absolute deviation. They use standard deviation as a measure of spread to interpret and analyze data.

Objectives

In this module, students will:

* interpret data displayed in pie charts (1)
* create a frequency table from raw data (1, 2)
* interpret data displayed in histograms (1, 2, 4)
* interpret data displayed in stem-and-leaf plots (2, 3)
* find measures of central tendency (2, 3, 4, 5)
* interpret data displayed in box-and-whisker plots (3)
* determine mean absolute deviation (4, 5)
* determine standard deviation (5).

Prerequisites

For this module, students should know:

* how to find the mean, median, and mode of a data set
* how to create histograms
* how to divide a circle into sectors representing given percentages
* how to create stem-and-leaf plots
* how to determine upper and lower quartiles
* how to determine absolute value.

 Flashbacks, for use at your discretion, appear in the Teacher Resources for this module. These brief problem sets provide a review of some prerequisite skills for each activity.

Planning Guide

Activity	Materials	Technology	Time Line
Activity **1**	▪ none	▪ spreadsheet ▪ graphing utility	2 days
Activity **2**	▪ stopwatches ▪ sample heart rate data (optional)	▪ graphing utility	2 days
Activity **3**	▪ metric rulers	▪ graphing utility	2 days
Activity **4**	▪ none	▪ spreadsheet ▪ graphing utility	3 days
Activity **5**	▪ none	▪ spreadsheet	2 days
Assessment Activities	▪ none	▪ none	3 days **Total: 14 days**

teacher note

A blackline master for the sample heart rate data appears in the Teacher Resources for this module.

Introduction

The context for much of this module is the analysis and interpretation of statistics gathered by a high school yearbook staff.

This activity reviews frequency tables, histograms, and pie charts (circle graphs).

teacher note

Some graphing utilities might not allow users to graph histograms with non-integer data entries.

Materials List

- none

Technology

- graphing utility (capable of creating histograms)
- spreadsheet

Student Outcomes

After completing the following exploration and discussion, students should be able to:

✳ create a frequency table

✳ create and interpret histograms

✳ create and interpret pie charts.

Exploration

In this exploration, students create and interpret several histograms using the same set of data. They should begin to recognize some of the payoffs and pitfalls associated with displaying statistical information in graphical form.

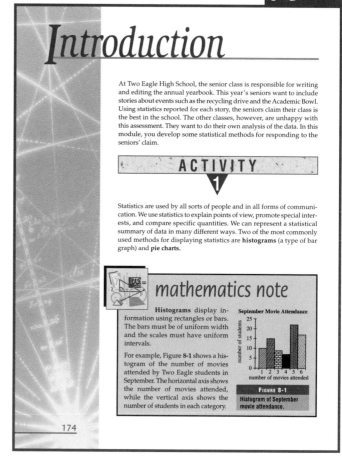

Introduction

At Two Eagle High School, the senior class is responsible for writing and editing the annual yearbook. This year's seniors want to include stories about events such as the recycling drive and the Academic Bowl. Using statistics reported for each story, the seniors claim their class is the best in the school. The other classes, however, are unhappy with this assessment. They want to do their own analysis of the data. In this module, you develop some statistical methods for responding to the seniors' claim.

ACTIVITY 1

Statistics are used by all sorts of people and in all forms of communication. We use statistics to explain points of view, promote special interests, and compare specific quantities. We can represent a statistical summary of data in many different ways. Two of the most commonly used methods for displaying statistics are **histograms** (a type of bar graph) and **pie charts.**

mathematics note

Histograms display information using rectangles or bars. The bars must be of uniform width and the scales must have uniform intervals.

For example, Figure **8-1** shows a histogram of the number of movies attended by Two Eagle students in September. The horizontal axis shows the number of movies attended, while the vertical axis shows the number of students in each category.

FIGURE 8-1
Histogram of September movie attendance.

174

Exploration

The seniors on the Two Eagle yearbook staff want to include the first semester honor roll in their annual publication. They chose the graph shown in Figure **8-2** to display their statistics.

FIGURE 8-2 A histogram of the first semester honor roll.

Notice the break in the vertical axis. In this case, the break indicates that the numbers from 0 to 19 are not shown on the graph.

In some cases, the type of information shown in Figure **8-2** can be interpreted more easily when displayed in a different form. One option is a **frequency table.**

mathematics note

A **frequency table** consists of two columns. One column contains a data item; the other displays the number of observed occurrences of that item. The number of occurrences of any particular data item is its **frequency.**

For example, the histogram in Figure **8-1** was generated from the frequency table shown in Figure **8-3**. This table summarizes the results of a survey of 80 students.

Number of Movies	Frequency
1	10
2	15
3	9
4	7
5	22
6	17
Total	80

FIGURE 8-3
Frequency table for September movie attendance.

a. Use the data presented in Figure 8-2 to create the corresponding frequency table.

b. Use your frequency table from Part **a** to create a histogram with a vertical axis that begins at 0 and ends at 30, without a break. Compare this new graph with the original in Figure **8-2. Note:** Save your frequency table and histogram for use later in this module.

c. Two Eagle High has a total of 104 freshmen, 81 sophomores, 110 juniors, and 128 seniors. Create another histogram to show the percentage of honor-roll students in each class. Compare this histogram with the one shown in Figure **8-2.**

Discussion

a. How accurately does the graph in Figure **8-2** portray the number of students from each class on the honor roll?

b. Compare your graphs from Parts **b** and **c** of the exploration. Which graph do you prefer? Explain your response.

c. How could the statistics encountered in the exploration be used to favor a particular class?

mathematics note

Pie charts (or circle graphs) consist of circular regions divided into sectors, each representing a percentage of the whole. For example, the pie chart in Figure 8-4 illustrates the same data as the histogram in Figure 8-1.

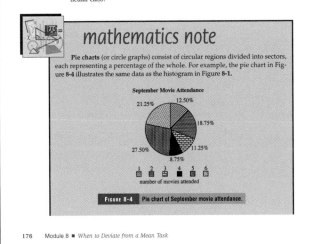

September Movie Attendance

21.25% 12.50%
18.75%
27.50% 11.25%
8.75%

number of movies attended
1 2 3 4 5 6

FIGURE 8-4 Pie chart of September movie attendance.

a. Sample frequency table:

Class	Students on Honor Roll
Freshman	21
Sophomore	20
Junior	24
Senior	29
Total	94

b. Students should recognize that the break in the vertical axis can visually exaggerate the difference between the number of seniors on the honor roll and the numbers from the other three classes. In the sample graph below, the differences among the classes are less prominent visually than in the original.

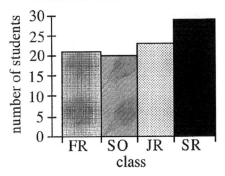

First Semester Honor Roll

c. The sample histogram below shows that the sophomore class had a larger percentage of its students on the honor roll than the seniors.

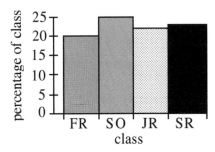

First Semester Honor Roll

Discussion

a. Sample response: The graph is visually misleading because of the break in the vertical axis. This makes the differences among classes appear more substantial than they actually are.

b. Students might argue that the graph that displays percentages is better because it allows a direct comparison among classes. However, the histogram from Part **b** indicates exactly how many students from each class are on the honor roll, and the percentage histogram does not.

c. Figure **8-2** suggests that the seniors had the best representation on the honor roll. The graph created in Part **b** of the exploration supports this same view but in a less exaggerated manner. The graph from Part **c** suggests that the sophomores had the best representation on the honor roll. The visual impact of that graph could be increased by adjusting the vertical axis as in Figure **8-2.**

d. Sample response: Round 27.50% down to 27% and round the other percentages to the nearest whole number.

Warm-Up

1. **a.** Sample frequency table.

Roll	Frequency
one	13
two	16
three	18
four	12
five	20
six	15

b. Sample histogram:

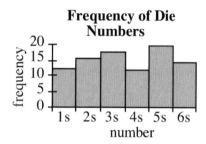

Frequency of Die Numbers

c. The following table shows the approximate angle measures.

Roll	Frequency	Central Angle
one	13	50°
two	16	61°
three	18	69°
four	12	46°
five	20	77°
six	15	57°

Assignment

Problems suitable for use as assessment items are identified by an asterisk (*).

* **1.1 a.** Sample graph:

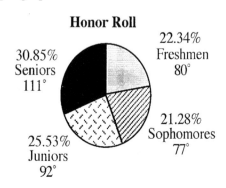

Honor Roll

22.34% Freshmen 80°

30.85% Seniors 111°

21.28% Sophomores 77°

25.53% Juniors 92°

As with the corresponding histogram, you can generate the pie chart in Figure 8-4 using a frequency table. Determine the percentages by dividing each frequency by the total. Then, to determine the measure of the central angle that should represent each frequency, multiply these percentages by 360°.

For example, 10 students attended 1 movie in September. This represents 10/80 or 12.5% of the total. The measure of the central angle for the corresponding sector of the circle is 0.125 • 360° = 45°.

d. The sum of the percentages in the pie chart in Figure **8-4** is 100%. How could you round each percentage to the nearest whole number, while maintaining a sum of 100%?

Warm-Up

1. The students in Mrs. Davis' math class rolled a die a total of 94 times with the following results: 13 ones, 16 twos, 18 threes, 12 fours, 20 fives, and 15 sixes.

   a. Create a frequency table to organize the data.

   b. Draw a histogram for the given information.

   c. Find the degrees of the central angle of each sector if this information were graphed in a pie chart.

Assignment

1.1 **a.** Use the frequency table from Part **a** of the exploration to construct a pie chart.

   b. Compare the pie chart to the histogram in Figure **8-2**. What advantages or disadvantages do you observe with the pie chart?

   c. If the number of students in the sophomore class doubled, while the number of sophomores on the honor roll remained the same, would you need to adjust your pie chart? Explain your response.

   d. Upon seeing your pie chart, one student commented, "The seniors had the largest percentage of their class on the honor roll." Explain why this is a misinterpretation of the pie chart.

b. Sample response: The pie chart presents a more accurate picture of the comparison of classes. It does not exaggerate the number of seniors on the honor roll compared to the number of underclassmen.

Visually, it might be more difficult to compare categories with close percentage values on a pie chart. Also, a pie chart is more difficult to construct than a histogram because it involves calculating percentages and measuring the number of degrees in a sector.

c. No. The pie chart represents only the students who made the honor roll. The percentages are calculated with the number of students from each class who made the honor roll divided by the total number who made the honor roll. The number of sophomores on the honor roll is unchanged, so this percentage remains constant.

d. The pie chart indicates that 31.18% of the students on the honor roll are seniors. This does not mean that 31.18% of all seniors made the honor roll.

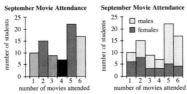

1.2 To display additional information on the same graph, a histogram can be "stacked." Both histograms below were created using information from the same survey.

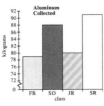

September Movie Attendance

September Movie Attendance
☐ males
■ females

a. Use the stacked histogram on the right to make an interpretation of the data that was not possible with the histogram on the left.

b. Explain why it might be difficult to use the stacked histogram to compare the numbers of male students in each attendance category.

1.3 Your frequency table from Part a of the exploration describes the number of students from each class on the first semester honor roll. Two Eagle High has a total of 104 freshmen, 81 sophomores, 110 juniors, and 128 seniors.

a. Create a stacked histogram that displays both these sets of information.

b. Using your stacked histogram, can you identify the class with the largest number of students on the first semester honor roll? Explain your response.

c. Using your stacked histogram, can you identify the class with the greatest percentage of students on the first semester honor roll? Explain your response.

1.4 The following graph summarizes the results of Two Eagle High's recycling drive. The yearbook staff plans to use this graph to show that the seniors collected more aluminum than any other class.

Aluminum Collected

---

b. In the sample graph, a reader can compare the heights of the lower bars to determine the class with the largest number on the honor roll. This would not be as simple if the honor roll bars were displayed on the top.

c. Although the percentages could be calculated, these values are not immediately evident from the sample graph.

* 1.4 a. Sample response: Redraw the vertical axis to include a complete scale from 0 to 92.

b. The sample histogram below shows the kilograms of aluminum collected per student (by class). By this measure, the sophomores appear more productive than the seniors.

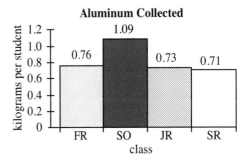

Aluminum Collected

1.5 a. 1. The following histogram shows that more females (21) were inducted into the Honor Society than males (18).

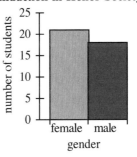

Induction in Honor Society

2. The following histogram shows that 45% of male applicants to the honor society were successful, while only 42% of female applicants were successful.

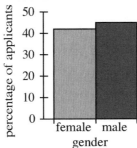

Induction in Honor Society

1.2 a. Answers will vary. Students might observe that the majority of the students surveyed were male, or that males had a greater tendency to attend more than 4 movies in September.

b. Sample response: It is not easy to compare the males because they do not have a common base line. The heights of the bars for the males takes time to calculate.

1.3 a. Sample graph:

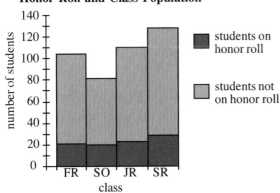

Honor Roll and Class Population

students on honor roll

students not on honor roll

3. The following histogram shows that more seniors (22) were inducted than juniors (17).

Induction in Honor Society

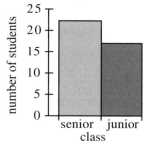

4. The following histogram shows that almost 57% of junior applicants to the honor society were successful, while only about 37% of the senior applicants were successful.

Induction in Honor Society

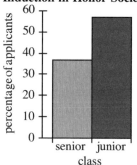

b. Sample response: Yes. Using only the statistics in the table, it is possible to create graphs that argue for or against each statement in Part **a**.

* * * * *

1.6 **a. 1.** Sample pie chart:

Comparative Land Areas of Four States

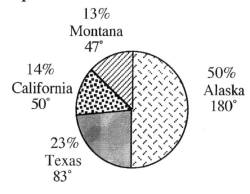

2. Judging from the pie chart, Texas is almost twice as big as California, Alaska is nearly four times as big as California, while California and Montana are about the same size.

a. How could you change the histogram to represent the freshman class more positively?

b. Two Eagle High has a total of 104 freshmen, 81 sophomores, 110 juniors, and 128 seniors. Using this information, create a graph which shows that a class other than the seniors was most effective in collecting aluminum for the recycling drive.

1.5 The numbers of males and females inducted in the Two Eagle High School Honor Society are displayed in the table below.

Class	Gender	No. of Applicants	No. Inducted
Junior	male	20	12
	female	10	5
Senior	male	20	6
	female	40	16

a. Using the data in this table, create a graph to support each of the following statements.

1. The females at Two Eagle High are better students than the males.

2. The males at Two Eagle High are better students than the females.

3. The honor society's selection process favored seniors.

4. The honor society's selection process favored juniors.

b. Do you think it is possible to use accurate statistics to support an inaccurate or deceptive position? Explain your response.

* * * * *

1.6 The following table shows the land area and 2003 population for Alaska, Texas, California, and Montana.

State	Land Area (km²)	2003 Population
Alaska	1,477,267	648,818
California	403,970	35,484,453
Montana	376,991	917,621
Texas	678,358	22,118,509

a. 1. Create a pie chart of the information on land area.

2. Use your chart to compare the areas of each of the following pairs of states: Alaska and Texas; Alaska and California; Alaska and Montana.

Module 8 ■ When to Deviate from a Mean Task 179

b. 1. Sample pie chart:

Comparative Populations of Four States

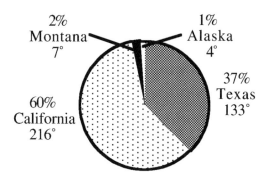

2. Sample response: Judging from the chart, the population of California is about 1.5 times larger than that of Texas. Visually, it is difficult to make this type of comparison with Montana or Alaska.

b. 1. Create a pie chart of the information on population.

2. Use this chart to compare the populations of each of the following pairs of states: California and Texas; California and Alaska; California and Montana.

1.7 The following table shows the land area and 2003 population of the five most densely populated states.

State	Land Area (km²)	2003 Population
Connecticut	12,550	3,483,372
Maryland	25,316	5,508,909
Massachusetts	20,300	6,433,422
New Jersey	19,215	8,638,396
Rhode Island	2,706	1,076,164

a. Jody claims that Rhode Island has the most people per square kilometer because it has the smallest area. Is her claim correct? Explain your response.

b. Use a histogram to compare the population densities of the five states.

1.8 Use each of the following types of graphs to emphasize a characteristic of your state.

a. a pie chart

b. a histogram.

Research Project

Design and write a survey on a topic of interest to your school. The survey should consist of no more than 10 carefully worded questions.

Give the survey to 30 people in your school.

After completing Activities **1–4** of this module, analyze the collected data using appropriate graphs and statistical measurements.

Prepare an oral presentation that describes the conclusions you drew from the results of the survey.

ACTIVITY 2

When researchers report statistical information, they often represent the elements of an entire data set with a single number. For example, instead of listing the size

1.8 Answers will vary. Students create histograms and pie charts that emphasize a characteristic of their home states.

Research Project

Students design surveys of no more than 10 questions to be administered to 30 people. You might wish to ask students to plan the survey and select questions as a class. Questions should provoke answers that lend themselves to statistical analysis—including histograms, pie charts, stem-and-leaf plots, box-and-whisker plots, and mean absolute deviation.

ACTIVITY 2

Students review stem-and-leaf plots, range, and the measures of central tendency.

In the assignment, they examine situations in which measures of central tendency alone do not allow conclusive analysis of data.

Materials List

■ stopwatch (or other timepiece that displays seconds; one per group)

■ sample heart rate data (optional)

Technology

■ graphing utility

teacher note

The mode is the item that occurs most frequently in a data set. If no item occurs more than once, then the mode does not exist. If two items have the same, highest frequency, then the data set is bimodal. If three items share the highest frequency, the set is trimodal.

1.7 a. Jody's claim is not correct. The population densities for each state are shown in the following table. Rhode Island's population density is the second highest, after New Jersey.

State	Population Density (people/km²)
Connecticut	278
Maryland	218
Massachusetts	317
New Jersey	450
Rhode Island	398

b. Sample histogram:

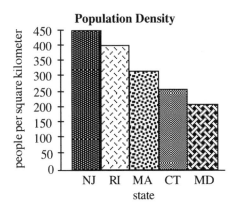

Population Density

Student Outcomes

After completing the following exploration, discussion, and assignment, students should be able to:

✳ find and interpret measures of central tendency (mean, median, and mode)

✳ gather and organize data

✳ create and interpret stem-and-leaf plots

✳ identify the range of a data set.

Exploration

 Note: If you do not wish to have students collect their own data, some sample data appears in the Teacher Resources for this module.

a–c. Students measure and record their own pulse rates three times during this exploration: while at rest, immediately after exercise, and after two minutes of recovery. For the second pulse reading, running in place for one minute is sufficient. Good results are obtained if students check the pulse in the neck area, count the rate for 15 sec, then multiply by 4.

d. Students should save all data for the assignment. For comparison, you might wish to ask students to separate data for males and females. The table below shows some sample data for 10 students.

e. Students should select a representative number for each of the three pulse rates taken.

of each class in your school, you might give the school's mean class size. In this case, the mean (or average) class size is a single statistic "representing" all class sizes. Statistics such as the mean, median, and mode are **measures of central tendency.**

Exploration

The Two Eagle High Physical Education Department administers a fitness test before allowing students to participate in sports. This test includes a check of the student's resting and active pulse rates. In this exploration, you collect and analyze data on pulse rates for three levels of activity.

a. After sitting quietly for a period of five minutes, measure and record your pulse rate (beats per minute).

b. Exercise for one minute. Immediately after exercising, measure and record your pulse rate again.

c. Rest from your exercise for two minutes. Measure and record your pulse rate one more time.

d. Organize the class data in a table. **Note:** Save this table for use in the assignment.

e. For each level of activity, determine a representative pulse rate for the class using a measure of central tendency.

Discussion

a. What were the representative pulse rates for your class? How did you choose these numbers?

b. How did changing the level of activity affect the representative pulse rate?

c. In discussing an individual's pulse rate, what additional information might be important?

d. Do you think that your class statistics are representative of the entire student body?

Warm-Up

1. Find the mean of each of the following sets of numbers.

   a. 7, 3, 5, 5, 4, 6

   b. 23, 53, 45, 17

   c. 9.3, 2.6, 4.4, 8.1, 5.9

Heart Rate (beats per minute)			
Student	**At Rest**	**Immediately After Exercise**	**Two Minutes After Exercise**
A	72	116	84
B	68	120	92
C	76	112	88
D	80	124	96
E	72	112	88
F	64	116	84
G	68	112	80
H	76	128	92
I	84	120	100
J	72	112	88
Mean	73.2	117.2	89.2
Median	72	116	88
Mode	72	112	88

2. Find the median of each set of numbers below.

   a. 4, 7, 9, 2, 2, 3, 5, 1

   b. 13.1, 15.2, 14.6, 13.35, 15.5, 14.16, 14.32, 15.07, 13.05

   c. 35, 72, 69, 44, 29, 14, 16, 83, 67, 88

3. Find the mode of each of the following sets.

   a. 1, 5, 3, 2, 3, 4, 5, 6, 5

   b. 68, 84, 75, 84, 95, 76, 75, 82, 97

   c. 4.3, 5.7, 6.2, 4.7, 5.5, 6.7, 5.2, 6.5

Assignment

2.1 The following table shows the number of siblings reported by nine students at Two Eagle High School.

Student	Number of Siblings
A	1
B	0
C	2
D	2
E	0
F	3
G	2
H	6
I	1

   a. Which measure of central tendency best represents the number of siblings per student? Justify your choice.

   b. Create a frequency table of this data. For example, because students B and E each have 0 siblings, the frequency for 0 siblings is 2.

   c. Use your frequency table to create the corresponding histogram. Represent the number of siblings on the horizontal axis and the frequency on the vertical axis.

2.2 Often we use measures of central tendency to describe an entire set of data. But in situations involving small data sets, measures of central tendency can be misleading.

   a. Identify four people in your community with different occupations. Make a table that displays each person's occupation and estimated annual income. Determine the mean, median, and mode of the income data.

182   Module 8 ■ *When to Deviate from a Mean Task*

3. **a.** 5

   b. 75 and 84

   c. This set has no mode.

Assignment

Problems suitable for use as assessment items are identified by an asterisk (*).

2.1 **a.** Sample response: Either the median or mode of 2 would serve as a good representation of the number of siblings because it is a whole number. The mean of approximately 1.89 is not the best because you cannot have a part of a person.

   b. Sample frequency table:

Number of Siblings	Frequency
0	2
1	2
2	3
3	1
4	0
5	0
6	1

   c. Sample histogram:

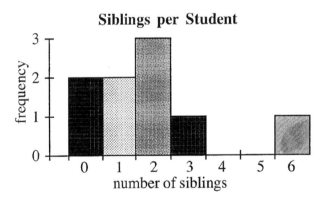

Siblings per Student

* 2.2 **a.** Sample table:

Occupation	Estimated Salary
teacher	$25,000
superintendent	$50,000
nurse	$25,000
custodian	$16,000
Mean	$29,000
Median	$25,000
Mode	$25,000

Discussion

a. Students are likely to select the mean as a representative number for the class. Typical means will range from 70–80 beats/min for resting pulses, 115–125 beats/min for active pulses, and 85–95 beats/min for pulse rates after a two-minute rest.

b. Sample response: The resting pulse rates produced the lowest mean. Exercise increased the mean. A two-minute rest lowered the mean but did not return it to the original resting rate.

c. Height, weight, age, and general health often influence pulse rate.

d. The class statistics are not likely to be representative of the entire school. During the teen years, pulse rates tend to decline with age. Seniors would be expected to have lower pulse rates than sophomores.

   Students may also discuss whether or not their class is a representative sample of the entire student body in terms of physical fitness or male/female ratio.

Warm-Up

1. **a.** 5

   b. 34.5

   c. 6.06

2. **a.** 3.5

   b. 14.32

   c. 55.5

b. Sample table:

Occupation	Estimated Salary
teacher	$25,000
superintendent	$50,000
nurse	$25,000
custodian	$16,000
baseball player	$6,000,000
Mean	$1,223,200
Median	$25,000
Mode	$25,000

c. Sample response: The mean is a good representative number for the salaries in Part **a** because they are all relatively close in value.

d. Sample response: The mean is not a good representative number for the incomes in the new group. It is distorted by the large difference in the baseball player's salary relative to the others.

e. When some data items differ from the majority of the data by a large amount, the mean is most affected. In these situations, the median might be a better representative (although it still may not be a good one). In the sample data given above, the mean is greatly affected, while the median and mode are not affected at all.

2.3 If no element occurs more than once in a data set, then the mode does not exist.

2.4 Answers will vary. Some students may mention that the mode may not be representative for sets with multiple occurrences of very high or very low numbers. Neither the mean, the median, nor the mode is necessarily representative when large differences exist within a data set. Measures of central tendency tend to be most useful when the values in a data set are closely grouped.

b. Add the occupation and estimated annual income of a professional athlete to your table. Determine the mean, median, and mode of the income data for this new group.

c. Does the mean income you calculated in Part **a** accurately represent the incomes of the original group? Explain your response.

d. Does the mean income you calculated in Part **b** accurately represent the incomes of the new group? Explain your response.

e. Which of the three measures of central tendency—mean, median, or mode—is most affected by data values very different from the majority of values? Which of the three measures of central tendency is affected the least?

2.3 Describe a set of data in which the mode does not exist.

2.4 Describe some possible pitfalls associated with using a measure of central tendency to describe a set of data.

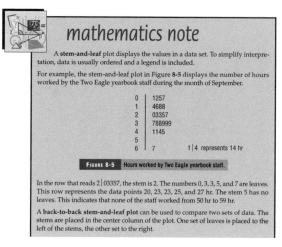

mathematics note

A **stem-and-leaf** plot displays the values in a data set. To simplify interpretation, data is usually ordered and a legend is included.

For example, the stem-and-leaf plot in Figure 8-5 displays the number of hours worked by the Two Eagle yearbook staff during the month of September.

```
0 | 1257
1 | 4688
2 | 03357
3 | 788999
4 | 1145
5 |
6 | 7          1|4 represents 14 hr
```

FIGURE 8-5 Hours worked by Two Eagle yearbook staff.

In the row that reads 2|03357, the stem is 2. The numbers 0, 3, 3, 5, and 7 are leaves. This row represents the data points 20, 23, 23, 25, and 27 hr. The stem 5 has no leaves. This indicates that none of the staff worked from 50 hr to 59 hr.

A **back-to-back stem-and-leaf plot** can be used to compare two sets of data. The stems are placed in the center column of the plot. One set of leaves is placed to the left of the stems, the other set to the right.

For example, the back-to-back stem-and-leaf plot in Figure 8-6 displays the same information on work hours as Figure 8-5. It also shows how those hours were distributed between the boys and the girls.

Girls		Boys
52	0	17
84	1	68
53	2	037
997	3	889
5	4	114
	5	
7	6	

4 | 1 | 6 represents 16 hr for boys and 14 hr for girls

FIGURE 8-6 Hours worked by girls and boys on the yearbook staff.

2.5 The **range** of a data set is the difference between the greatest data value and the least data value. The range provides one indication of how widely the data varies.

a. Determine the range of the data in Figure 8-5.

b. Can the range of a set of data be negative? Explain your response.

2.6 The heights in centimeters of 10 students at Two Eagle High are listed below. The heights of females are underlined.

153, 157, 163, 165, 166, 169, 170, 173, 176, 185

a. Determine the mean, median, and mode of the data.

b. Construct a stem-and-leaf plot of the data, using the first two digits of the heights as the stems and the last digits as the leaves.

c. Find the range of heights.

d. Create a histogram of the data using the following intervals for heights in centimeters: [150, 159], [160, 169], [170, 179], and [180, 189].

e. Separate the data into two categories: heights of female students and heights of male students. Use the data to make a back-to-back stem-and-leaf plot.

f. Use the back-to-back stem-and-leaf plot to create a stacked histogram.

2.5 a. The range is 66 hr.

 b. The range is the difference between the greatest data value and the least data value; therefore it cannot be negative.

* 2.6 a. The mean is 167.7 cm; the median is 167.5 cm. There is no mode.

 b. Sample stem-and-leaf plot:

 Heights of Students

 15 | 3 7
 16 | 3 5 6 9
 17 | 0 3 6
 18 | 5   15 | 3 represents 153 cm

 c. The range of heights is 185 – 153 = 32 cm.

 d. Sample histogram:

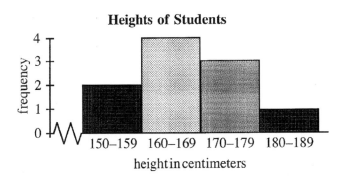

Heights of Students

 e. Sample back-to-back stem-and-leaf plot:

 Heights of Students

 female   male
      3 | 15 | 7
    9 5 | 16 | 3 6
    6 3 | 17 | 0
         | 18 | 5   5 | 16 | 3 represents 163 cm for male
                                     and 165 cm for female

 f. Sample stacked histogram:

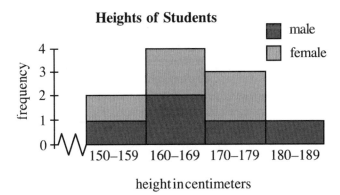

Heights of Students

male
female

2.7 a. Sample response: No. The advertiser could have driven 1000 new cars 1000 miles each. Most new cars do not break down during the first 1000 miles.

b. Sample response: Knowing the mean or median number of miles driven by each test car would provide a better measure of reliability.

2.8 a. Answers will vary. Students might claim that their class is in good, average, or poor physical condition.

b. Some possible weaknesses may include small sample size, lack of a truly random sample, unreliable measurements, or lack of knowledge about the connection between pulse rate and overall health.

✳ ✳ ✳ ✳ ✳

2.9 a. The tables at the bottom of the page show the mean and median for land area, 1990 population, and population density (in people per square kilometer) for the New England states and Mountain states.

b. Answers will vary. Students should use the data to support their preferences.

2.7 Advertisers often omit important information in their sales pitches. One advertisement in the Two Eagle yearbook claims that "after more than a million miles of testing, our automobiles had a repair-free record."

a. Does the "repair-free" statistic alone convince you that the cars are reliable? Describe one way in which a "million miles of testing" could fail to prove reliability.

b. To convince you that the cars are reliable, which measure of central tendency should the advertisement mention?

✳ ✳ ✳ ✳ ✳

2.9 a. Use measures of central tendency to compare the New England states with the Mountain states.

	State	Land Area (km²)	1990 Population
New England States	Connecticut	12,550	3,287,116
	Maine	79,939	1,227,928
	Massachusetts	20,300	6,016,425
	New Hampshire	23,231	1,109,252
	Rhode Island	2,706	1,003,464
	Vermont	23,956	562,758
Mountain States	Arizona	296,400	3,665,228
	Colorado	268,660	3,294,394
	Idaho	214,235	1,006,749
	Montana	376,991	799,065
	Nevada	284,397	1,201,833
	New Mexico	314,334	1,515,069
	Utah	212,816	1,722,850
	Wyoming	251,501	453,588

b. Would you rather live in the New England states or the Mountain states? Use the statistics from Part **a** to support your choice.

Module 8 ■ *When to Deviate from a Mean Task*   185

New England States			
	Area (km²)	**1990 Census**	**Population Density**
Mean	27,114	2,201,157	169
Median	21,766	1,168,590	155

Mountain States			
	Area (km²)	**1990 Census**	**Population Density**
Mean	277,417	1,707,347	6
Median	276,529	1,358,451	5

2.10 a. Create a back-to-back stem-and-leaf plot to represent the land areas of the states in the following two regions. (You might want to round these values before creating your stem-and-leaf plot.)

	State	Land Area (km²)
	Alabama	131,443
	Florida	139,852
	Georgia	150,010
Region 1	Mississippi	121,506
	North Carolina	126,180
	South Carolina	77,988
	Tennessee	106,759
	Illinois	143,987
	Indiana	92,904
Region 2	Iowa	144,716
	Michigan	147,136
	Ohio	106,067
	Wisconsin	140,673

b. Compare the land areas for the two regions.

ACTIVITY 3

To help identify potential athletes, the Athletic Department would like a profile of all Two Eagle High students. Larger hands give basketball or volleyball players an advantage, so the coaches of those two teams are especially interested in student hand spans. A hand span is the distance from the end of the thumb to the end of the little finger when the two are stretched as far apart as possible.

Exploration

The hand spans, in centimeters, of 22 sophomores at Two Eagle High School are listed below (hand spans of females are underlined): 15.4, 23.4, 19.9, <u>14.8</u>, 17.6, <u>19.3</u>, 20.7, 22.3, <u>20.0</u>, <u>16.4</u>, 18.1, <u>19.6</u>, <u>21.9</u>, 24.1, <u>17.5</u>, 23.9, 25.2, <u>18.5</u>, 24.1, <u>17.6</u>, <u>15.8</u>, 23.4.

186   Module 8 ■ *When to Deviate from a Mean Task*

2.10 a. In the following stem-and-leaf plot, land areas are rounded to the nearest 1000 km².

State Land Area in 1000 km²

Region 1		Region 2
8	7	
	8	
	9	3
7	10	6
	11	
62	12	
1	13	
0	14	14578
0	15	

$7|10|6$ represents 106,000 km² and 107,000 km²

b. Sample response: The land areas in Region 1 tend to be more spread out, and the land areas in Region 2 tend to accumulate near 140,000 km².

ACTIVITY 3

In this activity, students determine quartiles and create box-and-whisker plots.

teacher note

A brief assessment of the mathematical content in Activities **1, 2,** and **3**, for use at your discretion, appears in the Teacher Resources for this module.

Materials List

- metric rulers

Technology

- graphing utility (capable of creating box-and-whisker plots)

teacher note

Some types of technology do not display the outliers on a box-and-whisker plot.

Student Outcomes

After completing the following exploration and discussion, students should be able to:

✳ determine the median, lower and upper quartiles, interquartile range, and outliers of a data set

✳ create and interpret box-and-whisker plots.

Exploration

For the following exploration, you might wish to ask the class to collect and compile their own data for hand spans. This process, however, can prove time-consuming.

a. 1. <u>14.8</u>, 15.4, <u>15.8</u>, <u>16.4</u>, <u>17.5</u>, 17.6, <u>17.6</u>, 18.1, <u>18.5</u>, <u>19.3</u>, <u>19.6</u>, 19.9, <u>20.0</u>, 20.7, <u>21.9</u>, 22.3, 23.4, 23.4, 23.9, 24.1, 24.1, 25.2.

2. The median is 19.75 cm.

3. **Note:** When determining the upper and lower quartiles for a data set, the median is not counted as a data point.

     The upper quartile is 23.4 cm.

4. The lower quartile is 17.6 cm.

5. The interquartile range is 23.4 – 17.6 = 5.8 cm.

6. Any outliers must be greater than 23.4 + (5.8)(1.5) = 32.1 cm, or less than 17.6 – (5.8)(1.5) = 8.9 cm. In this case, there are no outliers.

b. In the five-point analysis for all 22 hand spans, the minimum is 14.8 cm, the lower quartile is 17.6 cm, the median is 19.75 cm, the upper quartile is 23.4 cm, and the maximum is 25.2 cm. The interquartile range is 5.8 cm. There are no outliers.

For the girls' hand spans, the minimum is 14.8 cm, the lower quartile is 16.4 cm, the median is 18.05 cm, the upper quartile is 19.6 cm, and the maximum is 21.9 cm. There are no outliers.

For the boys' hand spans, the minimum is 15.4 cm, the lower quartile is 19 cm, the median is 22.85 cm, the upper quartile is 24 cm, and the maximum is 25.2 cm. There are no outliers.

Sample box plots:

Two Eagle Sophomore Hand Spans

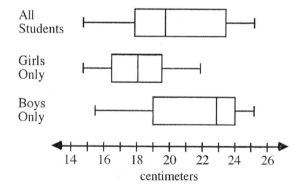

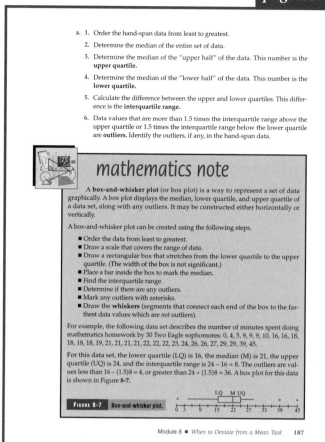

a. 1. Order the hand-span data from least to greatest.

2. Determine the median of the entire set of data.

3. Determine the median of the "upper half" of the data. This number is the **upper quartile.**

4. Determine the median of the "lower half" of the data. This number is the **lower quartile.**

5. Calculate the difference between the upper and lower quartiles. This difference is the **interquartile range.**

6. Data values that are more than 1.5 times the interquartile range above the upper quartile or 1.5 times the interquartile range below the lower quartile are **outliers.** Identify the outliers, if any, in the hand-span data.

mathematics note

A **box-and-whisker plot** (or box plot) is a way to represent a set of data graphically. A box plot displays the median, lower quartile, and upper quartile of a data set, along with any outliers. It may be constructed either horizontally or vertically.

A box-and-whisker plot can be created using the following steps.

- Order the data from least to greatest.
- Draw a scale that covers the range of data.
- Draw a rectangular box that stretches from the lower quartile to the upper quartile. (The width of the box is not significant.)
- Place a bar inside the box to mark the median.
- Find the interquartile range.
- Determine if there are any outliers.
- Mark any outliers with asterisks.
- Draw the **whiskers** (segments that connect each end of the box to the farthest data values which are *not* outliers).

For example, the following data set describes the number of minutes spent doing mathematics homework by 30 Two Eagle sophomores: 0, 4, 5, 9, 9, 9, 10, 16, 16, 18, 18, 18, 18, 19, 21, 21, 21, 22, 22, 22, 23, 24, 26, 26, 27, 29, 29, 39, 45.

For this data set, the lower quartile (LQ) is 16, the median (M) is 21, the upper quartile (UQ) is 24, and the interquartile range is 24 – 16 = 8. The outliers are values less than 16 – (1.5)8 = 4, or greater than 24 + (1.5)8 = 36. A box plot for this data is shown in Figure 8-7.

FIGURE 8-7 Box-and-whisker plot.

c. A hand span is the distance from the end of the thumb to the end of the little finger when the two are stretched as far apart as possible.

b. Create three different box-and-whisker plots of the hand-span data. One should display the data for all 22 students, one should display just the boys' hand spans, and one should display just the girls' hand spans. Compare the three plots. **Note:** Save these plots for use in the assignment.

c. Measure and record the span of your dominant hand in centimeters.

d. Add your hand-span measurement to the hand spans of all 22 students. Create a box-and-whisker plot for this new data set. Compare this plot to the plot for all 22 students from Part **b**.

e. Add your hand-span measurement to either the boys' or the girls' data. Create a box-and-whisker plot for this new set of data. Compare this plot to the corresponding plot from Part **b**.

Discussion

a. What would have more impact on a box-and-whisker plot—adding a data value within the interquartile range, or adding an outlier? Explain your response.

b. What advantages are there to using the median instead of the mean when describing a data set?

c. Is the mean of a data set readily identifiable in a box-and-whisker plot? Explain your response.

d. What are some of the advantages and disadvantages of using a box-and-whisker plot to illustrate data?

e. A box-and-whisker plot naturally leads to a so-called "five-point analysis" of a data set. What do you think these five points are?

Warm-Up

1. Find the range of each set below.

   a. 37.6, 55.3, 42.8, 61.1, 28.6, 84.9, 69.2

   b. 15, 42, 27, 13, 41, 35, 38, 55, 14

   c. 1.1, 1.5, 1.42, 1.06, 1.54, 1.32, 1.83, 1.8, 1.7, 1.73, 1.54

2. Find the median, lower quartile, upper quartile, and the interquartile range of each of the following sets of numbers.

   a. 23, 56, 76, 41, 54, 22, 72, 55, 46, 76

   b. 3.5, 2.2, 4.9, 3.6, 2.8, 4.5, 3.7, 3.9, 4.6

---

d. Answers will vary, depending on hand span. In the following sample plot, a hand span of 22.2 cm was added to the Two Eagle data. In this case, only the median changed (increasing from 19.75 cm to 19.9 cm).

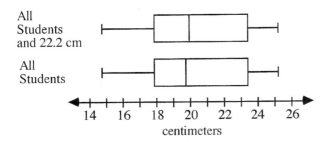

e. Answers will vary. As shown in the following sample graph, adding a hand span of 22.2 cm to the girls' data increased the median from 18.05 cm to 18.5 cm and the upper quartile from 19.6 cm to 20 cm.

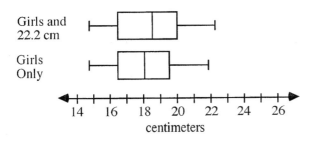

Adding a hand span of 22.2 cm to the boys' data lowered the median from 22.85 cm to 22.3 cm.

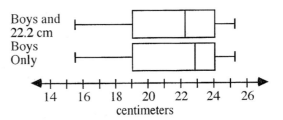

Discussion

a. Adding an outlier might affect the median because the number of data points would change from odd to even or vice versa. It also might affect the nearer quartile, which is determined in the same manner as the median. It is also possible that neither will be affected. If a new outlier has the same value as an existing one, the plot might not change at all. Otherwise, a new outlier would add an asterisk to the plot.

b. Sample response: The median is less affected than the mean by the addition of extreme values.

c. Sample response: No. A box-and-whisker plot only identifies the extreme values, the quartiles, and the median. This is not enough information to determine the mean of the data.

d. The biggest advantage of box-and-whisker plots is that they allow visual comparison of several sets of data on the same graph. They also give a general view of the spread in a set of data. One disadvantage is that very little other information about the data set is readily apparent. Another is that there is no clear picture of the location of individual items within the data set.

e. The five points identified graphically in a box plot are the minimum value, the maximum value, the median, the upper quartile, and the lower quartile.

Warm-Up

1. **a.** 56.3
   b. 42
   c. 0.77

2. **a.** median = 54.5; lower quartile = 41;
   upper quartile = 72; interquartile range = 31
   b. median = 3.7; lower quartile = 3.15;
   upper quartile = 4.55; interquartile range = 1.4

3. **a.** Any value x is an outlier if $x < 0.5$ or $x > 28.5$.

   b. Any value x is an outlier if $x < 2.3$ or $x > 69.5$.

Assignment

Problems suitable for use as assessment items are identified by an asterisk (*).

3.1 **a.** Yes. The lengths of the whiskers are determined by the most extreme data points that are not outliers (in other words, the greatest and least values within 1.5 times the interquartile range of the two quartiles, respectively.)

   b. Sample response: It is not possible to tell. It depends on the data set to which the value is added. See the answer to Discussion Part **a.**

   c. The addition of a data point within the interquartile range might or might not affect the median or the nearer quartile. See the answer to Discussion Part **a.**

3.2 The following sample responses use a hand span of 22.2 cm.

   a. My hand span is between the median (19.8 cm) and the upper quartile (23.4 cm) of the Two Eagle data. It is above the mean (20.0 cm) and below the two modes (23.4 cm and 24.1 cm).

   b. My hand span is greater than the largest value (21.9 cm) in the Two Eagle girls' data. It is above both the mean (18.1 cm) and the median (18.1 cm).

   c. My hand span is between the median (22.9 cm) and the lower quartile (19 cm) of the Two Eagle boys' data. It is above the mean (21.5 cm) and below the two modes (23.4 cm and 24.1 cm).

3.3 Sample response: Yes, this measurement is an outlier for the Two Eagle High data. It is more than 1.5 times the interquartile range greater than the upper quartile: $37 > 23.4 + (5.8)(1.5)$

3.4 **a.** Class III

   b. Class I (smallest range)

   c. Class III

   d. Box plots give little information about the distribution of individual data points; therefore this cannot be determined from the graph. By assuming that the data is evenly distributed, some students might guess Class II, because its lower quartile has the highest value.

   e. Class size is not displayed on the box plots, so it is not possible to identify the largest class.

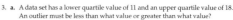
3. **a.** A data set has a lower quartile value of 11 and an upper quartile value of 18. An outlier must be less than what value or greater than what value?

   b. A data set has a lower quartile value of 27.5 and an upper quartile value of 44.3. An outlier must be less than what value or greater than what value?

Assignment

3.1 Use the box-and-whisker plots from Part **b** of the exploration to help answer the following questions about box-and-whisker plots in general. Explain your response for each one.

   a. Are the lengths of the whiskers related to the interquartile range?

   b. How would adding an outlier to the data affect the plot?

   c. How would adding a data point within the interquartile range affect the plot?

3.2 Using as many statistical measures as you can, describe how your hand span compares to each of the following:

   a. the hand spans of all 22 Two Eagle sophomores

   b. the hand spans of the sophomore girls

   c. the hand spans of the sophomore boys.

3.3 The world's tallest man, Robert Wadlow, had a hand span of about 37 cm. If this value were added to the data set in the exploration, would it be considered an outlier?

3.4 The following graph shows box plots for the number of sit-ups performed by three different classes at Two Eagle High.

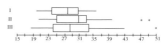

   a. Which class had the person who did the most sit-ups?

   b. For which class did the number of sit-ups vary the least?

   c. Which class had the greatest upper quartile?

   d. In which class did the bottom 25% perform the most sit-ups?

   e. Which class has the greatest number of students?

Module 8 ■ *When to Deviate from a Mean Task*   189

* 3.5 Answers and methods will vary. Sample response: I chose the value that the mean and median would share (83), then picked seven values equidistant on either side of this value: 76, 78, 79, 80, 82, 82, 82, and 84, 84, 84, 86, 87, 88, 90. This guarantees that the middle element is also the mean.

To choose an outlier, I determined the interquartile range for these 15 values, then multiplied the interquartile range by 1.5 and used it to help select the value for one outlier (43). Then I selected a second outlier an equal distance from the mean in the other direction (123).

My final data set has 17 items: 43, 76, 78, 79, 80, 82, 82, 82, 83, 84, 84, 84, 86, 87, 88, 90, 123.

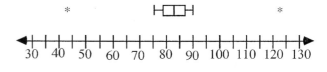

✳ ✳ ✳ ✳ ✳

3.5 Create a set of data with at least 16 items in which the mean and the median have the same value and there is at least one outlier. Explain the process you used to create the data set. Make a box plot of your data.

* * * * *

3.6 A survey conducted at two different universities, A and B, produced the following box plots.

Age of Students

a. Use the information in the plots to compare the students at university A to the students at university B.

b. Describe some information which might have been determined from the data but is not shown in the box plots.

3.7 a. Create a box plot for each of the following sets of data.

1. {5,5,5,5,30,30,30,30,70,70,70,70,95,95,95,95}

2. {5,6,7,28,37,41,50,61,68,76,89,92,95}

b. Compare the two plots.

c. Explain why a five-point analysis using box plots sometimes can be misleading.

d. Identify a type of graph that would better show the differences in the two data sets. Create the corresponding graphs.

ACTIVITY

4

Measures of central tendency are not always useful when comparing data sets. If the mean, median, and a mode of a data set are the same, or relatively close, other statistical measures are needed to provide a better picture of the data.

Exploration 1

Every year, Two Eagle High sponsors a competition between classes called the Academic Bowl. The rules for the contest are listed below.

190 Module 8 ■ *When to Deviate from a Mean Task*

---

d. A back-to-back stem-and-leaf plot might better represent the data.

second set   first set

7 6 5	0	5 5 5 5 5
	1	
8	2	
7	3	0 0 0 0 0
1	4	
	5	
8 1	6	
6	7	0 0 0 0 0
9	8	
5 2	9	5 5 5 5 5

7 | 3 | 0   represents 30 in the first data set and 37 in the second data set

ACTIVITY

4

In this activity, students examine data sets that are not adequately described by measures of central tendency.

Materials List

■ none

Technology

■ spreadsheet

■ graphing utility (capable of creating histograms)

 teacher note

Mean absolute deviation is introduced before standard deviation because of its ease of calculation and its direct link with distance from the mean.

Student Outcomes

After completing the following explorations and discussions, students should be able to:

✷ make decisions when data sets have the same measures of central tendency

✷ calculate and understand mean absolute deviation.

3.6 a. Sample response: The students at university A tend to be older than those at university B. Of those surveyed, about 75% of the students from university A are older than the oldest students at university B.

b. Sample response: The box plots do not show how many people were in the survey. They also don't allow you to see the actual ages of the students.

3.7 a–b. As shown below, the box plots for these two data sets are the same.

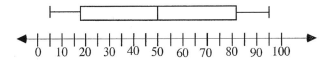

c. Sample response: It can be misleading because box plots do not show information about individual data points. A box plot only gives a general picture of the spread in a data set.

Exploration 1

Students discover that the graphs of several data sets with identical means and medians still might reveal some differences. Exploration **1** introduces the notion of spread as a measure of variability in a data set.

a. **Note:** Students should save their spreadsheets for use in Exploration **2**.

b. Sample histograms:

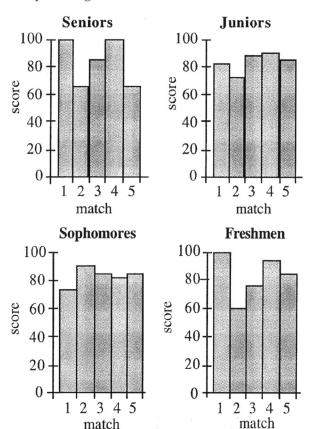

c. The mean for all teams is 83.2. The median for all teams is 85.

d. Using only the histograms and measures of central tendency, students may propose a number of methods for selecting a winner. The remainder of the activity, however, is designed to focus students on the spread in the data.

Discussion 1

a. Answers will vary. Using measures of central tendency, no clear winner emerges. Considering other criteria, each team won one match. All—except the seniors—also tied for the lead in one match. The seniors, however, have two of the three highest scores.

b. Judging from the histograms, the ranges in the scores for the juniors and sophomores are less than the ranges for the seniors and freshmen.

- Each class may enter only one team.
- Each team must consist of four students from one class.
- Each match is scored on a 100-point scale.
- Team scores are determined by averaging the scores of the four team members.
- Team members may work independently or cooperatively.
- Team members may change after any match.

The teams meet five times during the year, with the overall winner advancing to a state competition. Based on the information in Table **8-1**, the seniors believe that they should be declared the winners.

TABLE 8-1 ■ Results of the Academic Bowl

	Freshmen	Sophomores	Juniors	Seniors
Match 1	100	74	82	99
Match 2	60	90	72	66
Match 3	77	85	88	85
Match 4	94	82	89	100
Match 5	85	85	85	66

You have been selected as a judge for this year's contest. How will you choose a winner?

a. Enter the data from Table **8-1** in a spreadsheet. Record the scores for each team in its own column. **Note:** Save this spreadsheet for use in Exploration **2**.

b. Create a histogram for each team's scores. To simplify comparisons, all four histograms should be the same size and should have the same scales.

c. Use your histograms along with the measures of central tendency (mean, median, and mode) to determine the winner of the Academic Bowl.

d. Describe the process you used to choose a winner.

Discussion 1

a. Which class did you select as the winner? What criteria did you use?

b. Using the histograms you created in Part **b** of Exploration **1**, compare the range in scores for each class.

c. Would the difference in the range of scores for each class provide a reasonable criterion for selecting a winner? Explain your response.

d. Which of the rules for the competition might affect the range of scores? Explain your response.

Module 8 ■ *When to Deviate from a Mean Task*   191

c. Sample response: If the variation can be quantified, this might be used as a criterion for selecting a winner. This would reward the team that performed most consistently.

d. Two of the rules might affect the spread of scores—the one that allows teams to work cooperatively, and the one that permits teams to change members after each match.

Exploration 2

In Exploration **1**, you found that measures of central tendency alone might not provide enough information to select a winner for the Academic Bowl. Along with the mean, median, or mode, the variation among scores might be used to help determine a winner.

mathematics note

There are several methods for measuring variation in a set of data. One of these measures, **mean absolute deviation**, describes the average distance from the mean for the numbers in a data set.

The numbers in a data set with n items may be represented by symbols, such as $x_1, x_2, x_3, \ldots, x_n$. These symbols are **subscripted variables**, and the natural numbers $(1, 2, 3, \ldots, n)$ are the **subscripts**. The symbol x_1 (read "x sub one") represents the first number in the data set, the symbol x_2 (read "x sub two") represents the second number in the data set, and so on. In a data set with n items, the symbol x_n (read "x sub n"), represents the last number in the set.

For a set of data with n items represented by $x_1, x_2, \ldots, x_n$, the mean absolute deviation is given by:

$$\frac{|x_1 - \mu| + |x_2 - \mu| + \cdots + |x_n - \mu|}{n}$$

where the notation | | represents absolute value and μ, the lowercase Greek letter *mu*, is the mean of the data.

For example, consider the five match scores for the seniors in the Academic Bowl. The mean (μ) of these scores is 83.2. The distance from the mean for each score—in other words, the absolute value of the difference between the score and the mean—is shown in Figure **8-8**. The mean absolute deviation of the scores is the mean of these distances: $68.8/5 \approx 13.8$.

Score	Distance from Mean
99	15.8
66	17.2
85	1.8
100	16.8
66	17.2
Total	68.6

FIGURE 8-8
Distance from mean of the seniors' scores.

Exploration 2

This exploration introduces students to mean absolute deviation as a measure of spread.

a. Students may use a spreadsheet to determine the mean absolute deviation for each team's scores. (The mean for all teams was 83.2.) (See tables below.)

b. Any set of five equal scores will work. For example, the following set has a mean of 50 and a mean absolute deviation of 0: {50, 50, 50, 50, 50}.

c. Two sets of scores produce a mean absolute deviation of 24. These sets are {50, 50, 50, 100, 100} and {50, 50, 100, 100, 100}. In both sets of scores, the distance from each data point to the mean is as great as possible; therefore, the mean absolute deviation is as great as possible.

Seniors' Scores	Distance from Mean	Juniors' Scores	Distance from Mean
99	15.8	82	1.2
66	17.2	72	11.2
85	1.8	88	4.8
100	16.8	89	5.8
66	17.2	85	1.8
Mean Absolute Deviation	13.76	**Mean Absolute Deviation**	4.96

Sophomores' Scores	Distance from Mean	Freshmen's Scores	Distance from Mean
74	9.2	100	16.8
90	6.8	60	23.2
85	1.8	77	6.2
82	1.2	94	10.8
85	1.8	85	1.8
Mean Absolute Deviation	4.16	**Mean Absolute Deviation**	11.76

Discussion 2

a. Distances cannot be negative, so the absolute value function is used to express the difference between each data item and the mean as a non-negative value.

b. The expression $|x_i - \mu|$ is the distance from the mean for each data point. The sum of these distances, divided by the number of data points (n), is the average distance from the mean.

c. The distance from the top of each bar to the line is the distance between the data point and the mean. The mean of these distances is the mean absolute deviation.

d. Sample response: The histograms whose bars vary more in height have larger mean absolute deviations.

e. Answers will vary, depending on which team students initially chose as the winner. Adding mean absolute deviation as a criterion would make the sophomores a reasonable selection.

f. Students might reasonably expect the sixth score to fall within a range of values equal to the mean plus or minus the mean absolute deviation.

g. This question encourages students to consider the spread in a data set. Because the scores for the sophomores are clustered more closely around the mean than the scores from the other teams', a score of 95 seems more unlikely for the sophomores.

---

a. Use the data in Table **8-1** to determine the mean absolute deviation for each team's scores.

b. Create a set of scores using any five values from 50 to 100. Experiment with these values to obtain a set of scores with a mean absolute deviation of 0. Record your data set.

c. Create another set of scores with any five values from 50 to 100. Experiment with these to obtain a set of scores with a mean absolute deviation as great as possible. Record your data set.

Discussion 2

a. Why is absolute value used in the calculation of mean absolute deviation?

b. Mean absolute deviation is defined as the average distance from the mean for the numbers in a data set. How does the formula given in the mathematics note illustrate this definition?

c. Figure **8-9** below shows a histogram of the number of parking tickets issued by a traffic officer in five days. The horizontal line indicates the mean number of tickets per day. How is the distance from the top of each bar to the line related to mean absolute deviation?

FIGURE 8-9   Histogram of parking tickets.

d. How do the histograms from Exploration **1** reflect the fact that the mean absolute deviations for the teams are different?

e. How would considering the mean absolute deviation of each team's scores affect your choice for the winner of the Academic Bowl?

f. How might mean absolute deviation and measures of central tendency be used to predict a team's score in a sixth match?

g. Which team is least likely to score 95 in a sixth match? Explain your response.

Warm-Up

1. Evaluate each of the following expressions.

   a. $|5|$ b. $|-6|$

   c. $|3 - 7|$ d. $5|-2|$

   e. $|-4 \cdot -7|$ f. $|-35| \cdot |20|$

2. Evaluate each of the following using the given condition, if any.

   a. $|a|$, if $a > 0$ b. $|y|$, if $y < 0$

   c. $|x + y|$, if $x + y > 0$ d. $|a - b|$, if $a - b < 0$

   e. $-4|-2y|$, if $-2y < 0$ f. $|x^2 + y^2|$

3. Calculate the mean absolute deviation for each set of numbers.

   a. 87, 94, 72, 65, 97, 77

   b. 34.6, 54.6, 42.8, 51.5, 60.9, 22.7, 43.9

Assignment

4.1 The following graphs display the scores for each member of the junior and sophomore teams in the fifth match of the Academic Bowl.

The members of the junior team scored 85, 85, 75, and 95, while all the members of the sophomore team scored 85.

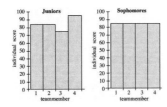

a. Can you differentiate between these two data sets using measures of central tendency alone? Explain your response.

b. Use the juniors' scores to describe how two unequal scores can have equivalent measures of deviation from the mean.

Warm-Up

1. a. $|5| = 5$

   b. $|-6| = 6$

   c. $|3 - 7| = 4$

   d. $5|-2| = 10$

   e. $|-4 \cdot -7| = 28$

   f. $|-35| \cdot |20| = 700$

2. a. $|a| = a$, if $a > 0$

   b. $|y| = -y$, if $y < 0$

   c. $|x + y| = x + y$, if $x + y > 0$

   d. $|a - b| = -a + b$, if $a - b < 0$

   e. $-4|-2y| = -8y$ if $-2y < 0$

   f. $|x^2 + y^2| = x^2 + y^2$

3. a. approximately 10.7

   b. 9.6

Assignment

Problems suitable for use as assessment items are identified by an asterisk (*).

4.1 a. Measures of central tendency are not adequate to differentiate between these two sets of scores. Although the graphs reveal some differences, the mean (85), median (85), and mode (85) are identical for both teams.

   b. The scores for students 3 and 4 on the junior team are 75 and 95, respectively. The distance from the mean score of 85 is 10 for both.

c. The mean absolute deviation would be reduced. The original set of scores has a mean absolute deviation of 5.0; the new set has a mean absolute deviation of 2.5. This occurs because the two revised scores are both closer to the mean.

d. Adding another score of 85 increases n in the formula for mean absolute deviation from 4 to 5, without increasing the sum of the distances from the mean. Therefore, the mean absolute deviation would be reduced.

4.2 a. The mean absolute deviation for each team's scores is shown below.

Class	Mean Absolute Deviation
Seniors	16.5
Juniors	5
Sophomores	0
Freshmen	8

b. Sample response: All the scores are the same: 85. As a result, the mean is 85 and the distance from each score to the mean is 0. The mean absolute deviation, therefore, is also 0.

c. Sample response: Because the seniors' scores are widely spread (mean absolute deviation 16.5), they probably worked independently. The same is likely to be true for the juniors, although the spread in their scores is not as great (mean absolute deviation 5.0). Because the sophomores' scores are identical, they appear to have worked as a cooperative group. The freshmen might have worked independently, or in two small groups because two pairs of scores are the same (mean absolute deviation 8).

4.3 a. Sample response: The score in match 5 for the seniors and the scores in matches 1 and 2 for the juniors all have a deviation greater than "an average amount."

b. Sample response: Because mean absolute deviation is the average of the deviations from the mean, I used it to determine the "average amount."

c. Sample response: The score in match 4 equals the mean score. The "missing" bar is actually a bar with a height of 0.

4.4 a. The upper end of the interval was determined by adding 13.8 to 83.2; the lower end of the interval was found by subtracting 13.8 from 83.2.

b. The mean absolute deviation is 0 when the data point has the same value as the mean.

c. Sample response: The interval that contains scores that are 2 mean absolute deviations from the mean is [69.4 – 13.8, 97 + 13.8] or [55.6, 110.8]. As it is not possible to score more than 100 points on the test, the interval would have to be [55.6, 100].

c. If team member 4 on the junior team scored 90 instead of 95, and team member 3 scored 80 instead of 75, how would this affect the mean absolute deviation? Explain why this occurs.

d. How would the mean absolute deviation be affected if a fifth member of the junior team scored 85? Explain your response.

4.2 The individual scores for the seniors in the fifth match of the Academic Bowl were 65, 99, 45, and 55. For the freshmen, the individual scores were 77, 93, 77, and 93.

a. Use this information, along with that given in Problem **4.1**, to determine the mean absolute deviation for the scores of each team in the fifth match.

b. Why can the mean absolute deviation for the sophomores' scores be determined without any calculations?

c. According to the rules for the Academic Bowl, team members may work independently or cooperatively. Describe the method that you think each team might have used. Explain your reasoning.

4.3 The two histograms below display the results of an academic bowl at a neighboring school. Each graph shows both the team scores and their distances from the mean for five matches.

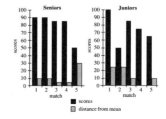

a. Identify the scores that deviate more than "an average amount" from the mean.

b. What statistical measure did you use to determine "an average amount" in Part **a**?

c. What is the significance of the missing bar in the fourth match for the juniors?

4.4 As described in the mathematics note, the mean of the Two Eagle seniors' five match scores is 83.2, with a mean absolute deviation of 13.8. The scores within 1 mean absolute deviation of the mean are contained in the interval [69.4, 97].

a. Describe how the interval [69.4, 97] was determined.

b. When is a data point 0 mean absolute deviations from the mean?

c. Determine the interval that contains scores within 2 mean absolute deviations of the mean. (*Hint*: Make sure that the extreme values in this interval make sense.)

4.5 The scores for the senior team in Problem **4.3** were 90, 89, 87, 86, and 51. The scores for the junior team were 100, 50, 85, 75, and 65.

a. Calculate the mean absolute deviation for each team's scores.

b. How does the mean absolute deviation describe the variation in scores for each team?

c. For each team, identify all scores more than 1 mean absolute deviation from the mean.

4.6 The winning team in the Academic Bowl advances to the state competition. In the past, teams that score at least 80 points typically place among the top three at state. Select a winning team from Two Eagle High and justify your choice.

＊ ＊ ＊ ＊ ＊

4.7 The table below shows some statistics for two basketball players at Two Eagle High. Rita is the leading scorer for the girls' team and Bernard is the leading scorer for the boys' team.

Player	Rita	Bernard
Average Points per Game	25	25
Mean Absolute Deviation (in Points per Game)	5	15
Points Scored in Last Game	35	35

a. Which player is the more consistent scorer? Explain your response.

b. For each player, identify the range of values that are within 1 mean absolute deviation of the mean.

c. Which player's performance in the last game is more impressive? Explain your response.

d. Both the boys' and girls' teams score an average of 60 points per game, with the same mean absolute deviation. Compare the range of the average scoring of Rita's teammates to that of Bernard's teammates.

4.8 At the end of the cross country season, the coach presents an award to the most improved runner. This award goes to the athlete whose time in the sixth race of the season is most extraordinary when compared with the mean time of the previous five races. The table below shows the times in each race for the top three candidates. Which runner should receive the award? Justify your choice.

	Runner 1	Runner 2	Runner 3
Race 1	25 min, 30 sec	20 min, 10 sec	22 min, 15 sec
Race 2	23 min, 45 sec	19 min, 50 sec	25 min, 20 sec
Race 3	24 min, 15 sec	21 min, 30 sec	20 min, 15 sec
Race 4	22 min, 5 sec	19 min, 45 sec	24 min, 25 sec
Race 5	21 min, 10 sec	18 min, 40 sec	20 min, 10 sec
Race 6	21 min, 5 sec	19 min, 20 sec	21 min, 45 sec

ACTIVITY 5

Mean absolute deviation can help you interpret a set of data when considered along with measures of central tendency. Another measure of the spread in a data set is **standard deviation.** Mean absolute deviation and standard deviation are usually close in value. However, standard deviation is preferred by statisticians because of its mathematical properties.

4.7 **a.** Sample response: Because the mean absolute deviation for Rita's scoring average is much smaller than Bernard's, she is the more consistent offensive player.

b. The range of values for Rita is from 20 to 30 points; for Bernard, the range is from 10 to 40 points.

c. Sample response: Rita's performance in the last game is more impressive because it is out of her range of "typical scores" (established by the mean, plus or minus the mean absolute deviation). Her typical range of points would be between 20 and 30 points per game, so 35 is an outstanding performance. Bernard's "typical scores" range from 10 points to 40 points. For him, a 35-point game is within the expected range.

d. If both teams average 60 points per game, Bernard's teammates must score in the range from 20 to 50 points, while Rita's teammates must score in the range from 30 to 40 points.

4.8 Sample response: Runner 1 should receive the award because her time in the sixth race is the only one more than 1 mean absolute deviation from her mean time for the previous five races (see table below).

ACTIVITY 5

In this activity, students investigate a more commonly encountered measure of variance—standard deviation.

teacher note

A brief assessment of the mathematical content in Activities **4** and **5,** for use at your discretion, appears in the Teacher Resources for this module.

---

* 4.5 **a.** The mean absolute deviation is 11.84 for the seniors and 14 for the juniors.

b. The mean absolute deviation for the juniors is higher, which means that the juniors' scores are spread more widely than the seniors'.

c. The seniors' score of 51 is more than 2 deviations from the mean. The juniors' scores of 50 and 100 are more than 1 mean absolute deviation from the mean.

4.6 Sample response: I would select the sophomores because they have the smallest mean absolute deviation and therefore score the most consistently around the mean of 83.2.

✳ ✳ ✳ ✳ ✳

	Runner 1	Runner 2	Runner 3
Race 1	1530 sec	1210 sec	1335 sec
Race 2	1425 sec	1190 sec	1520 sec
Race 3	1455 sec	1290 sec	1215 sec
Race 4	1325 sec	1185 sec	1465 sec
Race 5	1270 sec	1120 sec	1210 sec
Mean	1401 sec	1199 sec	1349 sec
Mean Absolute Deviation	82.8 sec	40.8 sec	114.8 sec

teacher note

Both mean absolute deviation and standard deviation can be treated as functions. If the derivative of the function exists, the deviation can be minimized. However, the absolute value function is not everywhere differentiable. For this reason, statisticians prefer standard deviation rather than mean absolute deviation as a measure of spread.

In this activity, students calculate standard deviation for data sets. The formula given in the mathematics note is for the standard deviation of a population (σ), not the standard deviation for a sample (s). In the formula for sample standard deviation, the sum of the squared differences is divided by ($n - 1$), rather than n.

The built-in functions in your technology might handle this calculation in different ways. For example, the most recent versions of Texas Instruments' TI-84, TI-89, and Voyage 200 calculators will report both sample and population standard deviations, although some older models may report only sample standard deviation. Similarly, some older versions of Microsoft Excel might calculate only sample standard deviation. You might wish to discuss these capabilities with students before assigning Problem **5.2**.

You also might wish to ask your students to investigate how *variance* is derived and related to standard deviation. Both are measures of spread that square the difference between each data point and the mean. The mean of these squared differences is the variance. The square root of the variance is the standard deviation.

Materials List

- none

Technology

- spreadsheet

Student Outcomes

After completing the following discussion, students should be able to:

✴ examine the differences between mean absolute deviation and standard deviation

✴ use standard deviation as a measure of data spread.

Discussion

a. Sample response: Both formulas use the differences between the mean and the data points, along with the number of data points in the set, to determine spread. They are different in that mean absolute deviation uses absolute value, whereas standard deviation uses the squares of the differences, then takes the square root.

b. Sample response: The differences are kept non-negative by squaring them.

mathematics note

Standard deviation is a common measure of the spread in a data set. To calculate it, first square the individual distance from the mean (the deviation) for each piece of data. Then find the mean of these squared deviations. The standard deviation is equal to the non-negative square root of the mean of the squared deviations.

Standard deviation is often represented by the symbol σ (the lowercase Greek letter *sigma*). For a population with n members represented by $x_1, x_2, \ldots, x_n$, where μ is the mean, the standard deviation is given by the formula below:

$$\sigma = \sqrt{\frac{(x_1 - \mu)^2 + (x_2 - \mu)^2 + \cdots + (x_n - \mu)^2}{n}}$$

For example, consider the scores for the freshman team in the fifth match of the Academic Bowl. The mean score (μ) is 85.25. The sum of the squared deviations may be calculated by using a spreadsheet, as shown in Figure **8-10**.

Score (x_n)	($x_n - \mu$)	($x_n - \mu$)^2
85	−0.25	0.06
74	−11.25	126.56
92	6.75	44.56
90	4.75	22.56
	Total	194.74

FIGURE 8-10 Determining standard deviation.

The mean of the sum of the squared deviations is 194.74/4 ≈ 48.69. The standard deviation is $\sqrt{48.69}$ ≈ 6.98.

Discussion

a. How are the formulas for standard deviation and mean absolute deviation similar? How are they different?

b. How is the difference between the mean and each data point kept positive in the formula for standard deviation?

c. What is the purpose of taking the square root of the mean squared deviation?

d. Why is it important to consider only the non-negative square root?

198   Module 8 ■ *When to Deviate from a Mean Task*

Warm-Up

1. Simplify each of the following radical expressions.

   a. $\sqrt{25}$ b. $\sqrt{3/4}$ c. $\sqrt{-5}$

   d. $\sqrt{\dfrac{3+5+8}{7}}$ e. $\sqrt{\dfrac{(3-7)^2}{8}}$ f. $\sqrt{\dfrac{(8-10)^2+(12-10)^2}{2}}$

2. Is the following equation true: $\sqrt{3^2 + 4^2} = 3 + 4$? Justify your response.

3. Calculate the standard deviation of each of the following sets of numbers.

   a. 3, 5, 8, 2, 4, 7, 1, 8, 6, 6

   b. 45, 47, 41, 42, 48, 43

   c. 19.2, 83.6, 34.5, 74.3, 99.4, 23.3, 52.4, 48.3

Assignment

5.1 In the five matches of Two Eagle's Academic Bowl, the senior team scored 99, 66, 85, 100, and 66. Calculate the mean and the standard deviation for these scores.

5.2 Many calculators have built-in functions to compute the mean and standard deviation for a set of data.

   Enter the Academic Bowl scores for the juniors (82, 72, 88, 89, and 85), the sophomores (74, 90, 85, 82, and 85), and the freshmen (100, 60, 77, 94, and 85) into your calculator.

   a. Use a calculator function to find the mean for each team's scores. One symbol commonly used to represent the mean is $\bar{x}$. What notation does your calculator use?

   b. Use a calculator function to find the standard deviation for each team's scores. One common notation for standard deviation is σ. What notation does your calculator use?

5.3 The past 12 drama performances at Two Eagle High attracted the following audiences: 220, 210, 180, 170, 120, 60, 40, 80, 110, 150, 200, and 260. This data is displayed in the line plot below. The mean for the 12 performances is identified by the middle arrow. The other two arrows indicate values 1 standard deviation from the mean.

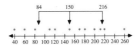

   a. How many performances were attended by an audience more than 1 standard deviation from the mean?

   b. In this data set, are there any audiences more than 2 standard deviations from the mean? Explain your response.

❋ ❋ ❋ ❋ ❋

5.4 The following table shows the mass in kilograms for the players on a high school football team.

54	85	78	67	75
75	76	75	80	85
62	90	88	79	68
55	95	65	85	92
62	83	72	90	88

   a. Find the mean mass for the players on the team.

   b. Calculate the standard deviation for the mass of the players.

   c. What percentage of the players have a mass more than 1 standard deviation from the mean?

   d. Are there any players whose masses are more than 2 standard deviations from the mean? If so, identify their masses.

5.5 The interval [230, 450] represents values within 1 standard deviation of the mean for a data set.

   a. Determine the mean of the data set.

   b. Determine the interval that represents values within 2 standard deviations of the mean.

   c. Determine the interval that represents values within 3 standard deviations of the mean.

---

c. The square root is taken to eliminate the effect of squaring the differences. It also returns the value of the deviation to its proper units.

d. Sample response: Standard deviation is a measure of spread; therefore it must be non-negative. A "negative spread" would have no meaning.

Warm-Up

1. a. 5   b. ≈0.866   c. undefined
   d. ≈1.512   e. ≈1.414   f. 2

2. Sample response: No, using the order of operations, 3 and 4 each must be squared before they are added. This gives the following result, $\sqrt{9 + 16} = \sqrt{25} = 5$, and $5 \neq 3 + 4$.

3. a. ≈2.32   b. ≈2.56   c. ≈27.2

Assignment

Problems suitable for use as assessment items are identified by an asterisk (*).

5.1 The mean is 83.2. From the equation below, the standard deviation is approximately 15.01.

$$\sigma = \sqrt{\dfrac{(99-83.2)^2 + (66-83.2)^2 + (85-83.2)^2 + (100-83.2)^2 + (66-83.2)^2}{5}}$$

5.2 a. Many calculators use $\bar{x}$ or μ to represent the mean. The mean score for all three teams is 83.2.

   b. To represent standard deviation, calculators may use σ, σx, or σ_x. The standard deviation for the juniors' scores is 6.1, for the sophomores' scores it is 5.3, and for the freshmen's scores it is 14.0.

5.3 a. There are 5 audiences more than 1 standard deviation from the mean.

   b. Sample response: No. The standard deviation is 66, so the audience would have to have been less than 18 or greater than 282 to be more than 2 standard deviations from the mean.

❋ ❋ ❋ ❋ ❋

* 5.4 a. The mean mass is 76.96 kg.

   b. The standard deviation is 11.3 kg.

   c. The interval of values within 1 standard deviation of the mean is [65.66, 88.26]. The masses of 9 of the 25 players, or 36%, fall outside this interval.

   d. The mass of 54 kg is more than 2 standard deviations from the mean.

5.5 a. The mean, 340, is the midpoint of the interval [230, 450].

   b. From Part a, one standard deviation equals 450 − 340 or 110. The interval of values within 2 standard deviations of the mean is 340 ± 2(110) or [120, 560].

   c. The interval of values within 3 standard deviations of the mean is 340 ± 3(110) or [10, 670].

teacher note

An additional assessment, for use at your discretion, appears in the Teacher Resources for this module.

Summary Assessment

1. Sample graph:

<pre>
        fifth   third
       period   period
                 |5| 2
                 |6| 0 6
         9 8 7 6 |7| 1 2 3 5 6 7 7 8
 8 5 5 4 3 2 0 0 |8| 0 2 4 5 8 9
 9 6 6 2 2 0 0 0 |9| 0
</pre>

    6|7|1   represents a score of 76 in
            fifth period and a score of
            71 in third period

2. The mean score for the third-period class is approximately 76.4. The mean score for the fifth-period class is approximately 86.1.

3. For the third-period class, the minimum is 52, the maximum is 90, the lower quartile is 72, the median is 77, and the upper quartile is 84. The score of 52 is an outlier.

    For the fifth-period class, the minimum is 76, the maximum is 99, the lower quartile is 80, the median is 85, and the upper quartile is 91.

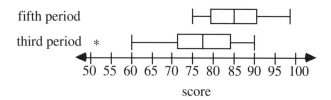

    Sample observations: Third-period test results are definitely below those for fifth period. The range of scores for third period is greater than the range of scores for fifth period.

Summary Assessment

At Two Eagle High, the biology teacher has two classes: third period and fifth period. Both classes take the same tests. On previous tests, the average score in each class has been very close.

On the most recent test, the third-period class received the following scores: 52, 60, 66, 71, 72, 73, 75, 76, 77, 77, 78, 80, 82, 84, 85, 88, 89, and 90.

On the same test, the fifth-period class received these scores: 76, 77, 78, 79, 80, 80, 82, 83, 84, 85, 85, 88, 90, 90, 90, 92, 92, 96, 96, and 99.

1. Create a back-to-back stem-and-leaf plot of this data.

2. Determine the mean test score for each class.

3. Create a box plot of the data for each class and write a summary of your observations.

4. a. Determine the standard deviation for the test scores from each class.

    b. What percentage of the scores in each class are within 1 standard deviation of the mean?

4. a. The standard deviation for the third-period scores is approximately 9.7. The standard deviation for the fifth-period scores is approximately 6.7.

    b. For the third-period class, the interval that contains scores within 1 standard deviation of the mean is [66.7, 86.1]. Thirteen of the 18 scores, or about 72%, are in this interval.

    For the fifth-period class, the interval that contains scores within 1 standard deviation of the mean is [79.4, 92.8]. Thirteen of the 20 scores, or about 65%, are in this interval.

Are You Just a Small Giant?

9

module

Overview

In this module, students investigate the relationship between physical dimensions and biological growth. Students examine linear measures and scale factors, determine the relationship of scale factors to area and volume in similar objects, and investigate the impact of growth on area, volume, and pressure.

Introduction: Students are introduced to similarity and scale factor.

Activity 1: Students use scale factors and proportions to solve for unknown measures in similar shapes.

Activity 2: Students develop the relationship between scale factors and areas in similar figures.

Activity 3: Students investigate the relationship between scale factor and volume for similar objects.

Activity 4: Students model data with power equations of the form $y = ax^b$ where b is a whole number.

Activity 5: Students investigate pressure as force per unit area.

Activity 6: Students explore limits on biological growth due to proportional changes in size, mass, and pressure.

teacher note

Activities **5** and **6** may be omitted without significant loss of mathematical content. However, if you plan to do Activity **6**, it is necessary to complete Activity **5** first.

If students do not complete Activities **5** and **6**, Problems **5** and **6** in the Module Assessment (included in the Teacher Resources for this module) should be omitted.

Objectives

In this module, students will:

* relate the constant of proportionality in direct proportions to the scale factor in similar figures (Introduction)

* use proportions and lengths to determine if objects are similar (1)

* use the relationships among scale factor, length, area, and volume for similar objects (1, 2, 3)

* examine how area changes as shapes change size proportionally (2)

* use squares and square roots (2, 3)

* examine how volume and mass change as objects change size proportionally (3)

* use cubes and cube roots (3)

182

✳ examine how the values of a and b affect graphs of power equations of the form $y = ax^b$ (4)

✳ model data with appropriate power equations (4)

✳ use mass or weight, along with area, to determine pressure (5)

✳ use relationships among mass, density, weight, and pressure to describe proportional changes in size (6).

Prerequisites

For this module, students should know:

✳ how to use ratios and solve proportions

✳ how to write, graph, and solve linear equations

✳ how to use absolute value

✳ how to find residuals

✳ how to evaluate exponential expressions.

 Flashbacks, for use at your discretion, appear in the Teacher Resources for this module. These brief problem sets provide a review of some prerequisite skills for each activity.

Planning Guide

Activity	Materials	Technology	Time Line
Introduction/Activity **1**	▪ rulers ▪ metersticks ▪ Wadlow template	▪ none	3 days
Activity **2**	▪ centimeter graph paper	▪ geometry utility	2 days
Activity **3**	▪ rulers ▪ metersticks ▪ unit cubes	▪ graphing utility ▪ spreadsheet	2 days
Activity **4**	▪ rulers ▪ metersticks ▪ centimeter graph paper	▪ graphing utility ▪ spreadsheet	2 days
Activity **5**	▪ rulers ▪ metersticks ▪ centimeter graph paper	▪ none	2 days
Activity **6**	▪ rulers ▪ metersticks ▪ centimeter graph paper ▪ tape	▪ graphing utility ▪ spreadsheet	3 days
Assessment Activities	▪ none	▪ graphing utility ▪ spreadsheet	4 days **Total: 18 days**

 teacher note

A blackline master of the Wadlow template appears in the Teacher Resources for this module.

Introduction

Similarity and proportionality are used throughout this module. You might wish to ask students to describe some examples of similar objects.

teacher note

The discussion of Wadlow's dimensions continues in Activity **1**. Figure **9-2** shows a visual comparison of Wadlow and his father. You may mark Wadlow's height and arm span on a wall for student comparisons. As students discuss their similarity to Wadlow, you might wish to point out that his height and arm span are nearly the same. This ratio is close to 1 for most people.

Student Outcomes

After completing the following discussion, students should be able to:

✳ relate the constant of proportionality in direct proportions to the scale factor in similar figures.

Discussion

a. Sample response: Yes, the enlarged image is similar to the original image because the ratios of corresponding lengths are proportional and they have the same shape.

b. A photographic image of a person is not similar to the actual person. Although the ratios of corresponding lengths will be proportional, a two-dimensional object cannot have the same shape as a three-dimensional one. A statue, on the other hand, is similar to its subject.

c. 1. Sample response: The scale factor tells how much the dimensions in the drawing have been reduced or enlarged from the dimensions in the actual object.

   2. Scale drawings of two-dimensional objects produce similar figures because the drawing has the same shape as the original object and the ratios of corresponding lengths are proportional.

      Two-dimensional scale drawings of three-dimensional objects do not produce similar figures because they do not have the same shape. Architectural models, however, are similar to the actual buildings.

d. $y = \dfrac{a}{b} x$

e. Yes, the equation in Part **d** represents a direct proportion in which a/b is the constant of proportionality.
   Note: The ratio a/b is also the scale factor.

Introduction

Robert Wadlow (1918–1940) was the world's tallest human, according to *The Guinness Book of World Records*. Wadlow's measurements at the time of his death are listed in Table **9-1**.

TABLE 9-1 ■ *Robert Wadlow's Measurements at Death*

Height	272 cm
Weight	1950 N
Mass	199 kg
Shoe Length	47 cm
Hand Length	32 cm
Arm Span	289 cm
Ring Size	25

How does your size and shape compare with Wadlow's? If Robert Wadlow were alive today, would the two of you look similar? The answer to this question depends on the definition of *similar*.

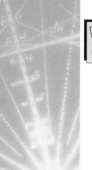

mathematics note

Two ratios, a/b ($b \neq 0$) and c/d ($d \neq 0$), are **proportional**, or **in proportion**, if:

$$\frac{a}{b} = \frac{c}{d}$$

When two such ratios are proportional, it is also true that a/c and b/d are proportional, where $c \neq 0$ and $d \neq 0$.

In mathematics, two objects are **similar** if they have the same shape and the ratios of corresponding lengths are proportional. The ratio of corresponding sides is the **scale factor**.

For example, Figure 9-1 shows two similar triangles, *ABC* and *DEF*.

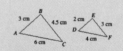

FIGURE 9-1 Two similar triangles.

Because *ABC* and *DEF* are similar, the ratios of corresponding sides are proportional and equal to the scale factor. In this case, the scale factor is 1.5.

$$\frac{AB}{DE} = \frac{BC}{EF} = \frac{AC}{DF} = 1.5$$

When two triangles are similar, the measures of the corresponding angles also are equal.

Discussion

a. When a photograph is enlarged, is the new image similar to the original? Explain your response.

b. Explain why a photographic image of a person is not similar to the actual person.

c. 1. How are scale factors used in scale drawings?

   2. Do scale drawings always produce similar figures?

d. Describe the equation that results when the following proportion is solved for *y*.

$$\frac{y}{x} = \frac{a}{b}$$

e. In the module "Oil: Black Gold," you learned that a direct proportion can be described by a linear equation of the form $y = mx$, where m is the constant of proportionality.

   Does the equation you described in Part **d** represent a direct proportion? If so, identify the constant of proportionality. If not, explain why not.

f. Describe some other examples of similar objects.

ACTIVITY
1

Are Robert Wadlow's dimensions proportional to those of other people? In this activity, you compare Wadlow's measurements at the time of his death with the measurements of other humans.

Exploration

In this exploration, you use proportions to investigate similarity in scale drawings. You also use proportions to determine if two people are similar.

Figure **9-2** shows a scale drawing of Robert Wadlow and his father.

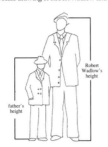

| FIGURE 9-2 | Scale drawing of Robert Wadlow and his father. |

a. Obtain a second scale drawing of Robert Wadlow and his father from your teacher.
   1. Measure Robert Wadlow's height, in centimeters, in both drawings.
   2. Determine the ratio of the height from Figure **9-2** to the height from the template.
b. 1. Measure the height, in centimeters, of Wadlow's father in both drawings.
   2. Determine the ratio of the height from Figure **9-2** to the height from the template.

208   Module 9 ■ *Are You Just a Small Giant?*

---

f. Sample response: Some stuffed animals are approximately similar to the corresponding real animals. Some toy trucks are similar to the corresponding real trucks. All circles are similar to each other.

ACTIVITY
1

Students continue their exploration of proportions and similarity.

Materials List

- metersticks (one per group)
- rulers (one per group)
- Wadlow template (one per student)

Student Outcomes

After completing the following exploration and discussion, students should be able to:

✳ use the relationship between the scale factor of similar objects and their corresponding lengths

✳ use proportions and corresponding lengths to determine if objects are similar.

Exploration

Students investigate similarity by measuring the height of two scale drawings of Robert Wadlow: one shown in Figure **9-2,** the other on a copy of the Wadlow template.

a. 1. In Figure **9-2,** Wadlow's image is 9.9 cm tall. In the template, Wadlow's image is 19.9 cm tall.
   2. The ratio of these two measurements is $9.9/19.9 \approx 0.5$.
b. 1. In Figure **9-2,** the image of Wadlow's father is 6.6 cm tall. In the template, the image of Wadlow's father is 13.2 cm tall.
   2. The ratio of the two measurements is $6.6/13.2 \approx 0.5$.

c. 1. Yes, the results in Parts **a** and **b** suggest that the images in the two drawings are proportional.

2. The two drawings have the same shape and are in proportion; therefore the drawings are similar.

d. Sample response:

$$\frac{\text{width of father's hat in Figure } \mathbf{9\text{-}2}}{\text{width of father's hat in template}} = \frac{1 \text{ cm}}{2 \text{ cm}} = 0.5$$

e. 1. Students should write the following ratio:

$$\frac{\text{actual height}}{\text{height in Figure } \mathbf{9\text{-}2}} = \frac{272 \text{ cm}}{9.9 \text{ cm}} \approx 27.5$$

2–3. Students should write and solve the proportion below:

$$\frac{272 \text{ cm}}{9.9 \text{ cm}} = \frac{\text{father's height}}{6.6 \text{ cm}}$$

$$\frac{272 \text{ cm} (6.6 \text{ cm})}{9.9 \text{ cm}} = \text{father's height}$$

$$181 \text{ cm} \approx \text{father's height}$$

f. 1. Students should write the following ratio:

$$\frac{\text{actual height}}{\text{height in template}} = \frac{272 \text{ cm}}{19.9 \text{ cm}} \approx 13.7$$

2–3. Students should write and solve the proportion below:

$$\frac{272 \text{ cm}}{19.9 \text{ cm}} = \frac{\text{father's height}}{13.2 \text{ cm}}$$

$$\frac{272 \text{ cm} (13.2 \text{ cm})}{19.9 \text{ cm}} = \text{father's height}$$

$$180 \text{ cm} \approx \text{father's height}$$

g. The two heights are approximately the same.

h. 1. Sample response: My height is 160 cm and my shoe length is 24.6 cm.

2. Sample response: The ratio of my height to Wadlow's height is:

$$\frac{160 \text{ cm}}{272 \text{ cm}} \approx 0.59$$

The ratio of my shoe length to Wadlow's shoe length is:

$$\frac{24.6 \text{ cm}}{47 \text{ cm}} \approx 0.52$$

We are not similar because the ratios are not equal.

i. 1. Sample response: My height is 160 cm and my shoe length is 24.6 cm. My friend's shoe length is 27.1 cm.

$$\frac{27.1 \text{ cm}}{24.6 \text{ cm}} = \frac{\text{friend's height}}{160 \text{ cm}}$$

$$\frac{27.1 \text{ cm} (160 \text{ cm})}{24.6 \text{ cm}} = \text{friend's height}$$

$$176 \text{ cm} \approx \text{friend's height}$$

c. 1. Do your results in Parts **a** and **b** indicate that the measurements in the two drawings are proportional?

2. Are the two drawings similar? Explain your response.

d. Provide additional evidence for (or against) your response to Part **c1** by taking a third measurement on each drawing and determining the ratio of the measurements.

e. 1. Write the ratio of Wadlow's actual height to the height of his image in Figure **9-2**.

2. Use this ratio and the height of Wadlow's father in Figure **9-2** to write a proportion that can be used to determine the father's actual height.

3. Determine the father's actual height.

f. Repeat Part **e** using the scale drawing on the template.

g. Compare the height you determined in Part **f** with the height you determined in Part **e3**.

h. 1. Measure your height and shoe length in centimeters.

2. Use these measurements to determine if you are similar to Robert Wadlow at the time of his death.

i. 1. Use your height and shoe length and the shoe length of a classmate to predict the height of that classmate.

2. Compare the predicted height with your classmate's actual height.

3. What do your results indicate about the two of you?

Discussion

a. Can you use your measurements from Part **h** of the exploration to make predictions about the measurements of other people? Explain your response.

b. If two polygons are similar, their corresponding sides are proportional. What is the relationship between their corresponding angles?

c. In the equation below, why can't *b* and *d* be equal to 0?

$$\frac{a}{b} = \frac{c}{d}$$

d. Use the terms *proportional*, *similar*, and *scale factor* to describe how a photocopier preserves similarity while enlarging or reducing.

2. Sample response: My friend's actual height is 180 cm. He is a little taller than I predicted using the ratios.

3. Sample response: The results appear to show that my friend and I are not similar. However, because the difference between the predicted height and the actual height is small, this could be explained by an error in measurement. Also, the different parts of the body do not always grow at the same rate. For example, your feet might grow before your height increases.

Discussion

a. Sample response: Given their shoe lengths, it is possible to predict the heights of other people using my measurements. However, these predictions may not be exact because I am not similar to everyone.

b. Corresponding angles of similar polygons are congruent.

c. Sample response: The values of *b* and *d* can't be 0 because you can't divide by 0.

d. Sample response: When a photocopier enlarges or reduces an image, you select a percentage. This is the scale factor. The resulting copy is similar to the original, and corresponding lengths are proportional.

Warm-Up

1. Solve each of the following proportions for x.

   a. $\dfrac{3}{8} = \dfrac{x}{56}$ b. $\dfrac{4}{7} = \dfrac{47}{x}$

   c. $\dfrac{x}{9} = \dfrac{13}{79}$ d. $\dfrac{1}{x} = \dfrac{22}{37}$

2. Which of the following equation(s) do not have the same solution as the one below?

$$\frac{14}{x} = \frac{84}{45}$$

   a. $\dfrac{14}{x} = \dfrac{45}{84}$ b. $\dfrac{84}{14} = \dfrac{45}{x}$ c. $\dfrac{x}{45} = \dfrac{14}{84}$

Assignment

1.1 Use Robert Wadlow's shoe length and height to estimate each of the following:

   a. the height of a similar person with a shoe length of 40 cm

   b. the shoe length of a similar person with a height of 165 cm.

1.2 a. A family of five all have proportional shoe lengths and heights. The shoe length and height, in centimeters, of one member of the family can be written as the ordered pair (21,126). Use these dimensions to complete the ordered pairs for the rest of the family.

     1. brother: (12, ____)   2. mother: (24, ____)

     3. sister: (____ , 108)   4. father: (____ , 216)

   b. In the following table, the ratios of corresponding lengths are expressed in the form "row:column." Use the ordered pairs from Part a to complete a copy of the table, expressing ratios in terms of whole numbers.

Family Member	father	mother	brother	sister
father	1:1	3:2		
mother				
brother			1:1	2:3
sister				

1.3 A person similar to you has a thumb length of 6.5 cm. Use your thumb length and height to estimate this person's height.

Assignment

Problems suitable for use as assessment items are identified by an asterisk (*).

1.1 a. Students may write and solve the following proportion:

$$\frac{\text{height}}{272 \text{ cm}} = \frac{40 \text{ cm}}{47 \text{ cm}}$$

$$\text{height} \approx 231 \text{ cm}$$

   b. Students may write and solve the following proportion:

$$\frac{\text{shoe length}}{47 \text{ cm}} = \frac{165 \text{ cm}}{272 \text{ cm}}$$

$$\text{shoe length} \approx 29 \text{ cm}$$

1.2 a. 1. brother: (12, 72)

      2. mother: (24, 144)

      3. sister: (18, 108)

      4. father: (36, 216)

   b. A completed table is shown at the bottom of the page.

1.3 Sample response: My thumb length is 5.5 cm and my height is 160 cm. If we are similar, the person's height can be estimated as follows:

$$\frac{\text{height}}{160 \text{ cm}} = \frac{6.5 \text{ cm}}{5.5 \text{ cm}}$$

$$\text{height} \approx 189 \text{ cm}$$

Warm-Up

1. a. $x = 21$

  b. $x = 82.25$

  c. $x = 1.48$

  d. $x = 1.68$

2. The equation in Part **a** does not have the same solution as the others.

Family Member	father	mother	brother	sister
father	1:1	3:2	3:1	2:1
mother	2:3	1:1	2:1	4:3
brother	1:3	1:2	1:1	2:3
sister	1:2	3:4	3:2	1:1

1.4 Students should measure their own heights and head circumferences, then compare ratios. Sample response: I am not similar to this baby. My ratio of head circumference to height is:

$$\frac{59 \text{ cm}}{160 \text{ cm}} \approx 0.37$$

The baby's ratio is:

$$\frac{33 \text{ cm}}{46 \text{ cm}} \approx 0.72$$

* 1.5 a. Sample response: Assuming that the image in the photograph is proportional to the real shoeprint, the length of the print can be found as shown below.

$$\frac{\text{real penny}}{\text{photo penny}} = \frac{\text{real footprint}}{\text{photo footprint}}$$

$$\frac{1.9 \text{ cm}}{0.8 \text{ cm}} = \frac{\text{real footprint}}{12 \text{ cm}}$$

$$29 \text{ cm} \approx \text{real footprint}$$

b. If the suspect is similar to Robert Wadlow, then the suspect's height can be found as follows:

$$\frac{\text{height of suspect}}{272 \text{ cm}} = \frac{29 \text{ cm}}{47 \text{ cm}}$$

$$\text{height of suspect} \approx 168 \text{ cm}$$

c. A detective also might consider other aspects of the print, such as the style of the shoe or the wear on the tread, to make predictions about the suspect's lifestyle or employment. Footprint photography and analysis are common topics of study for investigators.

✳ ✳ ✳ ✳ ✳

1.6 Sample response: My wrist circumference is 0.16 m and my height is 1.6 m. Assuming I am similar to the basketball player:

$$\frac{\text{wrist circumference}}{0.16 \text{ m}} = \frac{2.5 \text{ m}}{1.6 \text{ m}}$$

$$\text{wrist circumference} \approx 0.25 \text{ m}$$

1.7 a. Sample response: Yes, he will have time to finish the project. Using the following proportion, the typing will take 87.5 min.

$$\frac{2000 \text{ words}}{3500 \text{ words}} = \frac{50 \text{ min}}{x \text{ min}}$$

b. Using the proportion below, the amount of time needed is 10.5 min.

$$\frac{3 \text{ min}}{1000 \text{ words}} = \frac{x \text{ min}}{3500 \text{ words}}$$

1.4 A newborn baby is 46 cm long, with a head circumference of 33 cm. Are you similar to this baby? Explain your response.

1.5 During a criminal investigation, a detective photographed the print of a suspect's shoe next to the outline of a penny, as shown below.

a. Use this photograph to determine the length of the footprint.

b. Predict the suspect's height if the suspect is similar to Robert Wadlow.

c. What other useful predictions might the detective make from this footprint?

✳ ✳ ✳ ✳ ✳

1.6 A basketball player's height is 2.5 m. Assuming that the player's shape is similar to yours and that height is proportional to wrist circumference, determine the circumference of the player's wrist.

1.7 a. Theo can keyboard 2000 words in 50 min. He has 90 min available to enter a 3500-word essay in the computer. Will he be able to finish in time?

b. Theo requires 3 min per 1000 words to proofread a document. How much time will it take for him to proofread his essay?

c. Will Theo need more than 90 min to finish his essay if he also plans to proofread it? Explain your response.

1.8 The speed of an object caught in a whirlpool is inversely proportional to its distance from the whirlpool's center. If an object's speed is 7.8 cm/sec at a distance of 900 cm from the center, what is its speed at a distance of 10 cm from the center?

ACTIVITY 2

In **Activity 1**, you used scale factors to predict lengths in similar figures. In this activity, scale factors will be used to predict areas of similar figures.

Module 9 ■ *Are You Just a Small Giant?*   **211**

c. Sample response: Yes, he will need more time. The total time required is 87.5 + 10.5 = 98 min.

1.8 If speed and distance from the center are inversely proportional, then:

$$\text{speed} = \frac{k}{\text{distance}}$$

Substituting into this relationship,

$$k = (900 \text{ cm})7.8 \text{ cm/sec}$$

$$= 7020 \text{ cm}^2/\text{sec}$$

If the distance from the center is 10 cm, the speed is:

$$\text{speed} = \frac{7020 \text{ cm}^2/\text{sec}}{10 \text{ cm}}$$

$$= 702 \text{ cm/sec}$$

ACTIVITY 2

Students investigate the relationship between scale factor and area for similar objects.

Exploration

All squares are similar. How is the scale factor for two squares related to their areas? To answer this question, complete Parts **a–e**.

a. Table **9-2** lists the side lengths of nine different squares. Draw each of these squares on a sheet of centimeter graph paper.

TABLE 9-2 ■ Side Lengths of Squares

Square	Side Length (cm)
A	1.0
B	2.0
C	3.0
D	4.0
E	5.0
F	6.0
G	1.5
H	2.5
I	1.2

b. How do you think scale factors might be used to predict the areas of these squares?

c. Complete Table **9-3** using the formula for the area of a square.

TABLE 9-3 ■ Side Lengths and Areas of Squares

Square	Side Length (cm)	Area (cm²)
A	1	
B	2	
C	3	
D	4	
E	5	
F	6	
G	1.5	
H	2.5	
I	1.2	
J	z	
K	y	

Materials List

■ centimeter graph paper (one sheet per student)

Technology

■ geometry utility

teacher note

As an alternative to using a geometry utility in Part **g** of the exploration, students may use grid paper, measuring lengths and angles by hand.

Student Outcomes

After completing the following exploration and discussion, students should be able to:

✳ examine how area changes as figures change size proportionally

✳ use the relationships among scale factor, length, and area for similar objects

✳ use squares and square roots.

Exploration

In this exploration, students discover that, for two similar figures, the ratio of the areas is the square of the scale factor.

a–b. Students may estimate areas by counting squares on the graph paper. Some might observe that the relationship between the areas can be obtained by squaring the scale factor.

c. A completed Table **9-3** is shown below.

TABLE 9-3 ■ Side Lengths and Areas of Squares

Square	Side Length (cm)	Area (cm²)
A	1	1
B	2	4
C	3	9
D	4	16
E	5	25
F	6	36
G	1.5	2.25
H	2.5	6.25
I	1.2	1.44
J	z	z^2
K	y	y^2

d. A completed Table **9-4** is shown below.

e. The ratio of the areas is the square of the scale factor.

f. Answers will vary. Students consider this question in general in Part **h** of the discussion.

g. 1–3. Students should show that the ratio of corresponding sides (scale factor) is 2 and that the corresponding angles have equal measures.

---

d. Use the information in Table **9-3** to complete Table **9-4**, using whole numbers to express each ratio.

TABLE 9-4 ■ *Scale Factors and Ratios of Areas of Squares*

Squares	Ratio of Side Lengths (Scale Factor)	Ratio of Areas
A to B		
E to A		
B to D		
E to C		
I to A		
G to A		
J to F		
J to K		

mathematics note

To raise a fraction to a power n, where n is a non-negative integer, both the numerator and the denominator may be raised to the indicated power. In general,

$$\left(\frac{a}{b}\right)^n = \frac{a^n}{b^n}$$

where $b \neq 0$.

For example, the fraction 3/4 can be raised to the third power as follows:

$$\left(\frac{3}{4}\right)^3 = \frac{3^3}{4^3} = \frac{27}{64}$$

e. Use the information in Table **9-4** to describe the relationship between the scale factor for two squares and the ratio of their areas.

f. Predict whether the relationship between scale factor and area for squares is also true for similar triangles.

g. To test your prediction in Part **f**, complete Steps **1–4** below.

1. Using a geometry utility, construct a triangle *ABC*.

TABLE 9-4 ■ *Scale Factors and Ratios of Areas of Squares*

Squares	Ratio of Side Lengths (Scale Factor)	Ratio of Areas
A to B	1/2	1/4
E to A	5/1	25/1
B to D	1/2	1/4
E to C	5/3	25/9
I to A	6/5	36/25
G to A	3/2	9/4
J to F	$z/6$	$z^2/36$
J to K	z/y	z^2/y^2

2. Connect the midpoints of the sides of triangle *ABC* to form triangle *IGH*. Your construction should now resemble the one shown in Figure **9-3**.

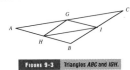

FIGURE 9-3   Triangles *ABC* and *IGH*.

3. Using the lengths of corresponding sides and the measures of corresponding angles, prove that triangles *ABC* and *IGH* are similar.

4. Determine the relationship between the scale factor of the two triangles and the ratio of their areas.

Discussion

a. Why are all squares similar?

mathematics note

A **square root** of a non-negative number a is a number s such that $s^2 = a$.

For example, because $5^2 = 25$, the number 5 is a square root of 25. Because $(-5)^2 = 25$, the number -5 is also a square root of 25.

The positive square root of a number is its **principal square root**. The principal square root of a is usually denoted by $\sqrt{a}$, although it may also be written as $\sqrt[2]{a}$. For example, $\sqrt[2]{25} = \sqrt{25} = 5$.

In general, an *n*th root of a non-negative number a is a number s such that $s^n = a$. The non-negative *n*th root of a is denoted as $\sqrt[n]{a}$.

The *n*th root of a fraction can be found by taking the *n*th root of the numerator and dividing it by the *n*th root of the denominator. In general,

$$\sqrt[n]{\frac{a}{b}} = \frac{\sqrt[n]{a}}{\sqrt[n]{b}}$$

where $b \neq 0$.

For example, the principal square root of 9/16 can be found as follows:

$$\sqrt[2]{\frac{9}{16}} = \sqrt{\frac{9}{16}} = \frac{\sqrt{9}}{\sqrt{16}} = \frac{3}{4}$$

b. When the side length of a square is doubled, what happens to the area of the square?

c. When the side lengths of a triangle are tripled, what happens to the area of the triangle?

d. If the area of a square is a cm², what is the side length of the square?

e. Consider two squares, one with an area of 49 cm² and another with an area of 1 cm². What is the scale factor for these squares?

f. In Table **9-4**, you recorded the ratio of the area of square J to the area of square K. What is the square root of this ratio?

g. Given the area of square A and the ratio of the side length of square A to the side length of square B, how could you determine the area of square B?

h. Do you think that the relationship between scale factor and the ratio of areas discovered in the exploration is true for all similar figures? Explain your response.

mathematics note

The ratio of the areas of two similar objects is the square of the ratio of the lengths of corresponding sides (the scale factor).

For example, if the scale factor for two similar objects is 4/5, the ratio of their areas is:

$$\left(\frac{4}{5}\right)^2 = \frac{4^2}{5^2} = \frac{16}{25}$$

Warm-Up

1. Calculate a real-number value for each square root below. Round non-integer values to the nearest hundredth.
   a. $\sqrt{121}$
   b. $\sqrt{56}$
   c. $\sqrt{-32}$
   d. $\sqrt{1}$
   e. $\sqrt{0}$
   f. $\sqrt{81/64}$

---

4. The ratio of the areas is 4/1. This is the square of the scale factor.

Discussion

a. Sample response: The four angles of a square are right angles and the four sides are of equal length. Therefore, for any two squares, the ratio of corresponding sides will be the same and the corresponding angles will have equal measures.

b. The area increases by a factor of 4.

c. The area increases by a factor of 9.

d. The side length is the square root of the area: $s = \sqrt{a}$.

e. The scale factor can be found by taking the square root of the ratio of the areas:

$$\sqrt{\frac{49}{1}} = \frac{\sqrt{7^2}}{\sqrt{1^2}} = \frac{7}{1} = 7$$

f. The square root of the ratio of the areas can be written as:

$$\sqrt{\frac{z^2}{y^2}} = \frac{\sqrt{z^2}}{\sqrt{y^2}} = \frac{z}{y}$$

teacher note

In Part **g** of the discussion, students are asked how to determine the area of a square given the area of a second square and the ratio formed by the side lengths of the two squares.

Students must understand the response given below to complete the assignment problems successfully.

g. Solve for the area of square B in the proportion:

$$\frac{\text{area of A}}{\text{area of B}} = \left(\frac{\text{side length of A}}{\text{side length of B}}\right)^2$$

h. The relationship between scale factor and the ratio of areas is true for any pair of similar figures. (For similar polygons, an argument can be constructed based on similar triangles.)

Warm-Up

1. a. 11
   b. 7.48
   c. undefined
   d. 1
   e. 0
   f. 9/8

2. See the completed table at the bottom of the page.
3. If the lengths of the sides are tripled, the perimeter is 3 times larger, and the area is 9 times larger.
4. If the area of a regular hexagon is quadrupled, the lengths of the sides are doubled.
5. The scale factor is $\sqrt{75/52} \approx 1.2 \approx 6/5$.

Assignment

Problems suitable for use as assessment items are identified by an asterisk (*).

2.1 Each length was multiplied by 15. This is the scale factor found by taking the square root of the ratio of the areas, 225/1.

2.2 The area of the larger circle is 10^2 or 100 times greater.

2.3 The area of the larger rectangle is $3^2 \bullet 80 = 720$ m^2.

2.4 **a.** The scale factor for the two pizzas is 41/30.

  b. The ratio of the areas is:

$$\left(\frac{41}{30}\right)^2 \approx 1.87$$

  c. If price were proportional to area, then

$$\left(\frac{41}{30}\right)^2 \approx \frac{x}{11.30}$$

  The 41-cm pizza should cost $21.11.

  d. At $18.95, the 41-cm pizza is a better buy because it costs less per square centimeter.

* 2.5 The ratio of foot areas is:

$$\frac{\text{Nelson's foot area}}{\text{pro's foot area}} = \frac{325}{468}$$

The scale factor (ratio of corresponding lengths) is therefore:

$$\frac{\sqrt{325}}{\sqrt{468}} \approx 0.83$$

Since the basketball player is 215 cm tall, Nelson's height is $215 \bullet 0.83 \approx 179$ cm.

2. Polygons A, B, C, D, E, F, G, and H are all similar polygons. Use this information to complete the following table.

Polygons	Ratio of Side Lengths	Ratio of Areas
A and B	1:6	
C and D		9/16
E and F	$m:n$	
G and H		s/t

3. If the lengths of the sides of a square are tripled, by what factor is the perimeter increased? By what factor is the area increased?

4. If the area of a regular hexagon is quadrupled, by what amount are the lengths of the sides increased?

5. The areas of two similar parallelograms are 75 cm^2 and 52 cm^2, respectively. What is the scale factor of their lengths?

Assignment

2.1 A figure is enlarged until its area is 225 times the area of the original figure. By what number was each length in the original figure multiplied?

2.2 A circle with a radius of 3 cm is enlarged by a scale factor of 10. How many times the area of the original circle is the area of the larger circle?

2.3 The sides of a rectangle with an area of 80 m^2 are enlarged by a scale factor of 3. Find the area of the larger rectangle.

2.4 Zino's Pizzeria charges $11.30 for a pizza with a diameter of 30 cm and $18.95 for a pizza with a diameter of 41 cm.

  a. The two pizzas are similar. Determine the scale factor when comparing the larger pizza to the smaller one.

  b. Find the ratio of their areas.

  c. Use the ratio of the areas and the price of the smaller pizza to determine a corresponding price for the larger pizza.

  d. Decide which pizza is the better buy and explain your reasoning.

2.5 A professional basketball player 215 cm tall has a footprint with an area of 468 cm^2. This basketball player and Nelson have similar bodies. If the area of Nelson's footprint is 325 cm^2, how tall is Nelson?

Polygons	Ratio of Side Lengths	Ratio of Areas
A and B	1:6	1:36
C and D	3/4	9/16
E and F	$m:n$	$m^2:n^2$
G and H	$\sqrt{s}/\sqrt{t}$	s/t

> **2.6** The size of a television screen typically is reported in terms of the length of its diagonal. For example, if a store advertises a 50-cm screen, this means that the length of the screen's diagonal is 50 cm.
>
> **a.** What is the ratio of the area of a 63-cm screen to the area of a 33-cm screen?
>
> **b.** What is the length of the diagonal for a screen with twice the area of a 33-cm screen?
>
> **2.7 a.** Determine the area of a right triangle with sides that measure 3 cm, 4 cm, and 5 cm.
>
> **b.** Use your answer to Part **a** to predict the area of a right triangle with sides that measure 18 cm, 24 cm, and 30 cm.
>
> **c.** Verify your prediction using the formula for the area of a triangle.
>
> ✶ ✶ ✶ ✶ ✶
>
> **2.8** Andreas and Jonalynn installed new carpeting in two of their bedrooms. The floors in both rooms are rectangles. The smaller of the two rooms is 3.2 m wide and 4.1 m long. The ratio of the widths of the two rooms is 1.2, while the ratio of the lengths is 1.6.
>
> **a.** Find the length and width of the larger room.
>
> **b.** Can the ratios of the widths and the lengths of the two rooms be used to determine the ratio of the areas? Explain your response.
>
> **c.** Find the areas of both rooms.
>
> **d.** What is the ratio of the areas of the two rooms? Does this ratio verify your response to Part **b**? Why or why not?
>
> **2.9** Damion's Turf Service charges $50.00 to clean a section of artificial turf 10 yd wide and 20 yd long. Excluding the end zones, a football field is 50 yd wide and 100 yd long. How much should the company charge to clean a football field? Explain your response.
>
> **2.10** The figure below shows four rectangles and their dimensions in centimeters.
>
>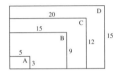
>
> **a.** Compare the perimeters and areas of these rectangles.
>
> **b.** Identify the rectangles that are similar and explain how you determined your response.
>
> Module 9 ■ *Are You Just a Small Giant?* **217**

2.9 The $50 section of turf and a football field are similar rectangles. The scale factor is 5; therefore, the ratio of areas is 25/1. To keep the price proportional to the area, the company should charge $1250 to clean a football field.

2.10 a. In the following table, the perimeters and areas for the four rectangles are listed from smallest to largest. For any pair, the ratio of the areas is the square of the ratio of the perimeters.

Rectangle	Perimeter	Area
A	16	15
B	48	135
C	64	240
D	80	375

b. Sample response: All of the rectangles are similar to each other. For any pair, the ratios of corresponding sides are equal and all angles are congruent.

2.6 a. Since the diagonal is a length measurement, the ratio of the diagonals is the scale factor: $63/33 \approx 1.9/1$. The ratio of the areas is the square of the scale factor: $(1.9)^2 \approx 3.6$.

b. If the ratio of the areas is 2, the scale factor is $\sqrt{2}$. The diagonal of the larger screen measures

$$\sqrt{2}\,(33) \approx 46.7 \text{ cm.}$$

2.7 a. $A = 0.5 \bullet 4 \bullet 3 = 6 \text{ cm}^2$

b. Sample response: These two right triangles are similar. The scale factor is 6, so the ratio of the areas is $6^2/1$. The area of the larger triangle is

$$6 \text{ cm}^2(36) = 216 \text{ cm}^2.$$

c. $A = 0.5 \bullet 24 \bullet 18 = 216 \text{ cm}^2$

✳ ✳ ✳ ✳ ✳

2.8 a. The larger room is 6.56 m long and 3.84 m wide.

b. Answers will vary. Sample response: No. The ratios of corresponding lengths are not equal, so the rectangles are not similar. (Some students might conjecture that the ratio will be $1.4^2 = 1.96$ because 1.4 is the mean of 1.2 and 1.6.)

c. The area of the smaller room is 13.12 m²; the area of the larger room is 25.19 m².

d. Answers will vary. The ratio of areas is 1.92.

ACTIVITY

In this activity, students explore the relationship between scale factor and volume for similar objects.

teacher note

A brief assessment of the mathematical content in Activities **1**, **2**, and **3**, for use at your discretion, appears in the Teacher Resources for this module.

Materials List

- unit cubes (27 per group)
- rulers (one per group)

Technology

- graphing utility
- spreadsheet

Student Outcomes

After completing the following exploration and discussion, students should be able to:

✳ examine how volume and mass change as objects change size proportionally

✳ use the relationships among scale factor, length, area, and volume of similar objects

✳ use cubes and cube roots.

Exploration

By building models with unit cubes, students investigate the relationship between scale factor and volume.

a. A completed table appears below.

Cube	Edge Length	Volume
A	1	1
B	2	8
C	3	27
N	n	n^3

ACTIVITY
3

In previous activities, you used scale factors to predict lengths and areas for similar figures. In this activity, scale factors are used to predict volumes of similar objects.

Exploration

a. 1. Using a set of unit cubes, create a cube with an edge length of 2 units. Determine the volume of this cube and record it in the appropriate cell of Table **9-5**.

TABLE 9-5 ■ Edge Length and Volume of Cubes

Cube	Edge Length	Volume
A	1	1
B	2	
C		27
N	n	

2. Determine the edge length of a cube with a volume of 27 units³ and record it in the appropriate cell of Table **9-5**.

3. Determine the volume of a cube with an edge length of n and record it in the appropriate cell of Table **9-5**.

b. 1. Use the information in Table **9-5** to complete Table **9-6**.

TABLE 9-6 ■ Ratios of Edge Lengths and Volumes

Cubes	Ratio of Edge Lengths (scale factor)	Ratio of Volumes
B to A	2/1	
B to C	2/3	
C to A		27/1
	a/b	

2. Describe the relationship between the ratio of the edge lengths (scale factor) for two cubes and the ratio of their volumes.

---

mathematics note

A **cube root** of a number a is a number b such that $b^3 = a$. Because $2^3 = 8$, for example, 2 is the cube root of 8.

The cube root of a is denoted by $\sqrt[3]{a}$. For example, $\sqrt[3]{-8} = -2$ and

$$\sqrt[3]{\frac{64}{125}} = \frac{\sqrt[3]{64}}{\sqrt[3]{125}} = \frac{4}{5}$$

Discussion

a. 1. What is the ratio of volumes for two cubes with volumes of 125 cm³ and 8 cm³?

2. What is the ratio of the edge lengths for these cubes?

b. In general, what is the relationship between the scale factor and the ratio of volumes for two cubes?

c. If a cube is enlarged until its volume is 64 times the original volume, by what scale factor has each edge length been multiplied?

d. If the volume of a cube is d cm³, what is the length of one edge?

e. Do you think that the relationship you described in Part **b** is true for all similar figures? Explain your response.

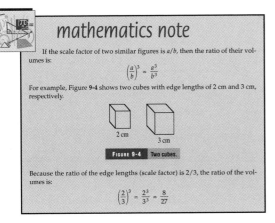

mathematics note

If the scale factor of two similar figures is a/b, then the ratio of their volumes is:

$$\left(\frac{a}{b}\right)^3 = \frac{a^3}{b^3}$$

For example, Figure 9-4 shows two cubes with edge lengths of 2 cm and 3 cm, respectively.

2 cm   3 cm

FIGURE 9-4 Two cubes.

Because the ratio of the edge lengths (scale factor) is 2/3, the ratio of the volumes is:

$$\left(\frac{2}{3}\right)^3 = \frac{2^3}{3^3} = \frac{8}{27}$$

f. Consider two similar pyramids. The smaller has a volume of 18 cm³. The sides of the larger pyramid are 3 times as long as the smaller pyramid's.

Describe how you could determine the volume of the larger pyramid.

Warm-Up

1. Calculate a real-number value for each cube root below. Round non-integer values to the nearest hundredth.

   a. $\sqrt[3]{343}$ b. $\sqrt[3]{-1728}$ c. $\sqrt[3]{592.704}$ d. $\sqrt[3]{-4913}$

2. Complete the following table.

Scale Factor	Ratio of Areas	Ratio of Volumes
3/5		
	25:4	
		$m^3 : n^3$
	s^2/t^2	
	u/v	

b. 1. A completed table appears below.

Cubes	Ratio of Edge Lengths (scale factor)	Ratio of Volumes
B to A	2/1	8/1
B to C	2/3	8/27
C to A	3/1	27/1
	a/b	a^3/b^3

2. Students should observe that the ratio of volumes is the cube of the scale factor.

Discussion

a. 1. The ratio of the volumes is 125/8.
   2. The scale factor is 5/2.
b. The ratio of the volumes is equivalent to the cube of the scale factor (ratio of the edge lengths).
c. Because $4 = \sqrt[3]{64}$, the scale factor is 4.
d. The length of each edge is $\sqrt[3]{d}$.
e. The relationship is true for all similar three-dimensional objects. For example, doubling the measurements of a room increases its volume by a factor of 8. Tripling the radius of a sphere increases its volume by a factor of 27.
f. Sample response: The ratio of volumes is $3^3:1$ or 27:1, so the volume of the larger pyramid is $18 \cdot 27 = 486$ cm³.

Warm-Up

1. a. 7
   b. –12
   c. 8.4
   d. –17
2. See the completed table below.

Scale Factor	Ratio of Areas	Ratio of Volumes
3/5	9/25	27/125
5:2	25:4	125:8
$m{:}n$	$m^2 : n^2$	$m^3 : n^3$
s/t	s^2/t^2	s^3/t^3
$\sqrt{u}/\sqrt{v}$	u/v	$(\sqrt{u})^3/(\sqrt{v})^3$

teacher note

In Problems **3.2**, **3.4**, and **3.6**, students extend the concept of similarity to eggs and fish. In living things, mass is not always strictly proportional to volume. To make their estimates, students should assume that densities are nearly equal among similar animals. **Note:** The biological literature cites fish as examples of living organisms that are truly close to similar.

Assignment

Problems suitable for use as assessment items are identified by an asterisk (*).

3.1 The ratio of the volumes is 1/343, so the scale factor is:

$$\sqrt[3]{\frac{1}{343}} = \frac{1}{7}$$

3.2 The scale factor is 2/1, so the ratio of their volumes is:

$$\left(\frac{2}{1}\right)^3 = \frac{8}{1}$$

3.3 a. Density is the ratio of mass to volume; therefore the density is:

$$\frac{261 \text{ g}}{33.5 \text{ cm}^3} \approx 7.8 \text{ g/cm}^3$$

b. The density of a pure substance is a constant; therefore the density of the larger sphere is the same: 7.8 g/cm³.

c. 3/2 = 1.5

d. Because volume varies as the cube of the scale factor, the ratio is:

$$\left(\frac{3}{2}\right)^3 = \frac{27}{8}$$

e. 1. The ratio of the volumes is the same as the ratio of the mass.

2. The ratio of the volumes is the cube of the scale factor.

* 3.4 From mouth to tail, the image of the smaller fish measures about 40 mm. The image of the larger fish measures about 48 mm. The scale factor between the fish is 48/40 = 1.2. Because the smaller fish is 25 cm long, the length of the larger fish is 25(1.2) = 30 cm.

The volume of the larger fish is greater by the cube of the scale factor: $1.2^3 \approx 1.7$. Assuming that mass is proportional to volume, its mass also should be greater by the cube of the scale factor. The smaller fish has a mass of 0.75 kg; therefore the mass of the larger

Assignment

3.1 Consider two spheres: the smaller has a volume of 1 m³, the larger has a volume of 343 m³. What is the scale factor for these spheres?

3.2 Two eggs are similar in shape. One egg is twice as long as the other. What is the ratio of their volumes?

science note

The **density** of a substance is the ratio of its mass to its volume. For example, the density of water is 1 g/cm³.

The density of any pure substance is a constant. Therefore, the mass of the substance is directly proportional to its volume. In other words, as the volume increases, so does the mass.

3.3 A steel sphere with a diameter of 4 cm has a volume of 33.5 cm³. Its mass is 261 g.

    a. What is the density of the sphere?

    b. What is the density of a steel sphere with a diameter of 6 cm?

    c. What is the scale factor between the 6-cm sphere and the 4-cm sphere?

    d. What is the ratio of the volume of the 6-cm sphere to the volume of the 4-cm sphere?

    e. How does the ratio of their volumes compare to:

       1. the ratio of their masses?

       2. the scale factor?

3.4 The two similar fish shown below are drawn to scale. The smaller fish is 25 cm long and has a mass of 0.75 kg. Assuming that the densities of the two fish are the same, use scale factor to estimate the length and mass of the larger fish.

* * * * *

fish is: $0.75(1.7) \approx 1.3$ kg. (This is not far from doubling the mass, which might surprise some students.)

* * * * *

3.5 Because the scale factor is 8/9, the ratio of the volumes is $(8/9)^3 \approx 0.7$. Therefore, an 8-inch pie should require 6(0.7) = 4.2 cups of apples.

3.6 If one egg has three times the circumference of another egg, then the scale factor is 3/1. Assuming that mass is proportional to volume, the ratio of the masses is the cube of the scale factor: 27/1.

ACTIVITY
4

Students collect data on shoe length and shoeprint area and model the data using equations of the form $y = ax^b$.

Materials List

■ metersticks (one per group)

■ rulers (one per group)

■ centimeter graph paper (one or two sheets per student)

3.5 A baker's favorite pie recipe calls for 6 cups of apples to make a 9-inch pie. How many cups of apples should he use to make a similar 8-inch pie?

3.6 The circumference of one egg is three times the circumference of another egg. If the two eggs are similar, what is the ratio of the mass of the larger egg to the mass of the smaller egg?

ACTIVITY 4

In Activity **2,** you discovered that when a square's side length is doubled, its area is quadrupled. In this activity, you examine the relationship between length and area from a graphical point of view.

Exploration

The area of a square is related to the length of its sides. The area of a shoe print is related to the length of the shoe. How are these two relationships similar? How are they different?

a. Figure 9-5 shows a scale drawing of a child's shoe print. Each square in the drawing represents an area of 1 cm². Use this drawing to estimate the actual length and area of the shoe print.

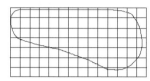

FIGURE 9-5 A child's shoe print.

b. Draw your own shoe print on centimeter graph paper. Measure its length and estimate its area.

c. 1. Collect and organize this information for the entire class. To this data set, add the child's data from Part **a** along with a shoe length of 0 cm and the corresponding area.

   2. Create a scatterplot of the class data. Let y represent area and x represent shoe length.

222   Module 9 ■ *Are You Just a Small Giant?*

Technology

- graphing utility
- spreadsheet

teacher note

If you choose to do Activity **5,** students should save their shoeprint data from Part **b** of the exploration for use later in the module.

In Part **e** of the exploration, you might wish to show students how to use a data point (x,y) to solve for a in the equation $y = ax^2$.

Student Outcomes

After completing the following exploration and discussion, students should be able to:

✳ examine how the values of a and b affect graphs of power equations of the form $y = ax^b$

✳ model data with appropriate power equations.

Exploration

a–b. Students can estimate area by counting squares. The child's shoeprint is approximately 13.5 cm long, with an area of approximately 57 cm².

c. 1. See sample data at the bottom of the page.
   2. See sample graph in Part **d1** on the next page.

Length (cm)	Area (cm²)	Length (cm)	Area (cm²)
0.0	0.0	27.0	237.0
13.5	57.0	29.0	248.0
20.0	115.0	29.0	251.0
23.0	140.0	29.0	252.0
25.0	170.0	29.5	262.0
26.0	182.0	30.0	275.0
26.0	190.0	30.5	251.0
26.0	203.0	31.0	262.0
26.5	210.0	31.8	300.0
27.0	228.0	33.5	336.0

d. 1. Sample graph:

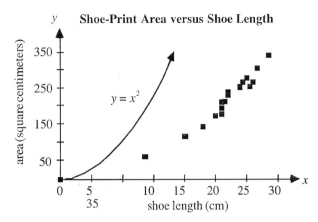

2. Sample response: The two graphs have the same general shape. As the length increases, the area increases. Although both graphs are nonlinear, the graph of $y = x^2$ is steeper than the scatterplot.

e. Students find an equation that models the data by experimenting with different values of a. For the sample data, the equation $y = 0.3x^2$ fits very well. Sample graph:

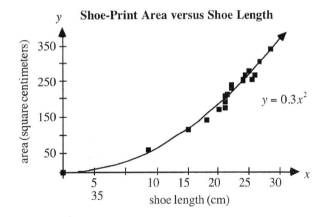

d. 1. Graph the formula for the area of a square on the same coordinate system as the scatterplot in Part **c**. Let y represent area and x represent side length.

2. Describe any similarities or differences you observe in the two graphs.

mathematics note

An equation of the form $y = ax^b$ is a **power equation**.

For example, the formula for the area of a square, $y = x^2$, is a power equation in which $a = 1$ and $b = 2$.

e. Find an equation of the form $y = ax^2$ that models the scatterplot in Part **c** by varying the value of a until the graph of the equation reasonably approximates the data points.

f. One way to determine if another power equation fits the data better than your equation from Part **e** is to compare the residuals.

1. Enter the class data in a spreadsheet with the following headings:

Length (x)	Area (y)	Predicted Area	Absolute Value of Residual

2. Use your model from Part **e** to determine the predicted area for each value of x.

3. Determine the absolute value of each residual.

4. Find the sum of the absolute values of the residuals.

g. Vary the value of a in your model of the form $y = ax^2$ to determine the equation that minimizes the sum of the absolute values of the residuals. Record this equation.

h. 1. Graph your equation from Part **g** on the same coordinate system as the scatterplot from Part **c** and print a copy of the resulting graph.

2. Mark the point on the scatterplot that represents your shoe length and area.

3. Mark the point on the curve that represents the ordered pair (x, y), where x is your shoe length and y is the predicted area. Connect this point to the point in Step **2**.

f. The values in the table at the bottom of the page were generated using the sample data given in Part **c** and the equation $y = 0.3x^2$.

g. For the sample data, the equation $y = 0.3x^2$ produces the smallest sum of the absolute values of the residuals for a rounded to the nearest tenth. The equation $y = 0.298x^2$ produces a slightly smaller sum (172).

h. This graph should be very similar to the sample graph shown in Part **e**. The segment drawn in Step **3** provides a graphic representation of the residual. Students will evaluate how well their models fit their own data points in Part **b** of the discussion.

Length (x)	Area (y)	Predicted Area	Absolute Value of Residual
0.0	0.0	0.0	0.0
13.5	57.0	54.7	2.3
20.0	115.0	120.0	5.0
23.0	140.0	158.7	18.7
25.0	170.0	187.5	17.5
26.0	182.0	202.8	20.8
26.0	190.0	202.8	12.8
26.0	203.0	202.8	0.2
26.5	210.0	210.7	0.7
27.0	228.0	218.7	9.3
27.0	237.0	218.7	18.3
29.0	248.0	252.3	4.3
29.0	251.0	252.3	1.3
29.0	252.0	252.3	0.3
29.5	262.0	261.1	0.9
30.0	275.0	270.0	5.0
30.5	251.0	279.1	28.1
31.0	262.0	288.3	26.3
31.8	300.0	303.4	3.4
33.5	336.0	336.7	0.7
		Sum	175.8

Discussion

a. Sample response: As shoe length increases, the area of the shoeprint increases by the square of the length.

b. Students should have obtained approximately the same equations.

c. Answers will vary. Students should recognize that the size of the residual is one measure of the accuracy of a model.

d. Sample response: The value of a affects the steepness of the curve. **Note:** At this point in the module, students have used only positive values for a. They continue their investigation of power equations in Problem **4.1**.

e. The ratio of the areas is 9 to 1.

Warm-Up

1. **a.** Sample table and graph:

x	−2	−1	0	1	2
y	5.2	1.3	0	1.3	5.2

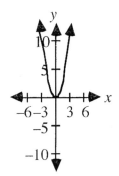

b. Sample table and graph:

x	−2	−1	0	1	2
y	−6.64	−0.83	0	0.83	6.64

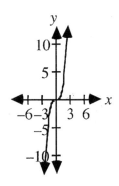

2. **a.** $x \approx 8.22$ or -8.22

   b. $x \approx 4.73$

Discussion

a. Describe the general relationship between shoe length and the area of a shoe print.

b. Compare your equation in Part **g**, along with its corresponding sum of the absolute values of the residuals, with those obtained by others in the class.

c. How well does your equation model the data for your own shoe length and area?

d. How does the value of a affect the graph of the equation $y = ax^2$?

e. If the lengths of two similar shoe prints have a scale factor of 3, what is the ratio of their areas?

Warm-Up

1. Complete the following table of values for each equation below. Then sketch a graph of each equation.

x	−2	−1	0	1	2
y					

   a. $y = 1.3x^2$ **b.** $y = 0.83x^3$

2. For each equation in Problem **1**, determine the value of x (to the nearest hundredth) when $y = 87.93$.

Assignment

4.1 In the exploration, you graphed equations of the form $y = ax^b$ where $b = 2$ and both the domain and range were limited to positive numbers. To observe how different values of a and b affect the graph of $y = ax^b$, use a graphing utility to complete Parts **a–c** below.

Sketch each set of graphs on a sheet of paper, using the same pair of axes for each set, and including the appropriate labels.

   a. Graph at least three examples of each of the following. Let the domain be the set of real numbers from –10 to 10. Include one value for a where $|a| < 1$.

   1. $y = ax^2$ where a is positive   **2.** $y = ax^2$ where a is negative

   b. Repeat Part **a** for $y = ax^3$.

   c. Repeat Part **a** for $y = ax^b$ where b is greater than 3.

   d. Describe how the values of a and b appear to affect the graph of $y = ax^b$.

teacher note

For Problems **4.3** and **4.4,** you might wish to select one student's data for use by the entire class.

Assignment

Problems suitable for use as assessment items are identified by an asterisk (*).

4.1 **a–c.** Students use technology to explore graphs of $y = ax^b$.

   d. Sample response: The value of a affects the steepness of the curve. The sign of a determines which quadrants contain the graph. The value of b changes the shape of the curve. If b is even, the curve resembles a parabola. If b is odd, the curve resembles the graph of $y = x^3$. The size of b also influences the steepness of the curve.

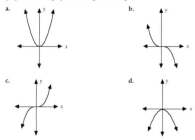

4.2 Each of the following graphs was generated by an equation of the form $y = ax^b$. For each one, determine two equations with different values of b that produce graphs with roughly the same general shape.

4.3 Assuming that Robert Wadlow is similar to you, estimate the area of his shoe print.

4.4 Neva is 170 cm tall. Estimate her shoe length and the area of her shoe print if she is similar to you.

4.5 The table below shows some data on the length and mass of bird eggs.

Type of Egg	Length (cm)	Mass (g)
hummingbird	1.3	0.5
black swift	2.5	3.5
dove	3.18	6.41
partridge	3.0	8.7
Arctic tern	4.2	18
grebe	4.3	19.7
Louisiana egret	4.5	27.5
very small chicken	5.2	44.8
mallard duck	6.17	80
very large chicken	6.5	85
great black-backed gull	7.62	111
Canada goose	8.9	197
condor	11.0	270
ostrich	17.0	1400

Module 9 ■ *Are You Just a Small Giant?* **225**

4.2 Answers will vary. Some possible equations are listed below:

a. $y = x^2$, $y = x^4$
b. $y = -x^3$, $y = -x^5$
c. $y = x^3$, $y = x^5$
d. $y = -x^2$, $y = -x^4$

* 4.3 Substituting Wadlow's shoe length from Table **9-1** (47 cm) into the equation $y = 0.3x^2$, the area of Wadlow's shoeprint is approximately 663 cm^2.

Note: It might help students to rewrite their equations using more meaningful variables, such as $A = 0.3s^2$. You may wish to discuss why the generic variables x and y are used in tools such as graphing calculators.

4.4 Sample response: My height is 160 cm and my shoe length is 24.6 cm. If Neva is similar to me, her shoe length can be found as follows:

$$\frac{\text{Neva's shoe}}{24.6 \text{ cm}} = \frac{170 \text{ cm}}{160 \text{ cm}}$$

$$\text{Neva's shoe} \approx 26.1 \text{ cm}$$

Using the equation from the exploration, the area of her shoeprint is:

$$y = 0.3x^2$$
$$= 0.3(26.1 \text{ cm})^2$$
$$\approx 204 \text{ cm}^2$$

Note: Even if the student and Neva are not similar, the same relationship between height and shoeprint area may hold.

4.5 a. Sample graph:

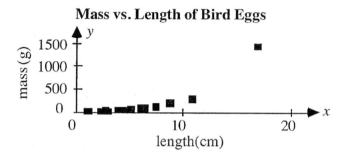

Mass vs. Length of Bird Eggs

b. One equation that models the data is $y = 0.28x^3$.

c. Sample response: The condor egg appears to be a little below the upward-curving trend of the other data points. The data point for the condor is (11,270). Substituting 11 into the power equation $y = 0.28x^3$ yields a predicted mass of 373 g, a difference of 103 g.

d. Substituting the length of the bald eagle's egg into the sample equation yields a mass of 108.9 g.

e. Sample response: The graph of the data for mass and length of bird eggs can be modeled by the equation $y = 0.28x^3$. This equation states that the mass of an egg is proportional to the cube of its length. In other words, as the length is increased by a scale factor of x, the mass of an egg increases by x^3.

✳ ✳ ✳ ✳ ✳

4.6 a. See sample graph in Part **c.**

b. One equation that models the data is $y = 4.54x^2$. The sum of the absolute values of the residuals is 0.267.

Time (x)	Distance (y)	Predicted Distance	Absolute Value of the Residual
0.00	0.000	0.000	0.000
0.05	0.000	0.011	0.011
0.10	0.017	0.045	0.028
0.15	0.072	0.102	0.030
0.20	0.152	0.182	0.030
0.25	0.256	0.284	0.028
0.30	0.387	0.409	0.022
0.35	0.539	0.556	0.017
0.40	0.717	0.726	0.009
0.45	0.920	0.919	0.001
0.50	1.144	1.135	0.009
0.55	1.393	1.373	0.020
0.60	1.668	1.634	0.034
0.65	1.889	1.918	0.029
		Sum	0.267

c. Sample graph:

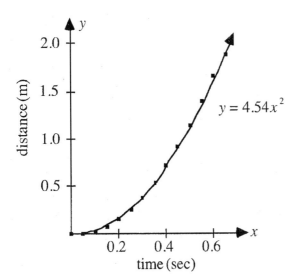

d. Using the sample equation given in Part **b**, the object would fall about 18.2 m in 2 sec.

a. Make a scatterplot of this data. Let y represent mass in grams and x represent length in centimeters.

b. Find an equation of the form $y = ax^3$ that models the data.

c. Which type of egg fits the curve least well? Explain your response.

d. The egg of a bald eagle is 7.3 cm long. Use your equation to predict the mass of this egg.

e. Write a paragraph summarizing the relationship between the length and mass of bird eggs.

* * * * *

4.6 The table below shows the data collected as an object fell through the air.

Time (sec)	Distance (m)	Time (sec)	Distance (m)
0.00	0.000	0.35	0.539
0.05	0.000	0.40	0.717
0.10	0.017	0.45	0.920
0.15	0.072	0.50	1.144
0.20	0.152	0.55	1.393
0.25	0.256	0.60	1.668
0.30	0.387	0.65	1.889

a. Create a scatterplot of this data. Let y represent distance in meters and x represent time in seconds.

b. Use the process described in Parts **e–g** of the exploration to find an equation that models the data.

c. Graph this equation on the same coordinate system as in Part **a.**

d. Use your model to predict how far the object will fall in 2 sec.

The soles of your feet place a certain amount of pressure on the ground when you stand upright. In this activity, you explore the differences in pressure created by wearing shoes with flat soles, shoes with small heels, or no shoes at all.

Students investigate pressure as force per unit area.

teacher note

Although this activity may be treated as optional, it must be completed if you wish to proceed to Activity **6.**

Materials List

■ metersticks (one per group)

■ rulers (one per group)

■ centimeter graph paper (one or two sheets per student)

science note

The kilogram is a unit of mass, even though it is often referred to as a metric unit of weight. Weight is a force determined by gravity. One metric unit of force is the **newton (N)**. On the surface of the earth, the weight of an object in newtons is its mass in kilograms multiplied by 9.8 m/sec² (the acceleration due to gravity).

For example, the weight in newtons of a 70-kg person can be calculated as follows:

$$70 \text{ kg} \cdot \frac{9.8 \text{ m}}{\text{sec}^2} = \frac{686 \text{ kg} \cdot \text{m}}{\text{sec}^2} = 686 \text{ N}$$

Exploration

a. 1. Place your shoeless foot on a sheet of centimeter graph paper and trace around it. Use the tracing to estimate the area of your footprint without shoes.

   2. Estimate the area of your shoe print when wearing shoes with flat soles. Assume that the bottom of your shoe makes complete contact with the ground.

   3. Estimate the area of your shoe print when wearing a shoe with small heels.

b. Compare the three areas determined in Part **a**.

c. Determine your weight in newtons.

d. Find the pressure, in newtons per square centimeter, that your feet place on the ground in each of the following situations. *Hint:* Because your weight is distributed over both feet, divide this weight by the area of two footprints.

   1. while not wearing shoes

   2. while wearing shoes with flat soles

   3. while wearing shoes with small heels

e. Compare the three pressures determined in Part **d**.

Discussion

a. When designing shoes for specific purposes, manufacturers often consider the amount of pressure that the foot places on the ground. For example, the sole on a running shoe typically has a greater area than the sole on a casual shoe.

Describe the purposes of some different types of shoes and the approximate area of the sole for each type.

Module 9 ■ *Are You Just a Small Giant?*   **227**

---

teacher note

For Step **2** of Part **a** in the following exploration, students may use the areas of the shoeprints found in the exploration in Activity **4**. For Step **3** of Part **a**, you might wish to ask some students to bring high-heeled shoes.

Student Outcomes

After completing the following exploration and discussion, students should be able to:

✳ use mass or weight, along with area, to determine pressure.

Exploration

Students discover that shoes which add area to the footprint lower the force per unit area on the ground (and vice versa). **Note:** This can be demonstrated visually by stepping into a box of soft sand.

a. 1. Students can estimate the area of a footprint by counting squares. Sample response: The area of my footprint is 400 cm².

2. This area should be larger than the area in Step **1**. Sample response: The area of my shoeprint is 420 cm².

3. This area should be considerably less than the area in Step **1**. Sample response: The area of my print while wearing a small-heeled shoe is 240 cm².

b. Sample response: The areas vary considerably. The area of the largest shoeprint is 175% of the area of the smallest shoeprint.

teacher note

The calculations in Part **c** below require mass in kilograms. To convert weights in pounds to kilograms, students should use the following:

$$1 \text{ lb} \approx 2.2 \text{ kg}.$$

c. Sample response: My weight in newtons can found by multiplying my mass in kilograms by 9.8 m/sec².

$$135 \text{ lbs} \cdot \frac{1 \text{ kg}}{2.2 \text{ lbs}} \cdot \frac{9.8 \text{ m}}{\text{sec}^2} = \frac{600 \text{ kg} \cdot \text{m}}{\text{sec}^2} \approx 600 \text{ N}$$

d. The following pressures were calculated using the sample responses given in Parts **a** and **c**.
1. without shoes:

$$\frac{600 \text{ N}}{2(400 \text{ cm}^2)} = 0.75 \text{ N/cm}^2$$

2. shoes with flat soles:

$$\frac{600 \text{ N}}{2(420 \text{ cm}^2)} \approx 0.71 \text{ N/cm}^2$$

3. shoes with small heels:

$$\frac{600 \text{ N}}{2(240 \text{ cm}^2)} = 1.25 \text{ N/cm}^2$$

e. Sample response: The three pressures vary by a considerable amount. The largest pressure exerted is approximately 176% of the least pressure exerted.

Discussion

a. Sample response: Hiking boots have large soles that spread your weight over a larger area. This makes them comfortable for long hikes. Shoes worn by rock climbers have small soles to increase the weight per unit area and improve the gripping power of the shoes.

Track shoes for racing also have small soles. Besides reducing the mass, this increases the weight per unit area and (along with spikes) improves traction. **Note:** In Problem **5.2**, students are asked to describe how snowshoes make it easier to walk on snow.

Module 9 ■ *Are You Just a Small Giant?*   **203**

b. Sample response: As the area of the shoeprint decreases, the force per unit area increases. High heels could damage floors made of wood or other substances.

c. Sample response: Four casters are sufficient to support the weight of a box spring and mattress. The weight of a waterbed must be distributed over a larger area.

Warm-Up

1. **a.** ≈ 44.55 kg
   b. ≈ 56.82 kg
   c. ≈ 65 kg
2. **a.** ≈ 33.3 N
   b. ≈ 110.7 N
   c. ≈ 5.35 N

Assignment

Problems suitable for use as assessment items are identified by an asterisk (*).

5.1 **a.** Sample response:

 print of Arlis' heel

b. Assuming half of her weight rests on the heel:

$$\frac{250\,\text{N}}{0.75\,\text{cm}^2} \approx 333\,\text{N/cm}^2$$

* **5.2** Snowshoes distribute the wearer's weight over a greater surface area, decreasing the force per unit area. Estimating the area of the snowshoe is difficult because of its shape and the webbing. However, multiplying its length by its width: 75 cm • 35 cm = 2625 cm². Even if the actual area is only one-third of 2625 or 875 cm², it still is more than three times the area of a typical adult shoeprint.

5.3 From Problem **4.3,** the area of one of Wadlow's shoeprints is 663 cm². From Table **9-1,** his weight is 1950 N. The pressure on the ground can be calculated as follows:

$$\frac{1950\,\text{N}}{2 \bullet 663\,\text{cm}^2} \approx 1.47\,\text{N/cm}^2$$

Students should compare this value with the pressures found in Part **d** of the exploration.

✳ ✳ ✳ ✳ ✳

b. Why do you think that high heels (and other shoes with small heel areas) are banned in some buildings?

c. Why does the frame of a bed with a mattress and box spring differ from the frame of a waterbed?

Warm-Up

1. Convert each of the following weights to mass in kilograms.
   a. 98 lb   **b.** 125 lb   **c.** 143 lb

2. Determine the weight in newtons of each of the following masses.
   a. 3.4 kg   **b.** 11.3 kg   **c.** 546 g

Assignment

5.1 Walking involves the smooth transfer of weight from one foot to the other. At the beginning of each step, about half your weight rests on the heel of the forward shoe.

   a. Arlis wears shoes with a heel area of 0.75 cm² each. Sketch the print of one heel.

   b. Arlis weighs 500 N. Estimate the pressure that the heel of her forward shoe places on the ground at the beginning of each step.

5.2 The diagram below shows the shape and dimensions of a typical snowshoe. Use this diagram to explain why snowshoes make it easier to stand or walk on snow.

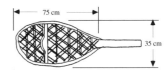

5.3 Assume that you and Robert Wadlow are similar. The area of Wadlow's shoe print is approximately 663 cm². Determine the pressure he places on the ground when standing upright. How does this amount differ from the pressure you place on the ground?

✳ ✳ ✳ ✳ ✳

5.4 The diagram below shows a block of lead in the shape of a rectangular prism. The density of lead is 11.34 g/cm³.

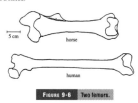

4.0 cm
5.0 cm
9.0 cm

a. Calculate the pressure, in newtons per square centimeter, that the block exerts on the floor.

b. Suppose that the lead block is balanced on top of a wooden cube with an edge length of 2.5 cm. Assuming that the cube adds no significant mass to this situation, determine the pressure that the combination of block and cube exerts on the floor.

c. Explain any differences you observe in the pressures calculated in Parts a and b.

5.5 When placed upright on its base, a cylinder exerts a pressure of 0.50 N/cm² on the floor. The radius of the base is 35 cm. What is the mass of the cylinder?

5.6 Gravity on the planet Mars is about 1/3 the gravity on Earth. How much pressure would you place on the Martian surface when standing upright?

ACTIVITY 6

The **femur**, or thigh bone, extends from the hip to the knee. In humans, two femurs (one in each leg) support the weight of the body. A horse, however, has four related bones to bear its weight. Figure **9-6** shows scale drawings of both a human femur and the femur of a horse.

5 cm

horse

human

Figure 9-6 Two femurs.

5.6 Students should select one of the pressures determined in Part **d** of the exploration. They should then divide this pressure by 3. Sample response: While standing upright without shoes, I exert a pressure of 0.75 N/cm² on Earth. The gravity on Mars is one-third the gravity on Earth, so my weight on Mars would be one-third my weight on Earth. Therefore, the pressure I would exert on the Martian surface is 0.25 N/cm².

ACTIVITY 6

Students make models of bones, compare the graphs of first-, second-, and third-degree curves, and investigate one limit to human growth.

Note: The Italian astronomer and physicist Galileo Galilei (1564–1642) wrote about the relative size and strength of materials in *Dialogues Concerning Two New Sciences*. A paperback edition of this work, translated by Henry Crew and Alfonso di Salvio, was published by Prometheus Books in 1991.

teacher note

This activity may be omitted without significant loss of mathematical content.

A brief assessment of the mathematical content in Activities **4, 5,** and **6,** for use at your discretion, appears in the Teacher Resources for this module.

Materials List

■ tape
■ metersticks (one per group)
■ rulers (one per group)
■ paper (two sheets per group)
■ centimeter graph paper (one sheet per student)

Technology

■ graphing utility
■ spreadsheet

5.4 **a.** The volume of the block is 180 cm³. Using the given density, the block has a mass of approximately 2040 g or 2.04 kg. Multiplying this mass by the acceleration due to gravity (9.8 m/sec²) gives a force of approximately 20 N. The area of the base is 45 cm²; therefore the pressure is:

$$\frac{20\,\text{N}}{45\,\text{cm}^2} \approx 0.44\,\text{N/cm}^2$$

b. The area of the cube's base is 6.25 cm²; therefore the pressure is:

$$\frac{20\,\text{N}}{6.25\,\text{cm}^2} = 3.2\,\text{N/cm}^2$$

c. Sample response: When the lead block is balanced on the cube, the weight is distributed over a smaller area. It is the same idea as distributing my weight over high-heeled shoes.

5.5 The area of the base is approximately 3848 cm². Multiplying this area by the pressure gives a force of 1924 N. Dividing this force by the acceleration due to gravity gives a mass of approximately 196 kg.

Student Outcomes

After completing the following exploration and discussion, students should be able to:

✳ use relationships among mass, density, weight, and pressure to describe proportional changes in size.

Exploration

Students investigate the relationship between area and volume.

a. The two models are obviously not similar. The ratio of the diameters is:

$$\frac{\text{femur diameter of horse}}{\text{femur diameter of human}} = \frac{4.5}{3} = 1.5$$

If the horse and human femurs were similar and 1.5 was the scale factor, the length of the horse femur would have to be 1.5 • 50.5 cm = 75.75 cm (almost twice its actual length). The actual ratio of the lengths is:

$$\frac{\text{femur length of horse}}{\text{femur length of human}} = \frac{39.5}{50.5} = 0.78$$

The circumference of the horse femur is 14.1 cm; the circumference of the human femur is 9.4 cm.

b. 1. Sample response: The area of a cross-section of the human femur is about 6 cm². The area of a cross-section of the horse femur is about 18 cm².

2–3. Using the formula for the area of a circle, the human and horse femurs have cross-sectional areas of approximately 7 cm² and 16 cm², respectively.

4. The horse femur has approximately 2.3 times the cross-sectional area of the human femur. Therefore, it is about twice as strong as a human femur. (Because a horse also has twice as many legs, the total cross-sectional area of leg bones in an individual horse is 4.6 times that of a human.)

c. 1–2. The height is doubled, so the scale factor is 2. Therefore, the diameter of the giant's femur is 2(3 cm) = 6 cm; the length is 2(50.5 cm) = 101 cm; and the circumference is 2(9.4 cm) = 18.8 cm. The cross-sectional area of the bone increases by the square of the scale factor: 2²(7 cm) = 28 cm².

How much weight can these bones support without breaking? In this activity, you build two model femurs and use them to investigate one limit to biological growth.

Exploration

a. Use paper cylinders to model each femur in Figure 9-6. The diameter of each cylinder should equal the smallest diameter of each bone.

Write the corresponding length, diameter, and circumference on each model. Compare the two models for similarity and record your observations.

b. Figure 9-7 shows that a **cross section** is the surface found by slicing an object perpendicular to its length.

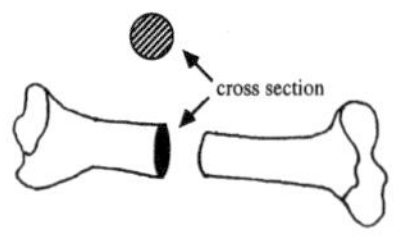

FIGURE 9-7 A cross section of bone.

1. Using centimeter graph paper, draw an accurate cross section of each femur. Estimate the area of each cross section in square centimeters.

2. Calculate the cross-sectional area of each femur and compare these values with your estimates.

3. Write the calculated cross-sectional area on each model.

4. The cross-sectional area of a bone is a good indicator of its relative strength. Compare the strength of the femurs shown in Figure 9-6.

c. The person whose femur appears in Figure 9-6 was 180 cm tall and weighed 600 N. Imagine a similar person who is twice as tall (a giant).

1. Use a strip of paper to make a cross-sectional model of the giant's femur, as shown in Figure 9-8.

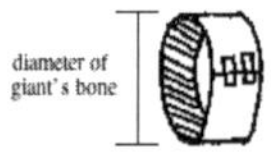

diameter of giant's bone

FIGURE 9-8 Paper model of cross section of bone.

2. Write the diameter, circumference, and cross-sectional area on your model.

3. Would the giant's bone have to support the same weight per square unit as the bone of the person who weighed 600 N? Explain your response.

4. Write a paragraph describing the femurs of the 600-N human and the giant, including the dimensions of the bones and the pressures on the cross-sectional areas.

5. The relationship between volume and area creates a tension on bone structure that affects the biological growth of animals. How might this tension affect the giant?

d. A vertical compression test measures how much pressure a bone can withstand before crushing. In one test, a human femur withstood a pressure of approximately 1200 N/cm².

Considering the results of this test, do you think that there is a limit on the size of humans? Explain your response.

e. To investigate this question further, create a spreadsheet with columns as in Table 9-7. Complete the spreadsheet using the data from Parts **a** and **b** of this exploration.

TABLE 9-7 ■ Scale Factor and Human Body Structure

Scale Factor	Body Height (cm)	Femur Diameter (cm)	Cross-sectional Area of Femur (cm²)	Body Weight (N)	Pressure on Femur (N/cm²)
1	180			600	
2					
3					
⋮					
30					

f. Considering the information in your spreadsheet, do you think that there is a limit on the size of humans? Explain your response.

g. Use the data in your spreadsheet to create the following:

1. a scatterplot of femur diameter versus scale factor

2. a scatterplot of the cross-sectional area of a femur versus scale factor

3. a scatterplot of body weight versus scale factor.

h. 1. Predict the shape of a scatterplot of pressure on the femur versus scale factor.

2. Create a scatterplot of pressure on the femur versus scale factor. How does the shape of the graph compare with your prediction?

Module 9 ■ *Are You Just a Small Giant?*   **231**

---

3. For the 600-N person, the pressure is:

$$\frac{600 \text{ N}}{2 \cdot 7 \text{ cm}^2} = 42.9 \text{ N/cm}^2$$

Volume increases as the cube of the scale factor. Because mass is directly proportional to volume and weight is directly proportional to mass, weight also increases as the cube of the scale factor. The giant's weight would therefore be $2^3 (600 \text{ N}) = 4800 \text{ N}$. Since the cross-sectional area has increased only as the square of the scale factor, the giant must support more weight per square centimeter of bone. For the giant, the pressure is:

$$\frac{4800 \text{ N}}{2 \cdot 28 \text{ cm}^2} \approx 85.7 \text{ N/cm}^2$$

4. Students should summarize their measurements and calculations and demonstrate their understanding of the relationship between mass and area. Sample response: The weight of the giant increased as the cube of the scale factor, but the bone cross-sectional area increased only as the square of the scale factor. Because the scale factor was 2, the giant's femurs bear twice the weight for each unit of cross-sectional area.

5. Sample response: As the tension on the bone structure increases, bones are more likely to break. A giant might be less mobile than a smaller person and more prone to fractures.

d. Sample response: Yes, when a human gets too tall, the bones of the femur would break.

teacher note

In Part **e** of the exploration, the formula used to calculate pressure in the right-hand column of the spreadsheet must account for two femurs per person. The table at the bottom of the page shows some possible formulas.

	A	B	C	D	E	F
1	Scale Factor	Body Height (cm)	Femur Diameter (cm)	Cross-Sectional Area of Femur (cm²)	Body Weight (N)	Pressure on Femur (N/cm²)
2	1	180	3	=(C2/2)^2*PI( )	600	=E2/(D2*2)
3	=A2+1	=$B$2*A3	=$C$2*A3	=(C3/2)^2*PI( )	=A3^3*600	=E3/(D3*2)
4	=A3+1	=$B$2*A4	=$C$2*A4	=(C4/2)^2*PI( )	=A4^3*600	=E4/(D4*2)

e. See Table 9-7 below for a sample spreadsheet: Area is rounded to the nearest whole number while pressure is rounded to the nearest tenth.

f. Answers will vary. As shown in the sample spreadsheet below, the pressure on the femur exceeds 1200 N/cm^2 when the scale factor is 29. This giant would be 57.6 m tall and weigh 14,633,400 N. Students might argue that other factors would limit a person's growth long before this size could be reached.

g. 1. Sample graph:

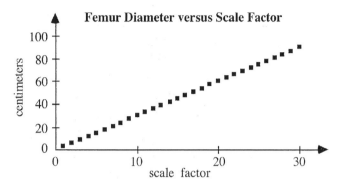

Femur Diameter versus Scale Factor

2. Sample graph:

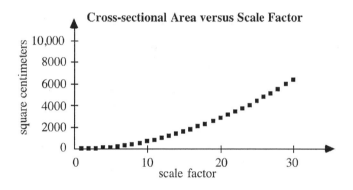

Cross-sectional Area versus Scale Factor

3. Sample graph:

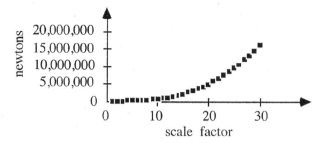

Body Weight versus Scale Factor

h. 1. Answers will vary. Because cross-sectional area increases as the square of the scale factor and weight increases as the cube of the scale factor, then pressure (or weight/area) increases linearly as the scale factor.

2. Sample graph:

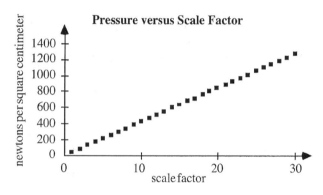

Pressure versus Scale Factor

TABLE 9-7 ■ Scale Factor and Human Body Structure

Scale Factor	Body Height (cm)	Femur Diameter (cm)	Cross-sectional Area of Femur (cm²)	Body Weight (N)	Pressure on Femur (N/cm²)
1	180	3	7	600	42.9
2	360	6	28	4800	85.7
3	540	9	64	16,200	126.6
⋮	⋮	⋮	⋮	⋮	⋮
28	5040	84	5542	13,171,200	1188.3
29	5220	87	5945	14,633,400	1230.7
30	5400	90	6362	16,200,000	1273.2

Discussion

a. What did you discover about the femurs of humans and horses?

b. Is it possible for a human to grow taller than Robert Wadlow? Explain your response.

c. Compare the three graphs you created in Part **g** of the exploration.

d. Describe the relationship between pressure on the femur and scale factor.

Warm-Up

1. Calculate the area of a circle with each of the following dimensions.

   a. $d = 4.7$ cm

   b. $r = 8\frac{3}{4}$ in.

   c. $d = 56.9$ m

2. A block of steel in the shape of a rectangular prism has a base 2 m by 3 m and a height of 5 m. A cubic meter of steel has a mass of about 8000 kg. Use this information to complete Parts **a–c**.

   a. Determine the mass of the block and the pressure (in N/m^2) it exerts on the ground.

   b. If the dimensions of the block were doubled, what would its volume be? What pressure would it exert on the ground?

   c. In general, what happens to the volume, mass, and pressure exerted on the ground as the dimensions of the block change by a given scale factor?

Assignment

6.1 The person whose femur is shown in Figure **9-6** weighed 600 N and was 180 cm tall. Assuming that your body is similar, use your height to estimate the pressure on your femur in newtons per square centimeter.

6.2 Assume that a human femur can withstand a pressure of approximately 1200 N/cm^2. Use your response to Problem **6.1** to determine the maximum weight that your femur can support. *Hint:* First, find the cross-sectional area of your femur.

6.3 Describe some other factors that might limit the maximum height of humans.

* * * * *

Discussion

a. Sample response: The femurs of humans and horses are not similar because corresponding lengths do not have the same ratios. Horse femurs, although shorter in length, have a larger diameter and are much stronger than human femurs.

b. If the strength of bone were the only limitation on human growth (and assuming that human bones can withstand a pressure 1200 N/cm^2 before crushing), then a human could be much larger than Wadlow, even considering the pressure when landing on one foot. However, the limitations on growth are much more complicated than this model suggests. You may ask students to consider, for example, the power of the pump required to circulate blood from head to toe in a person 52 m tall.

c. The three graphs show linear, quadratic, and cubic increases. Students should use the knowledge that area increases as the square of the scale factor and volume increases as the cube of the scale factor to help them interpret these graphs.

d. The pressure on the femur is directly proportional to the scale factor.

Warm-Up

1. a. ≈ 17.34 cm^2

   b. ≈ 240.53 in.^{2}

   c. ≈ 2542.81 m^2

2. a. The mass of the block is 240,000 kg. Its weight is $240{,}000 \cdot 9.8 = 2{,}352{,}000$ N. The pressure exerted is 392,000 N/m^2.

   b. The new dimensions would be 4 m by 6 m by 10 m. The volume would be 240 m^3. The pressure exerted would be 784,000 N/m^2.

   c. Sample response: As the dimensions of the block are increased or decreased by a scale factor, the volume and mass are increased or decreased by the cube of the scale factor. The pressure exerted is increased or decreased by the scale factor.

Assignment

Problems suitable for use as assessment items are identified by an asterisk (*).

6.1 Answers will vary. Sample response: The pressure on each femur in Figure **9-6** was 42.9 N/cm^2. Since I am 160 cm tall and the pressure on each femur is directly proportional to the scale factor:

$$\frac{\text{my pressure}}{42.9 \, \text{N/cm}^2} = \frac{160 \, \text{cm}}{180 \, \text{cm}}$$

$$\text{my pressure} \approx 38.1 \, \text{N/cm}^2$$

* 6.2 Answers will vary. Students may use height to estimate the cross-sectional area of each femur. Sample response: Since area increases as the square of the scale factor and my height is 160 cm, then the cross-sectional area of my femur is:

$$\frac{\text{area}}{7 \, \text{cm}^2} = \left(\frac{160 \, \text{cm}}{180 \, \text{cm}}\right)^2$$

$$\text{area} \approx 5.5 \, \text{cm}^2$$

Assuming that human bone can withstand a pressure of 1200 N/cm^2, the maximum weight can be found by multiplying the cross-sectional area by 1200. Therefore the maximum weight my femur will hold is:

$$5.5 \, \text{cm}^2 \cdot \frac{1200 \, \text{N}}{\text{cm}^2} = 6600 \, \text{N}$$

6.3 Answers will vary. Students may mention limits on blood circulation, muscle strength, and nutrition needed to sustain growth, and other biological and environmental factors.

✳ ✳ ✳ ✳ ✳

6.4 **a.** 1960 N

b. 19,600 N

c. The ratio of the heights of King Kong and an average gorilla is about 5.4/1. Because weight increases by the cube of the scale factor, the ratio of the weights would be:

$$\left(\frac{5.4}{1}\right)^3 \approx \frac{160}{1}$$

Therefore, King Kong would weigh about 310,000 N, which is much more than the femur could support.

6.5 The cross-sectional area of the dinosaur femur is $12.5^2 \cdot \pi \approx 491$ cm^2. The Tyrannosaurus has two femurs, so the total cross-sectional area is 2(491 cm^2) or 982 cm^2. For a weight of 35,000 N, the pressure is:

$$\frac{35000 \text{ N}}{982 \text{ cm}^2} \approx 36 \text{ N/cm}^2$$

For a weight of 62,000 N, the pressure is about 63 N/cm^2.

From Part **c** of the exploration, the pressure on a human femur for a 600-N person is 42.9 N/cm^2—a little less than the average of the two Tyrannosaurus calculations.

6.4 The mean height of male gorillas is approximately 1.8 m. Their mean mass is about 200 kg.

a. Determine the mean weight, in newtons, of male gorillas.

b. A gorilla's femur can support a maximum of 10 times the mean body weight. What is this maximum weight?

c. In one version of the story, the gorilla King Kong was supposed to be about 9.8 m tall. Is it possible for a gorilla like King Kong to exist? Explain your response.

6.5 The femur of a Tyrannosaurus in a Montana museum is 103 cm long and has a diameter of 25 cm. Scientists estimate that this dinosaur weighed between 35,000 N and 62,000 N. Which bone is subject to greater pressure: the femur of this Tyrannosaurus or the femur of a 600-N person? Explain your response.

Summary Assessment

Do you think that human siblings are similar? Use the data in the following table (or collect data from your own family) to support your response.

Sibling	Length of Foot (cm)	Circumference of Foot (cm)	Area of Footprint (cm²)	Body Weight (N)
A	15.0	35	61	93
B	19.5	45	101	208
C	23.0	54	149	340
D	30.0	70	251	756

In justifying your position, include examples of each of the following:

- proportionality
- scale factors
- linear equations of the form $y = ax$
- power equations of the forms $y = ax^2$ and $y = ax^3$
- square roots
- cube roots.

Your report should also include predictions made using scale factors, graphs, and equations, and should use residuals to determine how well an equation models a data set.

---

teacher note

An additional assessment, for use at your discretion, appears in the Teacher Resources for this module.

Summary Assessment

If students collect their own data, they probably will conclude that siblings are not similar. The data in the table, however, can be modeled very well by equations that indicate similarity. As shown in the graph below, for example, the equation $y = 2.3x$ models the relationship between foot length and circumference for all four siblings.

Circumference versus Length

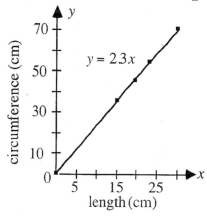

The table below shows the sum of the absolute values of the residuals for this model.

The fit appears to be good both from the graph end and the small residual sum.

Sibling	Length of Foot (x)	Circumference of Foot (y)	Predicted Circumference	Absolute Value of Residual
A	15	35	34.5	0.5
B	19.5	45	44.85	0.15
C	23	54	52.9	1.1
D	30	70	69	1
			Sum	2.75

Similarly, the equation $y = 0.27x^2$ models the relationship between foot length and footprint area.

Area versus Length

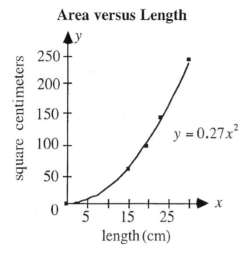

The equation $y = 0.28x^3$ models the relationship between foot length and weight.

Mass versus Length

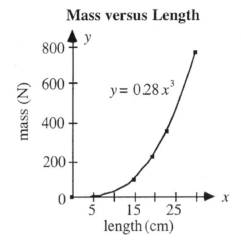

The first table below shows the sum of the absolute values of the residuals for this model.

The fit appears to be good both from the graph end and the small residual sum.

The second table below shows the sum of the absolute values of the residuals or this model.

The fit appears to be good both from the graph end and the small residual sum.

Sibling	Length of Foot (x)	Area of Footprint (y)	Predicted Area	Absolute Value of Residual
A	15	61	60.75	0.25
B	19.5	101	102.67	1.67
C	23	149	142.83	6.17
D	30	251	243	8
			Sum	16.09

Sibling	Length of Foot (x)	Body Weight (y)	Predicted Mass	Absolute Value of Residual
A	15	93	94.5	1.5
B	19.5	208	207.6	0.4
C	23	340	340.7	0.7
D	30	756	756	0
			Sum	2.6

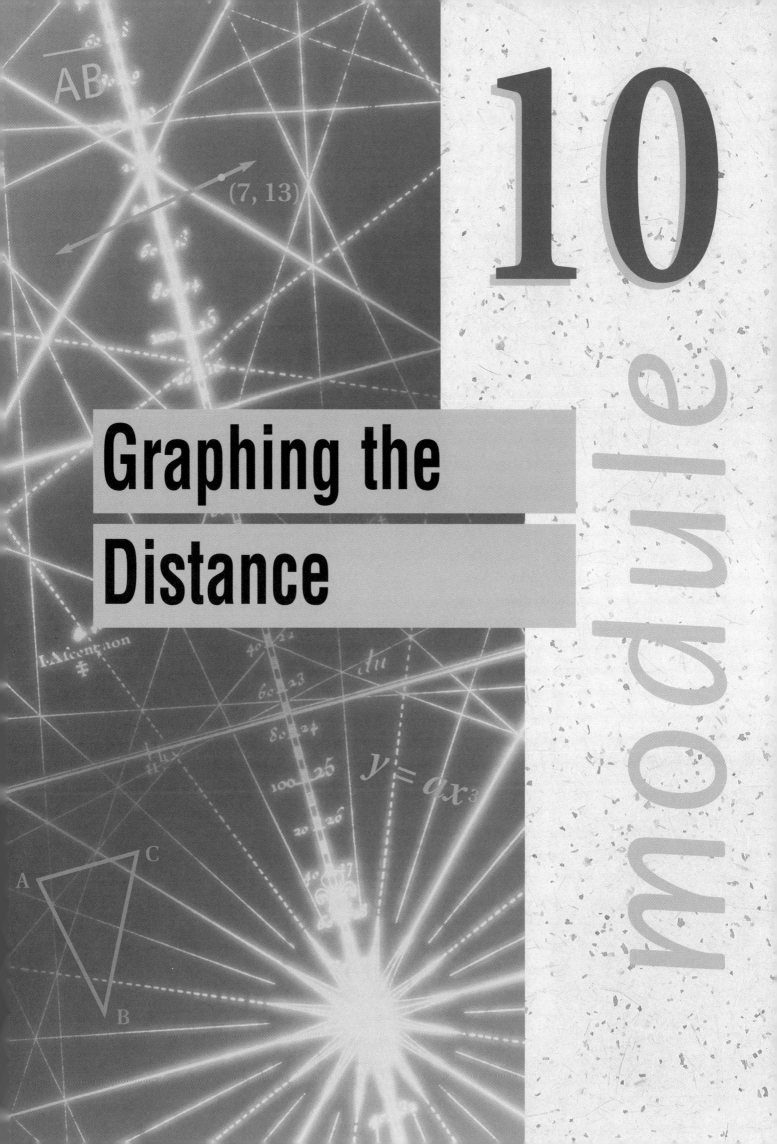

Graphing the Distance

Overview

This module uses distance-time graphs to investigate linear and quadratic functions.

Activity 1:   Students use a sonar range finder to create distance-time graphs for objects moving at constant speeds. Students use interval and inequality notation to describe portions of the graphs and determine average velocity as the slope of a line. They then approximate instantaneous velocity using narrowing intervals of average velocity.

Activity 2:   Students again use a sonar range finder to create distance-time graphs of objects moving at constant speeds. They determine appropriate linear models using residuals.

Activity 3:   Students graph and translate quadratic functions in vertex form. They also rewrite quadratic functions in vertex form to the general form $f(x) = ax^2 + bx + c$.

Activity 4:   Students use a sonar range finder to gather distance-time data for objects moving down an inclined plane and for objects in free fall. They determine appropriate quadratic models using residuals.

Objectives

In this module, students will:

✳ use interval and inequality notation (1)

✳ relate finite and infinite intervals to inequalities and graphs (1)

✳ calculate displacement for a given time interval (1)

✳ distinguish between speed and velocity (1)

✳ calculate average speed and average velocity (1)

✳ estimate instantaneous velocity (1)

✳ create distance-time graphs using motion detectors (1, 2, 4)

✳ interpret distance-time graphs (1, 2, 3, 4)

✳ relate distance, time, and velocity for an object moving at constant speed to the slope-intercept form of a line (2)

✳ calculate residuals and the sum of the squares of the residuals (2, 4)

✳ use linear regressions to model data (2)

✳ write and graph quadratic functions of the general form $f(x) = ax^2 + bx + c$ and the vertex form $f(x) = a(x - c)^2 + d$ (3)

✳ predict shapes of graphs from quadratics in vertex form (3)

✳ translate parabolas using the vertex form (3)

✳ apply the distributive property to expand the vertex form to the general form (3)

✳ calculate average acceleration (4)

✳ describe the height of a falling object using the formula $d(t) = -\dfrac{1}{2}gt^2 + v_0 t + d_0$ (4)

✳ use quadratic regressions to model data (4).

Prerequisites

For this module, students should know:

✳ how to identify graphs of linear, exponential, and power functions

✳ how to graph linear equations

✳ how to find the slope and x- and y-intercepts of linear graphs and equations

✳ how to write an equation for a line given two ponts on the line

✳ how to expand algebraic expressions using the distributive property

✳ how to make scatterplots

✳ how to calculate residuals

✳ how to solve equations in one variable

✳ how to interpret function notation

✳ how to evaluate functions for a given value.

 Flashbacks, for use at your discretion, appear in the Teacher Resources for this module. These brief problem sets provide a review of some prerequisite skills for each activity.

Planning Guide

Activity	Materials	Technology	Time Line
Activity 1	▪ graph paper	▪ sonar range finder ▪ science interface device ▪ graphing utility	2 days
Activity 2	▪ graph paper ▪ masking tape ▪ basketball or soccer ball ▪ track for ball	▪ sonar range finder ▪ science interface device ▪ graphing utility	2 days
Activity 3	▪ graph paper	▪ graphing utility	3 days
Activity 4	▪ graph paper ▪ masking tape ▪ basketball or soccer ball ▪ track for ball	▪ sonar range finder ▪ science interface device ▪ graphing utility	2 days
Assessment Activities	▪ none	▪ none	3 days **Total: 12 days**

 teacher note

Several different companies offer motion detectors or sonar range finders that collect distance-time data. This data can be transferred to a calculator or computer using a science interface device. For example, the Calculator Based Laboratory 2 (CBL 2) produced by Texas Instruments is a scientific interface that connects collecting devices to a graphing calculator. The CBL 2 connects to TI-84, TI-89, and TI-Voyage 200 calculators and comes with its own software. (You will need a TI Connectivity cable and the free TI Connect software to download the CBL 2 software first to a computer, then to your calculators.)

Self-contained units such as Texas Instruments' TI Ranger do not require a science interface. The unit connects directly to a calculator for data collection and transfer.

Introduction

Distance-time graphs represent one of the most common applications of graphing in engineering and physics.

In this activity, students use a sonar range finder and science interface device to investigate different kinds of motion.

Materials List

- graph paper (several sheets per student)

Technology

- sonar range finder (one per group)
- science interface device (one per group)
- graphing utility

teacher note

If you are unfamiliar with the range finder, science interface device, and related software, you might need to refer to appropriate manuals and practice with the equipment before introducing it to students. For example, some sonar range finders might have an interval of distances in which they operate most efficiently.

Actual collection of relevant, useful data in each experiment takes only a few seconds. However, students may require some time to become comfortable with the equipment. Careful and accurate setup, group cooperation, and multiple trial runs are necessary to obtain data sets that give good analytic results.

For Parts **b–d** of Exploration **2,** students may set their range finders to collect and graph data in real time. Refer to the range finder's manual to determine the appropriate settings.

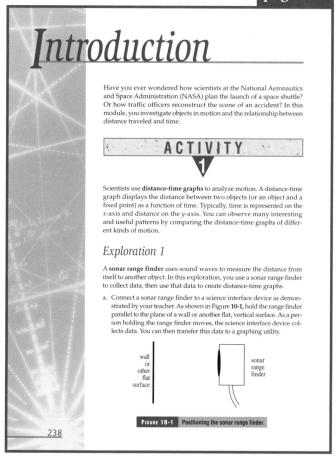

Introduction

Have you ever wondered how scientists at the National Aeronautics and Space Administration (NASA) plan the launch of a space shuttle? Or how traffic officers reconstruct the scene of an accident? In this module, you investigate objects in motion and the relationship between distance traveled and time.

ACTIVITY 1

Scientists use **distance-time graphs** to analyze motion. A distance-time graph displays the distance between two objects (or an object and a fixed point) as a function of time. Typically, time is represented on the x-axis and distance on the y-axis. You can observe many interesting and useful patterns by comparing the distance-time graphs of different kinds of motion.

Exploration 1

A **sonar range finder** uses sound waves to measure the distance from itself to another object. In this exploration, you use a sonar range finder to collect data, then use that data to create distance-time graphs.

a. Connect a sonar range finder to a science interface device as demonstrated by your teacher. As shown in Figure 10-1, hold the range finder parallel to the plane of a wall or another flat, vertical surface. As a person holding the range finder moves, the science interface device collects data. You can then transfer this data to a graphing utility.

FIGURE 10-1 Positioning the sonar range finder.

238

Student Outcomes

After completing the following explorations and discussions, students should be able to:

* create distance-time graphs using motion detectors

* interpret distance-time graphs

* distinguish between speed and velocity

* use interval notation

* relate finite and infinite intervals to inequalities and graphs

* calculate displacement over a given time interval

* calculate average speed and average velocity

* estimate instantaneous velocity.

b. Practice using a range finder, science interface, and graphing utility to generate distance-time graphs. Move the range finder toward the wall, then away from it, and observe the resulting graphs. Draw one of the graphs on a sheet of graph paper.

c. Use the range finder to create distance-time graphs that match the ones shown below. (This might take a few trials.) Record the method you used to create each graph.

1.

2.

3.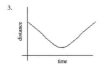

4.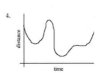

d. Figure **10-2** below shows a distance-time graph of data collected during the launch of a model rocket, where the distance is the rocket's height above the ground. After the rocket's engine ignited, it flew straight up. A few seconds after the engine burned out, it began to fall straight back toward the ground. Later, its parachute opened and slowed its descent.

FIGURE 10-2 Distance-time graph for a model rocket.

Point the range finder at the floor. By raising and lowering the range finder along a vertical path, create a distance-time graph whose shape resembles the graph in Figure **10-2.**

Exploration 1

a–b. Students practice generating distance-time graphs using the sonar range finder. Each point on a distance-time graph represents the distance (y) from the sonar range finder to a flat surface at a given time (x). Although graphs will vary according to the movements of the students holding the range finders, they should resemble connected scatterplots.

> **Note:** Students should recognize that distance-time graphs are not position plots. For example, the distance-time graph of a ball traveling straight up into the air and straight back down is not a vertical line.

c. Methods will vary. See sample responses in Part **d** of the following discussion.

d. Students should raise the range finder rapidly, then slowly move it toward the floor.

Discussion 1

a. Sample response: Each point represents how far away the range finder is from the wall at a given time.

b. Sample response: The *y*-intercept represents the distance the range finder is from the wall when it is first turned on (when the time is 0). The *x*-intercept represents the time when the distance between the range finder and the wall is 0.

c. Sample response: As the range finder and an object get farther apart, the data points are plotted farther away from the *x*-axis. As the range finder and the object get closer together, the data points fall closer to the *x*-axis. The steepness of the line segment between any two points is determined by the speed at which the distance between the range finder and the object is changing—the faster the speed, the steeper the line segment.

d. Sample response: To create the graph in Part **c1** of the exploration, move the range finder at a steady rate away from the wall.

    To create the graph in Part **c2,** do not move the range finder at all.

    To create the graph in Part **c3,** move the range finder at a steady rate toward the wall, then move it at a steady rate away from the wall.

    To create the graph in Part **c4,** move the range finder at a fairly steady rate toward the wall, then move it at the same rate away from the wall. This is followed by moving the range finder quickly toward the wall, then slowing the pace and continuing to move toward the wall. The range finder then is moved away from the wall at the slower rate; then the rate is slowed even more. The graph is competed by continuing to move slowly away from the wall, then increasing the rate and continuing to move away from the wall.

e. Sample response: At points *P* and *Q*, a change in direction occurs. At point *R*, the range finder is moving slowly away from the wall.

f. Sample response: Curved sections show motion in which the speed of the range finder is either increasing or decreasing, while straight sections represent motion at a constant rate.

Discussion 1

a. In Part **b** of Exploration **1,** you sketched a graph on a sheet of paper. What does each point on the graph represent?

b. On a distance-time graph, what do the *x*- and *y*-intercepts represent?

c. How does the motion of the range finder in Part **b** of Exploration **1** affect the resulting distance-time graph?

d. Describe how you moved the range finder to obtain each of the graphs in Part **c** of Exploration **1.**

e. Figure **10-3** shows a distance-time graph generated by moving a range finder toward and away from a wall. Describe what is happening to the range finder at points *P, Q,* and *R*.

FIGURE 10-3 A distance-time graph.

f. How does the kind of motion represented by a "curved" section of a distance-time graph differ from the motion represented by a "straight" section?

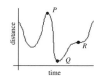

mathematics note

The set of all real numbers between two fixed endpoints is a **real-number interval.** Each endpoint may or may not be included in the interval.

One way to describe an interval is with an inequality. For example, the set of real numbers greater than or equal to 15 but less than 30 can be described by the inequality $15 \le x < 30$.

We also can describe a real-number interval using **interval notation.** In interval notation, a square bracket,] or [, indicates that the endpoint is included in the interval. A parenthesis,) or (, indicates that the endpoint is not included in the interval. For example, the interval described by the inequality $15 \le x < 30$ can be written as [15, 30).

240   Module 10 ■ *Graphing the Distance*

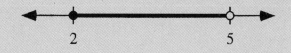

teacher note

Before proceeding to Part **h** of Discussion **1,** students should be aware of several different ways to represent an inequality. For example, the statement "*x* is greater than or equal to 2 but less than 5" can be represented using the interval [2, 5), the inequality $2 \le x < 5$, or by the following graph:

| | |
| 2 | 5 |

g. Consider the distance-time graph for a model rocket in Figure **10-2.** Use interval notation in your discussion of the following questions.

 1. Over what interval of time is the distance increasing? How is this indicated by the graph?

 2. Over what interval of time is the distance decreasing? How is this indicated by the graph?

 3. Over what interval of time is the distance increasing the fastest? How is this indicated by the graph?

 4. Over what interval of time is the distance decreasing the fastest? How is this indicated by the graph?

h. A set of real numbers greater than a given value increases without bound. Such a set of numbers is an **infinite interval.** The notation for an infinite interval uses ∞, the symbol for infinity, to indicate that the set does not end.

 For example, the interval of real numbers greater than or equal to 2, or $x \geq 2$, can be represented in interval notation as [2, ∞). Notice that a parenthesis,), is used with ∞.

 When describing sets of real numbers less than a given value, the symbol for negative infinity (−∞) is used.

 1. Describe the set of real numbers less than −6 using interval notation.

 2. Would you use an infinite interval to describe time in the flight of a model rocket? Explain your response.

 3. What set is described by (−∞, ∞)?

i. The average speed of an object during a time interval can be calculated by dividing distance traveled by time.

TABLE 10-1 ■ Distance-Time Data for a Model Rocket			
Time (sec)	Distance (m)	Time (sec)	Distance (m)
0	0	11	170.8
1	7.4	12	155.4
2	36.9	13	147.7
4	134.2	14	141.9
6	192.9	15	136.3
8	212.3	16	130.8
10	192.9		

 1. Using the data from Table **10-1,** determine the total distance traveled by the model rocket during the interval [6, 12].

 2. What is the rocket's average speed during the interval [6, 12]?

Module 10 ■ *Graphing the Distance* 241

j. Given the current location of an object moving at constant speed, what information would you need to predict the object's location in the future?

science note

Displacement is a change in the position of an object. It has both magnitude and direction.

For example, consider the distance-time data for the model rocket in Table **10-1.** At $t = 2$ sec, the rocket is 36.9 m above the ground. At $t = 6$ sec, it is 192.9 m above the ground. Its displacement during this time is 192.9 − 36.9 = 156.0 m. In this case, the magnitude of the rocket's displacement is 156.0, while its direction is positive (away from the ground).

From $t = 6$ sec to $t = 12$ sec, however, the rocket's position changes from 192.9 m above the ground to 155.4 m above the ground. Its displacement over this period is 155.4 − 192.9 = −37.5 m. In this case, the magnitude of the rocket's displacement is 37.5, while its direction is negative (toward the ground).

k. 1. Using the information in Table **10-1,** determine the displacement of the model rocket during the time interval [6, 12].

 2. Compare this displacement to the distance you determined in Part **i** of the discussion.

science note

Velocity is the rate of change in position with respect to time. Like displacement, velocity also has magnitude and direction.

Calculate the **average velocity** of an object by dividing its displacement by the change in time. For example, you can find the model rocket's average velocity between $t = 2$ sec and $t = 6$ sec as follows:

$$\frac{192.3 \text{ m} - 36.9 \text{ m}}{6 \text{ sec} - 2 \text{ sec}} = \frac{156.0 \text{ m}}{4 \text{ sec}} = 39 \text{ m/sec}$$

l. 1. Use the data in Table **10-1** to determine the rocket's average velocity during the time interval [6, 12].

242 Module 10 ■ *Graphing the Distance*

g. 1. Sample response: The distance is increasing over the interval (0,8), where x represents time in seconds. As you move from left to right along the x-axis, the corresponding y-values continue to increase in value.

 2. Sample response: The distance is decreasing over the interval (8,16). As you move from left to right along the x-axis, the corresponding y-values continue to decrease in value.

 3. Sample response: The distance is increasing the fastest over the interval [2,4]. This is the steepest part of the graph in which the rocket is rising.

 4. Sample response: The distance is decreasing the fastest over the interval [10,11]. This is the steepest part of the graph in which the rocket is falling.

h. 1. The set of real numbers less than −6 decreases without bound; therefore the interval notation uses −∞ and a left parenthesis: (−∞,−6). The right parenthesis shows that −6 is not included.

 2. Sample response: No. A rocket flight will begin and end. Infinite intervals only contain sets of real numbers that continue forever.

 3. This notation describes the set of all real numbers.

i. 1. The rocket went up 19.4 m during the interval [6, 8] and down 56.9 m during the interval [8, 12]. Therefore, the total distance traveled by the rocket during the interval [6, 12] is 76.3 m.

 2. The average speed of the rocket during the interval [6,12] is:

$$\frac{76.3 \text{ m}}{6 \text{ sec}} \approx 12.7 \text{ m/sec}$$

j. Sample response: You would need to know the direction in which the object is moving.

k. 1. The rocket is 192.9 m above the ground at $t = 6$. It is 155.4 m above the ground at $t = 12$. Therefore, the displacement of the rocket during the interval [6, 12] is −37.5 m.

 2. Sample response: The distance traveled by the rocket during the time interval [6, 12] is 76.3 m, while the displacement is −37.5 m. The negative sign indicates that at $t = 12$, the rocket is below its location at $t = 6$.

l. 1. The average velocity of the rocket during the interval [6, 12] is:

$$\frac{-37.5 \text{ m}}{6 \text{ sec}} = -6.25 \text{ m/sec}$$

Module 10 ■ *Graphing the Distance* 219

2. The magnitude is 6.25 m/sec. The direction is negative, which in this case means that the rocket is moving toward the ground.

3. Sample response: The rocket's average speed of 12.7 m/sec is different from the average velocity of –6.25 m/sec. This is because average velocity is defined as displacement divided by the change in time, and average speed is defined as distance traveled divided by the change in time.

Exploration 2

In this exploration, students estimate instantaneous velocity using intervals. The true instantaneous velocity at a given point in time is equal to the slope of the line tangent to the distance-time curve at that point. Students will encounter this basic concept of calculus in later modules.

Laser speed guns collect distance-time data as often as several hundred times per second to estimate instantaneous velocity.

a. Sample graph:

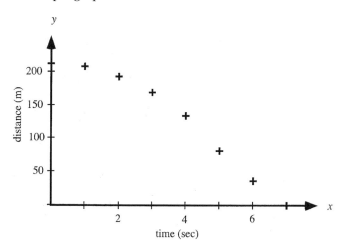

teacher note

Students should save their graphs for use in Discussion **1** of Activity **3**.

b. 1. The average velocity is:

$$\frac{(0 - 240) \text{ m}}{7 \text{ sec}} \approx -34.3 \text{ m/sec}$$

2. Students should connect the points (0,240) and (7,0).

3. The slope of the line equals the average velocity for this interval.

---

2. Describe the magnitude and direction of this average velocity.

3. Compare this average velocity to the average speed you determined in Part **i** of the discussion.

Exploration 2

Highway patrol officers use radar or laser speed guns to collect distance-time data about moving objects. These devices can give very accurate information about a car's **instantaneous velocity**—its velocity at a particular instant in time. In this exploration, you examine how to use distance-time data to approximate instantaneous velocity.

a. Table **10-2** below shows some distance-time data collected from a falling object. Create a scatterplot of this data.

TABLE 10-2 ■ Distance-Time Data for a Falling Object	
Time (sec)	Distance (m)
0	240.0
1	235.1
2	220.4
3	195.9
4	161.7
5	117.5
6	63.6
7	0.0

b. 1. Determine the average velocity for the time interval representing the entire fall.

2. Draw a line connecting the data points which correspond with the interval in Step **1**.

3. Determine the slope of the line in Step **2**. Compare its value with the average velocity for the interval.

c. One way to approximate the instantaneous velocity at a given time is to select an interval that contains that instant. Then you can use the average velocity for this interval to approximate the instantaneous velocity.

Suppose you want to approximate the instantaneous velocity at $t = 0.5$ sec. You could use the interval for the entire fall for your approximation, but is there a better choice?

1. Determine the average velocity for the time interval [0,5].

Module 10 ■ *Graphing the Distance*   243

c. 1. The average velocity is:

$$\frac{(117.5 - 240.0) \text{ m}}{(5 - 0) \text{ sec}} \approx -24.5 \text{ m/sec}$$

2. Draw a line connecting the data points which correspond with this interval.

3. Determine the slope of this line and compare it with the average velocity for the interval.

d. Other intervals that contain $t = 0.5$ sec might give different approximations. Repeat Part **c** for each of the following time intervals:

   1. [0,3]
   2. [0,2]
   3. [0,1]

e. Compare the average velocities you calculated in Parts **b–d**. Which value do you think is closest to the instantaneous velocity at $t = 0.5$ sec?

f. Use the data in Table **10-1** to estimate the instantaneous velocity at $t = 4.5$ sec as accurately as possible.

   Note: Save your scatterplot for use in Discussion **1** of Activity **3**.

Discussion 2

a. In Table **10-2**, what does an entry of 0 represent in each column?

b. What does a negative value for average velocity indicate about the motion of the object?

c. 1. Does the line you drew in Part **b** of Exploration **2** provide a good model for the data?

   2. What information does the line provide?

d. Using the graph from Part **a** of Exploration **2**, how can you tell when the object was moving at its greatest velocity?

e. Describe how you could approximate the instantaneous velocity of the object at $t = 6.5$ sec.

Warm-Up

1. Use interval notation to describe the set of real numbers represented by each of the following inequalities.

   a. $-2 \le x < 5$
   b. $x \ge 9$
   c. $12 > x > 7$
   d. $-4 \ge x$

2. Students should connect the points (0,240) and (5,117.5).

3. The slope of the line equals the average velocity for this interval.

d. In each case, the slope of the line equals the average velocity for the interval.

1. The average velocity is:

$$\frac{(195.9 - 240.0)\text{ m}}{(3 - 0)\text{ sec}} \approx -14.7 \text{ m/sec}$$

Students should connect the points (0,240) and (3,195.9).

2. The average velocity is:

$$\frac{(220.4 - 240.0)\text{ m}}{(2 - 0)\text{ sec}} \approx -9.8 \text{ m/sec}$$

Students should connect the points (0,240) and (2,220.4).

3. The average velocity is:

$$\frac{(235.1 - 240.0)\text{ m}}{(1 - 0)\text{ sec}} \approx -4.9 \text{ m/sec}$$

Students should connect the points (0,240) and (1,235.1).

e. Answers will vary. Sample response: Because the interval [0,1] is the smallest that contains $t = 0.5$ sec, it should provide the best estimate.

f. Using the time interval [4,5], the average velocity is:

$$\frac{(117.5 - 161.6)\text{ m}}{1 \text{ sec}} = -44.1 \text{ m/sec}$$

This is a reasonable estimate for the instantaneous velocity at $t = 4.5$ sec.

Discussion 2

a. Sample response: In the "time" column, an entry of 0 represents the beginning of data collection. In the "distance" column, 0 represents the point where the object makes contact with the range finder.

b. Sample response: In this case, a negative value for average velocity indicates that the object is closer to the range finder at the end of the interval than it was at the beginning of the interval.

c. 1. Sample response: No. A line is not a good model for the shape of this scatterplot.

   2. The slope of the line equals the average velocity for the interval.

d. Sample response: The scatterplot appears to be the steepest in the interval [6,7]. This would correspond with the greatest average velocity.

e. Answers will vary. Sample response: One way to approximate the velocity at a particular time is to find the average velocity for an interval that contains that time. For example, the average velocity during the interval [6,7] could be used to approximate the instantaneous velocity at $t = 6.5$ sec as -63.6 m/sec. The smaller the interval, the better the approximation.

Warm-Up

1. a. [−2,5)
   b. [9,∞)
   c. (7,12)
   d. (−∞,−4]

2. a. $-12 \le x \le -4$ **b.** $x \le 3$

  c. $-32 < x < 45$ **d.** $x \ge 0$

3. a. The average velocity for any interval shown on the graph is equivalent to $-10/3$ m/sec.

  b. Because the graph shows distance versus time for an object moving with constant velocity, the average velocity and slope are equivalent.

4. a. Sample response: The x-intercepts are $(-4,0)$, and approximately $(4.3,0)$. Because an x-intercept occurs when the y-value is 0, $(-4,0)$ can be identified from the table.

  b. Sample response: The function is increasing. As the x-values increase, the corresponding y-coordinates also increase.

  c. Sample response: The average rate of change is increasing. As the x-values increase, the steepness of the graph increases. This can be seen by calculating the average rate of change over the intervals $(0,2)$, $(2,4)$, and $(4,5)$. The average rates of change are -1, -6, and -7 respectively.

Assignment

Problems suitable for use as assessment items are identified by an asterisk (*).

1.1 a. Students should describe an object moving away from a fixed point at a constant speed.

  b. Students should describe an object moving toward a fixed point at a constant speed.

  c. Students should describe an object moving away from a fixed point and gradually slowing to a stop, then changing direction and gradually speeding up.

  d. Students should describe an object moving toward a fixed point at an increasing speed, slowing to a stop, moving away at an increasing speed, then again slowing to a stop.

* 1.2 a–d. Sample response:

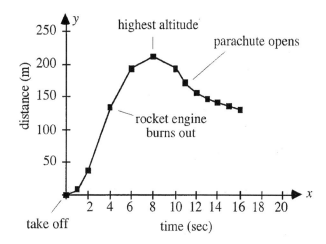

Note: Engine burnout and the parachute opening both correspond to inflection points in the graph. These are points

---

2. Write a corresponding inequality for each interval below.

  a. $[-12,-4]$

  b. $(-\infty,3]$

  c. $(-32,-45)$

  d. $[0,\infty)$

3. The graph below shows some distance-time data for an object.

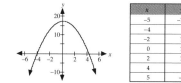

  a. What is this object's average velocity for any time interval shown on the graph?

  b. What is the relationship between this object's average velocity and the slope of the line? Explain your response.

4. Use the following graph and table to complete Parts **a–c** below.

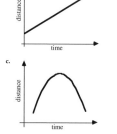

x	y
−5	−10
−4	0
−2	13
0	16
2	14
4	2
5	−5

  a. Describe the x-intercepts, if any. Explain how you used the table to help determine your response.

  b. Consider the interval of x-values $[-5,0)$. Are y-values increasing or decreasing over this interval? Explain your response.

  c. In general, the change in y-values over a given interval of x-values is the **average rate of change**.

  Consider the intervals of x-values $(0,2)$, $(2,4)$, and $(4,5)$. Is the average rate of change constant over these intervals? Explain your response.

Module 10 ■ *Graphing the Distance*   **245**

Assignment

1.1 Describe a real-world motion that could be represented by each of the distance-time graphs below.

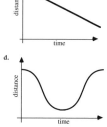

1.2 Sketch a copy of the distance-time graph in Figure **10-2.** On your copy, indicate the points at which you think the following events occurred:

  a. the rocket takes off

  b. the rocket's engine burns out

  c. the rocket reaches its highest altitude

  d. the parachute opens.

1.3 The table below contains data collected during the flight of a model rocket. Use the table to complete Parts **a–c.**

Time (sec)	Distance (m)	Time (sec)	Distance (m)
0	0	11	170.8
1	7.4	12	155.4
2	36.9	13	147.7
4	134.2	14	141.9
6	192.9	15	136.3
8	212.3	16	130.8
10	192.9		

246   Module 10 ■ *Graphing the Distance*

a. Determine the rocket's average speed during the time interval [6,10].

b. Determine the average velocity of the rocket during the same interval.

c. Explain why your responses to Parts **a** and **b** are different.

1.4 a. Determine the average velocity of the rocket in Problem **1.3** during the time interval [6,8].

b. Estimate the instantaneous velocity of the rocket at $t = 3$ sec. Describe how you determined your estimate.

1.5 The table below shows a space shuttle's distance from earth at various times during its initial vertical ascent.

Time (sec)	Distance (m)	Time (sec)	Distance (m)
24	1791	136	53,355
48	7274	160	66,809
72	15,539	184	78,374
96	27,920	208	88,117
120	43,326		

SOURCE: Johnson Space Center, Houston, Texas.

a. Create a distance-time graph of this data.

b. Based on this data, over what time interval does the space shuttle appear to start slowing down? Justify your response.

c. What is the average velocity of the space shuttle over the time interval [24,120]?

d. 1. Estimate the shuttle's instantaneous velocity, in meters per second, 195 sec after liftoff. Describe how you determined your estimate.

2. Express your response to Step **1** in kilometers per hour.

* * * * *

1.6 Sketch a distance-time graph that illustrates the motion of Little Red Riding Hood in the following paragraph:

Little Red Riding Hood left home and walked briskly down the road towards Grandmother's house. Along the way, she stopped to pick some violets growing beside the road. The Wolf saw her picking flowers and offered to show her a shortcut. He led Little Red Riding Hood on a winding path through the woods. After the path crossed the road for the third time at the place where she had picked the flowers, Little Red Riding Hood realized that she'd been tricked. She got back on the road and ran the rest of the way to Grandmother's house.

where the concavity of the graph changes from positive to negative or from negative to positive.

* 1.3 a. The average speed of the rocket during this interval is:

$$\frac{(212.3 \text{ m} - 192.9 \text{ m}) + (212.3 \text{ m} - 192.9 \text{ m})}{(10 \text{ sec} - 6 \text{ sec})} = 9.7 \text{ m/sec}$$

b. The average velocity of the rocket during the same interval is:

$$\frac{(192.9 - 192.9) \text{ m}}{(10 - 6) \text{ sec}} = 0.0 \text{ m/sec}$$

c. Sample response: The average velocity in this interval differs from the average speed because the rocket returned to the same altitude as at the beginning of the interval. This resulted in a displacement of 0 and an average velocity of 0 m/sec. The rocket actually went up 19.4 m, then back down the same distance.

1.4 a. The average velocity of the rocket during this interval is:

$$\frac{(212.3 - 192.9) \text{ m}}{(8 - 6) \text{ sec}} = 9.7 \text{ m/sec}$$

b. Sample response: By calculating the average velocity during the interval [2, 4], the instantaneous velocity at 3 sec can be approximated as follows:

$$\frac{(134.2 - 36.9) \text{ m}}{(4 - 2) \text{ sec}} \approx 48.6 \text{ m/sec}$$

1.5 a. Sample graph:

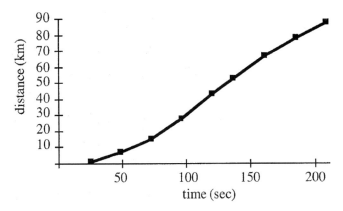

b. Sample response: The rocket appears to be moving more slowly in the interval [136, 160] than in the interval [120, 136]. For the interval [136, 160], the average velocity is:

$$\frac{(66.8 - 53.4)}{(160 - 136)} \approx 0.56 \text{ km/sec}$$

For the interval [120, 136], the average velocity is

$$\frac{(53.4 - 43.3)}{(136 - 120)} \approx 0.63 \text{ km/sec}$$

c. The average velocity is approximately 432.7 m/sec.

d. 1. Sample response: The instantaneous velocity at 195 sec can be estimated using the average velocity during the interval [184, 208]:

$$\frac{(88,117 - 78,374) \text{ m}}{(208 - 184) \text{ sec}} \approx 406 \text{ m/sec}$$

2. A velocity of 406 m/sec corresponds to approximately 1440 km/hr.

* * * * *

1.6 Answers will vary. Sample graph:

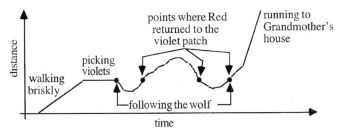

1.7 a. Sample graph:

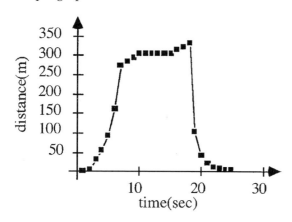

b. Sample response: The object first stopped moving away at the point (10,303), because the distance from the fixed point remains constant from 10 sec until 15 sec.

c. 1. The object began moving back toward the fixed point after 18 sec.

2. The velocity changed from positive to negative.

d. During this interval, the average velocity is:

$$\frac{(303-55)}{(10-4)} = \frac{248}{6} \approx 41 \text{ m/sec}$$

This value is positive; therefore the object was farther away from the fixed point at the end of the interval than at the beginning.

e. During this interval, the average velocity is:

$$\frac{(7-333)}{(23-18)} = \frac{-326}{5} \approx -65 \text{ m/sec}$$

This value is negative; therefore the object was closer to the fixed point at the end of the interval than at the beginning.

ACTIVITY 2

Students collect distance-time data for movement at a constant speed, then model their graphs using linear equations.

1.7 The table below shows the distances between an object and a fixed point over time.

Time (sec)	Distance (m)	Time (sec)	Distance (m)
1	2	14	303
2	5	15	303
3	33	16	313
4	55	17	323
5	94	18	333
6	160	19	104
7	273	20	41
8	283	21	20
9	293	22	11
10	303	23	7
11	303	24	5
12	303	25	3
13	303		

a. Create a distance-time graph of this data.

b. Which ordered pair (t,d), where d represents distance and t represents time, corresponds to the moment when the object first stopped moving away from the fixed point? Explain your response.

c. 1. When did the object start moving back toward the fixed point?

2. How did its velocity change at this time?

d. Calculate the average velocity of the object during the time interval [4,10]. What does this value tell you about the object's motion?

e. Calculate the average velocity of the object during the time interval [18,23]. What does this value tell you about the object's motion?

ACTIVITY 2

In the months before each launch, NASA engineers determine a space shuttle's longitude, latitude, altitude, and weight for every 0.04 sec of the flight. How are they able to predict these values with such accuracy and confidence?

248 Module 10 ■ *Graphing the Distance*

teacher note

Students unfamiliar with Newton's first law of motion might benefit from a discussion of the term *force*. Like velocity, force has both magnitude and direction. For example, a player's foot applies force to a soccer ball, while the wind applies force on a balloon. The resulting motion of the ball or balloon is in the same direction as that of the force. In Activity **4,** students investigate motion influenced by the force of gravity.

A brief assessment of the mathematical content in Activities **1** and **2,** for use at your discretion, appears in the Teacher Resources for this module.

Materials List

- graph paper (several sheets per student)
- masking tape
- basketball or soccer ball (one per group)
- track for ball (one per group; see sketch in the following teacher note)

At least some of the credit for scientists' ability to make such predictions must go to the English mathematician and physicist, Sir Isaac Newton (1642–1727). Newton used three concise laws of motion to describe the rules that govern the movement of objects both on earth and in space.

science note

A **force** is a physical quantity that can affect the motion of an object. Two familiar forces are gravity and friction.

According to Newton's **first law of motion**, an object in a state of rest or moving in a straight line at a constant speed will continue in that state unless acted on by a force.

Exploration

We can model a distance-time graph with a linear equation when the distance between an object and a fixed point changes at a constant rate. In this exploration, you use a range finder to explore the movement of a ball at a constant velocity.

a. Obtain a track, a ball, and the range-finder apparatus from your teacher. As shown in Figure **10-4,** place the track on a level surface and position the range finder at one end. Place the ball on the track approximately 0.5 m from the range finder.

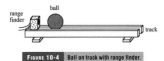

FIGURE 10-4 Ball on track with range finder.

b. Push the ball away from the range finder just hard enough so that it rolls to the end of the track. Collect distance-time data as the ball rolls.

c. Repeat Part **b** several times, increasing the force of the initial push each time. Observe how changing the ball's speed affects the resulting distance-time graphs.

d. Select a data set and graph from Part **c** that appears to describe the motion of the ball accurately. Determine the average velocity of the ball over the time interval represented by the graph.

Module 10 ■ *Graphing the Distance* 249

teacher note

The following diagram shows one possible design for the track. Vinyl raingutter also works well. For help with the track, you might wish to consult with the industrial arts or physics department at your school.

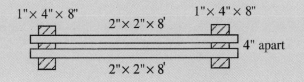

Technology

■ sonar range finder (one per group)
■ science interface device (one per group)
■ graphing utility

teacher note

You might wish to conduct Parts **a–c** of the exploration as a demonstration, then distribute the data to students for completion of Parts **d** and **e.**

Student Outcomes

After completing the following exploration and discussion, students should be able to:

✳ create and interpret distance-time graphs

✳ calculate residuals and the sum of the squares of the residuals

✳ use linear regressions to model data

✳ relate distance, time, and velocity for an object moving at constant speed to the slope-intercept form of a line.

Exploration

a–b. **Note:** Some sonar range finders have an interval of distances in which they operate most efficiently. Refer to the range finder's manual to determine this interval.

c. Students repeat the experiment several times and observe how the speed of the ball affects the graphs. **Note:** Due to friction, the movement of the ball on the track approximates movement at a constant velocity only for relatively short time intervals.

d. Students' graphs should look linear, with a positive slope. See the sample data set below and the corresponding graph on the following page:

Time (sec)	Distance (m)	Time (sec)	Distance (m)
0.000	0.580	1.200	1.126
0.200	0.667	1.400	1.216
0.400	0.757	1.600	1.302
0.600	0.848	1.800	1.394
0.800	0.934	2.000	1.488
1.000	1.028		

Module 10 ■ *Graphing the Distance* 225

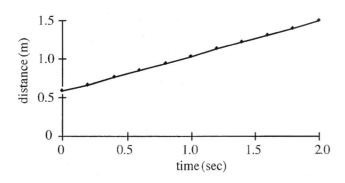

Based on this data, the average velocity of the ball is:

$$\frac{1.488 - 0.580}{2 - 0} = \frac{0.908}{2} = 0.454 \text{ m/sec}$$

e. Students may use a spreadsheet to calculate the sum of the squares of the residuals, then adjust their model to approximate the least sum.

f. The linear regression equation for the sample data given above is $d(t) = 0.455t + 0.576$.

Discussion

a. Sample response: The faster the ball moved down the track, the steeper the graph.

b. 1. Sample response: I used a spreadsheet to calculate the sum of the squares of the residuals, then adjusted the equation of the line until the sum was relatively small.

2. The slope of the graph is the ratio of the change in distance to the change in time; therefore the slope indicates the average velocity between two points in time.

3. The y-intercept represents the distance from the range finder to the ball at $t = 0$.

4. Sample response: Because the experiment started with the ball about 0.5 m away from the range finder, the line should not pass through the origin.

5. Answers will vary. Sample response: The equations are very similar. The values for slope and y-intercept are slightly different.

c. Sample response: The distance-time graph should be linear, but with a negative slope.

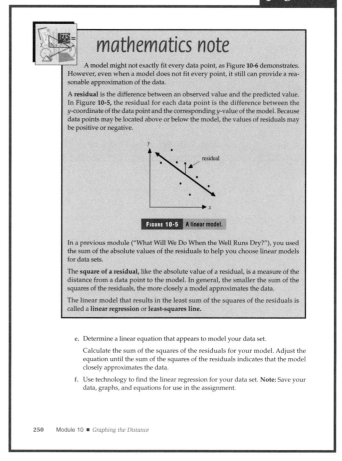

d. 1. Answers will vary. Sample response. The line hits most of the points and the residuals appear to be relatively small.

2. The ball's average velocity is the ratio of the change in distance to the change in time. This is also the slope of a line on a distance-time graph. In a function of the form $f(x) = mx + b$, m represents the slope of the line. Therefore, the value of m represents the average velocity of the ball.

Discussion

a. How did the ball's speed affect the graphs in Part **c** of the exploration?

b. In Parts **d** and **e** of the exploration, you found the ball's average velocity and determined a linear function to model its distance-time data.

   1. Describe how you determined the equation in Part **e**.

   2. What does the slope of the line indicate about the ball's movement?

   3. What does the *y*-intercept of the line represent?

   4. Should the line pass through the origin? Why or why not?

   5. How does your equation compare with the linear regression for the data set?

c. If you placed the ball at the far end of the track and pushed it toward the range finder, what would the resulting distance-time graph look like?

d. 1. How can you tell if an equation provides a good model of a distance-time graph?

   2. If the function that models the ball's distance-time data is written in the form $f(x) = mx + b$, which part of the equation represents the ball's average velocity? Explain your response.

   3. How could you determine the ball's instantaneous velocity in this situation?

e. Suppose that after collecting distance-time data for a ball on a ramp, the resulting graph can be modeled by a function of the form $d(t) = c$, where *c* is a constant. Describe the motion of the ball.

f. Describe some real-world situations that could be modeled with linear graphs of distance versus time.

Warm-Up

1. Complete a table of values for each of the following linear equations. Your table must include both the *x*- and *y*-intercepts, along with $x = -4$, $x = 6$, $y = -2$, and $y = 12$.

   a. $y = 3x - 5$

   b. $y = \frac{1}{2}x + 3$

   c. $2x + 5y = 1$

Warm-Up

1. **a.** Sample table:

x	−4	0	1	$1\frac{2}{3}$	$5\frac{2}{3}$	6
y	−17	−5	−2	0	12	13

   b. Sample table:

x	−10	−6	−4	0	6	18
y	−2	0	1	3	6	12

   c. Sample table:

x	−29.5	−4	0	0.5	5.5	6
y	12	1.8	0.2	0	−2	−2.2

3. Sample response: The ball is moving at a constant speed; therefore the instantaneous velocity is the same as the average velocity.

   Note: Mathematically, the slope between any two points on a distance-time graph represents the average velocity between these points. The defining feature of a straight-line graph is that the slope between any two points on the graph is always the same as the slope between any other two points on the graph. Thus, any estimate of the instantaneous velocity using an average velocity between two points will yield the slope of the line.

e. Sample response: The function indicates that the ball on the ramp remains a constant distance from the range finder, so the ball must be motionless.

f. Answers will vary. Students may describe any situation in which an object has constant velocity, such as a car driving along a straight highway at a constant speed.

2. **a.** $y = 5x + 3$

   b. $y = -3x + 2$

   c. $y = -\dfrac{1}{2}x + 2$

3. **a.** The function with the greatest y-intercept is $5x - 3y = 4$.

   b. The function with the greatest average rate of change (slope) is $y = 2x - 7$.

   c. The function with the greatest x-intercept is $y = 2x - 7$.

Assignment

Problems suitable for use as assessment items are identified by an asterisk (*).

2.1 Sample response: Velocity equals the change in distance divided by the corresponding change in time. Therefore, when the velocity remains constant, the ratio of the change in distance to the change in time also must be constant.

2.2 Answers will vary, depending on the data collected. The following sample responses use the equation $d(t) = 0.455t + 0.576$.

   a. After 1.7 sec, the ball was approximately 1.35 m from the range finder.

   b. The ball was 0.75 m away after approximately 0.4 sec.

   c. 1. If the track were long enough, and the ball's speed remained constant, the ball would be about 274 m away.

   2. Sample response: No. Because of friction, the ball will slow down and eventually come to a stop.

* 2.3 **a–b.** Sample table:

Time (sec)	Distance (m)	Interval (sec)	Average Velocity (m/sec)
0	0.50		
1	1.25	[0, 1]	0.75
2	2.00	[1, 2]	0.75
3	2.75	[2, 3]	0.75

   c. Sample response: Because the ball is moving at a constant velocity during the interval [0, 3], the instantaneous velocity at 2 sec is the same as the average velocity, 0.75 m/sec.

   d. Sample response: Each answer in Parts **b** and **c** is the slope of the line that models the data.

2. Determine the equation of the line that contains the points in each of the following tables.

   a.

x	y
-2	-7
0	3
2	13
5	28

   b.

x	y
-3	11
-1	5
0	2
3	-7

   c.

x	y
-4	4
-2	3
0	2
4	0

3. Consider the three linear functions $y = 2x - 7$, $5x - 3y = 4$, and $3x = 2y + 6$.

   a. Which of these functions has the greatest y-intercept?

   b. Which of these functions has the greatest average rate of change?

   c. Which of these functions has the greatest x-intercept?

Assignment

2.1 Describe how distance, velocity, and time are related when a ball is moving along a straight track at a constant rate.

2.2 Use the linear equation you found in Part **e** of the exploration to answer the following questions.

   a. How far was the ball from the range finder after 1.7 sec?

   b. When was the ball 0.75 m away from the range finder?

   c. 1. If the track were long enough, how far from the range finder would the ball be after 10 min?

   2. Do you think your prediction is accurate? Why or why not?

2.3 The function below describes the motion of a ball on a level track, where $d(t)$ represents distance in meters from a range finder and t represents time in seconds:

$$d(t) = 0.75t + 0.5$$

   a. Make a table showing the ball's distance from the range finder after 0 sec, 1 sec, 2 sec, and 3 sec.

   b. Add a column to your table that shows the average velocity of the ball during the following time intervals: [0,1], [1,2], and [2,3].

   c. What is the instantaneous velocity of the ball at $t = 2$ sec?

   d. How do your responses to Parts **b** and **c** relate to the equation that describes the ball's motion?

2.4 Describe a function that could be used to model the distance-time graph of each of the following:

    a. a ball that is not moving

    b. a ball moving at a constant velocity of 1 m/sec.

2.5 The table below shows a space shuttle's distance from earth at some specific times after liftoff.

Time (sec)	Distance (m)	Time (sec)	Distance (m)
72	15,539	136	53,355
96	27,920	160	66,809
120	43,326	184	78,374

SOURCE: Johnson Space Center, Houston, Texas.

    a. Create a distance-time graph of this data.

    b. 1. Determine a linear equation that closely models the data.

        2. What is the average velocity of the shuttle during the interval [72, 184]?

    c. Use the equation you found in Part **b** to predict the shuttle's altitude after 520 sec.

    d. Would it be reasonable to use this linear model to predict the shuttle's altitude at any time during its flight? Explain your response.

2.6 The table below shows some distance-time data collected as a model rocket returned to the ground under its parachute.

Time (sec)	Distance (m)	Time (sec)	Distance (m)
12	155.4	15	136.3
13	147.7	16	130.8
14	141.9	17	125.2

    a. Determine an equation that closely models the data.

    b. Use your equation to predict when the rocket will reach the ground.

    c. Do you think your prediction is reasonable? Why or why not?

* * * * *

2.4 **a.** Sample response: The graph is a horizontal line. The function that models it is of the form $d(t) = c$, where c is a constant that represents the distance the ball is from the range finder.

    b. Sample response: The graph is a line with a slope of 1. The function is of the form $d(t) = 1t + c$, where t represents time and c represents the ball's distance from the range finder at $t = 0$.

2.5 **a.** Sample graph:

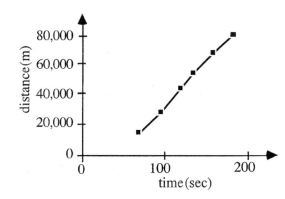

    b. 1. One linear equation that closely models the data is $d(t) = 573t - 25{,}832$.

        2. The average velocity is the slope of the line determined in Part **b1,** or approximately 573 m/sec.

    c. Assuming its motion continues according to the linear model, the shuttle's altitude after 520 sec would be about 272,000 m.

    d. Sample response: No. A linear model assumes that the velocity of the shuttle is constant. However, the shuttle does not fly in a straight line or at a constant speed.

2.6 **a.** One linear equation that closely models the data is $d(t) = -5.9t + 225$. Sample graph:

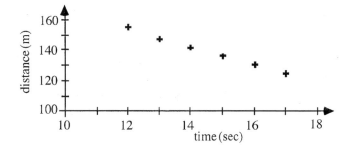

    b. Using the sample equation given above, the rocket should reach the ground at $t \approx 38$ sec.

    c. Sample response: The rocket appears to be falling at a constant speed. The equation fits the data very well, so the prediction seems reasonable.

✳ ✳ ✳ ✳ ✳

2.7 **a.** Equations **1** and **4** represent objects moving at the same average velocity because they have the same slope.

 b. The absolute value of the slope of a distance-time line represents the average speed. Equations **1** and **4** represent objects moving at the same average speeds, as do equations **2** and **5**.

 c. Equations **1** and **4** represent the fastest moving objects because they have the greatest speeds.

 d. Equations **2** and **5** represent the slowest moving objects because they have the lowest speeds.

 e. Equations **1, 2,** and **3** represent objects that started nearer to the range finder because the *y*-intercepts are smaller. Equations **4** and **5** represent objects that started farther from the range finder because the *y*-intercepts are larger.

In this activity, students explore the graphs of quadratic functions. (They will use these functions to model data in Activity **4.**)

Materials List

■ graph paper (several sheets per student)

Technology

■ graphing utility

2.7 Each of the linear functions below models a distance-time data set collected using a range finder:

 1. $d(t) = 3.5t + 1.3$ **2.** $d(t) = -1.2t + 1.3$

 3. $d(t) = 3.0t + 1.3$ **4.** $d(t) = 3.5t + 2.0$

 5. $d(t) = 1.2t + 2.0$

 a. Which functions represent objects moving at the same average velocity?

 b. Which functions represent objects moving at the same average speed?

 c. Which function(s) represent(s) the object that is moving the fastest?

 d. Which function(s) represent(s) the object that is moving the slowest?

 e. Which function(s) correspond(s) to the object that started nearest to the range finder? farthest from the range finder?

A C T I V I T Y

3

In the previous activity, you examined distance-time graphs of a ball moving at a constant speed. These graphs could be modeled by linear functions. But what type of function would you use to model a distance-time graph for an object whose speed was increasing or decreasing?

mathematics note

Quadratic expressions in a single variable are expressions in which the greatest exponent on the variable is 2. Because of this fact, they are also called **second-degree** expressions.

A quadratic expression in x can be written in the general form $ax^2 + bx + c$, where $a \neq 0$. The **coefficients** of x are a, b, and c.

For example, $3x^2 - 5x + 2$ is a quadratic expression of x written in the general form. The coefficients of x are 3, –5, and 2. The expression $rsx^2 + 2tx + v$ also is a quadratic expression. In this case, the coefficients of x are rs, $2t$, and v.

A function f is a **quadratic function** if $f(x)$ is defined as a quadratic expression in x. Quadratic functions also are called second-degree functions.

For example, $f(x) = -5x^2 + 3x - 7$ is a quadratic function.

A quadratic function can be written in the general form $f(x) = ax^2 + bx + c$, where $a \neq 0$.

254 Module 10 ■ *Graphing the Distance*

---

teacher note

The graph of a quadratic function is a parabola. Students can determine the coordinates of the vertex using the parabola's vertical line of symmetry. Given two points with the same *y*-coordinate, such as (3,2) and (7,2), the *x*-coordinate of the vertex is the average of the *x*-coordinates of the two known points. They can find the *y*-coordinate by substituting the *x*-coordinate into the quadratic function. For this example, the vertex is $(5, f(5))$.

This activity introduces students both to the general form and to the vertex form of a quadratic. Students should understand that they can find the general form by expanding the vertex form using the distributive property.

In Exploration **1,** students work with quadratic functions in vertex form in which the lead coefficient is 1. They will be introduced to quadratic functions with other lead coefficients in Exploration **2.**

Exploration 1

Before using quadratic functions to model distance-time data, you must discover more about their graphs.

The graph of a quadratic function is a **parabola**. For example, Figure **10-6** below shows two parabolas. When a parabola opens upward, its **vertex** occurs at the lowest point in the graph. When a parabola opens downward, its vertex occurs at the highest point in the graph.

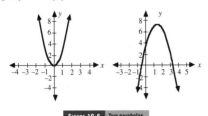

FIGURE 10-6 Two parabolas.

a. 1. Create a graph of the quadratic function $f(x) = x^2 - 6x + 14$.

2. Use your graph to identify the coordinates of the vertex.

3. A parabola is symmetric about a line, known as the **axis of symmetry**. Describe how you could locate the vertex using the axis of symmetry.

4. Write the equation for the axis of symmetry.

mathematics note

Quadratic functions may be written in several different forms, each with its own advantages. A **vertex form**, for instance, allows you to more easily identify the vertex.

A **vertex form** of a quadratic function is $f(x) = a(x - c)^2 + d$, where a, c, and d are real numbers and $a \neq 0$.

For example, the quadratic function $f(x) = x^2 - 6x + 14$ can be written in vertex form as $f(x) = (x - 3)^2 + 5$.

Student Outcomes

After completing the following explorations and discussions, students should be able to:

✴ write and graph quadratic functions of the general form $f(x) = ax^2 + bx + c$ and the vertex form $f(x) = a(x - c)^2 + d$

✴ predict shapes of graphs from quadratics in vertex form

✴ translate parabolas using the vertex form

✴ apply the distributive property to expand the vertex form to the general form.

Exploration 1

a. 1. Sample graph:

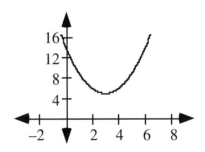

2. The vertex is located at (3,5).

3. Sample response: The vertex is located at the intersection of the line of symmetry and the parabola.

4. The equation for the axis of symmetry is $x = 3$.

b. 1. The graphs are the same.

2. Sample response: The coordinates of the vertex are (3,5). The number in the parentheses with x is the opposite of the x-coordinate. The number outside the parentheses is the same as the y-coordinate of the vertex.

c. 1. Sample response: Adding 2 to the function would move it up 2 units. The new function would be $f(x) = (x-3)^2 + 7$.

2. Sample response: Adding 6 to the number in the parentheses with the x would move it to the left 6 units. The new function would be $f(x) = (x+3)^2 + 5$.

3. Sample response: Subtracting 4 from the function would move it down 4 units. Subtracting 2 from the number in the parentheses with the x would move it to the right 2 units. The new function would be $f(x) = (x-5)^2 + 3$.

d. Students create graphs of quadratic functions without revealing the functions used. They exchange graphs with classmates, then try to identify the function from the graph.

Discussion 1

a. Sample response: The graph resembles half of a parabola.

b. Sample response: In a function of the form $f(x) = a(x-c)^2 + d$, the value of c is the x-coordinate of the vertex, and the value of d is the y-coordinate of the vertex.

c. Sample response: The vertex of the parabola for $p(x) = x^2$ is at (0,0). The vertex form of this function would be $p(x) = (x-0)^2 + 0$.

d. 1. $(x+2)^2 + 0$

2. $(x-5)^2 + 0$

3. $(x-0)^2 + 3$

4. $(x-0)^2 - 4$

e. 1. Sample response: Multiply 3 by x and 3 by -7. The resulting expression is $3x - 21$.

2. Sample response: Multiply x by $(x+4)$, then multiply -4 by $(x+4)$ and add the results. The resulting expression is:

$$(x^2 + 4x) + (-4x - 16) = x^2 + 0x - 16$$
$$= x^2 - 16$$

3. Sample response: Multiply $(x+5)$ by itself. This means multiply x by $(x+5)$, then multiply 5 by $(x+5)$ and add the results. The resulting expression is

$$x^2 + 10x + 25.$$

f. 1. Sample response: Multiply $(x-3)$ by itself and simplify. Finally, add 5 to the result. The resulting function is $f(x) = x^2 - 6x + 14$.

2. The functions are the same.

b. 1. Compare the graphs of $f(x) = x^2 - 6x + 14$ and $f(x) = (x-3)^2 + 5$.

2. Describe how the vertex form of a quadratic indicates the location of the vertex.

c. 1. How can you modify the function $f(x) = (x-3)^2 + 5$ to move its graph 2 units upward? (*Hint:* If the vertex moves, the rest of the parabola also must move.) Record your observations.

2. How can you modify the function $f(x) = (x-3)^2 + 5$ to move its graph 6 units to the left? Record the new function.

3. How can you modify the function $f(x) = (x-3)^2 + 5$ to move its graph down 4 units and to the right 2 units? Record the new function.

d. 1. Write a quadratic function in the form $f(x) = (x-c)^2 + d$ on a sheet of paper.

2. Create a graph of your equation.

3. Without revealing your equations, exchange graphs with a classmate.

4. Use your classmate's graph to determine the equation of the function.

Discussion 1

a. In Exploration 2 of Activity 1, you graphed some distance-time data for a falling object. What shape best describes the graph?

b. Describe how you can use the vertex form of a quadratic function to determine the coordinates of the parabola's vertex.

c. A **family** of functions is a set of functions that have a common **parent**. The parent of the family of quadratic functions is $p(x) = x^2$.

Describe how to write the function $p(x) = x^2$ in vertex form.

d. Describe how to write each of the following quadratic expressions in vertex form.

1. $(x+2)^2$

2. $(x-5)^2$

3. $x^2 + 3$

4. $x^2 - 4$

e. The **distributive property of multiplication over addition** provides the basis for multiplying two numbers together.

To find the product of 4 and 25, for example, you could express 25 as $(20 + 5)$ and distribute the 4 as follows:

$$4(20 + 5) = (4 \cdot 20) + (4 \cdot 5)$$
$$= 80 + 20$$
$$= 100$$

Exploration 2

a. Sample graph:

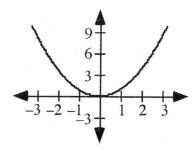

b. 1. $f(x) = (x-0)^2 + 1$

2. $f(x) = (x-0)^2 - 1$

3. $f(x) = (x-1)^2 + 0$

4. $f(x) = (x+1)^2 + 0$

Similarly, you could multiply 23 and 17 by expressing 23 as (20 + 3) and 17 as (20 – 3). Using the distributive property of multiplication over addition:

$$(20 + 3)(20 - 3) = 20(20 - 3) + 3(20 - 3)$$
$$= (400 - 60) + (60 - 9)$$
$$= 391$$

1. Describe how to use the distributive property to find the product of 3 and $(x - 7)$.

2. Describe how to use the distributive property to multiply $(x - 4)$ and $(x + 4)$.

3. Describe how to use the distributive property to expand $(x + 5)^2$.

f. 1. How could you use the distributive property to express $f(x) = (x - 3)^2 + 5$ in the general form $f(x) = ax^2 + bx + c$? (Recall from the order of operations that you must work with the exponent first.)

2. How does your result compare with the function you graphed in Part **a**: $f(x) = x^2 - 6x + 14$?

Exploration 2

In the following exploration, you continue your investigation of the graphs of quadratic functions.

a. Using a graphing utility, create a graph of the parent function of the quadratic family, $f(x) = x^2$.

b. Express each of the following functions in vertex form.

1. $f(x) = x^2 + 1$

2. $f(x) = x^2 - 1$

3. $f(x) = (x - 1)^2$

4. $f(x) = (x + 1)^2$

c. Create a graph of each quadratic function in Part **b** and compare it to the graph of the parent function.

d. To examine the influence of the value of a on functions of the form $f(x) = ax^2$, graph each function below on the same coordinate system as $f(x) = x^2$. Record your observations.

1. $f(x) = -x^2$

2. $f(x) = 3x^2$

3. $f(x) = \frac{1}{3}x^2$

4. $f(x) = -2x^2$

e. Write each of the functions in Part **d** in vertex form, $f(x) = a(x - c)^2 + d$.

c. 1. Sample response: As shown in the graph below, the new function (bold curve) is located 1 unit above the graph of $f(x) = x^2$.

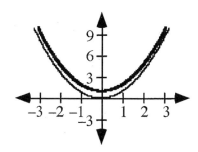

2. Sample response: As shown in the graph below, the new function (bold curve) is located 1 unit below the graph of $f(x) = x^2$.

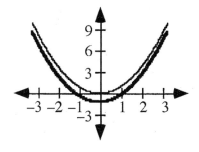

3. Sample response: As shown in the graph below, the new function (bold curve) is located 1 unit to the right of the graph of $f(x) = x^2$.

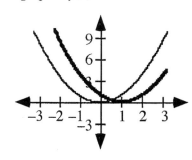

4. Sample response: As shown in the graph below, the new function (bold curve) is located 1 unit to the left of the graph of $f(x) = x^2$.

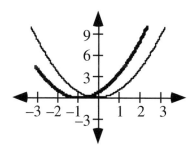

d. 1. Sample response: The graph of $f(x) = -x^2$ is a reflection of $f(x) = x^2$ in the x-axis.

2. Sample response: The graph of $f(x) = 3x^2$ appears to be narrower than that of $f(x) = x^2$.

3. Sample response: The graph of

$$f(x) = \frac{1}{3}x^2$$

appears to be wider than that of $f(x) = x^2$.

4. Sample response: The graph of $f(x) = -2x^2$ appears to be narrower than that of $f(x) = x^2$ and a reflection of $f(x) = x^2$ in the x-axis.

e. 1. $f(x) = -(x - 0)^2 + 0$

2. $f(x) = 3(x - 0)^2 + 0$

3. $f(x) = \frac{1}{3}(x + 0)^2 + 0$

4. $f(x) = -2(x - 0)^2 + 0$

f. Sample response: If d is positive, the graph of $f(x) = x^2$ is moved up d units. If d is negative, the graph is moved down d units.

   If c is positive, the graph of $f(x) = x^2$ is moved to the right c units. If c is negative, the graph is moved to the left c units.

   If $|a| > 1$, the graph appears to be narrower than the graph of $f(x) = x^2$. If $|a| < 1$, the graph appears to be wider than the graph of $f(x) = x^2$. If a is negative, the graph is reflected in the x-axis.

Discussion 2

a. Sample response: When a is negative, the graph is reflected in the x-axis. If $|a| > 1$, the graph appears to be narrower than the graph of the original function. If $|a| < 1$, the graph appears to be wider than that of the original function.

b. Sample response: When c is positive, the graph of the function is shifted c units to the right of the original function. When c is negative, the graph of the function is shifted c units to the left of the original function.

c. Sample response: When d is positive, the graph of the function is shifted d units up from the original function. When d is negative, the graph of the function is shifted d units down from the original function.

d. Sample response: The graph is a reflection of the graph of $f(x) = x^2$ in the x-axis. It is wider than the original function and its vertex is 4 units above the origin and 3 units to the right of the origin.

e. 1. Sample response: The y-intercept is the point where the graph of the function crosses the y-axis. The x-coordinate for this point is 0. If you locate 0 in the x-column of the table, the corresponding y-value is the y-coordinate of the y-intercept. If the function models the scatterplot exactly, the y-intercept is $(0,-7)$.

   2. Sample response: It is not possible to locate the exact x-intercepts from the table in Figure **10-7**. Because an x-intercept occurs where the graph crosses the x-axis, the y-values on either side of the intercept will have opposite signs. The signs change from positive to negative between $x = -2$ and $x = -1$. This indicates that an x-intercept is between -1 and -2. A reasonable approximation for this x-intercept is $(-1.8,0)$. The other x-intercept appears to be near $(-4.2,0)$.

   3. Sample response: When a parabola opens downward, the vertex occurs at the highest point. The greatest y-value in the table is 2. From the graph, the vertex is close to $(-3,2)$.

   4. Sample response: In a function of the form $f(x) = a(x - c)^2 + d$, the x-coordinate of the vertex equals the value of c, and the y-coordinate equals the value of d.

---

f. Experiment with other negative and positive values for the constants a, c, and d in functions of the form $f(x) = x^2 + d$, $f(x) = (x - c)^2$, and $f(x) = ax^2$. Compare the graph of each function to the graph of $f(x) = x^2$. Record your observations.

Discussion 2

a. How does the value of a appear to affect the graphs of functions of the form $f(x) = ax^2$?

b. How does the value of c appear to affect the graphs of functions of the form $f(x) = (x - c)^2$?

c. How does the value of d appear to affect the graphs of functions of the form $f(x) = x^2 + d$?

d. How would the graph of $f(x) = -0.5(x - 3)^2 + 4$ differ from the graph of $f(x) = x^2$?

e. Figure **10-7** below shows a scatterplot of the data in the table on the left. The scatterplot can be modeled by a quadratic function.

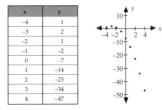

x	y
−4	1
−3	2
−2	1
−1	−2
0	−7
1	−14
2	−23
3	−34
4	−47

FIGURE 10-7   Data and scatterplot.

   1. Is it possible to identify the function's y-intercept from the table? If so, describe how. If not, describe how you could approximate it.

   2. Is it possible to identify the function's x-intercepts from the table? If so, describe how. If not, describe how you could approximate them.

   3. Describe how you would approximate the coordinates of the vertex.

   4. Describe how you could use the coordinates of the vertex to obtain the function $g(x) = a(x + 3)^2 + 2$.

5. To determine a function that models this data, you now must identify an appropriate value for *a*.

One method for finding a value for *a* is to select a data point (not the vertex) from the table, then substitute the values for *x* and $g(x)$ in $g(x) = a(x+3)^2 + 2$. For example, using the data point $(1, -14)$, you can solve for *a* as follows:

$$g(x) = a(x + 3)^2 + 2$$
$$-14 = a(1 + 3)^2 + 2$$
$$-14 = 16a + 2$$
$$-16 = 16a$$
$$-1 = a$$

Given this value for *a*, what function could be used to model this data?

f. 1. Select a different data point and determine another quadratic function $h(x)$ that could be used to model the data in Figure **10-7**.

2. Compare $g(x)$ and $h(x)$.

3. How could you determine which is a better model for the data?

g. Describe how you could rewrite any quadratic function in vertex form in the general form $f(x) = ax^2 + bx + c$.

Warm-Up

1. Write each of the quadratic functions below in the general form $f(x) = ax^2 + bx + c$.

   a. $r(x) = (x - 3)^2$
   b. $g(x) = (x + 5)^2 - 6$
   c. $h(x) = 2(x - 4)^2 - 7$
   d. $s(x) = -5(x + 1)^2 - 3$
   e. $t(x) = -(x + 2)^2 + 1$

2. Each of the following pairs of points satisfies a quadratic function. The first point in each pair is the vertex; the second is another point on the parabola. Write an equation for each function in vertex form.

   a. $(2,3), (1,0)$
   b. $(2,-4), (-3,3)$
   c. $(0,0), (4,-8)$
   d. $(-3,2), (0,-4)$

5. $g(x) = -(x + 3)^2 + 2$

f. 1. Answers will vary. If the point $(-4,0)$ is selected, the value of *a* is -2. The resulting quadratic function is $h(x) = -2(x + 3)^2 + 2$.

   2. Sample response: The absolute value of *a* in $h(x) = -2(x + 3)^2 + 2$ is greater than the absolute value of *a* in $g(x) = -(x + 3)^2 + 2$. This means that $h(x)$ would appear to be narrower than $g(x)$.

   3. Sample response: One way to compare models is to examine the sum of the squares of the residuals. The model with the lesser sum more closely approximates the data.

g. Sample response: Expanding the first equation using the distributive property results in the general form, as shown below.

$$f(x) = a(x - c)^2 + d$$
$$= a(x^2 - 2cx + c^2) + d$$
$$= ax^2 - 2acx + ac^2 + d$$
$$= ax^2 - 2acx + (ac^2 + d)$$

Warm-Up

1. a. $r(x) = x^2 - 6x + 9$
   b. $g(x) = x^2 + 10x + 19$
   c. $h(x) = 2x^2 - 16x + 25$
   d. $s(x) = -5x^2 - 10x - 8$
   e. $t(x) = -x^2 - 4x - 3$

2. a. $f(x) = -3(x - 2)^2 + 3$

   b. $f(x) = \dfrac{7}{25}(x - 2)^2 - 4$

   c. $f(x) = -0.5x^2$

   d. $f(x) = -\dfrac{2}{3}(x + 3)^2 + 2$

3. **a.** The x-intercepts are at $(-4,0)$ and $(3,0)$.

   b. The y-intercept is at $(0,-12)$.

   c. The approximate interval where the function is increasing is $(0,5]$.

   d. The approximate interval where the function is decreasing is $[-5,-1)$.

   e. Sample response: The point at which it changes from decreasing to increasing is between $x = -1$ and $x = 0$. A reasonable approximation would be $x = -0.5$.

4. Sample response: The data resembles a parabola with its vertex at $(-0.5,-12.5)$. Substituting this point and the data point $(-4,0)$ into the vertex form of a quadratic function and solving for a, the value of a is approximately 1.0. Therefore, one quadratic function that could be used to model the data is $f(x) = 1.0(x + 0.5) - 12.5$.

Assignment

Problems suitable for use as assessment items are identified by an asterisk (*).

3.1 a. $f(x) = (x - 3.5)^2 + 1.4$

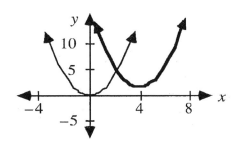

   b. $f(x) = -x^2$

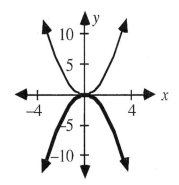

3.2 a–c. Sample response: Yes, it makes a difference. The graphs are shown below. The dotted graph shows the result when the move is done first. The solid graph shows the result when the reflection is done first.

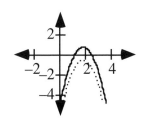

3. Use the following table of data to complete Parts **a–e** below.

x	y	x	y
−5	8	1	−10
−4	0	2	−6
−3	−6	3	0
−2	−10	4	8
−1	−12	5	18
0	−12		

   a. Identify the x-intercept(s).

   b. Identify the y-intercept(s).

   c. Determine the approximate interval(s) where the function appears to be increasing.

   d. Determine the approximate interval(s) where the function appears to be decreasing.

   e. Identify the point(s) where the function changes from increasing to decreasing or decreasing to increasing.

4. Determine a quadratic function that could be used to model the data in Problem **3**. Explain your response.

Assignment

3.1 Determine a function of the form $f(x) = a(x - c)^2 + d$ that represents each of the following changes to the function $f(x) = x^2$. Use graphs to support your responses.

   a. a move 3.5 units to the right and 1.4 units up

   b. a reflection in the x-axis

3.2 Does the order in which you make changes to the graph of a function affect the result? To investigate this question, complete Parts **a–c.**

   a. Create a graph of the function $f(x) = x^2$. Move the graph 3.5 units to the right and 1.4 units up, then reflect it in the x-axis.

   b. Create another graph of the function $f(x) = x^2$. Reflect the graph in the x-axis, then move it 3.5 units to the right and 1.4 units up.

   c. Compare your graphs from Parts **a** and **b.** What do you observe?

3.3 **a.** Write the function whose graph shows the following changes to the graph of $f(x) = x^2$: a reflection in the x-axis, followed by a move 3 units to the right and 2 units down.

b. To verify your response, graph $f(x) = x^2$ and the function from Part **a** on the same coordinate system.

c. Rewrite your function in Part **a** in the general form of a quadratic.

3.4 Determine a function of the form $f(x) = a(x - c)^2 + d$ whose graph is represented by the bold curve.

3.5 The distance-time data in the table below can be modeled by a quadratic function.

Time (sec)	Distance (m)	Time (sec)	Distance (m)
0.0	3.0	0.8	7.8
0.2	4.8	1.0	8.0
0.4	6.2	1.2	7.8
0.6	7.2	1.4	7.2

a. Create a scatterplot of the data.

b. Determine a quadratic function that models the data and graph it on the same coordinate system as in Part **a.**

c. Write the function in Part **b** in the general form of a quadratic.

✳ ✳ ✳ ✳ ✳

3.6 **a.** Write the function whose graph results in the following changes to the graph of $f(x) = x^2$: a reflection in the x-axis, followed by a move 2 units to the left and 6 units up.

b. To verify your response, graph $f(x) = x^2$ and the function from Part **a** on the same coordinate system.

c. Rewrite the function in Part **a** in the general form of a quadratic.

3.3 **a.** $f(x) = -(x - 3)^2 - 2$
b. Sample graph:

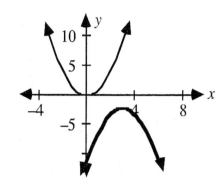

c. $f(x) = -x^2 + 6x - 11$

3.4 Sample response: $f(x) = x^2 + 3$.

3.5 **a.** Sample scatterplot:

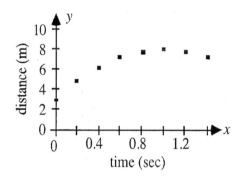

b. Sample response: $f(x) = -5(x - 1)^2 + 8$.

c. The general form for the function given in Part **b** is $f(x) = -5x^2 + 10x + 3$.

✳ ✳ ✳ ✳ ✳

3.6 **a.** $f(x) = -(x + 2)^2 + 6$
b. Sample graph:

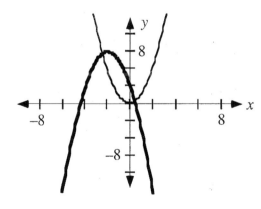

c. $f(x) = -x^2 - 4x + 2$

3.7 Sample response: $f(x) = (x + 2)^2 + 2$.

3.8 a. Sample graph:

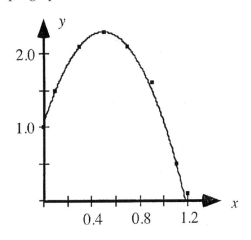

b. Answers will vary. Using (0.5,2.3) as the vertex and (0.1,1.5) as a point on the parabola, gives

$$f(x) = -5(x - 0.5)^2 + 2.3.$$

c. Using the sample response given in Part **b**:

$$f(x) = -5(x - 0.5)^2 + 2.3 = -5x^2 + 5x + 1.05.$$

ACTIVITY

In this activity, students use a range finder to collect data for a ball moving with constant acceleration. They then model this data with quadratic functions.

teacher note

A brief assessment of the mathematical content in Activities **3** and **4**, for use at your discretion, appears in the Teacher Resources for this module.

Materials List

- masking tape
- basketball or soccer ball (one per group)
- track for ball (one per group)

Technology

- sonar range finder (one per group)
- science interface device (one per group)
- graphing utility

3.7 Determine a function of the form $f(x) = a(x - c)^2 + d$ whose graph is represented by the bold curve.

3.8 The data in the table below can be modeled by a quadratic function.

x	$f(x)$	x	$f(x)$
0.0	1.0	0.7	2.1
0.1	1.5	0.9	1.6
0.3	2.1	1.1	0.5
0.5	2.3	1.2	0.1

a. Create a scatterplot of the data.

b. Determine a quadratic function that models the data and graph it on the same coordinate system as in Part **a**.

c. Rewrite the function in Part **b** in the general form of a quadratic.

ACTIVITY
4

According to legend, Isaac Newton "discovered" gravity after watching an apple fall from a tree. In this activity, you explore how the **acceleration** due to gravity affects the distance-time graphs of freely falling objects.

Student Outcomes

After completing the following discussions and exploration, students should be able to:

✴ create and interpret distance-time graphs for objects moving with constant acceleration

✴ calculate average acceleration

✴ use the sum of the squares of residuals to identify a model that closely approximates the data

✴ describe the height of a falling object using the formula

$$d(t) = -\frac{1}{2}gt^2 + v_0t + d_0$$

✴ use quadratic regressions to model data.

science note

Acceleration is the rate of change in velocity with respect to time.

For example, consider a car driving along a straight section of highway. Over time, the velocity of the car can increase, decrease, or remain the same. When the car's velocity increases, its acceleration is positive. When the car's velocity decreases, its acceleration is negative. If the car's velocity remains constant, its acceleration is 0.

You can determine the average acceleration of an object over a particular time interval by dividing the change in velocity by the change in time. For example, consider a model rocket launched straight into the air. At $t = 3$ sec, its velocity is 48.65 m/sec. At $t = 5$ sec, its velocity is 29.33 m/sec. Estimate the rocket's average acceleration during this period as follows:

$$\frac{29.33 \text{ m/sec} - 48.65 \text{ m/sec}}{5 \text{ sec} - 3 \text{ sec}} = -9.65 \text{ m/sec}^2$$

This means that during the time interval [3,5], the rocket's velocity decreased by an average of 9.65 m/sec for every second that passed.

Discussion 1

a. When you rolled a ball along a level track in Activity **2**, its velocity remained almost constant over time. If one end of the track was raised, and the ball rolled down the incline, do you think that its velocity also would remain constant? Explain your response.

b. As the ball continues down the track, how would the distances traveled in equal time intervals compare?

c. What do you think a graph of the distance-time data collected for a ball rolling down an inclined track will look like?

d. Describe the shape of a scatterplot that you would model with each of the following:

   1. a linear regression

   2. a quadratic regression

Exploration

In this exploration, you collect distance-time data for a ball rolling down an incline. You then use quadratic functions to model this data.

Discussion 1

a. Sample response: No. As the ball rolls down the track, its velocity would increase.

b. Sample response: Its velocity increases as the ball continues down the track; therefore the distance traveled in equal time intervals would increase.

c. Sample response: The graph will start near the origin of the coordinate system and curve upward and to the right. **Note:** The graph actually should resemble half of a parabola.

d. 1. Sample response: A linear regression would be used if the scatterplot resembles a line.

   2. Sample response: A quadratic regression would be used if the scatterplot resembles a parabola or a portion of a parabola.

Exploration

a–c. See initial instructions given in the exploration in Activity **2**. Students should repeat the experiment several times.

d. 1. See the sample data in the table at the bottom of the page and the graph below:

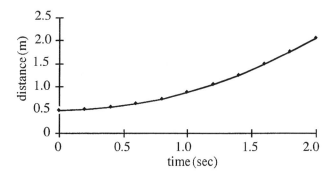

2. Students should use the techniques developed in Activity **3** to determine a model.

e. Students use the sum of the squares of residuals to identify a model that closely approximates the data. A quadratic function that closely models the sample data is $f(x) = 0.4x^2 + 0.5$. This process typically is reserved for lines, but it is one way to compare how well different quadratic equations model the same set of data.

f. Students use technology to generate a quadratic regression for their data. For the sample data given in Part **d** above, the quadratic regression found using technology is $y \approx 0.35x^2 + 0.03x + 0.49$.

a. Obtain a track, a ball, and the range-finder apparatus from your teacher. Set up the track and range finder as in Activity **2**, then use books or blocks to raise the end of the track with the range finder on it.

b. Place the ball approximately 0.5 m from the range finder and gently release it. (Do not push the ball down the track.) You should begin collecting distance-time data just before the ball is released.

c. Repeat Part **b** several times, then select a data set and graph that you think accurately describes the motion of the ball down the track.

d. 1. Edit your data set so that it contains only information collected as the ball was actually moving, beginning with the moment of its release.

2. Determine a quadratic equation that appears to model this data set.

e. Recall that a **residual** is the difference between an observed value and the corresponding value predicted by a model, and that the sum of the squares of the residuals can be used to evaluate how well a model fits a data set.

Calculate the sum of the squares of the residuals for your model. Adjust the equation until the sum of the squares of the residuals indicates that the model closely approximates the data. **Note:** Save your data set, graph, and equation for use later in the module.

f. In Activity **2**, you used linear regression equations to model data. Many calculators and computer software programs also can generate other types of regression equations, including exponential, power, and quadratic (or second-degree) regressions.

Use technology to determine a quadratic regression equation for your data set in Part **d**.

g. If the track were extremely steep, the ball's motion would be virtually a **free fall**. In physics, the term *free fall* refers to an object falling without air resistance and affected only by the force of gravity.

Remove the range finder from the track and point it at the floor from a height of approximately 60 cm. Hold the ball directly beneath the range finder at a height of about 10 cm. Release the ball.

You should begin collecting distance-time data just before the ball is released and stop after the ball hits the ground. Repeat this experiment several times, then select a data set and graph that you think accurately describes the motion of the ball.

h. Repeat Parts **d–f** using the data for the falling ball.

Discussion 2

a. 1. How did raising one end of the track affect the speed of the ball over time?

2. How is this effect displayed on the distance-time graphs?

Time (sec)	Distance (m)	Time (sec)	Distance (m)
0.000	0.494	1.200	1.053
0.200	0.506	1.400	1.254
0.400	0.552	1.600	1.489
0.600	0.630	1.800	1.755
0.800	0.740	2.000	2.048
1.000	0.881		

b. 1. Describe how to express the quadratic functions you found in Parts **d** and **h** of Exploration **2** in the general form of a quadratic function.

2. Compare each of these equations to the quadratic regression equation for the same data set.

c. How do the distance-time graphs and equations you found in this exploration compare with those you used to model a ball rolling on a level track in Activity 2?

d. Use your graphs from this exploration and the one in Activity 2 to answer the following questions.

1. Describe the shape of a distance-time graph when an object's acceleration is 0.

2. What influence does an object's acceleration have on the shape of its distance-time graph?

3. How does the magnitude of the acceleration affect the equations used to model the distance-time data?

science note

The acceleration due to gravity is a constant typically denoted by g. On earth's surface, the acceleration due to gravity is about $9.8 \, m/sec^2$ in a direction toward the earth's center. For comparison, the acceleration due to gravity on the moon's surface is about $1.6 \, m/sec^2$.

When an object is acted on only by gravity, its distance from the ground is described by the following function:

$$d(t) = -\frac{1}{2}gt^2 + v_0 t + d_0$$

where $d(t)$ represents the object's distance from the ground after t sec, g is the acceleration due to gravity, v_0 is the object's velocity in the vertical direction at $t = 0$, and d_0 is the object's distance above the ground at $t = 0$.

For example, consider a tennis ball dropped from a height of 10 m. Because the ball is dropped and not thrown, its initial velocity in the vertical direction is 0, or $v_0 = 0$. Its initial distance above the ground is 10 m, therefore $d_0 = 10$. On earth, the value of g is about $9.8 \, m/sec^2$. To calculate the ball's height above the ground after 1 sec, substitute these values into the equation for $d(t)$ as follows:

$$d(1 \, sec) = -\frac{1}{2}(9.8 \, m/sec^2)(1 \, sec)^2 + (0 \, m/sec)(1 \, sec) + 10 \, m$$
$$= -4.9 \, m + 0 \, m + 10 \, m$$
$$= 5.1 \, m$$

g–h. See the sample data in the table below.

One equation that closely approximates this data set is $f(x) = 5x^2 + 0.5$. The quadratic regression equation found using technology was

$$y \approx 4.4x^2 + 0.11x + 0.49.$$

Discussion 2

a. 1. Sample response: The speed of the ball gradually increased as the ball rolled down the track. The higher the end of the track was raised, the more rapidly the speed of the ball increased.

2. Sample response: This is seen on the distance-time graphs as an upward curve that gradually gets steeper.

b. 1. Responses will vary, based on the data collected in the exploration. The sample function given in Part **e** can be written as $f(x) = 0.4x^2 + 0.5$. The sample function in Part **g** can be written as $f(x) = 5x^2 + 0.5$.

2. Sample response: The two functions are similar, although the coefficients of corresponding terms are not equal. However, the values predicted by each model are approximately the same.

c. Sample response: The distance-time graphs from Activity **2** could be modeled by lines, while the graphs in this exploration are best modeled with parabolas.

d. 1. Sample response: When the acceleration is 0, the graph is linear.

2. Sample response: When an object is accelerating, the graph is curved, not straight. The greater the acceleration, the more quickly curve becomes steep.

3. Sample response: As the acceleration increases, the coefficient of the second-degree term also appears to increase.

Time (sec)	Distance (m)	Time (sec)	Distance (m)
0.00	0.490	0.12	0.564
0.02	0.493	0.14	0.590
0.04	0.500	0.16	0.621
0.06	0.510	0.18	0.652
0.08	0.524	0.20	0.690
0.10	0.543	0.22	0.721

e. 1. Responses will vary. The following sample response corresponds with a ball dropped from a height of 1.5 m:

$$d(t) = -4.9t^2 + 0t + 1.5$$

2. Sample response: The two functions are very different because they do not model the same distance. The formula in the science note describes a falling object's height above the ground. The equation from the exploration, $y \approx 4.4x^2 + 0.11x + 0.49$, describes a falling ball's distance from the range finder, where the range finder is held above the ball. This explains why the coefficient of the second-degree term is positive rather than negative, and the differences in the constant terms, which represent initial position.

The estimated value of g in the function from the exploration is about 8.8, which is less than the value of 9.8 given in the science note. This may be due to the influence of air resistance on the falling ball.

Warm-Up

1. a. Sample scatterplot:

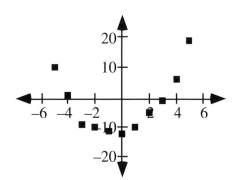

b. Sample scatterplot:

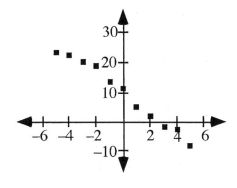

e. 1. Using the general formula described in the previous science note, write a quadratic function that should describe the distance from the ground over time of the falling ball in Part **h** of Exploration **2**.

2. Compare this function to the ones you determined in the exploration. Why do you think there are differences in these equations?

Warm-Up

1. Create a scatterplot of the data in each table below.

a.

x	y
−5	10
−4	1
−3	−9
−2	−10
−1	−11
0	−12
1	−10
2	−5
3	−1
4	6
5	19

b.

x	y
−5	22
−4	21
−3	19
−2	18
−1	13
0	11
1	5
2	2
3	−1
4	−2
5	−7

c.

x	y
−5	15
−4	3
−3	−10
−2	−11
−1	−9
0	−14
1	−10
2	−7
3	0
4	8
5	21

2. Describe an appropriate type of function to model each scatterplot in Problem **1**. Use technology to find the regression equation.

3. Solve each of the following equations for y when x = −2, x = 0, and x = 3.

a. $y = -11x^2 + 4x + 12$

b. $y = x^2 - 2.3x - 19$

c. $y - 12 = 4x - 11x^2$

c. Sample scatterplot:

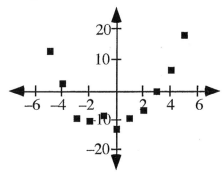

2. a. Sample response: Because the shape of the graph resembles a parabola, a quadratic regression would be appropriate. The regression equation for the data is $f(x) = x^2 + 0.9x - 12.3$.

b. Sample response: Because the shape of the graph is roughly linear, a linear regression would be appropriate. The regression equation for the data is $f(x) = -3.1x + 9.2$.

c. Sample response: Because the shape of the graph resembles a parabola, a quadratic regression would be appropriate. The regression equation for the data is $f(x) = 1.2x^2 + 0.8x - 13.3$.

b. One equation that approximates the data is $y = 3.05x^2$.

c. The following sample responses use the sample equation given in Part **b**.

1. 7625 m

2. $1.098 \cdot 10^6$ m = 1098 km

d. Sample response: The estimate for 50 sec should be valid because this time is contained in the interval for the data and the model equation fits the data points well. The estimate for 600 sec is not reasonable, because the model predicts that altitude continues to increase over time. In reality, the shuttle stops climbing and enters earth orbit at about 160,000 m.

e. Based on the equation in Part **b**, the time required to reach orbital altitude is approximately 229 sec, or about 4 min. Students may determine this value by solving the following equation for x:

$$160,000 = 3.05x^2.$$

* **4.2 a.** Sample response: Because the ball was not moving, the first two data points are eliminated. One equation that approximates the data is

$$f(x) = 1.1(x - 0.4)^2 + 0.02.$$

b. After 2 sec, the ball will be approximately 2.8 m from the range finder.

c. The ball would be 4 m away after about 2.3 sec.

3. **a.** When $x = -2$, $y = -40$. When $x = 0$, $y = 12$. When $x = 3$, $y = -75$.

b. When $x = -2$, $y = -10.4$. When $x = 0$, $y = -19$. When $x = 3$, $y = -16.9$.

c. Students should observe that this equation is equivalent to the one in Part **a**.

Assignment

Problems suitable for use as assessment items are identified by an asterisk (*).

* **4.1 a.** See the sample graph below.

4.3 a. Students may estimate instantaneous velocities by finding the average velocity for each 0.2-sec interval about a given time. Sample table:

Time (sec)	Velocity (m/sec)
0.5	1.1
0.7	1.5
0.9	2.0
1.1	2.4
1.3	2.8

b. Students estimate the acceleration by finding the change in the average velocity over time. The value of 2.0 in row 1 of the sample table below was found from the table in Part **a** above by dividing the change in average velocity (1.5 – 1.1 = 0.4 m/sec) by the change in time (0.7 – 0.5 = 0.2 sec).

Time Interval (sec)	Acceleration (m/sec^2)
[0.5, 0.7]	2.0
[0.7, 0.9]	2.5
[0.9, 1.1]	2.0
[1.1, 1.3]	2.0

c. Sample response: The acceleration appears to be roughly constant at approximately 2 m/sec^2.

4.4 a. The graph should be linear because the ball is moving away at a constant rate. Sample response:

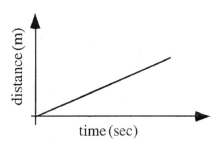

b. The graph should resemble the right side of a parabola with a positive leading coefficient. Sample response:

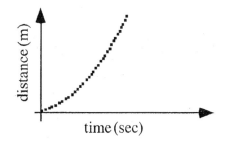

page 268

4.3 Use the data given in Problem **4.2** to complete Parts **a–c** below.

a. Estimate the ball's instantaneous velocity at each of the times listed in the following table.

Time (sec)	Velocity (m/sec)
0.5	
0.7	
0.9	
1.1	
1.3	

b. Use the values found in Part **a** to estimate the ball's average acceleration during each of the intervals listed in the table below.

Time Interval (sec)	Acceleration (m/sec^2)
[0.5, 0.7]	
[0.7, 0.9]	
[0.9, 1.1]	
[1.1, 1.3]	

c. How does the acceleration of the ball appear to change over time?

4.4 Sketch a distance-time graph that could represent each of the situations described below.

a. A ball moves away from a range finder with an acceleration of 0.

b. A ball moves away from a range finder with a positive acceleration.

c. A ball moves away from a range finder with a negative acceleration.

4.5 The distance-time graph below shows data collected during the flight of a model rocket. After its engine burns out, the primary force acting on the rocket is gravity.

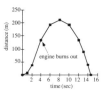

268   Module 10 ■ *Graphing the Distance*

c. The graph should resemble the left side of a parabola with a negative leading coefficient. Sample response:

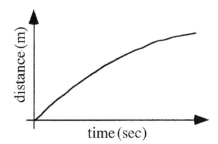

4.5 a. Velocity is the change in position over time; therefore the slope on a distance-time graph indicates the velocity. The slope is positive over the time interval (0, 8) and so is the velocity. The velocity is 0 at 8 sec where the rocket reaches its maximum distance above the ground. The velocity is negative, as indicated by negative slope, over the rest of the flight.

b. Sample response: Graph **3** represents a graph of the rocket's velocity for this interval. The graph shows positive velocity for the interval [4, 8), zero at $t = 8$, and negative for the remainder of the time.

a. Identify the locations on the graph where the velocity of the rocket is positive, zero, or negative.

b. Based on your responses to Part **a**, which of the graphs below represents a graph of velocity versus time for the interval [4,14]? Justify your choice.

1.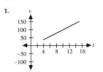

2.

3.

4.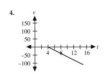

c. Using the graph you selected in Part **b**, describe a graph of the rocket's acceleration versus time over the same interval. Justify your response.

4.6 The table below shows the distance above the ground at various times for a bouncing ball.

Time (sec)	Distance (m)	Time (sec)	Distance (m)
0.00	0.0	0.48	0.933
0.08	0.301	0.56	0.878
0.16	0.549	0.64	0.762
0.24	0.736	0.72	0.583
0.32	0.865	0.80	0.342
0.40	0.929	0.88	0.0

a. Find a quadratic equation that closely models this data.

b. According to your model, when does the ball reach its highest point?

c. What is the velocity of the ball at the time it reaches this point?

d. What is the velocity of the ball at $t = 0$?

✳ ✳ ✳ ✳ ✳

4.7 Suppose that you have used a range finder to collect distance-time data for a freely falling object. Your data can be modeled by the function $d(t) = 4.9t^2$, where $d(t)$ represents distance in meters and t represents time in seconds.

a. Describe the motion of the object, including its initial velocity and initial distance from the range finder.

b. Use the model equation to estimate when the object was 4 m from the range finder.

4.8 Sir Isaac Newton once said that if he had seen farther than other scientists and mathematicians, this was because he had "stood on the shoulders of giants." One of those giants was Galileo Galilei (1564–1642), who died in the year of Newton's birth. In fact, Newton's first law of motion was actually a variation on Galileo's concept of inertia.

a. Besides describing inertia, Galileo theorized that, in the absence of air resistance, two objects of different sizes and weights dropped from the same height would reach the ground at the same time. What does Galileo's theory predict about the motions of an apple falling from a tree and the ball you dropped in the exploration?

b. On one of the Apollo missions to the moon, an astronaut demonstrated Galileo's theory by dropping a hammer and a feather from the same height. Given that the acceleration due to gravity on the moon is 1/6 that on earth, what function could be used to describe the two objects' distance from the lunar surface with respect to time?

c. If the hammer and feather were dropped from a height of 2 m, how long would it take them to reach the lunar surface?

d. If this demonstration were conducted on earth, how long would it take the hammer to reach the ground?

4.9 The data in the table below shows a rocket's distance above the ground at various times after launch. At $t = 2$ sec, the rocket's engine burned out. After this time, gravity is the primary force acting on the rocket.

Time (sec)	Distance (m)	Time (sec)	Distance (m)
2	36.9	8	212.3
4	134.2	10	192.9
6	192.9	11	170.8

a. Find a polynomial equation that closely fits the data.

b. Interpret the significance of each coefficient in your equation.

c. Sample response: The acceleration of the rocket is the change in velocity over time. This is equivalent to the slope on a velocity versus time graph. The velocity versus time graph is a line, so the slope is constant. Therefore, the acceleration is constant and its graph would be a horizontal line. This makes sense because the primary force acting on the rocket is gravity, and the acceleration due to gravity is a constant.

＊ 4.6 **a.** Sample response: $y = -4.8x^2 + 4.3x - 0.01$.

b. Using the model equation given above, the ball will reach its highest point after approximately 0.44 sec.

c. Sample response: At its highest point, the ball is changing direction. Therefore, its velocity is 0.

d. Using the model equation given above, the initial velocity is approximately 4.3 m/sec.

✳ ✳ ✳ ✳ ✳

4.7 **a.** Sample response: The function describes a situation in which the object is falling away from a range finder. The initial velocity is 0 m/sec. The initial distance from the range finder is 0 m.

b. It would take approximately 0.9 sec for the object to fall 4 m.

4.8 **a.** Galileo's theory predicts that if an apple and a ball are dropped from the same height, in the absence of air resistance, then they will hit the ground at about the same time.

b. $d(t) = -0.5\left(\dfrac{9.8}{6}\right)t^2 + d_0 \approx -0.8t^2 + d_0$

c. On the moon, it would take approximately 1.6 sec for both the hammer and the feather to reach the ground.

d. On the earth, it would take approximately 0.64 sec for both the hammer and the feather to reach the ground.

4.9 **a.** Sample response: $d(t) = -4.8t^2 + 58.1t + 37.1$.

b. Sample response: The first coefficient is approximately –0.5 g, while the second coefficient is the initial velocity of the rocket. The constant should describe the rocket's approximate distance above the ground at $t = 0$. In this case, however, it is closer to the distance at $t = 2$.

4.10 This data can be modeled well by a quadratic equation, such as $y = 3.22x^2 - 4.89x + 2.21$. Students may use graphs to defend their models.

Research Project

a. Newton's second law of motion can be expressed in a formula as $F = ma$, where F represents the applied force, m represents the mass of the object, and a represents the resulting acceleration. His third law of motion is often stated as "For every action (or force), there is an equal and opposite reaction."

b. To obtain more information about space shuttle launches, call or write the NASA Teacher Resource Room, Mail Code AP–4, Johnson Space Center, Houston, TX 77058; 713–483–8696. You also may contact NASA Dryden Flight Research Center, Public Affairs Office, Edwards, CA 93523; 805-258-3449; pao@dfrc.nasa.gov.

4.10 The table below shows a space shuttle's distance above the ground during the first seconds after liftoff. Find an equation that models this data. Explain why you think your model fits the data well.

Time (sec)	Distance (m)	Time (sec)	Distance (m)
0.00	0.00	7.68	153.31
1.92	6.10	9.60	249.63
3.84	33.53	11.52	371.86
5.76	81.69	13.44	519.99

SOURCE: Johnson Space Center, Houston, Texas.

Research Project

Select one of the following topics.

a. In addition to his three laws of motion, Isaac Newton also proposed a law of universal gravitation. Together, these few principles revolutionized the sciences of physics and astronomy. Write a report on Newton's contributions to the study of motion, including an explanation of the relationship among force, mass, and acceleration.

b. Scientists at NASA closely analyze each launch of the space shuttle and make a wealth of information available to the public. Contact the Johnson Space Center regarding a past or future shuttle flight. Write a report on the launch, including an analysis of the flight-path data.

Module 10 ■ *Graphing the Distance* 271

Summary Assessment

1. The distance-time data shown below was obtained by moving a book toward and away from a range finder taped to a desk.

Time (sec)	Distance (m)	Time (sec)	Distance (m)
0.0	1.393	2.4	1.856
0.4	1.145	2.8	1.838
0.8	0.851	3.2	1.549
1.2	0.682	3.6	1.308
1.6	0.859	4.0	0.841
2.0	1.328		

  a. Create a distance-time graph of this data.

  b. Describe what happens to the velocity of the book during the interval from 0 sec to 4 sec.

  c. Identify at least three different time intervals in which the book's average velocity is 0.

  d. During which 0.4-sec interval is the book moving the fastest?

  e. Find an equation that models the motion of the book during each of the following intervals:

    1. from 0 sec to 0.8 sec

    2. from 0.4 sec to 2.0 sec.

2. The following distance-time data was recorded for a falling ball:

Time (sec)	Distance (m)	Time (sec)	Distance (m)
0.00	0.42	0.45	0.84
0.05	0.42	0.50	1.00
0.10	0.42	0.55	1.19
0.15	0.42	0.60	1.40
0.20	0.42	0.65	1.63
0.25	0.44	0.70	1.89
0.30	0.50	0.75	2.17
0.35	0.59	0.80	2.06
0.40	0.70		

teacher note

An additional assessment, for use at your discretion, appears in the Teacher Resources for this module.

Summary Assessment

1. **a.** Sample graph:

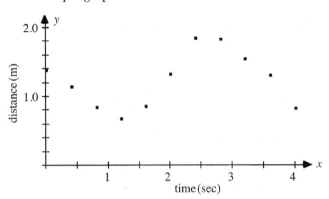

  b. Sample response: During the first 1.2 sec, the velocity is negative because the book is moving toward the range finder at a fairly constant speed. For the interval from 1.2 sec to about 2.6 sec, the velocity is positive because the book is moving away from the range finder at a fairly constant speed. For the interval from 2.6 sec to 4.0 sec, the velocity is again negative, indicating that the book is moving toward the range finder. The velocity is slowest from 2.4 sec to 2.8 sec and fastest from 2.0 sec to 2.4 sec.

  c. Answers will vary. Sample response: The average velocity is approximately 0 during the time intervals [0.8, 1.6], [0.8, 4.0], [1.6, 4.0], [2.4, 2.8], and [2.0, 3.6].

  d. The book is moving the fastest during the interval [2, 2.4]. In this time interval, the average velocity is 1.32 m/sec.

  e. **1.** The graph from 0 sec to 0.8 sec looks linear, so students may use a linear equation to model the motion of the book. One equation that closely approximates the data is

$$y = -0.68x + 1.4.$$

    2. The graph from 0.4 sec to 2.0 sec looks parabolic, so students may use a quadratic equation to model the motion of the book. One equation that closely approximates this data is

$$y = 0.84x^2 - 1.91x + 1.80.$$

2. a. Sample graph:

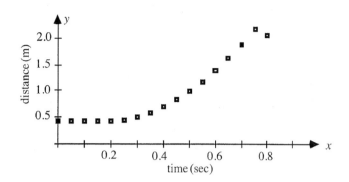

b. The ball was falling during the interval from 0.2 sec to 0.75 sec.

c. Answers will vary. Considering the known value for g and the initial position of the ball, some students might suggest the equation $y = 4.9x^2 + 0.42$, where x represents the time that the ball has been falling, as an appropriate model. Using technology, one quadratic equation that fits this data is

$$y = 4.97x^2 + 0.47x + 0.41.$$

d. Sample response: The coefficient of x^2 represents one-half of the acceleration due to gravity in m/sec^2, the coefficient of x represents the initial velocity in m/sec, and the constant represents the initial distance from the range finder.

e. 1. approximately 1.55 m/sec
  2. approximately 5.4 m/sec

f. Sample response: Because of the acceleration due to gravity, the average velocity of the falling ball should increase as time passes.

a. Create a distance-time graph for this data.

b. Describe the time interval for which the ball was actually falling.

c. Find an equation that models the distance-time graph for this interval.

d. Explain how the terms of the equation you found in Part c relate to the movement of the ball.

e. Calculate the average velocity of the ball during each of the following intervals:

  1. [0.25,0.35]

  2. [0.65,0.75]

f. Explain why the two average velocities you found in Part e are different.

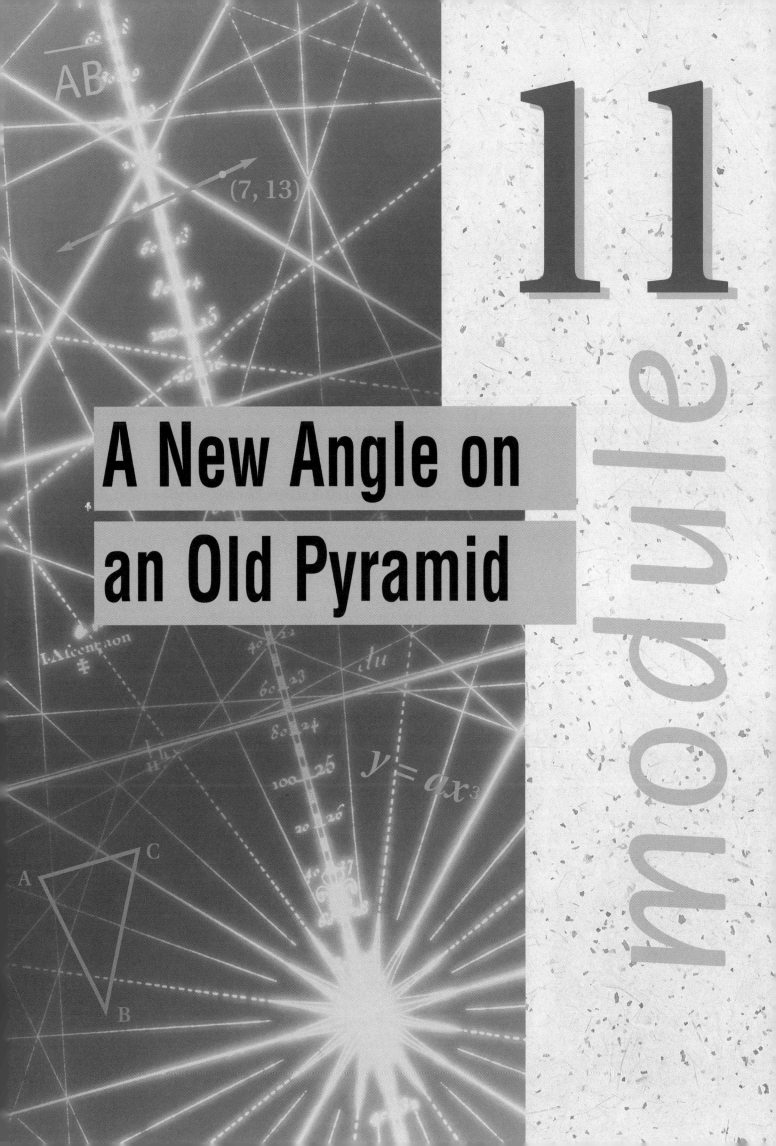

A New Angle on
an Old Pyramid

Overview

This module reviews similar triangles, the Pythagorean theorem, and triangle notation in the context of Egypt's Great Pyramid. Students explore the tangent, sine, and cosine ratios.

Activity 1:	Students use similar triangles to solve for unknown lengths and express triangle properties as conditional statements.
Activity 2:	Students use the Pythagorean theorem to find the lengths of sides of right triangles. They use its converse to distinguish among acute, obtuse, and right triangles. Students also explore the differences between planar and dihedral angles.
Activity 3:	Students investigate the tangent ratio and use it to calculate the lengths of sides of right triangles. They also use $\tan^{-1}$ to find the measures of angles in right triangles.
Activity 4:	Students investigate the sine and cosine ratios and use them to calculate the lengths of sides of right triangles. They also use $\sin^{-1}$ and $\cos^{-1}$ to find the measures of angles in right triangles.

Objectives

In this module, students will:

* use similarity to determine unknown measures in triangles (1)
* identify similar triangles using the AAA property (1)
* write conditional statements, identifying both hypothesis and conclusion (1)
* write converses of conditional statements (2)
* solve right-triangle problems using the Pythagorean theorem and its converse (2)
* classify triangles as acute, right, or obtuse based on the lengths of the three sides (2)
* identify segments that form a triangle using the triangle inequality property (2)
* develop the distance formula for two dimensions (2)
* define and identify dihedral angles (3)
* develop and apply the tangent ratio (3)
* use $\tan^{-1}$ to determine the measures of unknown angles in right triangles (3)
* use technology to develop a table of trigonometric values for the tangent, sine, and cosine ratios (3, 4)
* develop and apply the sine and cosine ratios (4)
* use $\sin^{-1}$ and $\cos^{-1}$ to determine the measures of unknown angles in right triangles (4).

Prerequisites

For this module, students should know:

✷ how to measure angles with a protractor

✷ how to solve proportions

✷ the definition of perpendicular

✷ how to solve equations of the form $x^2 + a = b$

✷ the sum of the measures of the interior angles of a triangle (180°)

✷ the definition of similarity for planar and three-dimensional shapes

✷ the definition of an altitude of a triangle or pyramid

✷ how to calculate scale factors for similar figures

✷ the definition of congruent geometric figures

✷ the definitions of acute, obtuse, and right triangles.

 Flashbacks, for use at your discretion, appear in the Teacher Resources for this module. These brief problem sets provide a review of some prerequisite skills for each activity.

Planning Guide

Activity	Materials	Technology	Time Line
Activity **1**	■ butcher paper ■ metersticks ■ centimeter rulers ■ protractors ■ triangle template	■ none	2 days
Activity **2**	■ puzzle template ■ scissors ■ string ■ graph paper	■ geometry utility ■ spreadsheet	2 days
Activity **3**	■ protractors ■ string ■ drinking straws ■ paper clips	■ geometry utility ■ spreadsheet	3 days
Activity **4**	■ protractors	■ geometry utility ■ spreadsheet	2 days
Assessment Activities	■ none	■ none	3 days **Total: 12 days**

 teacher note

Blackline masters of the templates appear in the Teacher Resources for this module.

In Activities **3** and **4,** students should set their technology to use degree measure (not radian measure).

Introduction

The construction of Egypt's Great Pyramid provides the context for most of the activities in this module.

teacher note

You might wish to use a model of a right square pyramid to help students visualize the altitude, slant heights, and lateral edges. You also might wish to point out that the altitude of a triangular face of a pyramid is *not* the altitude of the pyramid.

ACTIVITY
1

In this activity, students review similar triangles and proportional reasoning.

Materials List

- butcher paper (one sheet per group; approximately 1 m by 2 m)
- 30-cm rulers (one per group)
- protractors (one per group)
- metersticks (one per group)
- triangle template (one per student; a blackline master appears in the Teacher Resources for this module)

Student Outcomes

After completing the following exploration and discussion, students should be able to:

✳ use proportional reasoning to investigate data

✳ identify similar triangles and write proportions between corresponding sides

✳ write conditional statements.

Exploration

a. Students use protractors and rulers to construct a 90° corner.

Introduction

Tutankhamen and Khufu were kings of ancient Egypt. Khufu ruled around 2500 B.C., and Tutankhamen (King Tut) governed about 1200 years later. King Tut's artifacts are among the most popular items displayed in museums today. King Khufu built the Great Pyramid at Giza, one of the "seven wonders" of the ancient world.

Still standing after 4500 years, the Great Pyramid is an amazing architectural monument. Designed as Khufu's burial tomb, the structure is a regular square pyramid which originally stood 147 m high. Each side of its square base measured 230 m, as Figure 11-1 shows.

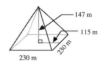

FIGURE 11-1 Dimensions of the Great Pyramid.

The Great Pyramid consists of about 2.3 million stone blocks, each with a mass of approximately 1000 kg. An estimated 100,000 laborers worked, possibly for 20 summers, to complete this engineering marvel. They used two basic kinds of stones: rectangular blocks and casing blocks. The casing blocks gave the faces of the pyramid a smooth, continuous slope.

The base of the Great Pyramid is nearly a perfect square. To build a structure of this size to such exacting specifications, the Egyptian engineers and surveyors must have applied some mathematics. Due to the lack of written records, however, historians are unsure about what mathematics the builders actually knew. In this module, you investigate some mathematical ideas that historians believe might have been used to build the pyramid.

278

ACTIVITY
1

Modern engineers use precise measuring tools to stake out the corners of a building's foundation before beginning construction. How did the Egyptians locate the corners of the Great Pyramid without the benefit of such tools? In this activity, you review some of the difficulties involved in performing this task.

Exploration

When two or more people make the same measurement, they may obtain different values. In some cases, a small difference in one measurement can have big consequences for another. In this exploration, you use proportions to investigate this possibility.

a. On a large sheet of paper, construct one corner of a square by following Steps **1–3** below. When marking points and line segments on the paper, make them dark enough to show through another sheet of paper.

1. Mark a point *C* near the lower left-hand corner of the paper, 5 cm from each edge.

2. Draw a line segment from point *C* to the lower right-hand corner of the paper. As shown in Figure **11-2**, place point *D* on the segment 30 cm from point *C*.

FIGURE 11-2 Segment from point *C* to point *D*.

3. Use a protractor and a meterstick to draw a line segment that passes through point *C*, is perpendicular to $\overline{CD}$, and has length of 1 m. Label the point at the end of the segment as *P*.

---

b. Compare the corner you created with those of others in the class by completing the following steps.

1. Select one group's sheet of paper from Part **a** on which to record the class results.

2. Place the selected sheet on top of another sheet and align the two drawings of $\overline{CD}$.

3. Mark the location of point P on the lower sheet on the top sheet.

4. Repeat Steps **2** and **3** until the information for the entire class has been collected on the selected sheet.

c. 1. On the common sheet of paper, identify the two locations of P that are farthest apart. Measure the distance between these points to the nearest millimeter.

2. Label these two points X and Y.

3. Express the length of $\overline{XY}$ in centimeters.

4. Draw $\triangle CXY$. The common sheet should now resemble the diagram in Figure **11-3.**

FIGURE 11-3 $\triangle CXY$ on the common sheet of paper.

d. Imagine that R is a point on $\overline{CX}$ 100 m from C, and S is a point on $\overline{CY}$ 100 m from C. Predict the distance between R and S.

Discussion

a. Why was there a difference between the corner you drew and those drawn by others in your class?

b. What type of triangle is $\triangle CXY$? What are its special features?

c. Two figures are **similar** when they have the same shape and corresponding sides are proportional. The symbol used to indicate similarity is ~. When $\triangle ABC$ is similar to $\triangle DEF$, explain why the notation $\triangle ABC \sim \triangle EDF$ is an incorrect way of expressing this similarity.

c. It is important to emphasize that this notation indicates corresponding sides and angles. For example, the statement $\triangle ABC \sim \triangle EDF$ indicates that $\angle B$ and $\angle D$ are corresponding angles and must be congruent, among other things. For the similar triangles in Figure **11-4,** this is incorrect.

Note: For the triangles in Figure **11-4,** there is only one correspondence between the angles and sides that results in a similarity relation. For some triangles, however, there can be several different similarity relations. If $\triangle ABC$ and $\triangle DEF$ are equilateral triangles, for example, then there are six different ways that angles and sides correspond: $\triangle ABC \sim \triangle DEF$, $\triangle ABC \sim \triangle EDF$, $\triangle ABC \sim \triangle FED$, $\triangle ABC \sim \triangle DFE$, $\triangle ABC \sim \triangle EFD$, and $\triangle ABC \sim \triangle FDE$.

teacher note

Because AAA similarity is not proved in this module, it will be referred to as a property. Students will receive a formal introduction to proof, and to theorems of triangle congruence, in the Level **2** module "So You Want to Build a House."

b. To illustrate the potential range of error, students mark their locations for point P on a common sheet of paper, as shown in Figure **11-3.**

c. The distance between X and Y may be as large as several centimeters.

d. Students should predict that the distance between R and S will be 100 times the distance between X and Y.

Discussion

a. Students should discuss the accuracy of their measurements, tools, and methods.

b. Because $\overline{CY}$ and $\overline{CX}$ are congruent, $\triangle CXY$ is an isosceles triangle. Because $\triangle CXY$ is isosceles, $\angle CXY$ and $\angle CYX$ are congruent.

d. Students should recognize that △*CXY* and △*CRS* are isosceles triangles with the same vertex angle, as shown below. Therefore, △*CXY* ~ △*CRS*.

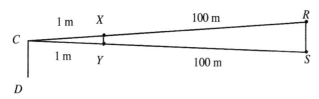

e. Because △*CXY* ~ △*CRS*, the corresponding sides are proportional. The distance *RS* can be found using the proportion below.

$$\frac{XY}{RS} = \frac{CX}{CR} = \frac{1}{100}$$

f. 1. Sample response: If three angles of one triangle are congruent to the corresponding angles of another triangle, then the two triangles are similar.

2. The hypothesis is "three angles of one triangle are congruent to the corresponding angles of another triangle."

3. The conclusion is "the two triangles are similar."

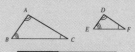

mathematics note

In plane geometry, when the angles of one triangle are congruent to the corresponding angles of another triangle, the triangles are similar. This is referred to as the **Angle-Angle-Angle (AAA) property.**

The symbol used to indicate congruence is ≅. For example, consider triangles *ABC* and *DEF* in Figure **11-4**. As shown by the markings, ∠*A* ≅ ∠*D*, ∠*B* ≅ ∠*E*, and ∠*C* ≅ ∠*F*. Because their corresponding angles are congruent, △*ABC* ~ △*DEF*.

FIGURE 11-4 Two similar triangles.

These triangles are similar, therefore the measures of their corresponding sides are proportional, as shown below.

$$\frac{AB}{DE} = \frac{AC}{DF} = \frac{BC}{EF}$$

d. In the exploration, which triangle is similar to △*CXY*? Explain your response.

e. How could you use the pair of similar triangles identified in Part **d** of the discussion to determine the distance between *R* and *S*?

mathematics note

A **conditional statement** is one that can be written in **if-then form.** A conditional consists of two parts: the **hypothesis** and the **conclusion.** The hypothesis is the "if" part of the conditional. The conclusion is the "then" part.

For example, consider the conditional statement, "If an animal is a German shepherd, then the animal is a dog." In this case, the hypothesis is "an animal is a German shepherd." The conclusion is "the animal is a dog."

f. 1. How would you write the AAA property as a conditional statement?

2. What is the hypothesis of the AAA property?

3. What is the conclusion of the AAA property?

Module 11 ■ *A New Angle on an Old Pyramid*   281

Warm-Up

1. The ratio of the lengths of two corresponding sides of two similar polygons is called the _____.

2. In the diagram below, *ABCD* ~ *WXYZ*. Use this fact to determine each of the following:

   a. the scale factor of *ABCD* to *WXYZ*

   b. the lengths *WX*, *XY*, and *YZ*

   c. the perimeters of *ABCD* and *WXYZ*

   d. the ratio of the perimeters of the quadrilaterals.

3. Use proportions to determine the values of *x* and *y* in the following triangles. (Angles which are marked in the same manner are congruent.)

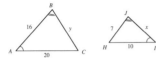

Assignment

1.1 Suppose that King Khufu ordered two different surveyors to stake the corners of the Great Pyramid. At 1 m from the first corner, the distance between the two surveyors' lines equaled the distance you measured in Part **c** of the exploration. How far apart will their two lines be after 230 m, the side length of the base of the Great Pyramid? Explain how you determined your response.

1.2 The Great Pyramid is a regular square pyramid. This means that the base is square, the altitude passes through the center of the base, and the four lateral faces are congruent isosceles triangles. To investigate some of the properties of these lateral faces, complete Parts **a–e** below.

   a. Cut an isosceles triangle from the template supplied by your teacher. Fold the triangle so that the line formed by the fold divides the triangle into two congruent parts, each a mirror image of the other. This line is a **line of symmetry**.

282   Module 11 ■ *A New Angle on an Old Pyramid*

---

teacher note

Each student will require a copy of the triangle template to complete Problem **1.2**. A blackline master appears in the Teacher Resources for this module.

Problem **1.3** extends the concept of similarity from planar figures to three-dimensional figures.

Assignment

Problems suitable for use as assessment items are identified by an asterisk (*).

1.1 Answers will vary, depending on the class value for *XY*. For example, if *XY* = 5 cm, then by similarity:

$$\frac{1}{0.05} = \frac{230}{x}$$

$$x = 11.5 \text{ m}$$

1.2 In this problem, students investigate the properties of isosceles triangles.

   a–b. The line of symmetry is perpendicular to the base and bisects the base.

Warm-Up

1. The ratio of the lengths of two corresponding sides of two similar polygons is called the scale factor.

2. **a.** 2.5

   b. 10.4; 5.6; 8

   c. 6.9; 27.6

   d. 2.5

3. Because △*ABC* ~ △*IJH*, the ratios of corresponding sides are proportional:

$$\frac{AC}{IH} = \frac{AB}{IJ} = \frac{BC}{JH}$$

$$\frac{20}{10} = \frac{16}{x} = \frac{y}{7}$$

Solving these proportions gives *x* = 8 and *y* = 14.

c. Sample response: If a triangle is an isosceles triangle, then the altitude from its vertex is a line of symmetry.

d. Sample response: If an isosceles triangle is folded along a line of symmetry, then two congruent right triangles are formed.

e. Sample response: If a line is a line of symmetry for an isosceles triangle, then it bisects the vertex angle.

1.3 Sample response: The base of each pyramid is a square; therefore the bases are similar. Each face is an isosceles triangle. Because the sum of the angles in a triangle is 180°, then $m\angle ACB = 180 - (m\angle CAB + m\angle CBA)$ and $m\angle DFE = 180 - (m\angle FDE + m\angle FED)$. Therefore, $\angle ACB \cong \angle DFE$. By the AAA Property, $\triangle ACB \sim \triangle DFE$. Because both the bases and the faces are similar, the pyramids are similar.

1.4 Sample response: The least amount of information needed is that two pairs of corresponding angles are congruent. This is because the sum of the measures of the angles in a triangle is 180°. Therefore, if two pairs of angles are congruent, then the third pair also must be congruent and the AAA Property would apply.

1.5 a. Because the two right triangles with heights h and k also share another angle, then they have two pairs of congruent, corresponding angles. Therefore, they are similar triangles. Because they are similar, the ratios of corresponding sides are equal.

b. Sample response: Given two right triangles with one set of corresponding acute angles congruent, the third set of angles are also congruent, making the triangles similar.

c. Sample response: If an acute angle in one right triangle is congruent to an acute angle in another right triangle, then the two triangles are similar by the AAA property.

b. Use a protractor and a ruler to determine the relationship between the line of symmetry and the base of the triangle.

c. What is the relationship between the triangle's altitude drawn from the vertex and its line of symmetry? Describe this situation using a conditional statement.

d. When the isosceles triangle is folded along its line of symmetry, what type of triangle is formed? Describe this situation using a conditional statement.

e. What is the relationship between the line of symmetry for the isosceles triangle and its vertex angle? Describe this situation using a conditional statement.

1.3 Two pyramids are similar when their bases are similar and their faces are similar. The diagram below shows two regular square pyramids. As shown by the corresponding markings, $\angle CAB$ and $\angle FDE$ are congruent. Are these pyramids similar? Explain your response.

1.4 What is the least amount of information necessary to determine if two triangles are similar? Explain your response.

1.5 a. The diagram below shows a cross section of a regular square pyramid where h is the height of the pyramid. The ancient Egyptians were aware that the ratios h/k and b/a are equal. Explain why this relationship is true.

b. Describe a simple rule for determining when two right triangles are similar.

c. Write your rule in Part **b** as a conditional statement.

Module 11 ■ *A New Angle on an Old Pyramid*   283

1.6 One source of information on ancient Egyptian mathematics is the Rhind Papyrus, a scroll about 5.5 m long and 33 cm wide. Written about 1650 B.C. by a scribe named Ahmes, the Rhind Papyrus is a practical handbook of mathematical problems.

As shown in the diagram on the right (not drawn to scale), one of these problems asks for the height of a square pyramid given certain measurements.

Find the height of the pyramid in cubits. **Note: In** ancient Egypt, the *cubit* was a unit of measurement based on the distance from the elbow to the tip of the fingers in an average person's forearm.

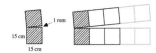

1.7 When placing the giant stone blocks on some levels of the Great Pyramid, workers had to align the blocks edge to edge and corner to corner. The task was similar to installing a tile floor—except on a much larger scale. In the diagram below, two square tiles have been placed with one pair of corners touching. The other pair of corners, however, has a gap of 1 mm. If the next tiles are aligned exactly with these two (as shown in the diagram), then how wide will the gap be after 3 m of tile have been installed? Explain your answer using similar triangles.

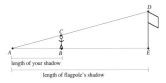

1.8 Your math class has been asked to determine the height of the school flagpole. Since you have no tools to actually measure the flagpole, the class devised a method which involves similar triangles. The diagram below shows a sketch of this situation.

---

* **1.6** Sample response: In the following diagram, $\triangle ADE \sim \triangle AFB$ by the AAA Property.

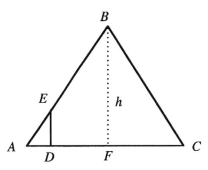

Because the triangles are similar, the ratios of corresponding sides are proportional:

$$\frac{AD}{AF} = \frac{ED}{h}$$

$$\frac{5/2}{230} = \frac{3}{h}$$

$$h = 276 \text{ cubits}$$

1.7 In the diagram below (not drawn to scale), $AB = AC = 15$ cm and $BC = 1$ mm.

After 3 m of tile are installed, $AD = AE = 3$ m and $\triangle ADE$ is similar to $\triangle ABC$. Therefore,

$$\frac{DE}{BC} = \frac{AD}{AB}$$

$$\frac{x}{0.001} = \frac{3}{0.15}$$

$$x = 0.02 \text{ m} \text{ or } 2 \text{ cm}$$

✳ ✳ ✳ ✳ ✳

1.8 **a.** Sample response: The two triangles are similar by the AAA property. They are right triangles that share a common angle.

b. Because the lengths of the corresponding sides of the similar triangles are proportional,

$$\frac{CB}{AB} = \frac{DE}{AE}$$

Solving the proportion for DE gives the height of the flagpole.

1.9 Sample response: The object should be 168 cm away from the front of the camera. The pyramids are similar, so the corresponding lengths are proportional. Solving for d (distance the camera is from the object) in the following proportion results in the distance being 168 cm.

$$\frac{20}{5} = \frac{d}{42}$$

1.10 Sample response: If two triangles are similar, then their altitudes are proportional. In the diagram below, for example, $\triangle LHK \sim \triangle QMP$. Because $\angle LKJ \cong \angle QPN$ and $\angle LJK \cong \angle QNP$, then $\triangle LJK \sim \triangle QNP$. Because these triangles are similar, their corresponding sides $\overline{LJ}$ and $\overline{QN}$ are proportional. These segments are also the altitudes of $\triangle LHK$ and $\triangle QMP$.

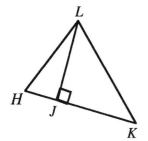
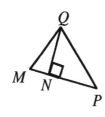

ACTIVITY 2

In this activity, students review the Pythagorean theorem, then develop its converse using a geometry utility.

teacher note

A brief assessment of the mathematical content in Activities **1** and **2,** for use at your discretion, appears in the Teacher Resources for this module.

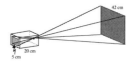

a. Explain why triangles *ABC* and *AED* are similar.

b. Describe how to use the properties of similar triangles to find the height of the flagpole.

1.9 A pinhole camera consists of a sealed box with a pinhole opening at one end and a piece of film at the opposite end. When light enters the box through the pinhole, an inverted image is projected on the film.

Consider a pinhole camera 20 cm long, as shown in the diagram below, containing a square piece of film, 5 cm on each side. The object to be photographed occupies a square 42 cm on each side.

If the photographer wants the image to exactly fill the film, how far away should the camera be placed? Explain your reasoning. (*Hint:* The lines in the diagram indicate the corresponding vertices of the object and the image. The two pyramids formed are similar.)

1.10 When two triangles are similar, are their corresponding altitudes proportional? Write your answer as a conditional statement. Use diagrams to help support your response.

ACTIVITY 2

The ancient Egyptians did not measure angles in degrees, so they must have used other methods than those in Activity **1** to make their corners "right." One theory suggests that the Egyptians used a rope subdivided by knots into 12 congruent segments. To make a corner, the rope was formed into a triangle with sides of 3, 4, and 5 units. As Figure **11-5** shows, the special characteristics of this kind of triangle might have allowed the Egyptians to form a right angle. In this activity, you examine such triangles and develop a method for deciding when a corner is "right."

FIGURE 11-5
A 3-4-5 triangle.

Materials List

■ scissors (one pair per group)

■ 30–40 cm lengths of string (one per student)

■ puzzle template (one per student; a blackline master appears in the Teacher Resources for this module)

■ graph paper

Technology

■ geometry utility

■ spreadsheet

Student Outcomes

After completing the following exploration, discussion, and assignment, students should be able to:

✴ use the converse of the Pythagorean to classify a triangle as acute, right, or obtuse

✴ use the triangle inequality property to determine if three segments can form a triangle.

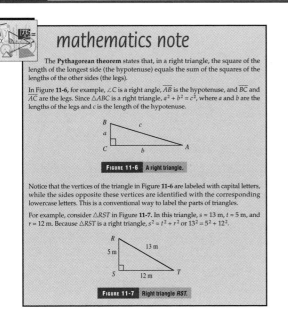

mathematics note

The **Pythagorean theorem** states that, in a right triangle, the square of the length of the longest side (the hypotenuse) equals the sum of the squares of the lengths of the other sides (the legs).

In Figure **11-6**, for example, $\angle C$ is a right angle, $\overline{AB}$ is the hypotenuse, and $\overline{BC}$ and $\overline{AC}$ are the legs. Since $\triangle ABC$ is a right triangle, $a^2 + b^2 = c^2$, where a and b are the lengths of the legs and c is the length of the hypotenuse.

FIGURE 11-6 A right triangle.

Notice that the vertices of the triangle in Figure 11-6 are labeled with capital letters, while the sides opposite these vertices are identified with the corresponding lowercase letters. This is a conventional way to label the parts of triangles.

For example, consider $\triangle RST$ in Figure **11-7**. In this triangle, $s \approx 13$ m, $t \approx 5$ m, and $r \approx 12$ m. Because $\triangle RST$ is a right triangle, $s^2 \approx t^2 + r^2$ or $13^2 \approx 5^2 + 12^2$.

FIGURE 11-7 Right triangle *RST*.

Exploration

In this exploration, you use a geometry utility and the Pythagorean theorem to investigate triangles. Although the Pythagorean theorem is evident in the rope triangle described above, it is the **converse** of this theorem that would have been more useful to the Egyptians.

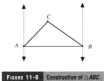

mathematics note

The **converse** of a conditional statement in the form "If A, then B" is the statement "If B, then A." The converse of a true conditional statement may or may not be true.

For example, consider the following conditional statement:

"If the country is Egypt, then the Nile River passes through the country."

The converse of this statement is:

"If the Nile River passes through a country, then the country is Egypt."

Because the Nile flows through other countries besides Egypt, the first conditional statement in this example is true, but its converse is not.

a. 1. Write the Pythagorean theorem as a conditional statement.
  2. Write the converse of the Pythagorean theorem as a conditional statement.
  3. Do you think that the converse is true?

b. Use a geometry utility to test the truth of the converse of the Pythagorean theorem by completing Steps 1–5.

  1. Construct $\triangle ABC$ and two lines perpendicular to the base $\overline{AB}$, as shown in Figure **11-8**.

FIGURE 11-8 Construction of $\triangle ABC$.

  2. Create a table with headings like those in Table **11-1** below.

TABLE 11-1 ■ *Triangle Data*

$m\angle C$	AB	AC	BC	$(AB)^2 - [(AC)^2 + (BC)^2]$

Exploration

a. 1. If a triangle is a right triangle, then the square of the length of the longest side equals the sum of the squares of the lengths of the other sides.
  2. The converse of the Pythagorean theorem may be stated as follows: "If the square of the length of the longest side equals the sum of the squares of the lengths of the other sides, then the triangle is a right triangle."
  3. Students may or may not believe that the converse is true.

teacher note

Before allowing students to proceed with Step **2** of Part **b,** you may wish to ensure that the lines constructed through points A and B are perpendicular to $\overline{AB}$.

b. By keeping point C within the given constraints, all obtuse or right triangles generated will have $\overline{AB}$ as the longest side. Sample data:

$m\angle C$	AB	AC	BC	$(AB)^2 - [(AC)^2 + (BC)^2]$
62.2°	1.59	1.38	1.66	−2.14
135°	1.59	0.55	1.16	0.89
90°	1.59	0.95	1.27	0

c. 1. obtuse

   2. acute

   3. right

teacher note

You might wish to remind students that the longest side of a triangle is opposite the angle with greatest measure.

Discussion

a. The expression $(AB)^2 - [(AC)^2 + (BC)^2]$ represents the difference between the square of the side opposite $\angle C$ and the sum of the squares of the other two sides. This expression equals 0 when $m\angle C = 90°$. At this point, $\triangle ABC$ is a right triangle, where $\overline{AB}$ is the hypotenuse and $\overline{AC}$ and $\overline{BC}$ are the legs. In this case, the Pythagorean theorem is restated as $c^2 - (a^2 + b^2) = 0$, where c is the length of the hypotenuse and a and b are the lengths of the legs.

b. 1. Sample response: In obtuse triangles, the square of the length of the side opposite the obtuse angle is greater than the sum of the squares of the lengths of the other two sides. This is shown by a positive value in the right-hand column of Table **11-1.**

   2. If a triangle is an obtuse triangle, then the square of the length of the side opposite the obtuse angle is greater than the sum of the squares of the lengths of the other two sides.

c. 1. Sample response: In acute triangles, the square of the length of any side is less than the sum of the squares of the lengths of the other two sides. This is shown by a negative value in the right-hand column of Table **11-1.**

   2. If a triangle is an acute triangle, then the square of the length of any side is less than the sum of the squares of the lengths of the other two sides.

d. From the data in Table **11-1,** students should observe that the converse of the Pythagorean theorem appears to be true. **Note:** It should be pointed out that the exploration does not constitute a proof.

e. Sample response: Measure the length a and the width b of the corner and consider these the legs of a potential right triangle. Then measure the potential hypotenuse c of the triangle. If these lengths satisfy the equation $a^2 + b^2 = c^2$, then the triangle is a right triangle and the angle is a right angle.

---

3. Record the appropriate measurements for $\triangle ABC$ in Table **11-1.**

4. Move point C to another location between the two lines (but without touching either line). Record the appropriate measurements in Table **11-1.**

5. Repeat Step **4** for several other locations of C. Include some positions that make $m\angle C$ acute (less than 90°), some that make it a right angle (exactly 90°), and some that make it obtuse (greater than 90° but less than 180°).

c. 1. When the value of $(AB)^2 - [(AC)^2 + (BC)^2]$ is positive, is $\angle C$ acute, right, or obtuse?

   2. When the value of $(AB)^2 - [(AC)^2 + (BC)^2]$ is negative, is $\angle C$ acute, right, or obtuse?

   3. When the value of $(AB)^2 - [(AC)^2 + (BC)^2]$ is 0, is $\angle C$ acute, right, or obtuse?

Discussion

a. How is the expression $(AB)^2 - [(AC)^2 + (BC)^2]$ related to the equation for the Pythagorean theorem, $a^2 + b^2 = c^2$?

b. 1. In an obtuse triangle, two angles are acute and one is obtuse. The longest side is opposite the obtuse angle. Based on your data in Table **11-1,** describe how the sides of an obtuse triangle are related.

   2. How would you express this relationship as a conditional statement?

c. 1. In an acute triangle, all three angles are acute. Based on your data in Table **11-1,** describe how the sides of an acute triangle are related.

   2. How would you express this relationship as a conditional statement?

d. Does the converse of the Pythagorean theorem appear to be true? Explain your response.

e. How could you use the converse of the Pythagorean theorem to determine if a corner is "square"?

Warm-Up

1. Each of the following sets of numbers represents the side lengths of a triangle. Identify whether the triangle is right, acute, or obtuse. Justify your responses.

   a. 9, 15, 12

   b. 8, 8, 8

   c. 14, 11, 23

288   Module 11 ■ *A New Angle on an Old Pyramid*

Warm-Up

1. a. These lengths form a right triangle.

   b. These lengths form an acute triangle.

   c. These lengths form an obtuse triangle.

2. Find the missing length in each right triangle below.

a.

b.

c.

d.

3. Consider the following conjecture: "When the diagonals of a quadrilateral are perpendicular, the quadrilateral is a rhombus."

   a. Write this conjecture as a conditional statement.

   b. Write the converse of the statement in Part **a.**

Assignment

2.1 The scholars of Babylon recorded much of their mathematics on clay tablets. Many of these tablets still exist. One remarkable tablet, designated "Plimpton 322," dates from sometime around 1900 B.C. This fragment of a once larger tablet contains several columns of numbers.

The table below shows a portion of the contents of Plimpton 322, and some numbers (in parentheses) that historians believe were in the original tablet. Each row of three numbers in the table is a *triple*.

Side 1	Side 2	Side 3
(120)	119	169
(72)	65	97
(60)	45	75
(360)	319	481

   a. Use the converse of the Pythagorean theorem to determine what type of triangle—acute, obtuse, or right—is formed when each triple in the table represents the lengths of the sides of a triangle.

   b. If you double each number in a triple from Plimpton 322, does the resulting triple still show the same relationship you described in Part **a**? Explain your response.

---

2. **a.** $m \approx 8.5$

   b. $z \approx 4.2$

   c. $q \approx 10.1$

   d. $y \approx 136.2$

3. **a.** If the diagonals of a quadrilateral are perpendicular, then the quadrilateral is a rhombus.

   b. If a quadrilateral is a rhombus, then its diagonals are perpendicular to each other.

---

teacher note

Students require string to complete Problem **2.2.**

The puzzle template is needed for Problem **2.3.** A blackline master appears in the Teacher Resources for this module.

In Problem **2.4,** students explore the triangle inequality property. You may supply string, paper strips, or other manipulatives.

In Problem **2.7,** students develop the distance formula for two dimensions.

Assignment

Problems suitable for use as assessment items are identified by an asterisk (*).

2.1 **a.** Students should verify that, when used as the lengths of the sides of a triangle, each triple in the table makes the Pythagorean equation true. Because the converse of the Pythagorean theorem is true, these triangles are all right triangles. For example, using the triple in the first row:

$$120^2 + 119^2 \stackrel{?}{=} 169^2$$

$$28{,}561 = 28{,}561$$

   b. Any multiple of a Pythagorean triple is also a Pythagorean triple. For example, suppose a, b, and c are whole numbers and $a^2 + b^2 = c^2$. Then $2a$, $2b$, and $2c$ are whole numbers and:

$$(2a)^2 + (2b)^2 = 4(a^2 + b^2)$$

$$= 4(c^2)$$

$$= (2c)^2$$

In general, if $a^2 + b^2 = c^2$, then $(ma)^2 + (mb)^2 = m^2(a^2 + b^2) = m^2(c^2)$.

2.2 By using the string to form a 3-4-5 triangle, students can create one right angle for the square. The other right angles may be formed in a similar manner. Students can then verify that their figures are squares by calculating the lengths of the diagonals. The diagonals of a square are congruent, perpendicular, and bisect each other. If the side length of a square is 3 units, the diagonal length is approximately 4.2 units.

2.3 Sample arrangement:

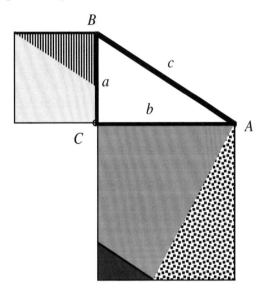

Note: Although this puzzle provides a graphic illustration of the Pythagorean relationship as a statement about areas, any demonstration of the Pythagorean theorem by the puzzle method should be treated with caution. Many math puzzles ask students to cut up a rectangle with an area of, for example, 80 cm², then rearrange the pieces to obtain a rectangle with an area of 81 cm². You may emphasize that a visually convincing demonstration does not constitute a proof.

2.4 **a.** Answers will vary. Sample response: (2, 3, 6); (1, 4, 5); (9, 10, 25).

   b. Sample response: The two shorter sides cannot meet to form the third vertex of the triangle.

   c. Any three segments whose lengths satisfy the inequality $a + b \leq c$ will not form a triangle.

   d. Sample response: If the sum of the lengths of any two segments is less than the length of a third segment, then the three segments will not form a triangle.

2.5 **a.** Using the Pythagorean theorem, $20^2 = x^2 + 10^2$. Solving for x, $x = \sqrt{300} \approx 17.3$.

   b. Using the Pythagorean theorem, $x^2 = 12^2 + 13^2$. Solving for x, $x = \sqrt{313} \approx 17.7$.

   c. Because this is a square pyramid, the altitude intersects the center of the base. The length of one leg of the right triangle is therefore 50 m. Using the Pythagorean theorem, $150^2 = x^2 + 50^2$. Solving for x, $x = \sqrt{20,000} \approx 141.4$.

2.2 To create a surveying tool similar to the one the Egyptians might have used, mark 12 congruent segments on a string. Considering the length of each segment as 1 unit, form a square whose sides are exactly 3 units long. (Do not use protractors or other tools to help set your corners.) Verify that your result is a square.

2.3 Although the early Babylonians were aware of the relationship represented in the Pythagorean theorem, they had not yet developed the algebraic notation we use today. Instead, they used a sort of "geometric algebra."

The following diagram shows a right triangle *ABC* with squares constructed on each side. Five shaded pieces subdivide the largest square. Obtain a template from your teacher and cut out the shaded pieces from the largest square. Arrange the pieces so that they exactly fill the two smaller squares. Explain how your arrangement geometrically demonstrates the algebraic expression $a^2 + b^2 = c^2$.

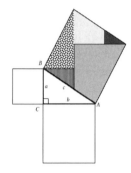

2.4 Given three segments, it is not always possible to use them to form a triangle.

   a. Identify at least three different sets of three segments that do not form triangles.

   b. Explain why each set of segments does not form a triangle.

   c. Describe the relationship that exists among the lengths of three segments when they cannot be used to form a triangle.

   d. Rewrite your response to Part **c** as a conditional statement.

2.5 Determine the unknown length *x* in each of Parts **a**–**e** below. The pyramids in Parts **c**–**e** are regular square pyramids.

a.

b.

c.

d.

e.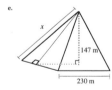

2.6 Without constructing the triangles, determine if the three lengths in each of the following sets would form an acute triangle, an obtuse triangle, a right triangle, or no triangle.

   a. 5, 12, 13

   b. 6, 8, 12

   c. 7, 10, 19

   d. 13, 8, 15

2.7 Use the properties of right triangles to find the distance between each pair of points in Parts **a–d**. (In Part **a**, an appropriate triangle has been drawn for you. In Part **d**, use an expression to represent the distance.)

a.

b.

c.

d.

2.8 Some of the granite blocks used in the Great Pyramid are 8.2 m long and 1.2 m thick. Each block has a mass of 49 metric tons, and some of them are set 61 m above the base of the pyramid.

Egyptologists believe that the builders used inclined ramps to raise the stone blocks to these levels. As shown in the diagram below, some researchers have suggested that the incline ratio (slope or rise:run) of these ramps was 1:3.

The dimensions of the completed Great Pyramid are shown in the diagram below. If the capstone (the stone on the top) is 1 m tall, how long was the ramp required to raise it?

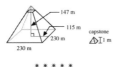

＊ ＊ ＊ ＊ ＊

d. From the diagram below, the height of the triangular face can be found as follows: $z^2 + 50^2 = 200^2$; $z = \sqrt{37{,}500}$.

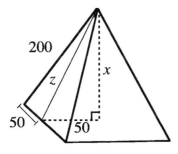

Substituting z^2 for in the equation below:

$$x^2 + 50^2 = z^2$$

$$x = \sqrt{35{,}000} \approx 187 \text{ m}$$

e. From the diagram below, the height of the triangular face can be found as follows: $z^2 = 147^2 + 115^2$; $z = \sqrt{34{,}834}$.

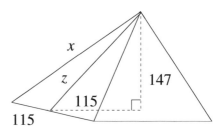

Substituting z^2 for in the equation below:

$$x^2 = z^2 + 115^2$$

$$x = \sqrt{48{,}059} \approx 219 \text{ m}$$

2.6 **a.** Because $13^2 = 5^2 + 12^2$, these lengths form a right triangle.
   b. Because $12^2 > 6^2 + 8^2$, these lengths form an obtuse triangle.
   c. Because $7 + 10 < 19$, no triangle is possible. (See Problem **2.4.**)
   d. Because $13^2 + 8^2 > 15^2$, these lengths form an acute triangle.

2.7 **a.** $AC = 2$; $BC = 3$. Because $2^2 + 3^2 = 13$, $AB = \sqrt{13}$.
   b. Because $5^2 + 4^2 = 41$, $DE = \sqrt{41}$.
   c. Because $(4-1)^2 + (-1-3)^2 = 25$, the length of the segment is 5.
   d. The distance between two points (x_1,y_1) and (x_2,y_2) is:

$$\sqrt{(x_1 - x_2)^2 + (y_1 - y_2)^2}$$

＊ 2.8 Because the Great Pyramid is 147 m tall, the ramp would have had to rise $(147 - 1)$ or 146 m above the ground. Therefore, the "run" of the ramp can be found as follows:

$$\frac{146}{x} = \frac{1}{3}$$

$$x = 3(146) = 438 \text{ m}$$

Using the Pythagorean theorem, the length of the ramp is $\sqrt{438^2 + 146^2}$, or approximately 462 m.

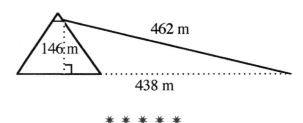

＊ ＊ ＊ ＊ ＊

2.9 Sample response: If the corners of the foundation are right angles, the lengths of the diagonals can be determined using the Pythagorean theorem.

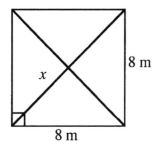

The sides are 8 m on each side; therefore:

$$8^2 + 8^2 = x^2$$

$$x = \sqrt{128} \approx 11.3 \text{ m}$$

2.10 a. The triangles formed are isosceles.

b. Because each triangle is isosceles, the altitude is perpendicular to the base and also bisects the base.

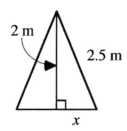

Using the Pythagorean theorem,

$$2^2 + x^2 = 2.5^2$$

$$x = 1.5 \text{ m}$$

Because x represents half the length of the base of the isosceles triangle, the length of the base is 3 m.

Therefore, the perimeter of the octagon is $3 \cdot 8 = 24$ m. Adding the lengths of the diagonals, the total length of the wood necessary for the floor supports is $24 + (4 \cdot 5) = 44$ m.

ACTIVITY 3

Students are introduced to the tangent (the first of the trigonometric ratios examined in this module) by investigating triangular ratios found in the casing blocks of the Great Pyramid. These casing blocks were cut with great accuracy using a constant slope. Although the ancient Egyptians might not have used trigonometry, they were aware of the ratios of a casing block's length to its height. This ratio essentially represents our concept of the cotangent of an angle.

2.9 Leah and Harlan are building a concrete foundation for their new garage. The foundation is a square 8 m on each side. After marking the boundaries, they decide to measure the diagonals to confirm that the corners are right angles. If the corners are right angles, how long should the diagonals be?

2.10 After finishing their garage, Leah and Harlan decide to build a gazebo in their backyard. (A gazebo is a small, roofed structure with open sides.) As shown in the diagram on the right, the floor of their gazebo is a regular octagon. The floor supports lie along the perimeter and the diagonals of the octagon.

a. The diagonals of the octagon form eight congruent triangles. What type of triangles are these?

b. An altitude drawn from the center of the octagon to the base of each triangle is 2 m long. Each diagonal is 5 m long. Determine the total length of the wood required for the floor supports.

ACTIVITY 3

Judging from the information recorded on Plimpton 322, the ancient Babylonians (and the ancient Egyptians too, perhaps) were aware of some uses for the ratios of the sides of right triangles. These ratios are important in many modern applications, from architecture to navigation. The study of these ratios and their properties is the focus of **trigonometry**. In this activity, you explore how the ancient Egyptians might have used some basic trigonometric ideas in the construction of the pyramids.

Exploration

The Great Pyramid of Giza has 203 distinct levels or steps, like those shown below in Figure **11-9**. These steps are not all the same height.

FIGURE 11-9   Pyramid steps.

Module 11 ■ *A New Angle on an Old Pyramid*   **293**

Materials List

Note: The materials listed below are required for the research project.

■ protractors (one per student)

■ drinking straws (one per student)

■ string

■ paper clips (one per student)

Technology

■ geometry utility

■ spreadsheet

After the steps were built, casing blocks were used to give the pyramid's walls their smooth outer surface. To create a smooth slope, the outer faces of all the casing blocks—regardless of their height—had to be slanted at the same angle to their bases. Figure **11-10** shows a portion of a pyramid wall with three casing blocks.

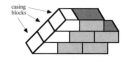

FIGURE 11-10 A portion of a pyramid wall with casing blocks.

An angle formed by two intersecting planes is a **dihedral angle.** The measure of a dihedral angle is the measure of the angle whose sides are the two rays formed by the intersections of the faces and a plane perpendicular to the edge. As shown in Figure **11-11,** the measure of the dihedral angle of the Great Pyramid is 52°.

FIGURE 11-11 The dihedral angle of the Great Pyramid's casing blocks.

Figure **11-12** shows cross-sectional drawings of the casing blocks for the bottom and top steps of the Great Pyramid. The bottom step is 141 cm thick, while the top step is 56 cm thick. The heights of the remaining 201 steps lie somewhere between these two values.

FIGURE 11-12 Cross-sections of two casing blocks.

To maintain a constant dihedral angle measure of 52°, the stonecutters had to be very precise. However, the Egyptians did not measure blocks using angles or degrees. Instead, they used a relationship called the *seqt,* the ratio of the horizontal "run" of a slope to its vertical "rise." The seqt of the bottom casing block in Figure **11-12,** for example, is $x/141$. In this exploration, you experiment with a ratio from trigonometry related to the Egyptian seqt.

---

a. 1. On a geometry utility, construct a horizontal line. Construct and label two points A and C on the line.

2. Construct a line perpendicular to $\overline{AC}$ through C. Label a point B on the perpendicular.

3. Construct $\overline{AB}$. Your construction should now resemble the one shown in Figure **11-13.**

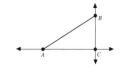

FIGURE 11-13 Construction of right triangle.

4. Hide the lines and construct $\overline{AC}$ and $\overline{BC}$, as shown in Figure **11-14.** Note: Save this construction for use in Activity **4.**

FIGURE 11-14 Right triangle.

5. Drag point B until $m\angle A = 52°$ (the measure of the dihedral angle of the Great Pyramid).

b. Measure the legs of right triangle ABC and calculate the ratio below.

$$\frac{\text{length of leg opposite } \angle A}{\text{length of leg adjacent to } \angle A}$$

Note: For convenience, this ratio will be referred to in this module as the ratio "opposite/adjacent."

c. Drag point C along the horizontal line to form other right triangles.

1. As the lengths of the legs change, describe any patterns you observe in the ratios of the lengths.

2. Explain why these right triangles are similar.

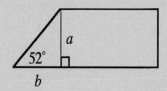

teacher note

You might wish to emphasize that the measure of a dihedral angle is the measure of the angle whose sides are the two rays formed by the intersections of the faces and a plane perpendicular to the edge (as shown in Figure **11-11**).

Students may create paper representations of the cross sections of casing blocks, using various values of a from 10 to 30 cm.

These models can then be used to illustrate the smooth, continuous slope that casing blocks gave to the sides of a pyramid.

For the following exploration, students should set their geometry utility to use degree measure, not radian measure.

Student Outcomes

After completing the following exploration and discussion, students should be able to:

✳ identify the tangent ratio in a right triangle

✳ use the tangent ratio to determine the measures of unknown sides and angles

✳ understand the difference between the tan⁻¹ and keys on a graphing utility.

Exploration

a. Students construct a right triangle with an acute angle measure of 52°.

b. For the angle measure of 52°, the ratio is approximately 1.28.

c. 1. The ratio remains constant for all these right triangles.

2. All these triangles have congruent angle measures of 90°, 52°, and 38°, so the triangles are similar by the AAA Property.

d–e. Students should realize that each acute angle measure is associated with a unique ratio. Sample table:

$m\angle A$	opposite/adjacent	$\tan\angle A$
52°	1.28	1.28
15°	0.268	0.268
30°	0.577	0.577
45°	1.00	1.00
60°	1.73	1.73
75°	3.73	3.73

f. Sample response: The inverse tangent of each value from Part **e** is the measure of the corresponding angle in Table **11-2**.

Discussion

a. Because the triangles generated are all similar to the first triangle, the corresponding ratios are equal.

b. Students should realize that because they all started with the same angle measure, the ratio of opposite to adjacent (the tangent) is the same, regardless of the right triangle used.

c. Sample response: As the measure of the angle gets larger, the tangent value gets larger.

d. The tangent of an acute angle measure in a right triangle is the ratio of the opposite to adjacent, while the seqt is the ratio of adjacent to opposite. The tangent is the multiplicative inverse of the seqt.

e. 1. Sample response: I would find the value in the right-hand column of the table. The measure of the angle is the value in the left-hand column of the same row

   2. Sample response: The inverse tangent commands reports the angle measure which corresponds to a particular tangent value.

f. Sample response: When the measure of an acute angle in a right triangle is 45°, the lengths of the two legs are equal. Because the lengths of the legs are equal, the ratio of opposite to adjacent is 1.

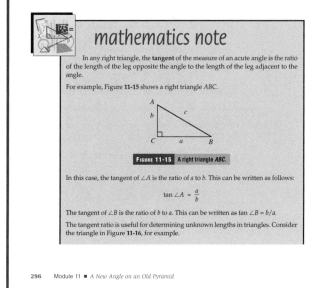

d. Create a table with headings like those in Table **11-2**. Drag point *B* to change the measure of ∠*A* and record the ratio of the length of the leg opposite ∠*A* to the length of the leg adjacent to ∠*A*.

TABLE 11-2 ■ Ratios of Length of Opposite Leg to Adjacent Leg

$m\angle A$	opposite/adjacent
52°	
15°	
30°	
45°	
60°	
75°	

mathematics note

In any right triangle, the **tangent** of the measure of an acute angle is the ratio of the length of the leg opposite the angle to the length of the leg adjacent to the angle.

For example, Figure **11-15** shows a right triangle *ABC*.

FIGURE 11-15 A right triangle *ABC*.

In this case, the tangent of ∠*A* is the ratio of *a* to *b*. This can be written as follows:

$$\tan\angle A = \frac{a}{b}$$

The tangent of ∠*B* is the ratio of *b* to *a*. This can be written as $\tan\angle B = b/a$.

The tangent ratio is useful for determining unknown lengths in triangles. Consider the triangle in Figure **11-16**, for example.

296   Module 11 ■ *A New Angle on an Old Pyramid*

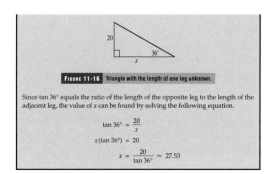

FIGURE 11-16 Triangle with the length of one leg unknown.

Since tan 36° equals the ratio of the length of the opposite leg to the length of the adjacent leg, the value of *x* can be found by solving the following equation.

$$\tan 36° = \frac{20}{x}$$

$$x(\tan 36°) = 20$$

$$x = \frac{20}{\tan 36°} \approx 27.53$$

e. Add a column to Table **11-2** and label it "tan ∠*A*." Using technology, find and record the tangent of each angle measure in the left-hand column. Compare your results with the ratios in the column labeled "opposite/adjacent."

f. Many calculators feature a key labeled "tan⁻¹." This represents the inverse tangent command. Use technology to determine and record the inverse tangent of each value you determined in Part **e**. Describe any patterns you observe.

Discussion

a. In Part c of the exploration, what pattern did you observe in the ratio opposite/adjacent? Explain why this pattern occurs.

b. Compare the values you recorded in Table **11-2** with others in your class. Describe any similarities or differences you observe.

c. What happens to the tangent as the measure of an acute angle changes?

d. How is the tangent related to the Egyptian seqt?

e. 1. Given that the tangent of an angle is approximately 1.73, how could you use the values in Table **11-2** to determine the measure of the angle?

   2. Describe how this process is related to the tan⁻¹ key on a calculator.

f. Why would you expect tan 45° to equal 1?

Module 11 ■ *A New Angle on an Old Pyramid*   297

Warm-Up

1. What is the definition of a dihedral angle?

2. Determine the unknown measure in each triangle below.

a.

b.

c.

d.

e.

f.

Assignment

3.1 The figure below shows a cross-sectional drawing of the Great Pyramid and a cross-sectional drawing of a casing block.

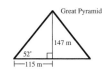

a. Explain why the right triangle shown in the casing block is similar to the right triangle shown in the Great Pyramid.

b. Determine the value of x in the casing block using each of the following methods:

   1. proportions and similar triangles   2. the tangent ratio.

Warm-Up

1. A dihedral angle is the angle formed by two intersecting planes.

2. **a.** $x \approx 4.9$
   b. $z \approx 84.1$
   c. $t \approx 3.6$
   d. $k \approx 784.5$
   e. $n \approx 32.6°$
   f. $q \approx 74.2°$

teacher note

Because a solution to Problem **3.5** requires several steps, it provides a good opportunity for group work. To assess students' understanding of the tangent ratio and its application, you may ask groups to present their solutions to the class.

Assignment

Problems suitable for use as assessment items are identified by an asterisk (*).

* **3.1 a.** Sample response: The right triangle in the casing block and the right triangle in the Great Pyramid both have angles that measure 52° and 90°. Therefore, the remaining angles in the two triangles also have the same measure. By the AAA Property, the triangles are similar.

   b. 1. Using proportions,

$$\frac{x}{60} = \frac{115}{147}$$

$$x \approx 47 \text{ cm}$$

   2. Using the tangent ratio,

$$\tan 52° = \frac{60}{x}$$

$$x \approx 47 \text{ cm}$$

3.2 a. $x/50 = \tan 52°$; $x \approx 64$ cm

b. $120/x = \tan 52°$; $x \approx 94$ cm

c. $x^2 = 100^2 + 128^2$; $x = \sqrt{26{,}384} \approx 162$ cm

* 3.3 Sample response:

cross-section of pyramid

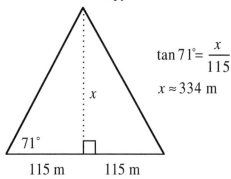

$$\tan 71° = \frac{x}{115}$$

$$x \approx 334 \text{ m}$$

71°

115 m   115 m

3.4 In their responses, students should describe the connections among tan 90°, dividing by 0, and the results displayed on their calculators.

* 3.5 a. Using the tangent ratio,

$$\tan 50° = \frac{x}{94.5}$$

$$x \approx 113 \text{ cm}$$

b. Considering the right triangle formed by the height at which the 50° angle was abandoned:

$$\tan 50° = \frac{73.5}{x}$$

$$x \approx 61.7 \text{ cm}$$

The width of the pyramid where the angle changes is therefore about 189 − 2(61.7) or 65.6 m.

The height of the upper part of the pyramid is:

$$\tan 37° = \frac{x}{32.8}$$

$$x \approx 24.7 \text{ cm}$$

The total height of Bent Pyramid is

$$73.5 + 24.7 = 98.2 \text{ m.}$$

3.2 The following diagrams show three casing blocks from the Great Pyramid. Determine the unknown length in each case.

a.

52°

50 cm

b.

120 cm

52°

x

c.

128 cm

52°

100 cm

3.3 Consider a pyramid whose base has the same dimensions as the Great Pyramid's. If its casing blocks have dihedral angle measures of 71° instead of 52°, how tall is the pyramid? (*Hint:* Use the given information to sketch an appropriate triangle.)

3.4 Examine the value of the tangent ratio for angles with measures close to 90°. Describe what a calculator displays for tan 90° and explain why this occurs.

3.5 King Khufu's father, Snefru, built a pyramid at Dashur known as the Bent Pyramid. As shown in the diagram below, the base of the Bent Pyramid is a square 189 m on each side. The 50° dihedral angle measure at its base was abandoned after construction reached a height of 73.5 m. A smaller angle measure, about 37°, was used to finish the pyramid.

50°

189 m

a. How tall would the Bent Pyramid have been if completed using the 50° dihedral angle measure?

b. How tall is the actual Bent Pyramid?

3.6 Find the unknown lengths and angle measures in each of the following triangles.

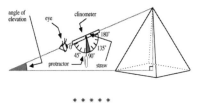

a.

b.

c.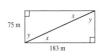

d.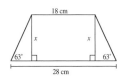

3.7 The ancient Egyptians used the ratio a/b to measure the slant of the casing block below. Express this ratio in terms of the tangent of the measure of the block's dihedral angle.

3.8 A clinometer measures angle of elevation. The simple clinometer shown in the diagram below consists of a drinking straw, a weighted string, and a protractor. Using this tool, the angle of elevation (the shaded angle in the diagram) is the difference between the angle indicated by the weighted string and 90°. Use this diagram to describe how a clinometer—along with some knowledge of trigonometry—could be used to calculate the height of a pyramid.

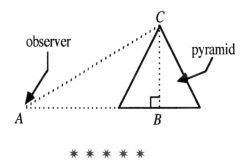

* * * * *

3.9 a. Find the unknown angle measures in the figure below.

b. Find the unknown lengths in the following figure.

3.10 When describing the roof of a house, the ratio of the vertical distance to the horizontal distance is often referred to as *pitch*. The figure below shows a roof with a pitch of 2/5. Determine the measure of the angle which this roof makes with the horizontal.

Research Project

Construct a clinometer like the one described in Problem **3.8**. Use your clinometer to estimate the height of your school, a flagpole, or some other tall object. Describe the methods you used to make each estimate. If possible, find the actual height of the object and compare this value to your estimate. Discuss some possible explanations for any differences you observe.

3.6 **a.** $x = 10/\tan 30° \approx 17$ cm
   b. $x = \tan^{-1}(20/20) = 45°$
   c. $y = 125(\tan 70°) \approx 343$ m
   d. $y = \tan^{-1}(150/450) \approx 18°$;
      $x = \tan^{-1}(450/150) \approx 72°$

3.7 Because the tangent of the dihedral angle is b/a, the Egyptians' ratio can be expressed as $1/\tan \theta$, where θ is the measure of the dihedral angle.

3.8 Sample response: In the diagram below, the clinometer measures the angle of elevation at point A, where the observer is standing. The length of segment AB, the distance from the observer to the center of the pyramid, could be measured. The tangent ratio can then be used to calculate the length of segment BC—which is the height of the pyramid.

* * * * *

3.9 **a.** $x = \tan^{-1}(75/183) \approx 22°$ and
      $y = \tan^{-1}(183/75) = 68°$

   b. $x = \dfrac{28 - 18}{2} \cdot \tan 63° \approx 9.8$ cm

3.10 $x = \tan^{-1}(2/5) \approx 22°$

Research Project

Students may build clinometers like the one shown in Problem **3.8** or develop their own designs. Their responses should include a discussion of possible sources of error.

ACTIVITY 4

In this activity, students explore two other right-triangle ratios that are constant for a given acute angle: sine and cosine.

teacher note

A brief assessment of the mathematical content in Activities **3** and **4,** for use at your discretion, appears in the Teacher Resources for this module.

Materials List

- protractors (one per student)

Technology

- geometry utility
- spreadsheet

Student Outcomes

After completing the following exploration and discussion, students should be able to:

✳ identify the sine and cosine ratios in a right triangle

✳ use the sine and cosine ratios to determine the measures of unknown sides and angles

✳ recognize the existence of other trigonometric ratios

✳ identify the difference between the sin and $\sin^{-1}$ keys, and the cos and $\cos^{-1}$ keys, on a graphing utility.

ACTIVITY 4

The word *trigonometry* is derived from the Greek words for "three-angle measurement." Right-triangle trigonometry involves the relationships among the sides and angles of right triangles. The tangent ratio is only one of these relationships.

As noted in Activity **3**, the Egyptians used the seqt. In Plimpton 322, the Babylonians worked with yet another such ratio. In this activity, you explore some other trigonometric ratios and examine their usefulness as problem-solving tools.

Exploration

a. Consider △*ABC* in Figure **11-17**. In Activity **3**, you found that the tangent ratio for a given measure of ∠*A* remains the same for all right triangles that contain that angle. List all the other ratios that you think will remain constant for ∠*A*.

Figure 11-17 Right triangle *ABC*.

b. Using your construction of a right triangle from Activity **3**, measure ∠*A* and the sides of △*ABC*. Calculate all the ratios that exist among the lengths of the sides.

c. Drag point C to create other, similar right triangles. Verify that the ratios you identified in Part **a** remain constant.

d. Create a table with headings like those in Table **11-3** below. Use your geometry utility to complete the table.

TABLE 11-3 ■ Ratios of Lengths in Right Triangles		
m∠A	opposite/hypotenuse	adjacent/hypotenuse
5°		
15°		
30°		
45°		
60°		
75°		

302   Module 11 ■ *A New Angle on an Old Pyramid*

---

teacher note

To complete Parts **d–e** of the exploration, students may use the table feature in a geometry utility instead of a spreadsheet.

Exploration

a–c. Answers will vary. Students list all ratios that they believe will remain constant for a given acute angle. The six possible ratios are *a/b, a/c, b/a, b/c, c/a,* and *c/b.*

d–e. To demonstrate that the ratios do not depend on the triangle used, you may ask students to compare values for Table **11-3.** See sample table below.

m∠A	opposite/hypotenuse	adjacent/hypotenuse	sin∠*A*	cos∠*A*
5°	0.087	0.996	0.087	0.996
15°	0.259	0.966	0.259	0.966
30°	0.5	0.866	0.5	0.866
45°	0.707	0.707	0.707	0.707
60°	0.866	0.5	0.866	0.5
75°	0.66	0.259	0.966	0.259

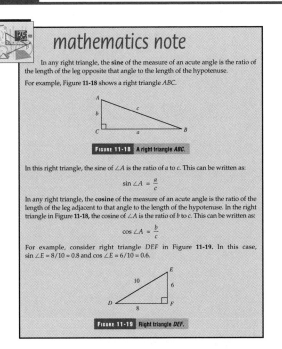

mathematics note

In any right triangle, the **sine** of the measure of an acute angle is the ratio of the length of the leg opposite that angle to the length of the hypotenuse.

For example, Figure **11-18** shows a right triangle ABC.

FIGURE 11-18 A right triangle ABC.

In this right triangle, the sine of $\angle A$ is the ratio of a to c. This can be written as:

$$\sin \angle A = \frac{a}{c}$$

In any right triangle, the **cosine** of the measure of an acute angle is the ratio of the length of the leg adjacent to that angle to the length of the hypotenuse. In the right triangle in Figure **11-18**, the cosine of $\angle A$ is the ratio of b to c. This can be written as:

$$\cos \angle A = \frac{b}{c}$$

For example, consider right triangle DEF in Figure **11-19**. In this case, $\sin \angle E = 8/10 = 0.8$ and $\cos \angle E = 6/10 = 0.6$.

FIGURE 11-19 Right triangle DEF.

e. Add two columns to Table **11-3** using the headings "sin $\angle A$" and "cos $\angle A$." Use technology to determine the sine and cosine of each angle measure in the left-hand column. Compare your results with the ratios in the columns labeled "opposite/hypotenuse" and "adjacent/hypotenuse."

f. Use your geometry utility to determine the minimum and maximum values of sin $\angle A$ and cos $\angle A$ in right triangle ABC.

g. Many calculators feature keys labeled "sin^{-1}" and "cos^{-1}." These represent the inverse sine and inverse cosine commands, respectively. Use the values you determined in Part **e** to experiment with these commands. Describe any patterns you observe.

Discussion

a. Describe how the two ratios in Table **11-3** are related to sin $\angle A$ and cos $\angle A$.

b. What trends did you observe in the values of sine and cosine as the measure of $\angle A$ increased?

c. What is the measure of $\angle A$ when sin $\angle A$ and cos $\angle A$ are equal?

d. 1. Describe the information you would need to find the measure of an angle using the inverse sine command.

2. Describe the information you would need to find the measure of an angle using the inverse cosine command.

e. In a right triangle ABC where $\angle C$ is the right angle, sin $\angle A$ equals cos $\angle B$. Explain why this occurs.

Warm-Up

1. Use the right triangle below to answer Parts **a–d**.

a. For $\angle B$ which trigonometric ratio is represented by 5/13?

b. For $\angle A$, which trigonometric ratio is represented by 5/13?

c. For $\angle B$, which trigonometric ratio is represented by 12/5?

d. For $\angle A$, which trigonometric ratio is represented by 12/13?

2. Determine the unknown length or angle measure in each of the three right triangles below.

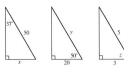

f. Students should determine that the minimum and maximum values of $\sin \angle A$ and $\cos \angle A$ are 0 and 1, respectively.

g. Students should observe that the appropriate inverse of each value from Part **e** is the measure of the corresponding angle in Table **11-3**.

Discussion

a. In a right triangle, $\sin \angle A$ = opposite/hypotenuse and $\cos \angle A$ = adjacent/hypotenuse.

b. Answers will vary. Some students will observe that, as $m \angle A$ increases, $\sin \angle A$ increases from 0 to 1 and $\cos \angle A$ decreases from 1 to 0.

c. When $m \angle A = 45°$, both the sine and cosine of $\angle A$ are approximately 0.707.

d. 1. Sample response: You would need to know the length of the side of the right triangle opposite the angle and the length of the hypotenuse.

2. Sample response: You would need to know the length of the side of the right triangle adjacent to the angle and the length of the hypotenuse.

e. Students should recognize that the side adjacent to $\angle A$ is opposite $\angle B$, and vice versa.

$$\sin \angle A = \frac{BC}{AB} = \cos \angle B$$

Warm-Up

1. **a.** cosine
   b. sine
   c. tangent
   d. cosine

2. $x \approx 30$; $y \approx 31$; $z \approx 53°$

$$\tan 37° = \frac{x}{50} \qquad \cos 50° = \frac{20}{y} \qquad \cos z° = \frac{3}{5}$$

$$x \approx 30 \qquad\qquad y \approx 31 \qquad\qquad z \approx 253°$$

3. The height of the triangle is approximately 5.3 cm.

Assignment

Problems suitable for use as assessment items are identified by an asterisk (*).

* **4.1 a.** $h = 160 \cdot \sin 44° \approx 111$ m;
  $l = 2(160 \cdot \cos 44°) \approx 230$ m
  b. $x = 120/\sin 52° \approx 152$ cm
  c. The length of the ramp is $100/\sin 25° \approx 237$ m.
  4.2 $x = \cos^{-1}(75/100) \approx 41°$
  4.3 Sample response:

$$\frac{\sin\angle A}{\cos\angle A} = \frac{\text{opposite/hypotenuse}}{\text{adjacent/hypotenuse}}$$

$$= \frac{\text{opposite}}{\text{hypotenuse}} \cdot \frac{\text{hypotenuse}}{\text{adjacent}}$$

$$= \frac{\text{opposite}}{\text{adjacent}}$$

$$= \tan\angle A$$

---

3. Find the height of an isosceles triangle if the vertex angle measures 48° and the congruent legs have a length of 5.8 cm.

Assignment

4.1 a. The figure below shows a cross-section of a pyramid. Use trigonometric ratios to determine the height h and the length l.

b. The figure below shows a cross-section of a casing block. Determine the unknown length x.

c. To move stones to the top of a pyramid, the Egyptians may have built a ramp of sand. If the pyramid in the diagram below is 100 m tall and the incline of the ramp is 25°, determine the length of the ramp.

4.2 Use appropriate technology and the inverse cosine command to find the unknown angle measure x in the figure below.

4.3 Use the definitions of the sine, cosine, and tangent ratios to prove that the following equation is true.

$$\tan \angle A = \frac{\sin \angle A}{\cos \angle A}$$

4.4 a. Using △ABC below, explain why sin 65° = cos 25° and tan 65° = 1/tan 25°.

b. Generalize your response to Part a for all pairs of acute angles whose measures add up to 90°. Use technology to verify this conjecture.

4.5 The diagram below shows the base angles on a face of the Great Pyramid. Determine the measure of these angles.

base angles

* * * * *

4.6 On a highway, a uniform grade of 4% means that there is a rise of 4 m for every 100 m of horizontal distance.

a. If you are driving up a road with a 4% grade, what angle measure does the path of your car make with the horizontal?

b. What is your change in elevation after traveling 32 m on this road?

4.7 Workers building the Great Pyramid used scaffolding to raise themselves to an appropriate height. The scaffold in the diagram below lifted stone masons to a height 4 m above the previous level. The measure of the angle between each crosspiece and vertical support is 60°. What is the length of the crosspiece? Describe how you determined your response.

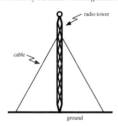

crosspiece

4.8 Determine the measure of the angle that the roof in the following diagram makes with the horizontal.

4.9 A radio tower is anchored to the ground by four cables, two of which are shown in the figure below. Each cable is bolted to the tower 20 m above the ground. The angles formed by the cables with the ground measure 60°.

radio tower

cable

ground

a. How many meters of cable have been used to anchor the tower?

b. How far is it from the bottom of the tower to the anchor point of each cable?

4.4 a. By the definitions of sine and cosine, sin 65° and cos 25° in triangle ABC are both a/c, while tan 65° = a/b and tan 25° = b/a.

b. If ∠A and ∠B are the acute angles of a right triangle, then sin∠A = cos∠B and tan ∠A = 1/tan ∠B. In other words, sin∠A = cos(90° − ∠A), cos∠A = sin(90° − ∠A), and tan∠A = 1/tan(90° − ∠A)

4.5 Using the Pythagorean theorem, the side of the triangular face is approximately 187 m long. Designating one of the base angles as ∠A,

$$\tan\angle A \approx \frac{187}{115}$$

$$m\angle A \approx 58°$$

* 4.6 a. $\tan^{-1}(4/100) \approx 2.3°$

b. The change in elevation is 32 • sin(2.3°) ≈ 1.3 m. Sample diagram (not drawn to scale):

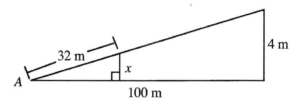

4.7 Using the diagram, the length (d) of the crosspiece can be calculated by solving for d in

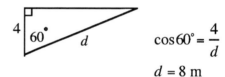

$$\cos 60° = \frac{4}{d}$$

$$d = 8 \text{ m}$$

4.8 $\cos^{-1}(4/4.5) \approx 27°$

4.9 a. The total length of cable is 4(20/sin 60°) ≈ 92 m.

b. The distance from the bottom of the tower to each anchor point is:

$$\frac{20}{\tan 60°} \approx 11.5 \text{ m}$$

Module 11 ■ *A New Angle on an Old Pyramid*   **273**

teacher note

An additional assessment, for use at your discretion, appears in the Teacher Resources for this module.

Summary Assessment

1. In the following sample diagram (not drawn to scale), x represents the width of the Nile and y represents the distance from the observer to the center of the pyramid's base.

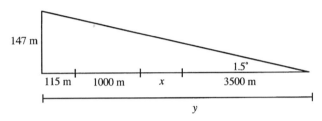

Because $\tan 1.5° = 147/y$, $y \approx 5614$ m. The width of the Nile, therefore, is about 999 m.

2. Because F is the center of the square base, DF is 115 m. Given that DE is 77 m, the Pythagorean theorem can be used to find the length of FE (the hypotenuse of right triangle FDE):

$$115^2 + 77^2 = (FE)^2$$

$$FE \approx 138 \text{ m}$$

In right triangle CFE, $m\angle CEF$ can be found using the inverse tangent:

$$m\angle CEF = \tan^{-1}\left(\frac{147}{138}\right)$$

$$\approx 47°$$

The measure of the dihedral angle is 52°; therefore the angles have different measures. **Note:** This problem demonstrates the need for a specific definition of the measure of a dihedral angle (see Activity **3**).

3. Sample response: Using the inverse tangent, $m\angle B = \tan^{-1}(6/10) \approx 31°$. Because $\angle C$ is a right angle, $m\angle A \approx 59°$.

In right triangle BEF,

$$\sin 31° = \frac{EF}{5}$$

$$EF \approx 2.6 \text{ m}$$

In right triangle ACD,

$$\sin 59° = \frac{CD}{6}$$

$$CD \approx 5.1 \text{ m}$$

Summary Assessment

1. The annual flooding of the Nile River was an important part of life for the ancient Egyptians. Imagine that you must determine the width of the Nile at its crest near the Great Pyramid. You know the distance from the edge of the pyramid to the near bank is 1 km, and that you are 3.5 km from the opposite bank. From where you are standing, the angle of elevation to the pyramid's peak is approximately 1.5°. Use the figure below to help calculate the width of the Nile.

2. In the diagram of the Great Pyramid below, $\angle CDF$ and $\angle CEF$ are angles with one side in the plane of the pyramid's base and the other in the plane of one of its faces. The dihedral angle CDF measures 52°. The length of $\overline{DE}$ is 77 m. Triangles CFD, CFE, and FDE are all right triangles. Use the Pythagorean theorem and trigonometric ratios to show that the measure of the dihedral angle is different from $m\angle CEF$.

3. A truss is a combination of beams used to support the roof of a building. The diagram below shows some dimensions for a truss for a house. Use the measures indicated in the diagram to determine the lengths of segments EF, DF, and CD.

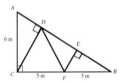

Using the Pythagorean theorem, AB can be found as follows:

$$6^2 + 10^2 = (AB)^2$$

$$(AB) \approx 11.7 \text{ m}$$

Again using the Pythagorean theorem,

$$(AD)^2 + 5.1^2 = 6^2$$

$$(AD) \approx 3.1 \text{ m}$$

and

$$(BE)^2 + 2.5^2 = 5^2$$

$$(BE) \approx 4.3 \text{ m}$$

Therefore, DE is $11.7 - 3.1 - 4.3 = 4.3$ m.

Because DE and EF are now known and DEF is a right triangle, DF can be found as follows:

$$4.3^2 + 2.6^2 = DF^2$$

$$DF \approx 5 \text{ m}$$

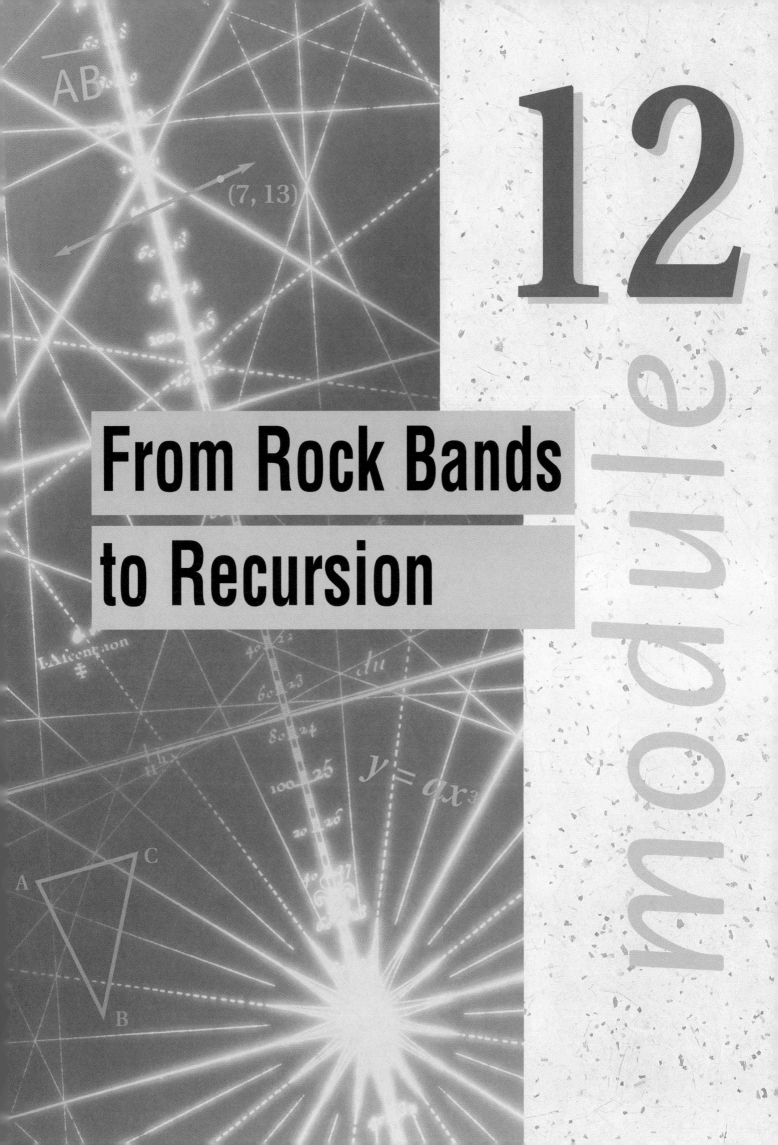

From Rock Bands to Recursion

Overview

In this module, students use spreadsheets to investigate arithmetic and geometric sequences.

Activity 1:   Students graph arithmetic sequences and develop their corresponding recursive formulas.

Activity 2:   Students develop explicit formulas for arithmetic sequences, compare the graphs to those of linear equations, and use arithmetic series as problem-solving tools.

Activity 3:   Students graph geometric sequences, develop their corresponding recursive formulas, and use finite geometric series as problem-solving tools.

Activity 4:   Students develop explicit formulas for geometric sequences and compare the graphs to those of exponential equations.

Objectives

In this module, students will:

* investigate number patterns (1, 2, 3, 4)

* develop arithmetic sequences (1, 2)

* write and evaluate recursive formulas for arithmetic sequences (1, 2)

* evaluate arithmetic series (2)

* write and evaluate explicit formulas for arithmetic sequences (2)

* compare linear equations and explicit formulas for arithmetic sequences (2)

* compare the graphs of linear equations and arithmetic sequences (2)

* develop geometric sequences (3, 4)

* write and evaluate recursive formulas for geometric sequences (3)

* compare the graphs of arithmetic and geometric sequences (3, 4)

* evaluate geometric series (3)

* write and evaluate explicit formulas for geometric sequences (4)

* compare exponential equations and explicit formulas for geometric sequences (4)

* compare the graphs of exponential equations and geometric sequences (4).

Prerequisites

For this module, students should be able to:

✳ recognize the graphs of linear equations and exponential equations

✳ write and graph linear equations in slope-intercept form

✳ represent multiplication as repeated addition

✳ represent repeated multiplication using exponents

✳ write and graph exponential equations.

 Flashbacks, for use at your discretion, appear in the Teacher Resources for this module. These brief problem sets provide a review of some prerequisite skills for each activity.

Planning Guide

Activity	Materials	Technology	Time Line
Activity 1	▪ graph paper (optional)	▪ spreadsheet ▪ graphing utility	3 days
Activity 2	▪ graph paper (optional)	▪ spreadsheet ▪ graphing utility	2 days
Activity 3	▪ graph paper (optional)	▪ spreadsheet ▪ graphing utility	2 days
Activity 4	▪ graph paper (optional)	▪ spreadsheet ▪ graphing utility	2 days
Assessment Activities	▪ graph paper (optional)	▪ spreadsheet ▪ graphing utility	3 days **Total: 12 days**

Introduction

The sales, performances, and travels of a rock band provide a context for investigating sequences throughout the module. (Students revisit the patterns created by stacks of blocks in Problem **2.8**.)

Students use tables and spreadsheets to explore patterns found in the number of performances made by a rock band. These patterns are arithmetic sequences.

Materials List

■ graph paper (optional)

Technology

■ spreadsheet
■ graphing utility

Student Outcomes

After completing the following exploration and discussion, students should be able to:

✳ investigate number patterns

✳ develop arithmetic sequences

✳ write recursive formulas for arithmetic sequences

✳ evaluate recursive formulas for arithmetic sequences.

teacher note

Students should understand how to identify the common difference before beginning Part **e** of the exploration.

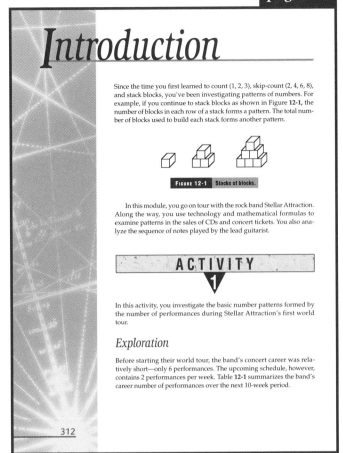

Introduction

Since the time you first learned to count (1, 2, 3), skip-count (2, 4, 6, 8), and stack blocks, you've been investigating patterns of numbers. For example, if you continue to stack blocks as shown in Figure **12-1**, the number of blocks in each row of a stack forms a pattern. The total number of blocks used to build each stack forms another pattern.

FIGURE 12-1 Stacks of blocks.

In this module, you go on tour with the rock band Stellar Attraction. Along the way, you use technology and mathematical formulas to examine patterns in the sales of CDs and concert tickets. You also analyze the sequence of notes played by the lead guitarist.

ACTIVITY
1

In this activity, you investigate the basic number patterns formed by the number of performances during Stellar Attraction's first world tour.

Exploration

Before starting their world tour, the band's concert career was relatively short—only 6 performances. The upcoming schedule, however, contains 2 performances per week. Table **12-1** summarizes the band's career number of performances over the next 10-week period.

312

TABLE 12-1 ■ *Performances by Stellar Attraction*

No. of Weeks on Tour	Total No. of Performances
1	8
2	10
3	12
4	14
⋮	⋮
10	26

a. Complete Table **12-1** for each of the next 10 weeks.

b. Record any patterns you observe in the table.

c. Use the patterns you discovered to answer the following questions.

    1. After how many weeks will the band have given 24 performances?

    2. How many performances will they have given after 12 weeks?

    3. After 16 weeks, Stellar Attraction will have performed 38 times. What will be the total number of performances after 18 weeks?

mathematics note

A **sequence** is an ordered list. Each item in the list is a **term** of the sequence.

The terms of a sequence may be represented by symbols, such as $p_1, p_2, p_3, \ldots, p_n$. These symbols are **subscripted variables**, and the natural numbers $(1, 2, 3, \ldots, n)$ are the **subscripts.** The symbol p_1 (read "p sub one") represents the first term of the sequence, the symbol p_2 (read "p sub two") represents the second term of the sequence, and so on. The symbol p_n (read "p sub n"), represents the **general,** or **nth, term** of a sequence.

For example, consider the following ordered list of numbers 16, 18, 20, 22, 24, ... In this sequence, $p_1 = 16$, $p_2 = 18$, $p_3 = 20$, and so on.

Exploration

a. A completed table appears below.

No. of Weeks on Tour	Total No. of Performances
1	8
2	10
3	12
4	14
5	16
6	18
7	20
8	22
9	24
10	26

b. Sample response: In the left-hand column, the pattern begins with 1, then adds 1 to each successive cell. In the right-hand column, the pattern begins with 8, then adds 2 to each successive cell.

c. **1.** 9 weeks

    2. 30 performances

    3. 42 performances

d. Sample spreadsheet:

No. of weeks (n)	Total No. of Performances (p_n)
1	8
2	10
3	12
⋮	⋮
48	102
49	104
50	106

e. The recursive formula for the sequence is:

$$\begin{cases} p_1 = 8 \\ p_n = p_{n-1} + 2,\ n > 1 \end{cases}$$

Discussion

a. The numbers in the left-hand column are found by starting with 1, then adding 1 to the previous number. The numbers in the right-hand column are found by starting with 8, then adding 2 to the previous number.

b. 1. The value of n is 20.

2. The value of p_{20} is 46.

3. The value of n is 7.

4. The value of p_7 is 20.

c. This can be expressed as $p_{30} = 66$.

d. The sequences are both arithmetic because they both have a common difference between any two successive terms. The first column has a common difference of 1, and the second column has a common difference of 2.

Warm-Up

1. a. A recursive formula is shown below. The next three terms are 43, 50, 57.

$$\begin{cases} a_1 = 7 \\ a_n = a_{n-1} + 6,\ n > 1 \end{cases}$$

b. A recursive formula is shown below. The next three terms are $-39, -46, -53$.

$$\begin{cases} a_1 = 3 \\ a_n = a_{n-1} - 7,\ n > 1 \end{cases}$$

c. A recursive formula is shown below. The next three terms are 54.5, 62.2, 69.9.

$$\begin{cases} a_1 = 8.3 \\ a_n = a_{n-1} + 7.7,\ n > 1 \end{cases}$$

d. 1. Create a spreadsheet with headings like those shown in Table **12-2** below. The entries in the right-hand column represent the total number of performances at the end of each week. They also represent the terms of a sequence.

TABLE 12-2 ■ *Performances Spreadsheet*

No. of Weeks on Tour (n)	Total No. of Performances (p_n)
1	8
2	10
3	12
4	14
⋮	⋮
50	

2. Use the spreadsheet to determine the total number of performances after each week for the next 50 weeks.

mathematics note

A **recursive formula** is a rule for finding any term in a sequence by using the preceding term(s). The process of using a recursive formula is known as **recursion**.

An **arithmetic sequence** is a sequence in which every term after the first is found by adding a constant value to the preceding term.

The recursive formula for calculating any term in an arithmetic sequence is:

$$\begin{cases} a_1 = \text{first term} \\ a_n = a_{n-1} + d,\ n > 1 \end{cases}$$

where a_1 is the first term, a_n is the nth term, a_{n-1} is the term preceding a_n, and d is the **common difference** between any two consecutive terms, $a_n - a_{n-1}$.

For example, consider the sequence in which the first term (a_1) is 27 and the common difference (d) between any two consecutive terms is 5. The recursive formula for this sequence is:

$$\begin{cases} a_1 = 27 \\ a_n = a_{n-1} + 5,\ n > 1 \end{cases}$$

Using this formula, the first four terms of the sequence can be found as follows:

$$a_1 = 27$$
$$a_2 = a_{2-1} + d = a_1 + d = 27 + 5 = 32$$
$$a_3 = a_{3-1} + d = a_2 + 5 = 32 + 5 = 37$$
$$a_4 = a_{4-1} + 5 = a_3 + d = 37 + 5 = 42$$

e. Find a recursive formula for the sequence in the right-hand column of Table **12-2**.

Discussion

a. How did you use the patterns you described in Part **b** of the exploration to complete Table **12-2**?

b. Use the sequence in the right-hand column of Table **12-2** to answer the following questions.

1. What is the value of n for p_{20}?

2. What is the value of p_{20}?

3. If $p_n = 20$, what is the value of n?

4. When $n = 8$, what is the value of p_{n-1}, the term before p_n?

c. How can you use subscript notation to express the fact that the 30th term of a sequence is 66?

d. Explain why the sequence found in each column of Table **12-2** is an arithmetic sequence.

Warm-Up

1. For each arithmetic sequence below, write a recursive formula, then list the next three terms.

a. 7, 13, 19, 25, 31, 37, . . .

b. 3, −4, −11, −18, −25, −32, . . .

c. 8.3, 16, 23.7, 31.4, 39.1, 46.8, . . .

2. Consider the following recursive formula:
$$\begin{cases} a_1 = 13 \\ a_n = a_{n-1} + 6, \; n > 1 \end{cases}$$

   a. What is the common difference?

   b. What is the first term in the sequence?

   c. What are the next three terms in the sequence?

   d. What does the n in the equation represent? What does $n-1$ represent?

3. Write recursive formulas for the arithmetic sequences described below.

   a. The first term is 5 and the common difference is –8.

   b. The first term is –7.6 and the common difference is 3.9.

Assignment

1.1 For their next performance, Stellar Attraction must drive from St. Louis, Missouri, to Portland, Oregon: a distance of 3290 km. They can average 100 km per hour during the trip.

   a. Create a spreadsheet with headings like those in the table below. Let h represent the number of hours driven and k_h represent the number of kilometers remaining after each hour.

Hours Driven (h)	Kilometers Remaining (k_h)
1	3190
2	3090
3	2990
⋮	⋮

   b. During which hour does the band arrive in Portland?

   c. What is the value of k_5?

   d. How many kilometers remain after the band has driven for 13 hr? Express your answer using subscript notation.

   e. For how many hours has the band been driving when they are 1390 km from Portland? Express your answer in subscript notation.

   f. What is the value of k_{h-1} when $k_h = 2290$?

   g. Write a recursive formula that describes the pattern for k_h.

---

2. a. 6

   b. 13

   c. 19, 25, 31

   d. The variable n represents the number of the term and $n-1$ represents the term before the nth term.

3. a. $\begin{cases} a_1 = 5 \\ a_n = a_{n-1} - 8, \; n > 1 \end{cases}$

   b. $\begin{cases} a_1 = -7.6 \\ a_n = a_{n-1} + 3.9, \; n > 1 \end{cases}$

Assignment

Problems suitable for use as assessment items are identified by an asterisk (*).

1.1 a. Sample spreadsheet:

Hours Driven	Kilometers Remaining	Hours Driven	Kilometers Remaining
1	3190	18	1490
2	3090	19	1390
3	2990	20	1290
4	2890	21	1190
5	2790	22	1090
6	2690	23	990
7	2590	24	890
8	2490	25	790
9	2390	26	690
10	2290	27	590
11	2190	28	490
12	2090	29	390
13	1990	30	290
14	1890	31	190
15	1790	32	90
16	1690	33	–10
17	1590		

   b. They arrive in Portland during hour 33.

   c. $k_5 = 2790$

   d. Because 1990 km remain after 13 hr, $k_{13} = 1990$.

   e. When they are 1390 km from Portland, the band has traveled 19 hr: $k_{19} = 1390$.

   f. Because the term before 2290 is 2390, $k_9 = 2390$.

   g. The recursive formula for kilometers remaining to Portland is:

$$\begin{cases} k_1 = 3190 \\ k_n = k_{n-1} + (-100), \; n > 1 \end{cases}$$

1.2 a. $t_1 = 790$, $t_2 = 1003$, $t_3 = 1216$, $t_4 = 1429$, $t_5 = 1642$

b. Ticket sales exceed 2200 for the first time on the eighth day; $t_8 = 2281$.

c. $t_{n+1} = t_{10} = 2707$

d. The recursive formula is:

$$\begin{cases} t_1 = 790 \\ t_n = t_{n-1} + 213, \ n > 1 \end{cases}$$

e. Sample response: This is not a good assumption. Although the average daily sales was 213 tickets, this does not mean that 213 tickets were sold every day.

* 1.3 A positive common difference produces an increasing sequence. A negative common difference produces a decreasing sequence.

1.4 a. The first term is 9.0.

b. The next four terms are 9.5, 10.0, 10.5, and 11.0.

1.5 The recursive formula is:

$$\begin{cases} t_1 = 3 \\ t_n = t_{n-1} + 4, \ n > 1 \end{cases}$$

* 1.6 a. Answers will vary. Sample response:

$$6, 17, 28, 39, \ldots.$$

b. For the sample sequence in Part **a**, the common difference is 11.

c. The recursive formula for the sample sequence in Part **a** is:

$$\begin{cases} t_1 = 6 \\ t_n = t_{n-1} + 11, \ n > 1 \end{cases}$$

1.7 Sample response: For $t_1 = 5$, the sequence is 5, 8, 11, 14, 17, ... For $r_1 = -4$, the sequence is –4, –1, 2, 5, 8, 11, 14, ... The two sequences are similar because they both increase by a constant of 3. The first sequence is a subset of the second. The two sequences are different because they have different first terms.

✳ ✳ ✳ ✳ ✳

1.2 After arriving in Portland, the band finds that concert tickets have been selling well. The ticket agency sold 790 tickets on the first day. During the next 20 days, they sold an average of 213 tickets per day.

a. Let n represent the number of days that tickets have been on sale and t_n represent the total number of tickets sold after n days. Express the first 5 terms of this sequence using subscript notation.

b. Using the sequence from Part **a**, on what day did total sales exceed 2200 tickets? Express your answer using subscript notation.

c. What is the value of t_{n+1} when $t_n = 2494$?

d. Write a recursive formula that describes the pattern of ticket sales.

e. To complete Parts **a–d**, you assumed that the pattern of ticket sales was an arithmetic sequence where $t_1 = 790$ and $t_{21} = 790 + 20(213)$. Do you think that this is a reasonable assumption?

1.3 In some arithmetic sequences, the numbers increase with each successive term. In others, the numbers decrease with each successive term. What can you say about the common differences used to form these sequences?

1.4 Consider the following recursive formula:

$$\begin{cases} t_1 = 9.0 \\ t_n = t_{n-1} + 0.5, \ n > 1 \end{cases}$$

a. What is the value of the first term of this sequence?

b. What are the next four terms of this sequence?

1.5 Find a recursive formula for the arithmetic sequence 3, 7, 11, 15, ...

1.6 **a.** Create your own arithmetic sequence.

b. What is the common difference for your sequence?

c. Write a recursive formula for your sequence.

1.7 In a paragraph, compare the two sequences described by the formulas shown below.

$$\begin{cases} t_1 = 5 \\ t_n = t_{n-1} + 3, \ n > 1 \end{cases} \quad \text{and} \quad \begin{cases} r_1 = -4 \\ r_n = r_{n-1} + 3, \ n > 1 \end{cases}$$

* * * * *

> **1.8** The *National Geographic* magazine is published 12 times per year. Each edition of the magazine is approximately 0.8 cm thick.
>
>   **a.** Imagine that your parents started collecting *National Geographic* in the year you were born. How much shelf space would they need to display their collection at the end of this year?
>
>   **b.** Write a recursive formula that describes the amount of shelf space needed at the end of a year. Let the first term of the sequence be the width of the shelf when you were in kindergarten.
>
>   **c.** Use your recursive formula to predict how much shelf space will be required when you are 60 years old.
>
> **1.9** **a.** Melinda has $51.00 and spends $3.00 per week. Write a recursive formula to describe the amount of money m_n Melinda has at the beginning of week *n*.
>
>   **b.** Kris has $11.00 and saves an additional $2.00 per week. Write a recursive formula to describe the amount of money k_n Kris has at the beginning of week *n*.
>
>   **c.** When will Melinda and Kris have the same amount of money?
>
> **1.10** Consider the following recursive formula:
>
>
>
> $$\begin{cases} t_1 = 1 \\ t_2 = 1 \\ t_n = t_{n-2} + t_{n-1} \text{ for } n > 2 \end{cases}$$
>
>   **a.** Find t_3.
>
>   **b.** Generate the first 10 terms of the sequence.
>
>   **c.** Create a scatterplot of the first 10 terms of the sequence versus the term number.
>
>   **d.** Is the sequence an arithmetic sequence? Justify your response.
>
> ## ACTIVITY 2
>
> The band's record company tracks the number of compact discs (CDs) that Stellar Attraction sells each week. During the week of June 10–16, the band sold 9050 copies. Sales projections indicate that the band can expect weekly sales to increase by an average of 2353 copies each week for the next year. These projections are shown in Table **12-3** on the next page.
>

1.8 Answers will vary, depending on student ages.

a. The sample response given below is for a 14-year-old.

$$\frac{0.8 \text{ cm}}{1 \text{ issue}} \left(\frac{12 \text{ issues}}{1 \text{ yr}} \right) (14 \text{ yr}) \approx 134 \text{ cm}$$

b. The shelf space needed for each year (the common difference) is 0.8 • 12 = 9.6 cm. In the following sample response, the student is 5 years old in kindergarten.

$$\begin{cases} w_1 = 9.6(5) = 48 \\ w_n = w_{n-1} + 9.6, \ n > 1 \end{cases}$$

c. Students may use a spreadsheet or table to answer this question. It will take 576 cm of shelf space for 60 yr of *National Geographic*.

Years	Shelf Space (cm)
1	9.6
2	19.2
3	28.8
⋮	⋮
58	556.8
59	566.4
60	576

1.9 **a.** The recursive formula is:

$$\begin{cases} m_1 = 51 \\ m_n = m_{n-1} - 3, \ n > 1 \end{cases}$$

b. The recursive formula is:

$$\begin{cases} k_1 = 11 \\ k_n = k_{n-1} + 2, \ n > 1 \end{cases}$$

c. Melinda and Kris will both have $27.00 at the beginning of the ninth week. Using subscript notation, $m_9 = k_9 = 27$.

1.10 **a.** Using the recursive formula, $t_3 = t_1 + t_2 = 1 + 1 = 2$.

b. The recursive formula generates the Fibonacci sequence. The first 10 terms of the sequence are 1, 1, 2, 3, 5, 8, 13, 21, 34, and 55.

c. Sample scatterplot:

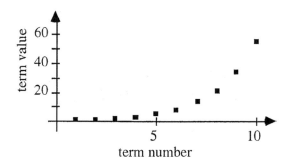

d. The sequence is not an arithmetic sequence. Although the terms are generated by addition, the difference between terms is not constant.

ACTIVITY 2

This activity continues the exploration of arithmetic sequences through the experiences of the rock band.

> ### teacher note
>
>
> A brief assessment of the mathematical content in Activities **1** and **2**, for use at your discretion, appears in the Teacher Resources for this module.

Materials List

■ graph paper (optional)

Technology

- spreadsheet
- graphing utility

Student Outcomes

After completing the following exploration and discussion, students should be able to:

✳ write explicit formulas for arithmetic sequences

✳ evaluate explicit formulas for arithmetic sequences

✳ create scatterplots of arithmetic sequences

✳ compare recursive and explicit formulas for an arithmetic sequence

✳ compare an explicit formula to the equation of a line in slope-intercept form

✳ evaluate arithmetic series.

Exploration

Students develop an explicit formula for an arithmetic sequence.

a. A completed Table **12-4** appears below.

page 319

TABLE 12-3 ■ *Weekly CD Sales*

Week	Week No.	CD Sales
June 10–16	1	9050
June 17–23	2	11,403
June 24–30	3	13,756
July 1–7	4	16,109
⋮	⋮	⋮
December 23–29	29	
⋮	⋮	⋮
June 2–8	52	

If the projections are accurate, how many CDs will the band sell during the last week of December? When will the total number of copies sold exceed 1 million? The predicted values for weekly sales represent an arithmetic sequence, so you could use a recursive formula to answer these questions. However, using a recursive formula can be time consuming. In this activity, you develop another type of formula that will allow you to respond more quickly.

Exploration

The two left-hand columns in Table **12-4** show the term number and terms for an arithmetic sequence. The two right-hand columns show expanded (and equivalent) forms of the term values. In this exploration, you use the patterns in this table to develop another type of formula for the sequence.

TABLE 12-4 ■ *Patterns within Arithmetic Sequences*

Term Number (n)	Term (p_n)	Recursive Form of p_n	Another Form of p_n
1	27	27	27 + (0 • 2)
2	29	27 + 2	27 + (1 • 2)
3	31	27 + 2 + 2	27 + (2 • 2)
⋮			
7			

a. Complete Table **12-4** for the first seven terms of the sequence. Record any patterns you discover.

TABLE 12-4 ■ *Patterns within Arithmetic Sequences*

Term Number (n)	Term (p_n)	Recursive Form of p_n	Another Form of p_n
1	27	27	27 + (0 • 2)
2	29	27 + 2	27 + (1 • 2)
3	31	27 + 2 + 2	27 + (2 • 2)
4	33	27 + 2 + 2 + 2	27 + (3 • 2)
5	35	27 + 2 + 2 + 2 + 2	27 + (4 • 2)
6	37	27 + 2 + 2 + 2 + 2 + 2	27 + (5 • 2)
7	39	27 + 2 + 2 + 2 + 2 + 2 + 2	27 + (6 • 2)

b. Write an expression that represents the number of 2s added to the first term to form the *n*th term.

c. Use the pattern in the far right-hand column to write a formula for p_n in terms of *n*.

d. Create a scatterplot of the data in the two left-hand columns of the table. Use the horizontal axis for the term number (*n*) and the vertical axis for the term value (p_n).

e. Find an equation that models the scatterplot and graph it on the coordinate system from Part **d**.

Compare this equation to the one you wrote in Part **c**.

Discussion

a. 1. In the sequence shown in Table **12-4,** how many 2s would you have to add to find p_{21}?

2. How many 2s would have to be added to 27 to find p_n?

b. 1. Describe the formula you wrote for p_n using *n* as a variable.

2. Use this formula to determine the values of p_{47} and p_{100}.

mathematics note

An **explicit formula** for calculating any specific term in an arithmetic sequence is:

$$a_n = a_1 + d(n - 1)$$

where a_n is the *n*th term, a_1 is the first term, and *d* is the common difference between any two consecutive terms, $a_n - a_{n-1}$.

For example, consider the arithmetic sequence 8, 14, 20, 26, ... In this sequence, the first term is 8 and the common difference is 6. The explicit formula for this sequence is $a_n = 8 + 6(n-1)$. This formula can be used to find the 20th term of the sequence as follows:

$$a_{20} = 8 + 6(20 - 1)$$
$$= 8 + 6(19)$$
$$= 122$$

The sum of the terms of an arithmetic sequence is an **arithmetic series.**

For example, consider the arithmetic sequence 8, 14, 20, 26. The corresponding arithmetic series is 8 + 14 + 20 + 26, or 68.

b. $(n - 1)$

c. $p_n = p_1 + (n - 1)2 = 27 + (n - 1)2$

d–e. The linear equation $y = 2x + 25$ models the scatterplot exactly. When the formula in Part **c** is expanded, the two equations are equivalent with p_n and *n* corresponding with *y* and *x*, respectively.

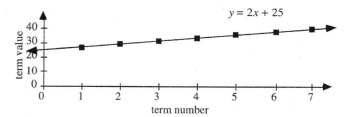

Discussion

a. 1. The number of 2s is 1 less than 21, or 20.

2. The number of 2s is 1 less than *n*, or $n - 1$.

b. 1. One possible formula is $p_n = 27 + (n - 1)2$.

2. $p_{47} = 119$; $p_{100} = 225$

c. In general, the x-values (or domain) for a linear equation are the set of all real numbers, and the n-values (or domain) for an arithmetic sequence are the set of natural numbers. (The context of a problem may limit the domain of a linear equation.) Therefore, the graph of a linear equation is a set of connected points (or continuous line), and the graph of a sequence is a set of disconnected points.

d. Sample response: The scatterplot of an arithmetic sequence always can be modeled well by a linear equation because an arithmetic sequence always has a constant difference and a line always has a constant slope.

e. 1. Both a_n and y represent the values on the y-axis, or the range.

   2. Both n and x represent the values on the x-axis, or the domain.

   3. The difference d and the slope m are equal because they both represent the ratio of the change in y-values to the change in x-values:

   $$m = \frac{y_2 - y_1}{x_2 - x_1} = \frac{a_n - a_{n-1}}{n - (n - 1)} = \frac{d}{1}$$

   4. The y-intercept b is the value of the linear equation at $x = 0$. The value of the explicit formula at $n = 0$ would be the difference between a_1 and d. Therefore, $a_1 - d = b$.

f. An explicit formula is easier to use when the previous term is not known. For example, the 100th term of the arithmetic sequence in Table **12-4** would be easier to find using an explicit formula rather than a recursive formula.

g. Answers may vary. The following proof substitutes b for $(a_1 - d)$, m for d, and x for n:

$$\begin{aligned} a_n &= a_1 + d(n - 1) \\ &= dn + (a_1 - d) \\ &= dn + b \\ &= mx + b \end{aligned}$$

c. How does the graph of a linear equation differ from the graph of an arithmetic sequence?

d. Do you think that the scatterplot of an arithmetic sequence can always be modeled by a linear equation in slope-intercept form, $y = mx + b$? Why or why not?

e. Using the distributive property, the explicit formula for an arithmetic sequence, $a_n = a_1 + d(n - 1)$, can be written as $a_n = a_1 + dn - d$. Using the associative property, it can also be written as $a_n = dn + (a_1 - d)$.

   Assuming that the equation $y = mx + b$ models the same arithmetic sequence, describe the relationship between each of the following:

   1. the nth term a_n and y

   2. the term number n and x

   3. the difference d and the slope m

   4. the first term a_1 and the y-intercept b

f. In what types of situations would an explicit formula be easier to use than a recursive formula?

g. Using the relationships described in Part **e** of the discussion, show that the explicit formula for an arithmetic sequence, $a_n = a_1 + d(n - 1)$, is equivalent to the linear equation of the form $y = mx + b$ that models the same sequence.

Warm-Up

1. Write an explicit formula for each arithmetic sequence below.

   a. 13, 18.3, 23.6, 18.9, 34.2, 39.5, ...

   b. 22, 14, 6, -2, -10, -18, ...

   c. -17, 2, 21, 40, 59, 78, ...

2. Consider the explicit formula $a_n = 5 + 7.5(n - 1)$.

   a. What is the first term of the sequence?

   b. What is the common difference?

   c. What is the 23rd term of the sequence?

3. Write an explicit formula for each arithmetic sequence described below, then find its 50th term.

   a. The first term is 31 and the common difference is -16.

   b. The first term is -12 and the common difference is 7.

Warm-Up

1. **a.** $a_n = 13 + 5.3(n - 1)$
   b. $a_n = 22 - 8(n - 1)$
   c. $a_n = -17 + 19(n - 1)$

2. **a.** 5
   b. 7.5
   c. 170

3. **a.** $a_n = 31 - 16(n - 1)$
   b. $a_n = -12 + 7(n - 1)$

Assignment

2.1 Table **12-3** shows that weekly CD sales for Stellar Attraction are expected to increase by an average of 2353 copies per week for the next 52 weeks after June 10–16.

 a. If this projection is accurate, how many CDs will be sold during the week of December 23–29?

 b. When will the total number of CDs sold exceed 1 million?

2.2 Stellar Attraction is playing at the Jan-San Amphitheater. The amphitheater has 120 seats in the front row, 136 seats in the second row, and 152 seats in the third row. This pattern continues from row to row. The last row has 584 seats.

 a. Write an explicit formula to determine the number of seats in any row of the theater.

 b. How many seats are in the 16th row?

 c. How many rows are in the theater?

 d. How many total seats are in the theater?

2.3 Imagine that you work as an usher at the Jan-San Amphitheater. Your starting wage is $4.25 per hour. Periodically, you will receive a raise of $0.10 per hour. Write an explicit formula to calculate your hourly wage after n raises.

2.4 **a.** Before the concert begins, the Jan-San Amphitheater contains 85 employees. The doors open to the public at 6:00 P.M. Between 6:00 P.M. and 6:15 P.M., an average of 9 people per second enter the theater. Let p_n represent the number of people in the theater after n seconds.

 1. List the first 5 terms of the sequence.

 2. Identify the common difference d.

 3. Write an explicit formula of the form $a_n = a_1 + d(n-1)$.

 4. Determine the number of people in the amphitheater at 6:15 P.M.

 b. When the concession stands open, they have a supply of 8500 L of soft drinks. Soft drink sales average 110 L per minute throughout the evening. Let l_n represent the number of liters remaining after n minutes.

 1. List the first 5 terms of the sequence.

 2. Identify the common difference d.

 3. Write an explicit formula of the form $a_n = a_1 + d(n-1)$.

 4. Determine how long the supply of soft drinks will last.

Assignment

Problems suitable for use as assessment items are identified by an asterisk (*).

2.1 **a.** The data for weekly sales form an arithmetic sequence. The explicit formula for this sequence is: $S_n = 9050 + 2353(n-1)$. Because the week of December 23–29 is week 29:

$$S_{29} = 9050 + 2353(29-1) = 74{,}934$$

 b. Sales exceed 1 million during the 26th week. Students may use a spreadsheet to solve this problem as shown below:

n	S_n	Total Sales
1	9050	9050
2	11,403	20,453
3	13,756	34,209
⋮	⋮	⋮
25	65,522	932,150
26	67,875	1,000,025

2.2 **a.** Sample response: $t_n = 120 + 16(n-1)$.

 b. There are 360 seats in the 16th row.

 c. There are 30 rows in the theater.

 d. There are 10,560 seats in the theater. Students may use a spreadsheet to solve this problem.

Row	Seats	Total Seats
1	120	120
2	136	256
3	152	408
⋮	⋮	⋮
28	552	9408
29	568	9976
30	584	10,560

* **2.3** Sample response: $w_n = 4.25 + 0.10(n-1)$.

* **2.4 a. 1.** The first five terms are 94, 103, 112, 121, and 130.

 2. The common difference $d = 9$.

 3. An explicit formula is $p_n = 94 + 9(n-1)$.

 4. 8185 people

 b. 1. The first five terms are 8500, 8390, 8280, 8170, and 8060.

 2. The common difference $d = -110$.

 3. An explicit formula is $l_n = 8500 + (-110)(n-1)$ or $l_n = 8500 - 110(n-1)$.

 4. The supply will last approximately 78 min.

2.5 a. In the following recursive formula, c_1 is the amount of money that the cashier started with and c_n represents the total amount of money in the cash register after n minutes.

$$\begin{cases} c_1 = \$50 \\ c_n = c_{n-1} + \$2.15, \ n > 1 \end{cases}$$

b. In the explicit formula below, c_n represents the amount of money in the cash register after n minutes, $50 is the amount that the cashier started with, and $2.15 is the amount taken in each minute.

$$c_n = \$50 + \$2.15(n - 1)$$

c. In the following linear equation, y represents the amount of money in the cash register after x minutes, x represents the number of minutes that the cash register has been open, and 47.85 is the y-intercept.

$$y = 2.15x + 47.85$$

Note: You may point out that, in this situation, the possible values for x are the natural numbers.

✳ ✳ ✳ ✳ ✳

2.6 a. There will be 93 members after 12 months. This can be calculated using the following explicit formula:

$$a_{12} = 38 + 5(12 - 1) = 93$$

b. Using the corresponding arithmetic series, $38 + 43 + 48 + \cdots + 93 = 786$ stamps.

* 2.7 a–b. Sample response: An equation of the line is $y = 2x + 5$ or $t_n = 2n + 5$. The graph below shows that an arithmetic sequence is linear.

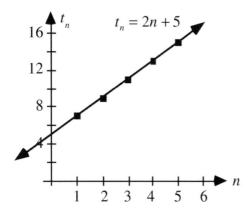

c. The explicit formula for the arithmetic sequence is $t_n = 7 + 2(n - 1)$, which simplifies to $t_n = 2n + 5$. This is the same as the linear equation in Part **b.**

2.5 A cashier starts the evening with $50.00 in the drawer. During the next 45 minutes, an average of $2.15 per minute is added to the drawer. Let c_n represent the number of dollars in the drawer at the end of n minutes.

a. Write a recursive formula for this sequence of the form

$$\begin{cases} c_1 = \text{first term} \\ c_n = c_{n-1} + d, \ n > 1 \end{cases}$$

Explain what each term in the formula represents.

b. Write an explicit formula for this sequence of the form

$$c_n = c_1 + d(n - 1)$$

Explain what each term in the formula represents.

c. Write an equation of the form $y = mx + b$ that models this sequence. Explain what each term in the equation represents.

✳ ✳ ✳ ✳ ✳

2.6 Brianna chairs the membership committee of a club with 33 members. To meet club goals, she plans to recruit 5 new members each month.

a. If Brianna meets her membership goals, how many members will the club have after the next 12 months?

b. Each club member receives a monthly newsletter. If each newsletter requires one stamp to mail, how many stamps will be needed during the next year?

2.7 a. Create a scatterplot of the data in the following table.

n	t_n
1	7
2	9
3	11
4	13
5	15

b. Write an equation for the line that fits the data. Graph this equation on your coordinate system from Part **a.** What does this graph tell you about an arithmetic sequence?

c. Write an explicit formula to determine t_n. How does this compare with the equation you wrote in Part **b?**

Module 12 ■ *From Rock Bands to Recursion*   323

2.8 Raul works in a supermarket. He is stacking blocks of cheese for a dairy display. The diagram on the right shows the first three layers, top to bottom, in his display.

layer 1　　layer 2　　layer 3

a. Make a sketch of the next three layers in the display.

b. Let l_n represent the number of blocks in layer n. Find the first six terms of this sequence.

c. Is the sequence you wrote in Part b an arithmetic sequence? Justify your response.

d. Write a formula to describe this sequence.

e. Raul plans to build a display with seven layers. How many blocks of cheese will there be in the stack?

2.9 Another supermarket employee is creating a pyramid of oranges for a produce display. The diagram on the right shows the first three levels, top to bottom, in this display.

level 1　　level 2　　level 3

a. Make a sketch of the next three levels in the display.

b. Let l_n represent the number of oranges in level n. Find the first six terms of this sequence.

c. Is the sequence you wrote in Part b an arithmetic sequence? Justify your response.

d. Write both recursive and explicit formulas to describe this sequence.

e. How many oranges are there in a 10-level display?

ACTIVITY 3

In Activities **1** and **2**, you examined how arithmetic sequences can be modeled by linear equations. However, just as there are many different types of equations, there are many different types of numerical sequences. In this activity, you explore a type of sequence that can be used to model a projected increase in sales.

Exploration

Before starting their next concert tour, Stellar Attraction releases a second CD. During the first week, 500 copies are sold. The band's manager predicts sales will double each week that the band is on tour.

---

* 2.8 a. The next three layers are shown below.

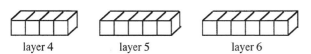
layer 4　　　layer 5　　　layer 6

b. The first six terms of the sequence are 1, 2, 3, 4, 5, and 6.

c. The sequence is an arithmetic sequence because there is a constant difference of 1.

d. Students can describe the sequence recursively or explicitly. The recursive formula is:

$$\begin{cases} l_1 = 1 \\ l_n = l_{n-1} + 1, \ n > 1 \end{cases}$$

The explicit formula is:

$$\begin{aligned} l_n &= 1 + 1(n - 1) \\ &= 1 + (n - 1) \\ &= n \end{aligned}$$

e. $1 + 2 + 3 + 4 + 5 + 6 + 7 = 28$ blocks of cheese

2.9 a. The next three levels in the display are shown below.

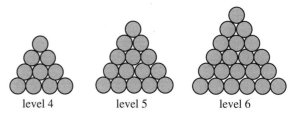
level 4　　　　level 5　　　　level 6

b. The first six terms of the sequence are 1, 3, 6, 10, 15, and 21.

c. The sequence is not an arithmetic sequence because the difference between successive terms is not constant.

d. A recursive formula is:

$$\begin{cases} l_1 = 1 \\ l_n = l_{n-1} + (n - 1), \ n > 1 \end{cases}$$

An explicit formula is:

$$l_n = \frac{n(n + 1)}{2}$$

e. Using the corresponding series,

$1 + 3 + 6 + 10 + 15 + 21 + 28 + 36 + 45 + 55 = 220$ oranges.

ACTIVITY 3

In this activity, students explore geometric sequences using recursion and graphs.

Materials List

■ graph paper (optional)

Technology

■ spreadsheet
■ graphing utility

Student Outcomes

After completing the following exploration and discussion, students should be able to:

✳ develop geometric sequences

✳ write recursive formulas for geometric sequences

✳ evaluate recursive formulas for geometric sequences

✳ evaluate geometric series.

teacher note

Students should understand how to identify the common ratio before beginning Part **c** of the exploration.

Exploration

a. A completed table for weeks 10–12 appears below.

Week	Weekly Sales	Total Sales
1	500	500
2	1000	1500
3	2000	3500
⋮	⋮	⋮
10	256,000	511,500
11	512,000	1,023,500
12	1,024,000	2,047,500

b. Sample response: The pattern in the "Weekly Sales" column begins with 500. The value for each successive cell is the value in the previous cell multiplied by 2. The pattern in the "Total Sales" column also begins with 500. The value for each successive cell is the value in the previous cell plus the weekly sales for the next week.

a. The band's concert tour will last 12 weeks. Table **12-5** shows the manager's predictions for both weekly sales and total sales during this period. Complete the table.

TABLE 12-5 ■ *Projected CD Sales*

Week	Weekly Sales	Total Sales
1	500	500
2	1000	1500
3	2000	3500
⋮	⋮	⋮
12		

b. Record any patterns you observe in the table.

mathematics note

A **geometric sequence** is a sequence in which every term after the first is found by multiplying the preceding term by a constant value.

The recursive formula for calculating any term in a geometric sequence is:

$$\begin{cases} g_1 = \text{first term} \\ g_n = g_{n-1}(r), \ n > 1 \end{cases}$$

where g_1 is the first term, g_n is the nth term, g_{n-1} is the term preceding g_n, and r is the **common ratio** between any two consecutive terms, g_n/g_{n-1}.

For example, consider the sequence in which the first term (g_1) is 4 and the common ratio (r) between any two consecutive terms is 5. The recursive formula for this sequence is:

$$\begin{cases} g_1 = 4 \\ g_n = g_{n-1}(5), \ n > 1 \end{cases}$$

Using this formula, the first four terms of the sequence can be found as follows:

$$g_1 = 4$$
$$g_2 = g_{2-1}(r) = g_1(r) = 4(5) = 20$$
$$g_3 = g_{3-1}(r) = g_2(r) = 20(5) = 100$$
$$g_4 = g_{4-1}(r) = g_3(r) = 100(5) = 500$$

The sum of the terms of a geometric sequence is a **geometric series.**

For example, consider the geometric sequence 3, 12, 48, 192. The corresponding geometric series is 3 + 12 + 48 + 192, or 255.

c. In Table **12-5**, the numbers in the "Weekly Sales" column form a geometric sequence.

1. Find the common ratio for this sequence.

2. Write a recursive formula for this sequence.

3. Determine the corresponding geometric series.

Discussion

a. Describe the patterns you observed in the numbers in Table **12-5**.

b. Use these patterns to answer the following questions:

1. After 12 weeks, what are the predicted total sales?

2. What are the predicted weekly sales for week 10?

3. During what week are total sales predicted to exceed 1 million?

c. Why do the numbers in the "Weekly Sales" column form a geometric sequence?

d. Do the numbers in the "Total Sales" column also form a geometric sequence? Why or why not?

e. If the band extends their tour for 12 more weeks, should they expect sales to continue the predicted pattern? Explain your response.

Warm-Up

1. For each of the following geometric sequences, write a recursive formula, then list the next three terms.

   a. 4, 4.8, 5.76, 6.912, 8.2944, 9.95328, . . .

   b. 24, 12, 6, 3, 1.5, 0.75, . . .

   c. 2, –6, 18, –54, 162, –486, . . .

2. Consider the following recursive formula:

$$\begin{cases} g_1 = 3.2 \\ g_n = g_{n-1} \bullet 5, \ n > 1 \end{cases}$$

   a. What is the common ratio?

   b. What is the first term?

   c. What are the next four terms?

3. Write a recursive formula for each geometric sequence described below.

   a. The first term is 4.4 and the common ratio is 3.1.

   b. The first term is –3 and the common ratio is 7.

c. 1. The common ratio 2/1 is or 2.

   2. Sample formula:

$$\begin{cases} g_1 = 500 \\ g_n = g_{n-1}(2), \ n > 1 \end{cases}$$

   3. The geometric series is 2,047,500.

Discussion

a. See sample response to Part **b** of the exploration.

b. 1. 2,047,500

   2. 256,000

   3. week 11

c. The numbers form a geometric sequence because they have a common ratio of 2 between any two successive terms.

d. The numbers do not form a geometric sequence because they do not have a common ratio. For example, the ratio between the first two terms is $1500/500 = 3/2$, but the ratio between the second and third terms is $3500/1500 = 7/3$.

e. Sample response: No. If the pattern continues, the total sales would be unrealistically high—over 8 billion. This is more than the world population.

Warm-Up

1. **a.** A recursive formula is shown below. The next three terms are 11.9943936, 14.3327232, 17.19926784.

$$\begin{cases} g_1 = 5 \\ g_n = g_{n-1} \bullet 1.2, \ n > 1 \end{cases}$$

   b. A recursive formula is shown below. The next three terms are 0.375, 0.1875, 0.09375.

$$\begin{cases} g_1 = 24 \\ g_n = g_{n-1} \bullet 0.5, \ n > 1 \end{cases}$$

   c. A recursive formula is shown below. The next three terms are 1458, –4374, 13122.

$$\begin{cases} g_1 = 5 \\ g_n = g_{n-1} \bullet (-3), \ n > 1 \end{cases}$$

2. **a.** 5

   b. 3.2

   c. 16, 80, 4000, 20000

3. **a.** $\begin{cases} g_1 = 4.4 \\ g_n = g_{n-1} \bullet 3.1, \ n > 1 \end{cases}$

   b. $\begin{cases} g_1 = -3 \\ g_n = g_{n-1} \bullet 7, \ n > 1 \end{cases}$

Assignment

Problems suitable for use as assessment items are identified by an asterisk (*).

3.1 a. Sample recursive formula:

$$\begin{cases} t_1 = 4 \\ t_n = t_{n-1} \bullet 7, \ n > 1 \end{cases}$$

b. Sample recursive formula:

$$\begin{cases} t_1 = 9 \\ t_n = t_{n-1} \bullet 2.1, \ n > 1 \end{cases}$$

c. Sample recursive formula:

$$\begin{cases} t_1 = 144 \\ t_n = t_{n-1} \bullet \dfrac{1}{4}, \ n > 1 \end{cases}$$

* 3.2 a. Sample graph of the sequence in Problem **3.1a:**

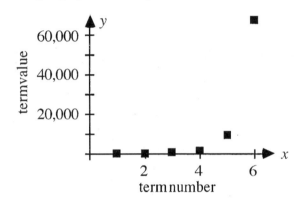

Sample graph of the sequence in Problem **3.1b:**

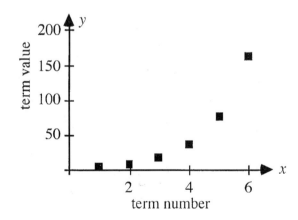

Sample graph of the sequence in Problem **3.1c:**

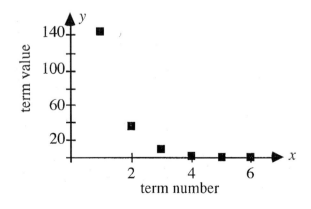

Assignment

3.1 Determine a recursive formula for each of the following geometric sequences:

a. 4, 28, 196, 1372, . . .

b. 9, 18.9, 39.69, . . .

c. 144, 36, 9, 9/4, . . .

3.2 a. Create a scatterplot of the first six terms of each geometric sequence in Problem **3.1.** Let *x* represent the term number and *y* represent the value of the term.

b. Compare the graphs of the three sequences.

3.3 As soon as the concert tour ends, Stellar Attraction's manager predicts that CD sales will begin to decline. Over the next 8 weeks, sales should fall by 75% each week.

a. Use this information to extend Table **12-5** for weeks 13–20.

b. The numbers in the "Weekly Sales" column for weeks 12–20 form a geometric sequence. Write a recursive formula for this sequence. (The first term is the weekly sales for week 12.)

c. Does your formula work after week 18? Explain your response.

d. What are the predicted weekly sales for week 20?

e. What are the predicted total sales for week 20?

3.4 Following the concert at the Jan-San Amphitheater, an enterprising group of students offers to clean the arena at the following rate: $0.01 for the first barrel of garbage, $0.02 for the second barrel, and $0.04 for the third barrel, with this doubling pattern continuing for each additional barrel.

a. Create a table with the following column headings. Complete this table for 20 barrels of garbage.

Barrel Number	Charge per Barrel	Total Charge

b. If the students want to earn at least $500, how many barrels of garbage must they collect?

c. The manager of the amphitheater has budgeted $1000 to clean up after the concert. How many barrels of garbage must the students collect to exceed this budget?

* * * * *

Module 12 ■ *From Rock Bands to Recursion*   **327**

b. Sample response: All three graphs appear to be exponential. Graphs **a** and **b** increase. Graph **c** decreases.

3.3 a. The following table is an extension of Table **12-5** (created in the exploration).

Week	Weekly Sales	Total Sales
12	1,024,000	2,047,500
13	256,000	2,303,500
14	64,000	2,367,500
15	16,000	2,383,500
16	4000	2,387,500
17	1000	2,388,500
18	250	2,388,750
19	62.5	2,388,812.5
20	15.625	2,388,828.125

b. Sample recursive formula:

$$\begin{cases} t_{12} = 1,024,000 \\ t_n = t_{n-1} \bullet 0.25, \ n > 12 \end{cases}$$

c. Sample response: After week 18, the formula yields fractional CDs sold. If these values are treated as approximations, however, the formula is still valid.

page 328

3.5 Consider the pattern of dots shown in the following diagram.

a. Draw the next picture in this pattern.

b. Represent this pattern as a sequence.

c. Is this sequence a geometric sequence? Explain your response.

d. Write a recursive formula for the sequence.

e. Graph the sequence as a scatterplot. Represent the term number on the x-axis and the value of the term on the y-axis.

3.6 As part of a holiday sales promotion, a clothing store plans to reduce the price of its $20.00 shirts by 10% each week.

a. Will the sale prices from week to week represent a geometric sequence? Explain your response.

b. The store originally paid $12.00 for each shirt. In what week will the store begin to lose money on the sale items?

c. The store manager decides to stop the sale in the week before shirt prices fall below $12.00. If you buy one shirt during each week of the sale, how much money will you spend?

3.7 Shahid and Yasmir borrowed money to buy their house. Their monthly payment includes the cost of the loan, insurance, and property taxes. During the first year of the loan, the monthly payment is $350.00. In each year following the first, the monthly payment rises by 2%.

a. Write a recursive formula that describes the monthly payment in any year.

b. Determine when the monthly payment will be more than $500.00.

c. Shahid and Yasmir must pay a total of $150,238.41 to pay off their loan. During what year will this occur?

ACTIVITY 4

As mentioned in Activity **3**, Stellar Attraction's manager predicted that the weekly sales of their CD would double each week. The predicted sales for the next 10 weeks form a geometric sequence. The two left-hand columns in Table **12-6** show the term number and terms for this sequence. The other three columns show expanded (and equivalent) forms of the term values.

328   Module 12 ■ *From Rock Bands to Recursion*

---

d. There will be 15 or 16 CDs sold during week 20.

e. The predicted total sales are 2,388,828.

* 3.4 a. Sample table:

Barrel Number	Charge per Barrel	Total Charge
1	$0.01	$0.01
2	$0.02	$0.03
3	$0.04	$0.07
4	$0.08	$0.15
⋮	⋮	⋮
15	$163.84	$327.67
16	$327.68	$655.35
17	$655.36	$1310.71
18	$1310.72	$2621.43
19	$2621.44	$5242.87
20	$5242.88	$10,485.75

b. To earn at least $500.00, the students must collect 16 barrels of garbage.

c. When the students collect 17 barrels of garbage, the manager will be $310.71 over budget.

＊ ＊ ＊ ＊ ＊

3.5 a. The next picture in this pattern is shown below.

b. This pattern can be represented as the sequence 1, 2, 4, 8, 16, ...

c. Sample response: This is a geometric sequence because each term after the first is formed by multiplying the preceding term by the common ratio of 2.

d. A recursive formula for the sequence from Part **b** is:

$$\begin{cases} t_1 = 1 \\ t_n = 2 \bullet t_{n-1}, \ n > 1 \end{cases}$$

e. Sample graph:

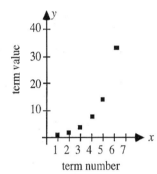

3.6 a. Sample response: Yes, the sale prices will form a geometric sequence. The sale price for each week is found by multiplying the previous week's price by a common ratio of 0.9.

b. In week 6, the sales price would be $11.81.

c. $20.00 + $18.00 + $16.20 + $14.58 + $13.12 = $81.90

3.7 a. Sample recursive formula:

$$\begin{cases} y_1 = 350 \\ y_n = y_{n-1} \bullet 1.02, \ n > 1 \end{cases}$$

b. The monthly payment will be more than $500.00 during year 20.

c. The loan will be paid in full after 27 years, 3 months.

ACTIVITY 4

In this activity, students continue their investigation of geometric sequences using explicit formulas and exponential equations.

teacher note

A brief assessment of the mathematical content in Activities **3** and **4**, for use at your discretion, appears in the Teacher Resources for this module.

Materials List

- graph paper (optional)

Technology

- spreadsheet
- graphing utility

Student Outcomes

After completing the following exploration and discussion, students should be able to:

✳ create scatterplots of geometric sequences

✳ write explicit formulas for geometric sequences

✳ evaluate explicit formulas for geometric sequences

✳ compare recursive and explicit formulas for a geometric sequence

✳ compare the explicit formula of a geometric sequence to an exponential equation.

Exploration

a. $t_n = 500 \cdot 2^{(n-1)}$

b. Students should use the explicit formula from Part **a** in their spreadsheets. Sample spreadsheet:

	A	B	C
	Term No.	Recursive Form	Explicit Form
1	(n)	of t_n	of t_n
2	1	500	500*2^(A2-1)
3	2	(B2)*2	500*2^(A3-1)
4	3	(B3)*2	500*2^(A4-1)
5	4	(B4)*2	500*2^(A5-1)
⋮	⋮	⋮	⋮

	A	B	C
	Term No.	Recursive Form	Explicit Form
1	(n)	of t_n	of t_n
2	1	500	500
3	2	1000	1000
4	3	2000	2000
5	4	4000	4000
⋮	⋮	⋮	⋮
9	8	64000	64000
10	9	128000	128000

TABLE 12-6 ■ *Patterns within Geometric Sequences*				
Term Number (n)	Term (t_n)	Recursive Form of t_n	Expanded Recursive Form of t_n	Explicit Form of t_n
1	500	500	500	500
2	1000	500 • 2	500 • 2	500 • 2^1
3	2000	1000 • 2	500 • 2 • 2	500 • 2^2
4	4000	2000 • 2	500 • 2 • 2 • 2	500 • 2^3
⋮	⋮	⋮	⋮	⋮

In this activity, you use the patterns in this table to investigate explicit formulas for geometric sequences.

Exploration

a. Develop an explicit formula for the sequence of terms, t_n, in Table **12-6**.

b. Create a three-column spreadsheet that duplicates the following three columns from Table **12-6**.

Term Number (n)	Recursive Form of t_n	Explicit Form of t_n

c. 1. Extend the spreadsheet to at least $n = 10$.

   2. Compare the values in the two right-hand columns in your spreadsheet.

d. Add a fourth column to the spreadsheet that determines the ratio of each term to its preceding term, t_n/t_{n-1} where $n > 1$.

e. Create a scatterplot of the sequence. Let x represent the term number and y represent the value of each term.

f. Find an equation that models the scatterplot and graph it on your coordinate system from Part **e**.

Compare this equation to the formula you wrote in Part **a**.

Discussion

a. 1. Using the explicit form of t_n described in Table **12-6**, what power of 2 is multiplied by 500 to determine t_{19}?

   2. How is the power of 2 in each row related to the value of n in that row?

---

c. In the sample spreadsheet shown above, the values in columns B and C are equal to t_n.

d. The fourth column produces a constant ratio of 2.

e–f. The exponential equation $y = 250 \cdot 2^x$ models the scatterplot exactly. Using the laws of exponents, this equation can be rewritten as $y = 250 \cdot 2^1 \cdot 2^{(x-1)}$, which equals $y = 500 \cdot 2^{(x-1)}$. This equation is equivalent to the formula found in Part **a**.

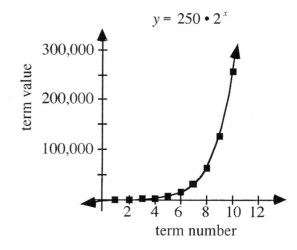

$y = 250 \cdot 2^x$

b. 1. Describe a formula based on the value of n that could be used to calculate the value of t_n.

    2. Use this formula to calculate t_7.

c. What do you observe about the ratio found in Part **d** of the exploration?

d. How is this ratio related to the formula described in Part **b** of the discussion?

mathematics note

An **explicit formula** for calculating any specific term in a geometric sequence is:

$$g_n = g_1 r^{n-1}$$

where g_n is the nth term, g_1 is the first term, and r is the common ratio between any two consecutive terms, g_n/g_{n-1}.

For example, consider the geometric sequence 6, 24, 96, 348, 1536, ... For this sequence, the first term is 6 and the common ratio 4. The explicit formula for this sequence is: $g_n = 6(4)^{n-1}$. Using this formula, the seventh term of the sequence can be found as follows:

$$g_7 = 6(4)^{7-1} = 6(4)^6 = 6(4096) = 24{,}576$$

e. Do you think that the scatterplot of a geometric sequence can always be modeled by an exponential equation? Why or why not?

f. How does the graph of an exponential equation differ from the graph of a geometric sequence?

g. Using the laws of exponents, the equation $y = ab^x$ can be rewritten as $y = a \cdot b^1 \cdot b^{x-1}$, which is equivalent to $y = (ab)b^{x-1}$. Assuming that this equation models the same geometric sequence as the explicit formula $g_n = g_1 r^{(n-1)}$, describe the relationship between each of the following:

    1. the nth term g_n and y 2. n and x

    3. the common ratio r and b 4. the first term g_1 and a

h. When is an explicit formula for a geometric sequence easier to use than the recursive formula?

i. Using the relationships described in Part **g** of the discussion, show that the explicit formula for a geometric sequence, $g_n = g_1 r^{(n-1)}$, is equivalent to the exponential equation of the form $y = ab^x$ that models the same sequence.

Discussion

a. 1. $t_{19} = 500 \cdot 2^{18}$

    2. The power of 2 equals $n - 1$.

b. 1. $t_n = 500 \cdot 2^{n-1}$, $n \geq 1$

    2. $t_7 = 500 \cdot 2^6 = 32{,}000$

c. The ratio is the same for each pair of successive terms.

d. The common ratio is the base of the exponent in the explicit formula.

e. The scatterplot of a geometric sequence always can be modeled by an exponential equation because a geometric sequence has a constant ratio between successive terms. This constant ratio corresponds with the value of b in an exponential equation of the form $y = ab^x$.

f. In general, the x-values (or domain) for an exponential equation are the set of all real numbers, and the n-values (or domain) for a geometric sequence are the set of natural numbers. (The context of a problem may limit the domain of an exponential equation.) Therefore, the graph of an exponential equation is a set of connected points (or a continuous curve), and the graph of a geometric sequence is a set of disconnected points.

g. 1. Both g_n and y represent the values on the y-axis, or the range.

    2. Both n and x represent the values on the x-axis, or the domain.

    3. The common ratio r and the value of b are the same because b represents the amount by which y is multiplied for every unit increase in x.

    4. The first term g_1 equals the y-value when $x = 1$, and a is the y-value when $x = 0$. Therefore, $g_1 = ab$. Because b equals the common ratio r, $g_1 = ar$.

h. The explicit formula is easier to use when the previous term is not known. For example, the 20th term of the geometric sequence in Table **12-5** would be easier to find by using the explicit formula rather than the recursive formula.

i. Answers may vary. The following proof substitutes ar for g_1, b for r, and x for n:

$$\begin{aligned} g_n &= g_1 r^{n-1} \\ &= ar(r)^{n-1} \\ &= ar^n \\ &= ab^x \end{aligned}$$

Warm-Up

1. **a.** $g_n = -2.4 \cdot 1.3^{n-1}$
   b. $g_n = 13 \cdot (-3)^{n-1}$
   c. $g_n = -4 \cdot 2.4^{n-1}$
2. **a.** 3.1
   b. 7
   c. 21.7, 67.27, 208.537
3. **a.** $g_n = -2.4 \cdot 1.3^{n-1}$
   b. $g_n = 9 \cdot 0.8^{n-1}$

Assignment

Problems suitable for use as assessment items are identified by an asterisk (*).

* **4.1 a.** The sequence is geometric. The explicit formula is $t_n = 0.5(5)^{n-1}$. The 10th term is 976,562.5.
  b. The sequence is not geometric because there is no common ratio between successive terms.
  c. The sequence is geometric. The explicit formula is $t_n = 4(-3)^{n-1}$. The 10th term is –78,732.
  d. The sequence is geometric. The explicit formula is $t_n = 1000(1/4)^{n-1}$. The 10th term is approximately 0.00381.

4.2 a. $1 + 3 + 9 + 27 + 81 = 121$
  b. $2 + 5 + 12.5 + 31.25 + 78.125 = 128.875$
  c. $0.5 + 1 + 2 + 4 + 8 + 16 + 32 + 64 = 127.5$
  d. $125 + 25 + 5 + 1 + 0.2 + 0.04 = 156.24$

* **4.3** Sample response: The ball will come to rest after about the eighth bounce. This was calculated using the following table, with heights rounded to 2 decimal places.

Bounce	Height (m)
Start	24.00
1	8.00
2	2.67
3	0.89
4	0.30
5	0.10
6	0.03
7	0.01
8	0.00
9	0.00
10	0.00

---

page 331

Warm-Up

1. Write an explicit formula for each of the following geometric sequences.
   a. 4000, 2000, 1000, 500, 250, 125, ...
   b. 13, –39, 117, –351, 1053, –3159, ...
   c. –4, –9.6, –23.04, –55.296, –132.7104, 318.50496, ...

2. Consider the explicit formula $g_n = 7 \cdot 3.1^{n-1}$.
   a. What is the common ratio?
   b. What is the first term?
   c. What are the next three terms?

3. Write an explicit formula for each geometric sequence described below.
   a. The first term is –2.4 and the common ratio is 1.3.
   b. The first term is 9 and the common ratio is 0.8.

Assignment

4.1 Identify each of the following sequences as geometric or not geometric. For each geometric sequence, write an explicit formula and find the 10th term. Explain why each of the remaining sequences is not geometric.
   a. 0.5, 2.5, 12.5, 62.5, ...
   b. 15, 150, 300, 900, ...
   c. 4, –12, 36, –108, ...
   d. 1000, 250, 62.5, 15.625, ...

4.2 Write the geometric series for each sequence below and find the corresponding sum.
   a. 1, 3, 9, 27, 81
   b. 2, 5, 12.5, ..., 78.125
   c. 0.5, 1, 2, ..., 64
   d. 125, 25, 5, ..., 0.04

4.3 At one of Stellar Attraction's concerts, an exuberant fan hits a beach ball into the air. The ball falls onto the stage from a height of 24 m. The height of each bounce is approximately one-third the height of the preceding bounce. Predict the number of bounces the ball will take before coming to rest. Justify your response.

Module 12 ■ *From Rock Bands to Recursion*   331

---

page 332

4.4 Describe the possible range of values for the common ratio in each of the following:
   a. an increasing geometric sequence
   b. a decreasing geometric sequence.

* * * * *

4.5 Consider the pattern of dots shown in the following diagram.

• : :: ::::

   a. If this pattern is expressed as a geometric sequence, what are the values for t_1 and r?
   b. Write an explicit formula that describes this pattern.
   c. Use your formula to determine the value of t_{14}.

science note

Sound is produced by vibrating objects. The frequency of a sound wave equals the frequency of the vibrating object.

The international unit of frequency is the **hertz (Hz)**, which represents one cycle per second. For example, a sound with a frequency of 220 Hz is produced by an object vibrating at 220 cycles per second.

332   Module 12 ■ *From Rock Bands to Recursion*

4.6 When a guitar string vibrates, the guitar produces sound. The rate at which the string vibrates determines the note. A string vibrating at 220 Hz produces the note A immediately below middle C. The note A immediately above middle C vibrates at 440 Hz. The frequencies of consecutive A notes form a geometric sequence.

Note	Frequency
A	
A	
A	
A	440 Hz
middle C	
A	220 Hz
A	
A	
A	
A	

a. Complete the table for all A notes above and below middle C.

b. Write a recursive formula that describes this sequence.

c. The average young person can hear sounds with frequencies from 20 Hz to 20,000 Hz. Which of the notes in the table in Part **a** could be heard by concert fans? Defend your response.

4.7 Annaborg has been offered two summer jobs, each for 12 weeks. The job at Plouvier's Pottery pays $5.00 per hour, with a 10% increase in the hourly wage every two weeks. The job at Brocklebank's Bakery pays $6.50 per hour, with a $0.10 increase in the hourly wage every two weeks.

a. Which type of sequence, arithmetic or geometric, best describes the wages offered by Plouvier's Pottery? Justify your response.

b. Which type of sequence, arithmetic or geometric, best describes the wages offered by Brocklebank's Bakery? Justify your response.

c. Write an explicit formula that describes the wages for each job.

d. If Annaborg wants to make as much money as possible, which job should she take? Justify your response.

4.4 **a.** In increasing geometric sequences, the common ratio is greater than 1.

b. In decreasing geometric sequences, the common ratio is between 0 and 1.

✳ ✳ ✳ ✳ ✳

4.5 **a.** If this pattern is expressed as a geometric sequence, $t_1 = 1$ and $r = 2$.

b. An explicit formula that describes this pattern is $t_n = 2^{n-1}$.

c. $t_{14} = 8192$

4.6 **a.** A completed table appears below.

Note	Frequency
A	3520
A	1760
A	880
A	440
middle C	
A	220
A	110
A	55
A	27.5
A	13.75

b. Two possible formulas are shown below:

$$\begin{cases} t_1 = 13.75 \\ t_n = t_{n-1}(2), \ n > 1 \end{cases} \qquad \begin{cases} t_1 = 3520 \\ t_n = t_{n-1}(0.5), \ n > 1 \end{cases}$$

c. The fans would hear all of the notes in the table except the fifth A below middle C.

* 4.7 **a.** A geometric sequence best describes the wages offered by Plouvier's Pottery because each hourly wage after the first is formed by multiplying the preceding wage by the common ratio of 1.10.

b. An arithmetic sequence best describes the wages offered by Brocklebank's Bakery because every hourly wage after the first is formed by adding the constant value of 0.10 to the preceding wage.

c. An explicit formula that describes the wages for Plouvier's Pottery is $P_n = 5(1.10)^{n-1}$. An explicit formula that describes the wages for Brocklebank's Bakery is $B_n = 6.5 + 0.10(n - 1)$.

d. If Annaborg wants to make as much money as possible, she should work for Brocklebank's Bakery. If she works 1 hr every 2 weeks, her total salary after 12 weeks for Plouvier's Pottery would be:

$5.00 + $5.50 + $6.05 + $6.66 + $7.32 + $8.05 = $38.58

Her corresponding salary for Brocklebank's Bakery would be:

$6.50 + $6.60 + $6.70 + $6.80 + $6.90 + $7.00 = $40.50

Therefore, her total salary at Brocklebank's Bakery will always exceed her total salary at Plouvier's Pottery, as long as she can work the same number of hours at either job.

teacher note

An additional assessment, for use at your discretion, appears in the Teacher Resources for this module.

Summary Assessment

1. Answers will vary. Sample response: Both residents used one year's data to predict the future. Mrs. Stephens assumed that the growth would continue arithmetically with a common difference of 35. She used the recursive formula:

$$\begin{cases} p_1 = 350 \\ p_n = p_{n-1} + 35, \ n > 1 \end{cases}$$

or the explicit formula $p_n = 350 + 35(n - 1)$. Mr. Aloishan assumed that the growth would continue geometrically with a common ratio of 1.1. He used the recursive formula:

$$\begin{cases} p_1 = 350 \\ p_n = p_{n-1}(1.1), \ n > 1 \end{cases}$$

or the explicit formula $p_n = 350(1.1)^{n-1}$. Mr. Aloishan is more concerned than Mrs. Stephens because the geometric sequence results in faster growth than the arithmetic sequence.

2. Answers will vary. Sample response: It will take between over 126,839 yr to cancel the debt using Plan A. This is calculated by:

4,000,000,000,000/(365 • 24 • 60 • 60) ≈ 126,839.2 yr

Under Plan B, the debt will be paid off during the 42nd year. This is found by using the following table:

Year	Debt (dollars)
1	3,999,999,999,999
2	3,999,999,999,997
3	3,999,999,999,993
⋮	⋮
41	1,800,976,744,449
42	−398,046,511,103

Plan A would be affordable but it takes too long. Plan B pays off faster, but the last payments are not feasible. Interest payments are not considered under either plan.

Summary Assessment

1. In 1990, the village of Bone Gap had a population of 350 people. By the end of 1991, the population had grown to 385. Many long-time residents grew concerned about the future of their community. At a town meeting, two different predictions were made.

   Mrs. Stephens presented the following graph and argued that residents should not be concerned about growth.

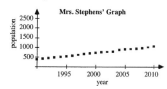

Mr. Aloishan, however, presented the graph below and argued that life in Bone Gap would change dramatically.

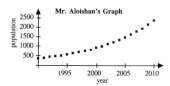

Based on these two graphs and the initial data, explain how the two residents reached their conclusions. Include formulas for each graph.

2. Imagine that the following two plans were proposed at the time that the U.S. national debt reached $4 trillion.

   ■ Plan A: Balance the budget to eliminate additional accumulation of debt. Reduce the debt by $1.00 per second until the debt is canceled.

   ■ Plan B: Balance the budget to eliminate additional accumulation of debt. Reduce the debt by $1.00 in the first year, $2.00 in the second year, $4.00 in the third year, and continue to double the reduction until the debt is canceled.

   Use the ideas and tools in this module to analyze the two plans. Which one do you think is better? Defend your choice.

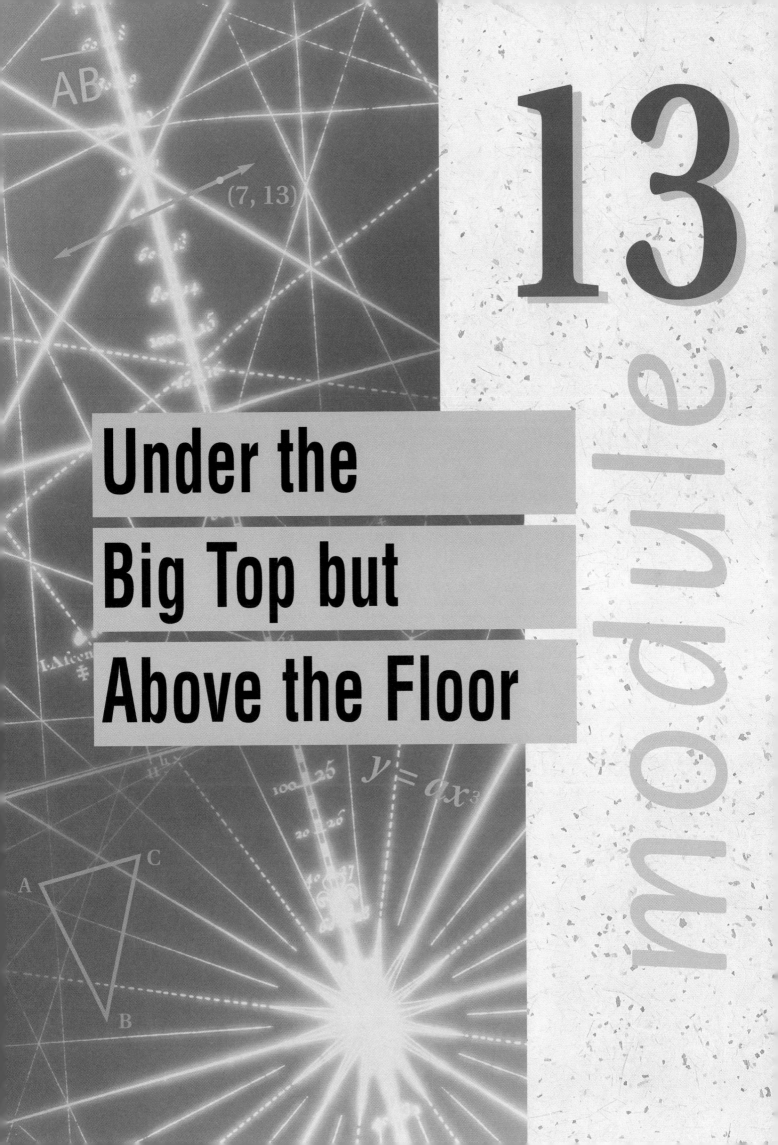

Under the Big Top but Above the Floor

Overview

In this module, students are introduced to linear programming. They define feasible regions by graphing inequalities determined by vertical, horizontal, and oblique lines. They find the coordinates of corner points both graphically and algebraically. They then use the corner principle to find optimum values for linear objective functions.

Introduction:	Students review writing and graphing inequalities on a number line.
Activity 1:	Students write inequalities, graph them on a coordinate plane, and learn to identify solution sets.
Activity 2:	Students use the substitution method to determine solutions to systems of equations and to identify corner points of a system of inequalities.
Activity 3:	Students determine the feasible region for a system of inequalities.
Activity 4:	Students write systems of inequalities to represent the constraints of a problem, use the corner principle, and find a solution that optimizes an objective function.

Objectives

In this module, students will:

* graph inequalities on a number line (Introduction)
* investigate number patterns (1, 2, 3, 4)
* write and graph linear inequalities (1, 2, 3)
* use linear inequalities to define regions graphically (1, 2, 3)
* solve systems of linear equations (2)
* determine the feasible region for a system of linear inequalities (3, 4)
* find the corner points for a feasible region (3, 4)
* determine the optimum values for linear objective functions (4).

Prerequisites

For this module, students should know:

* how to write and graph inequalities with one variable
* how to determine the coordinates of points which satisfy equations and inequalities
* how to determine the slope of a line
* how to find the equation of a line given the coordinates of two points
* how to graph equations of the form $y = mx + b$

✳ how to solve an equation for one variable in terms of another

✳ how to determine simple probabilities.

 Flashbacks, for use at your discretion, appear in the Teacher Resources for this module. These brief problem sets provide a review of some prerequisite skills for each activity.

Planning Guide

Activity	Materials	Technology	Time Line
Introduction	■ none	■ none	1 day
Activity **1**	■ graph paper ■ rulers	■ graphing utility	2 days
Activity **2**	■ graph paper ■ rulers	■ graphing utility	3 days
Activity **3**	■ graph paper ■ red dice ■ white dice ■ rulers	■ graphing utility	3 days
Activity **4**	■ graph paper ■ rulers ■ Roll-a-rama template	■ graphing utility	2 days
Assessment Activities	■ graph paper ■ rulers	■ graphing utility	3 days **Total: 14 days**

 teacher note

A blackline master of the template appears in the Teacher Resources for this module.

Introduction

Students play the game "Guess My Number" to review writing and graphing inequalities on a number line.

Materials List

■ none

teacher note

The game Guess My Number is best played in pairs. Students should read Part **a** only, then play the game. This should encourage them to experiment with winning strategies. Part **b** of the exploration guides them toward a specific strategy and reviews mathematical symbolism. Students should understand the significance of inclusive and non-inclusive inequalities ($\leq$ and $\geq$ versus $<$ and $>$). You might wish to compare strategies discovered in Part **a** of the exploration (in pairs or as a class) before proceeding to Part **b**.

Student Outcomes

After completing the following exploration and discussion, students should be able to:

✳ write and graph inequalities on a number line

✳ describe an efficient strategy for identifying a selected number in a given interval.

Exploration

a. Students should record both the questions asked and the information they received from each answer. As errors or arguments occur, ask students to use their records to identify mistakes or settle disputes.

  One possible strategy is to ask questions that reduce the range of possible numbers by half each time.

b–c. Students write their questions as inequalities and record the corresponding responses on a number line. For example, one question might be "Is $x > 0$?" If the response is "No," the following graph may be drawn to represent the remaining possibilities for the opponent's number:

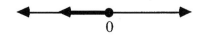

Introduction

Every year at Dantzig High School, the mathematics club sponsors a school carnival. The club designs game booths to earn money. As booths compete to attract more customers, the atmosphere grows festive. Many students dress in crazy costumes. Balloons, tinsel, and streamers are everywhere, and the aromas of pizza, popcorn, and hot dogs waft through the gym.

The first game booth that you visit is "Guess My Number." Inside the booth, Yvette stands next to a tumbling basket of numbers. Yvette picks a number from the basket. You must now guess the number by asking questions which can be answered by "yes" or "no." If you guess correctly using seven or fewer questions, you win a prize.

Exploration

In this exploration, you play Guess My Number with a classmate and try to develop a winning strategy.

a. To play Guess My Number with a classmate, each of you should select an integer in the interval $[-50,50]$. Do not reveal your number to your classmate. Take turns asking yes-or-no questions until you discover each other's number. Record the questions asked, the answers given, and the number of questions.

  Play the game at least twice and consider some strategies you might use to guess correctly with the fewest questions.

b. Play Guess My Number at least two more times, using only questions that include inequalities (for example, "Is your number less than 5?"). Record each question using inequality symbols. Record the responses on a number line.

c. Play Guess My Number at least three more times, using questions that include inequalities.

Discussion

a. If your opponent must choose an integer in the interval $[-50,50]$, can you develop a strategy that guarantees you will know the number in seven questions or less?

Discussion

a. It is possible to identify the number using seven questions or less. Each question divides the set of integers into two subsets. Reducing the original set of integers by "halves" with each question results in the following maximum cardinal numbers for successive subsets: 101 possibilities, 51 possibilities, 26 possibilities, 13 possibilities, 7 possibilities, 4 possibilities, 2 possibilities, and 1 possibility.

b. What do you think the minimum number of questions would be to determine an integer in the interval [–75,75]?

The next booth you visit is "Guess My Location." The object of this game is to determine the exact location of your opponent's point on a grid. Pablo and Lisa are ahead of you at the booth. Watch them play while you wait for your turn. Figure **13-1** shows the beginning of their game.

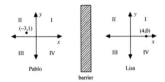

FIGURE 13-1   Pablo and Lisa play Guess My Location.

Pablo asks, "Is $x > 0$?"

Lisa answers, "Yes."

Pablo knows that Lisa's point must be in quadrant I, quadrant IV, or on the positive x-axis.

Lisa asks, "Is $y \leq 0$?"

"No," answers Pablo.

Lisa knows that Pablo's point is above the x-axis.

It's Pablo's turn again. "Is $y \geq 0$?" he asks.

"Yes," answers Lisa.

Pablo knows that Lisa's point can only be in the first quadrant or on the positive x-axis.

---

b. Using the same reasoning as in Part **a** above, the minimum number of questions is eight. The successive numbers of possibilities are 151, 76, 38, 19, 10, 5, 3, 2, and 1.

ACTIVITY

1

In this activity, students play a game that depends on their ability to write and graph systems of linear inequalities.

Materials List

- graph paper (five sheets per student)
- rulers (one per student)

Technology

- graphing utility

Student Outcomes

After completing the following discussions and explorations, students should be able to:

✳ graph horizontal and vertical inequalities on a coordinate plane

✳ determine if a boundary line is part of the solution set

✳ use the mathematical conjunction *and* to describe regions on a coordinate plane

✳ use conjunctions to narrow a solution set

✳ determine if a corner point (vertex) is part of the solution set

✳ describe the constraints for a given problem involving horizontal and vertical inequalities.

Discussion 1

a. 1. Sample response: The points in the shaded region all have *y*-coordinates greater than –3.
   2. $y \geq -3$
b. 1. Sample response: The graph is a vertical line passing through the *x*-axis at $x = 5$.
   2. Sample response: The graph of $x < 5$ is shaded to the left of the line $x = 5$ since all the *x*-coordinates to the left of the line are less than 5.
   3. The points lying on $x = 5$ should not be included since the *x*-values that satisfy the inequality must be less than 5. This can be shown by representing the boundary as a dashed line.
c. Each inequality has an infinite number of solutions.
d. 1. Any ordered pair that satisfies the two inequalities $x \geq -2$ and $y < 3$ is acceptable. Sample response: (3,–2).
   2. There is an infinite number of points in the combined solution set of the inequalities.
e. Sample response: For $x \geq 2$, any point with an *x*-coordinate of 2 or more is included in the solution set. For $y < -7$, only points with *y*-coordinates less than –7 are included.

   Inequalities which use the symbols $\leq$ and $\geq$ have graphs whose borders are included. Inequalities which use the symbols $>$ and $<$ have borders that are not included.

Exploration 1

Students should read the example and the rules before playing "Guess My Location." During the game, they should record both their questions and the information received.

You may model some questions and responses or, after a few minutes of play, ask students to share their game strategies.

To minimize potential sources of confusion in the first game, you also might wish to specify a range of coordinates for the board. For example, you might specify that the game board be defined by the interval [–10, 10] for both *x* and *y*. If time allows, pairs of students can agree on different intervals for their next games.

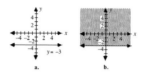

Discussion 1

a. The graph of the equation $y = -3$ is shown in Figure **13-2a** below. As the shaded region in Figure **13-2b** demonstrates, the line separates the plane into two parts or **half planes**.

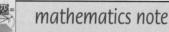

FIGURE 13-2 Graphs of $y = -3$ and the half-plane above $y = -3$.

   1. What must be true about the coordinates of all the points in the shaded region in Figure **13-2b**?
   2. How can you use inequality notation to describe the *y*-coordinates of the points either on or above the line $y = -3$?
b. The line $x = 5$ defines the boundary for the inequality $x < 5$.
   1. Describe what the graph of $x = 5$ would look like on a coordinate system.
   2. Would a graph of $x < 5$ be shaded to the right or to the left of $x = 5$? Explain your response.
   3. Should the boundary be a part of the graph of $x < 5$? Explain your response.

mathematics note

The graph of a linear inequality is a shaded region that represents the **solution set** of the inequality. The solution set contains all the points, or solutions, that make the inequality true. The graph of a linear equation forms the **boundary line** for the region. A solid boundary indicates that the points on the line are part of the solution set. A dashed boundary indicates that the points on the line are not part of the solution set.

For example, Figure **13-3a** shows the graph of $x \geq -2$ and Figure **13-3b** shows the graph of $y < 3$.

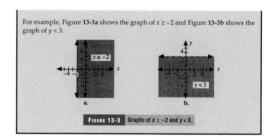

FIGURE 13-3 Graphs of $x \geq -2$ and $y < 3$.

c. How many points are in the solution set for each inequality in Figure **13-3**?
d. 1. Identify the coordinates of a point that is in the solution set of both inequalities in Figure **13-3**.
   2. How many points are in the solution set that satisfies both inequalities?
e. Explain why the point (2,–7) is in the solution set for $x \geq 2$ but not for $y < -7$.

Exploration 1

In this exploration, you play Guess My Location with a classmate. Read Parts **a–d** before beginning play.

a. Each player makes a game sheet by drawing a coordinate system on a sheet of graph paper. Both game sheets should have the same scales on the *x*- and *y*-axes.

   Place a book upright between the two game sheets so that neither player can see the other's graph.
b. Both players choose and mark a point on their game sheets, without revealing the point's location to the opponent. The coordinates of the point must be integers.
c. Players take turns asking yes-or-no questions involving inequalities, to gain information about the location of the opponent's point.

   Record each question you ask as an inequality. Record each answer you receive as the graph of an inequality on your coordinate system.
d. The first player to identify the coordinates of the opponent's point wins the game. If a player guesses incorrectly, then that player loses the next turn.

Discussion 2

a. Describe the strategies you used to play Guess My Location.

b. Assume that your opponent's point is located in the third quadrant. What two mathematical statements would describe this region?

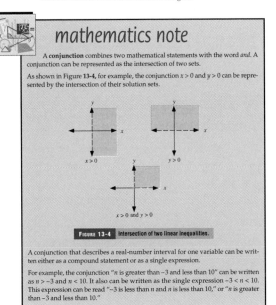

mathematics note

A **conjunction** combines two mathematical statements with the word *and*. A conjunction can be represented as the intersection of two sets.

As shown in Figure **13-4**, for example, the conjunction $x > 0$ and $y > 0$ can be represented by the intersection of their solution sets.

FIGURE 13-4 Intersection of two linear inequalities.

A conjunction that describes a real-number interval for one variable can be written either as a compound statement or as a single expression.

For example, the conjunction "n is greater than -3 and less than 10" can be written as $n > -3$ and $n < 10$. It also can be written as the single expression $-3 < n < 10$. This expression can be read "-3 is less than n and n is less than 10," or "n is greater than -3 and less than 10."

c. For all points in the first quadrant, the x- and y-coordinates are greater than 0. Does the conjunction shown in Figure **13-4** represent these points? Explain your response.

d. Imagine that Pablo asked Lisa "Is $x > 0$ and $y < 0$?"

1. If Lisa answers "Yes," in what quadrant(s) could her point be located? Explain your response.

2. If Lisa answers "No," in what quadrant(s) could her point be located? Explain your response.

e. What conjunction describes the intersection of the two inequalities shown in Figure **13-5**?

FIGURE 13-5 Two inequalities and their intersection.

Exploration 2

Imagine that Pablo and Lisa replay the original game of Guess My Location shown in Figure **13-1**. Pablo has chosen the point $(-3,1)$ and Lisa has chosen $(4,0)$. This time they ask questions that use conjunctions.

"Is $x > 0$ and $y < 0$?" asks Pablo.

"No," Lisa responds.

Pablo knows that the point is not in quadrant IV.

Now it's Lisa's turn. She asks, "Is $x \le 0$ and $y \ge 0$?"

Pablo answers, "Yes."

Lisa knows that the point is in quadrant II.

Now Pablo asks, "Is $x \ge 0$ and $y \ge 0$?"

"Yes," answers Lisa.

Following Pablo and Lisa's example, play another game of Guess My Location. For this game, use the two additional rules described in Parts **a** and **b**.

Discussion 2

a. Answers will vary. In one possible strategy, students might ask questions that eliminate possible regions for the point until only one point is left. In another strategy, students could identify the quadrant in which the point is located, then subdivide that quadrant repeatedly until the point is identified.

b. $x < 0$ and $y < 0$

c. Yes, the conjunction $x > 0$ and $y > 0$ represents all points in the first quadrant. (The points on the x and y-axes are not included in any quadrant.)

d. 1. Lisa's point must be located in Quadrant IV because it is the only quadrant where $x > 0$ and $y < 0$.

2. If Lisa says "yes," her point would be in Quadrant IV. She answered "no," so it must be located in Quadrants I, II, or III.

e. $x \ge -1$ and $y > -2$

Exploration 2

In this version of Guess My Location, students must ask questions in the form of conjunctions. One part of the question must refer to x and the other to y. **Note:** One game should take 10–15 minutes.

Discussion 3

a. Sample response: With two-part questions, a "yes" answer makes it possible to eliminate a larger portion of the playing grid. If the answer is "no," however, you do not know to which part of the question the answer refers.

b. The intersection of the two boundaries, $x = 0$ and $y = 0$, is the point with coordinates $(0,0)$. This point is not in the solution set because it does not satisfy the two inequalities.

   Note: You may ask students how they would change the question to include this corner point. If the conjunction were $x \geq 0$ and $y \leq 0$, the point would be included in the solution set.

c. Any point in the first quadrant, such as $(4,5)$, has a positive x-coordinate and a positive y-coordinate. Because any positive x-coordinate is greater than 0 and any positive y-coordinate is greater than 0, all the ordered pairs in the first quadrant are solutions to this conjunction.

d. The y-coordinates are "constrained" or restricted to positive real numbers.

e. Using simple inequalities, this region can be described as $x \geq -3$ and $y \geq -4$ and $y < 2$. It also can be described by the conjunction $x \geq -3$ and $-4 \leq y < 2$.

Warm-Up

Note: In all of the following sample graphs, both the x- and y-axes are marked in increments of 1 unit.

1. Sample graph:

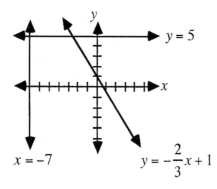

---

page 344

   a. Each question must be a conjunction.

      b. One mathematical statement in the conjunction must refer only to x; the other statement must refer only to y.

Discussion 3

   a. What advantages or disadvantages did you notice when using conjunctions to play Guess My Location?

   b. Consider Pablo's first conjunction, "Is $x > 0$ and $y < 0$?" The intersection of the two boundary lines for these inequalities, $x = 0$ and $y = 0$, is referred to as a **corner point** or **vertex**.

      Is this corner point part of the solution set for the conjunction? Explain your response.

   c. How do you know that a point in the first quadrant is a solution to $x > 0$ and $y > 0$?

   d. Consider the points in the solution set of $x > 0$ and $y > 0$. The x-coordinates of these points must be positive real numbers. This condition on the x-coordinates is called a **constraint**.

      Describe the constraints on the y-coordinates of the points in this solution set.

   e. How could you use conjunctions to describe the region shown in Figure 13-6?

FIGURE 13-6   A region defined by conjunctions.

Warm-Up

   1. Graph and label the following lines on the same coordinate grid.

      a. $y = 5$

      b. $x = -7$

      c. $y = -(2/3)x + 1$

344   Module 13 ■ *Under the Big Top but Above the Floor*

2. a. Sample graph:

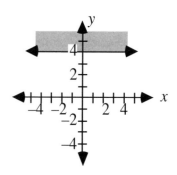

b. $y \geq 4$

c. See sample graph in Part **a.**

d. Answers will vary. Sample response: $(-5, 4.75)$, $(0,8)$, $(12,12)$.

e. There are no constraints on the x-coordinates.

f. All y-coordinates must be greater than or equal to 4.

2. **a.** Sketch a graph of the line $y = 4$.

   b. Write an inequality to describe all the points located on and above the line.

   c. Shade the region that corresponds to the solution set of the inequality.

   d. Write the coordinates of at least three points included in the solution set.

   e. Describe the constraints on the x-coordinates of the points in the solution set.

   f. Describe the constraints on the y-coordinates of the points in the solution set.

3. Graph each of the following on a separate coordinate grid.

   a. $x < 9$

   b. $y \geq -4$

   c. $y \leq -4$ and $x > 2$

4. The following graph shows the four quadrants of the coordinate plane. Use conjunctions of linear inequalities to describe each quadrant. **Note:** The x- and y-axes are not included in any quadrant.

5. **a.** On a coordinate plane, graph the region defined by the intersection of the linear inequalities $x \geq -4$ and $y \leq 2$.

   b. Select a point in the intersection of the two inequalities that is not on a boundary. Verify that the point is a solution to both inequalities.

   c. Select a point outside the shaded region. Verify that the point is not a solution for at least one of the inequalities.

   d. Select a point on a boundary. Is this point a solution to both inequalities? Explain your response.

   e. Identify the corner point of the conjunction.

c.

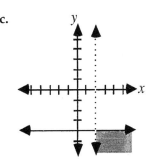

4. Sample response:

Quadrant	Conjunction
I	$x > 0$ and $y > 0$
II	$x < 0$ and $y > 0$
III	$x < 0$ and $y < 0$
IV	$x > 0$ and $y < 0$

5. **a.** Sample graph:

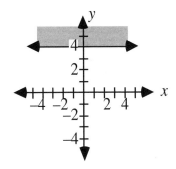

b. Answers will vary. Students should substitute the x- and y-values of their selected points in the inequalities. These values should make both inequalities true. For example, the point $(0,1)$ satisfies both inequalities because $0 \geq -4$ and $1 \leq 2$.

c. Answers will vary. For example, the point $(0,3)$ does not satisfy both inequalities because 3 is not less than or equal to 2.

d. Answers will vary. For example, the point $(-4,1)$ satisfies both inequalities because $-4 \geq -4$ and $1 \leq 2$.

e. The corner point is the intersection of the two boundaries, $(-4,2)$.

3. Sample graphs:

a.

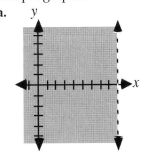

b.

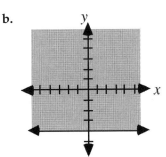

Assignment

Problems suitable for use as assessment items are identified by an asterisk (*).

1.1 a. 1. $y \le -4$

     2. $x > 1$ and $y \ge 1$

     3. $x \ge -1$, $x \le 4$, $y \ge -1$, and $y \le 2$ (this also can be written as $-1 \le x \le 4$ and $-1 \le y \le 2$)

  b. 1. There are no corner points on this region.

     2. (1,1) by using the corner point definition in Discussion **3** Part **b.**

     3. (−1,2), (4,2), (−1,−1), and (4,−1)

1.2 Answers will vary. Students should test their inequalities with the point (0,−2). Sample response: "Is $x \ge 0$ and $y < 0$?" and "Is $x \ge -1$ and $y < -1$?"

* 1.3 a. Sample graph:

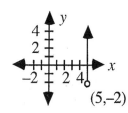

(5,−2)

  b. The graph formed is a vertical ray pointed upwards, with an open endpoint at (5,−2).

1.4 a. The point is located in the region defined by the following system of inequalities: $x \ge 4$, $y \ge 1$, and $y \le 5$. Sample graph:

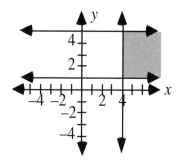

Assignment

1.1 a. Use inequalities to describe the shaded region in each of the following graphs.

1.   **2.**

3.

  b. Identify the coordinates of any corner points for each shaded region in Part **a.**

1.2 In a game of Guess My Location, your opponent chooses the point with coordinates (0,−2). Using conjunctions, write two different questions about this point that will receive a "yes" answer.

1.3 In another game of Guess My Location, you ask the question, "Is $x = 5$ and $y > -2$?" Your opponent answers, "Yes."

  a. On a coordinate plane, graph the set of all points that fit this information.

  b. Describe the graph formed.

1.4 The tables in Parts **a** and **b** show some questions and answers from two different games of Guess My Location. For each game, graph the "smallest" region that contains all possible solutions and use linear inequalities to describe the region.

a.

Question	Answer
Is $x \ge 0$ and $y \ge 0$?	Yes
Is $x \le 2$ and $y \ge 0$?	No
Is $x \ge 3$ and $y \ge 1$?	Yes
Is $x \ge 4$ and $y \le 5$?	Yes

b.

Question	Answer
Is $x \geq 0$ and $y \leq 0$?	Yes
Is $x \geq 5$ and $y \geq -3$?	No
Is $x \leq 4$ and $y \geq -3$?	Yes

* * * * *

1.5 A cash register contains bills and coins. Using the horizontal axis to represent the value of the bills and the vertical axis to represent the value of the coins, draw a graph to describe each of the following statements:

a. The cash register contains at least $50.00 in bills and no more than $25.00 in coins.

b. The cash register contains less than $100.00 in bills and at least $10.00 in coins.

c. The cash register contains more than $75.00 in bills and no more than $50.00 in coins.

* * * * *

1.6 Use linear inequalities to describe each shaded region in Parts **a–c.**

a.

b.

c.

b. The point is located in the region defined by the following system of inequalities: $x \geq 0$, $x \leq 4$, $y \geq -3$, and $y \leq 0$ (this also may be written as $0 \leq x \leq 4$ and $-3 \leq y \leq 0$). Sample graph:

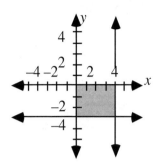

1.5 Sample graphs:

a.

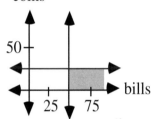

b.

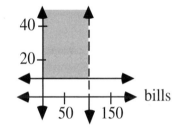

c.

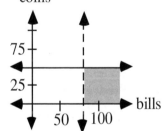

* * * * *

1.6 **a.** $-3 \leq x \leq -1$ and $y \geq -2$

b. $1 \leq x \leq 2$ and $-2 \leq y \leq 1$

c. $x \geq -2$ and $-1 \leq y < 2$

* 1.7 Sample graphs:

a.

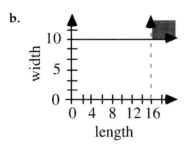

b.

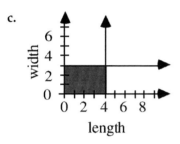

c.

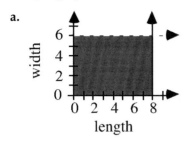

1.7 Terry, Stan, and Lindsey are designing vegetable gardens. Using the horizontal axis to represent length and the vertical axis to represent width, draw a graph to describe each of the following statements.

  a. Terry decides that her garden should be no more than 8 m long and less than 6 m wide.

  b. Stan decides his garden should be more than 16 m long and at least 10 m wide.

  c. Lindsey decides that her garden should be at most 4 m long and no more than 3 m wide.

ACTIVITY 2

Anton and Sharline are the school champions at Guess My Location. In this activity, you investigate some of the tools they use to analyze the game.

Exploration 1

Anton and Sharline are playing Guess My Location. Both players have selected points with x- and y-coordinates between −10 and 10. After receiving an answer to his first question, Anton shades his game sheet as shown in Figure **13-7**.

The points A, B, C, and D in Figure **13-7** lie at the intersections of the dashed line, the solid line, and the lines that define the right-hand and lower limits of the grid. The solid line through points A and C also passes through $(0,−3)$ and $(1,−1)$. The horizontal dashed line has a y-intercept of 7.

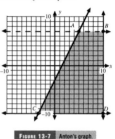

FIGURE 13-7 Anton's graph.

ACTIVITY 2

In this activity, students are introduced to the substitution method of solving a system of linear equations. Conjunctions are used to describe regions bounded by oblique lines.

teacher note

A brief assessment of the mathematical content in Activities **1** and **2**, for use at your discretion, appears in the Teacher Resources for this module.

Materials List

■ graph paper (several sheets per student)

Technology

■ graphing utility

a. Determine the equation of each line that borders the shaded region in Anton's graph.

mathematics note

A **system of linear equations** is a set of two or more equations whose graphs are lines. A **solution** to a system of linear equations is a point where all the lines intersect. The coordinates of this point satisfy all the equations in the system. For example, consider the following system of linear equations:

$$\begin{cases} y = 2x + 3 \\ y = x + 1 \end{cases}$$

Figure **13-8** shows that the graphs of the two lines intersect at the point with coordinates $(−2,−1)$. Substituting −2 for x and −1 for y shows that this point is a solution to the system, because $−1 = 2(−2) + 3$ and $−1 = −2 + 1$ are both true.

FIGURE 13-8 Solution to a system of linear equations.

b. To shade the region shown in Figure **13-7**, what question might Anton have asked? What answer must Sharline have given?

c. In Figure **13-7**, point C is one of the corner points of the shaded region.

  1. Identify the system of linear equations that intersect at point C.

  2. Estimate the coordinates of point C as accurately as possible.

  3. Determine if the coordinates that you estimated in Step **2** are a solution to the system of linear equations.

Discussion 1

a. The shaded region in Figure **13-7** contains the location of Sharline's point. Anton used the limits of the grid, one solid line, and one dashed line to define the boundaries of the region.

1. If Anton had wanted to define the same region using two dashed boundary lines, how could he have modified his question?
2. If Anton had wanted to use two solid boundary lines, how could he have modified his question?

b. What points are eliminated from a solution set when a dashed boundary line replaces a solid boundary line?

c. The shaded region in Figure 13-7 shows the solution set for a system of linear inequalities. Which of the corner points are included in this solution set?

d. The corner point C appears to have at least one coordinate that is not an integer. Did you find the exact coordinates of this point? Explain your response.

e. The exact coordinates of a point where two lines intersect is the solution to the corresponding system of equations. To find these exact coordinates, you can use a method involving substitution.

For example, Table 13-1 lists the steps necessary to find the solution to one system of equations by substitution.

TABLE 13-1 ■ Substitution Method for Solving a System of Equations	
Consider the given system of equations.	$\begin{cases} y = 2x - 3 \\ y = 7 \end{cases}$
Since y = 7 in this case, substitute 7 for y.	$7 = 2x - 3$
Solve the resulting equation for x.	$5 = x$
Write the solution to the system in the form (x, y).	$(5, 7)$

To check the solution, you can substitute the coordinates of the point in each of the original equations in the system. If $x = 5$ and $y = 7$, then $y = 2x - 3 = 2(5) - 3 = 7$, which is true. Therefore, $(5,7)$ is a solution to the equation $y = 2x - 3$. Because $(5,7)$ is also a solution to the equation $y = 7$, then it is a solution to the system of equations.

1. Why are the coordinates of point C in Exploration 1 a solution to a system of linear equations?
2. How does the substitution method compare with the method you used in Part c of Exploration 1?

Exploration 2

Figure 13-9 shows a graph of three linear equations. Point B is the intersection of $5x - 5y = 4$ and $3x + y = 8$.

350   Module 13 ■ *Under the Big Top but Above the Floor*

Student Outcomes

After completing the following explorations and discussions, students should be able to:

✳ determine the solution to a system of linear equations by substitution

✳ determine the corner points of a conjunction with oblique boundary lines using substitution.

Exploration 1

Students are introduced to systems of linear equations.

a. The equations of the boundary lines are $y = 7$, $y = 2x - 3$, $x = 10$, and $y = -10$.

b. One possible question is: "Is $y < 7$ and $y \le 2x - 3$?" For this question, Sharline must answer "Yes."

c. 1. The system of equations is:
$$\begin{cases} y = -10 \\ y = 2x - 3 \end{cases}$$

2. From the graph, the coordinates appear to be approximately $(-3.5, -10)$.

3. Students may substitute the estimated coordinates for point C in their system of equations. The point $(-3.5, -10)$ is a solution.

teacher note

Part **d** of Discussion **1** is designed to show that an exact answer can be difficult to identify using a graph. This demonstrates the need for an algebraic method of finding solutions.

Discussion 1

a. 1. Sample response: "Is $y < 2x - 3$ and $y < 7$?"
   2. Sample response: "Is $y \le 2x - 3$ and $y \le 7$?"

b. When the boundary line is dashed, the points on the boundary line are not included in the solution set.

c. Points C and D are included in the solution set because they occur at the intersections of two solid lines.

d. Sample response: The coordinates of C appear to be approximately $(-3.5, -10)$. From the graph there is no way to determine the exact value of the x-coordinate.

e. 1. The corner point C is defined by the intersection of the lines $y = -10$ and $y = 2x - 3$. According to the mathematics note, a solution to a system of linear equations is the point where the lines intersect. The coordinates of point C satisfy the equations of both lines.

   2. Sample response: The method I used is similar to the substitution method. Since C is on the line $y = -10$, the y-coordinate is -10. Substituting this value in the equation $y = 2x - 3$ results in the following value for x:

$$-10 = 2x - 3$$
$$-7 = 2x$$
$$-3.5 = x$$

Therefore, the coordinates of point C are $(-3.5, -10)$.

teacher note

Before beginning Part **b** of Exploration **2**, you might wish to review how to solve an equation of the form $Ax + By = C$ for either x or y.

Exploration 2

To find the coordinates of the corner points of a region, students use substitution to solve several systems of linear equations.

a. Sample response: The coordinate of point B are approximately (2.3,1.5).

b. 1. Sample response: Solve the equation $3x + y = 8$ for y to get $y = -3x + 8$. Then substitute this expression for y in the other equation:

$$5x - 5y = 4$$
$$5x - 5(-3x + 8) = 4$$
$$5x + 15x - 40 = 4$$
$$20x = 44$$
$$x = 2.2$$

Substituting 2.2 for x in $3x + y = 8$ gives a y-value of 1.4. The exact coordinates of point B are (2.2,1.4).

2. Student estimates should be fairly close to the exact values.

3. Students should substitute as follows:

$$3x + y = 8 \qquad\qquad 5x - 5y = 4$$
$$3(2.2) + 1.4 \overset{?}{=} 8 \quad \text{and} \quad 5(2.2) - 5(1.4) \overset{?}{=} 4$$
$$8 = 8 \qquad\qquad\qquad 4 = 4$$

c. Point A is the intersection of the line $3x + y = 8$ and the line $3y - x = 6$. Solving this system of equations by substitution yields the coordinates (1.8,2.6).

   Point C is the intersection of the line $5x - 5y = 4$ and the line $3y - x = 6$. Solving this system of equations by substitution yields the coordinates (4.2,3.4).

Discussion 2

a. Sample response: Yes, the coordinates estimated by looking at the graph were close to the actual values.

b. Sample response: One way to confirm the solution to a system of linear equations is to graph the lines and estimate the coordinates of the point of intersection. Another, more exact method is to substitute the coordinates of the solution into each equation, then check to see that a true statement results.

c. The system of linear inequalities for region ABC is: $5x - 5y \leq 4$, $3x + y \geq 8$, and $3y - x \leq 6$.

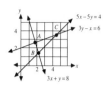

FIGURE 13-9 Three linear equations.

a. Estimate the coordinates of point B in Figure **13-9**.

b. Table **13-2** lists the steps necessary to find the solution to another system of equations by substitution.

TABLE 13-2 ■ Substitution Method for Solving a System of Linear Equations

Consider the given system of equations.	$\begin{cases} 2x + 3y = 6 \\ 9y - 4x = 13 \end{cases}$
Solve one of the equations for y.	$y = 2 - \dfrac{2}{3}x$
Substitute for y in the other equation.	$9\left(2 - \dfrac{2}{3}x\right) - 4x = 13$
Solve for x.	$x = \dfrac{1}{2}$
Substitute for x in one of the original equations.	$2\left(\dfrac{1}{2}\right) + 3y = 6$
Solve the resulting equation for y.	$y = \dfrac{5}{3}$
Write the solution to the system in the form (x, y).	$\left(\dfrac{1}{2}, \dfrac{5}{3}\right)$

To check the solution, you can substitute the coordinates of the point in each of the original equations.

$$2x + 3y = 6 \qquad\qquad 9y - 4x = 13$$
$$2\left(\frac{1}{2}\right) + 3\left(\frac{5}{3}\right) \overset{?}{=} 6 \quad \text{and} \quad 9\left(\frac{5}{3}\right) - 4\left(\frac{1}{2}\right) \overset{?}{=} 13$$
$$1 + 5 = 6 \qquad\qquad\qquad 15 - 2 = 13$$

Module 13 ■ *Under the Big Top but Above the Floor*   351

1. Use the method described in Table **13-2** to find the exact coordinates of point *B* in Figure **13-9**.

2. Compare your solution with the estimate you made in Part **a**.

3. Check your solution by substituting the coordinates of the point in each of the original equations.

c. Repeat Parts **a** and **b** for points *A* and *C* in Figure **13-9**.

Discussion 2

a. Did your estimated coordinates for points *A*, *B*, and *C* support the solutions you found by solving systems of equations?

b. Describe how to confirm the solution to a system of linear equations.

c. What system of linear inequalities could be used to describe the triangular region in Figure **13-9** with corner points *A*, *B*, and *C*? Assume that the region includes the lines defining its boundaries.

Warm-Up

1. Each graph below shows two intersecting lines. Use the graph to determine the equation of each line and the coordinates of their point of intersection. Substitute the coordinates of the point in each equation to verify your solution.

a.   b.

c.

2. Solve each of the following systems of equations using the substitution method. Check your solutions by graphing the system and verifying the coordinates of the point of intersection.

a. $y = x + 1$ and $y = 3x - 3$ b. $x + y = 10$ and $2x - 4y = 2$

c. $y = x + 7$ and $y = -2x + 6$ d. $3x + y = 10$ and $4x + 1 = y$

---

2. The solutions to each system of equations is shown in the graphs below.

a.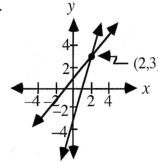
(2,3)

b.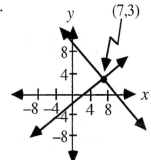
(7,3)

c.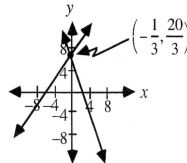
$\left(-\dfrac{1}{3}, \dfrac{20}{3}\right)$

d.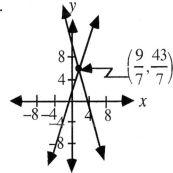
$\left(\dfrac{9}{7}, \dfrac{43}{7}\right)$

Warm-Up

1. **a.** The point of intersection is $(-4,-5)$.

$$\begin{cases} y = -5 \\ y = 2x + 3 \end{cases}$$

b. The point of intersection is $(1,1)$.

$$\begin{cases} y = x \\ y = -3x + 4 \end{cases}$$

c. The point of intersection is $(-2,2)$.

$$\begin{cases} y = x + 4 \\ y = -x \end{cases}$$

3. a. Sample graph

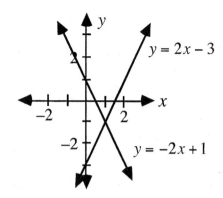

b. $y \leq 2x - 3$
c. $y \geq -2x + 1$
d. Sample response: (3,1), (3,–2).
e. The point of intersection is (1,–1).

teacher note

The following assignment problems offer several opportunities for students to work in groups.

---

page 353

3. a. Graph the lines $y + 3 = 2x$ and $y + 2x = 1$ on the same coordinate system.

b. Write a linear inequality that describes the region below the line $y + 3 = 2x$ and includes the line.

c. Write a linear inequality that describes the region above the line $y + 2x = 1$ and includes the line.

d. List the coordinates of two points that satisfy both inequalities.

e. Use the substitution method to identify the point of intersection of $y + 3 = 2x$ and $y + 2x = 1$.

Assignment

2.1 a. Draw the region defined by the following system of inequalities: $x \geq 0$, $y \geq 0$, $x \leq 8$ and $y \leq 8$.

b. Describe the shape of this region.

c. Identify the corner points, or vertices, of the region.

d. Rewrite the system of inequalities in Part **a** so that the boundaries are not included in the region.

e. Write the equations of three different lines that divide the region in Part **a** into two parts with equal area.

2.2 Graph the region defined by each of the following inequalities:

a. $y > 4x - 3$

b. $y \leq -2x + 7$

c. $-3x + 2y \geq 6$

2.3 a. Graph the following system of inequalities:

$$\begin{cases} x + y \leq 6 \\ y \geq -2 \\ x \geq -2 \\ x \leq 4 \end{cases}$$

b. Describe the shape of the region.

c. List the coordinates of its vertices.

2.4 Use a system of linear inequalities to describe the shaded region in the graph shown on the right.

Module 13 ■ *Under the Big Top but Above the Floor*   353

Assignment

Problems suitable for use as assessment items are identified by an asterisk (*).

2.1 a. Sample graph:

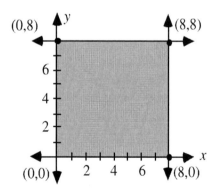

b. The shape of this region is a square.
c. (0,8), (8,8), (0,0), (8,0)
d. $x > 0$, $y > 0$, $x < 8$, $y < 8$
e. Sample response: $y = 4$, $x = 4$, and $y = x$.

2.2 Sample graphs:

a.

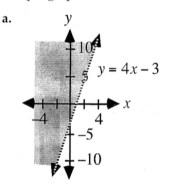

b.

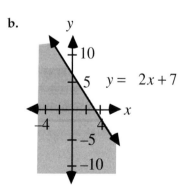

2.5 The Cronin and Nakagomi families are going camping together. At 9:00 A.M., the Cronins leave town traveling at an average speed of 90 km/hr. The Nakagomis don't leave until 9:20 A.M., but they drive at an average speed of 100 km/hr. Use a system of linear equations to determine how long it will take the Nakagomis to catch up with the Cronins. How far down the highway will the two families be before they meet?

2.6 The school library adds new books to its collection every year. According to library policy, the librarian can buy no more than 45 books each year. The number of new fiction books can be no more than half the number of nonfiction books.

   a. Let x represent the number of nonfiction books and y represent the number of fiction books. Write a system of inequalities that describes the constraints on book purchases.

   b. Graph the system of inequalities you created in Part **a.**

   c. Identify the coordinates of the points of intersection.

   d. What information do these coordinates represent?

   e. Given these constraints, what is the greatest number of fiction books the librarian can buy in a year? Justify your response.

          ✶ ✶ ✶ ✶ ✶

2.7 Graph the region defined by each of the following systems of inequalities:

   a. $y > 4x - 3$ and $y \le -2x + 7$

   b. $y \le -2x + 7$ and $-3x + 2y \ge 6$

2.8 Jasmine has $290.00 and saves $5.00 per week. Alan has $200.00 and saves $8.00 per week.

   a. Write equations that describe the amount of money each person has after any week w.

   b. In how many weeks will the two have the same amount of money?

2.9 In a basketball game, a player made at least five baskets (2 points each), at least four free throws (1 point each), and scored a total of no more than 20 points. (Assume no three-point baskets were made.)

   a. Write a system of three inequalities to describe this situation.

   b. Graph this system of inequalities. Use the horizontal axis to represent the number of baskets and the vertical axis to represent the number of free throws.

   c. List the set of ordered pairs that satisfy this system of inequalities.

c.

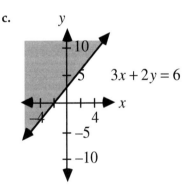

2.3 a. Sample graph:

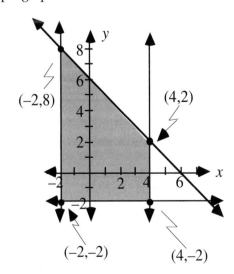

b. Students may describe the shape as a quadrilateral or a trapezoid.

c. $(-2,8), (-2,-2), (4,-2), (4,2)$

2.4 The shaded region may be described by the following system of inequalities:

$$\begin{cases} x \ge 0 \\ y \ge 0 \\ y \le -2x + 6 \text{ or } y + 2x \le 6 \end{cases}$$

2.5 Sample response: The time it takes for the Nakagomis to catch the Cronins can be found by solving the following system of equations:

$$\begin{cases} y = 90\left(x + \dfrac{1}{3}\right) \\ y = 100x \end{cases}$$

The solution $x = 3$ indicates that it will take 3 hr for the Nakagomis to catch up. Traveling at 100 km/hr, they will be 300 km down the road.

∗ 2.6 a. Sample system of equations:

$$\begin{cases} x \ge 0 \\ y \ge 0 \\ x + y \le 45 \\ y \le 0.5x \end{cases}$$

b. Sample graph:

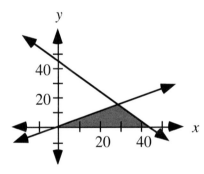

c. The points of intersection are (0,0), (45,0), and (30,15).

d. Sample response: The x-coordinate indicates the number of nonfiction books bought. The y-coordinate indicates the number of fiction books bought.

e. Sample response: The y-coordinate indicates the number of fiction books that can be purchased. The intersection point that satisfies the restrictions and has the greatest y-coordinate is (30,15).

          ✶ ✶ ✶ ✶ ✶

2.7 Sample graphs:

a.

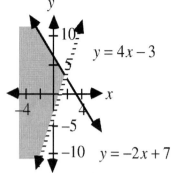

$y = 4x - 3$

$y = -2x + 7$

b.

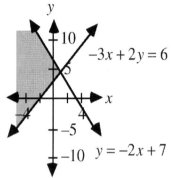

$-3x + 2y = 6$

$y = -2x + 7$

2.8 **a.** Sample response: The equation $j = 290 + 5w$ represents the amount of money for Jasmine. The equation $a = 200 + 8w$ represents the amount of money for Alan.

b. As shown below, the two must save for 30 weeks to have the same amount of money:

$$200 + 8w = 290 + 5w$$
$$w = 30$$

Note: You may point out that a given system of equations might not have integer solutions.

2.9 **a.** This situation can be described by the following system of three inequalities, where b represents the number of baskets and f represents the number of free throws:

$$\begin{cases} b \geq 5 \\ f \geq 4 \\ 2b + f \leq 20 \end{cases}$$

b. Note: In this context, both b and f must be integers. Sample graph:

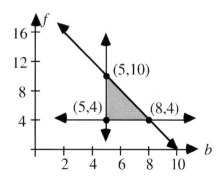

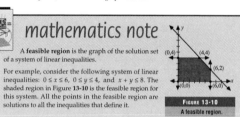

Another booth at the carnival features a game called "Roll-a-rama." This game offers many winning outcomes. In this activity, you examine the chances of winning at Roll-a-rama.

Exploration

In Roll-a-rama, players roll one white die and one red die. One roll of each die is considered a game. To win, the following must be true:

- the number on the red die must be at least 2 but no more than 5
- the sum of the two dice must be less than or equal to 7.

a. Play Roll-a-rama 10 times and record your results.

b. Determine the experimental probability of winning a game.

c. List all the possible rolls in Roll-a-rama.

d. Determine the theoretical probability of winning a game.

Discussion

a. Are you more likely to win or lose when playing Roll-a-rama?

b. Do you think it is possible to find a strategy that increases the probability of winning? Explain your response.

c. If all the possible rolls were graphed on a coordinate plane where the roll on one die is represented on the x-axis and the roll of the other die is represented on the y-axis, what would the graph look like?

mathematics note

A **feasible region** is the graph of the solution set of a system of linear inequalities.

For example, consider the following system of linear inequalities: $0 \leq x \leq 6$, $0 \leq y \leq 4$, and $x + y \leq 8$. The shaded region in Figure 13-10 is the feasible region for this system. All the points in the feasible region are solutions to all the inequalities that define it.

Figure 13-10
A feasible region.

Module 13 ■ *Under the Big Top but Above the Floor* 355

c. The set of ordered pairs that satisfy the system of inequalities is: (5,4), (6,4), (7,4), (8,4), (5,5), (6,5), (7,5), (5,6), (6,6), (7,6), (5,7), (6,7), (5,8), (6,8), (5,9), and (5,10).

ACTIVITY 3

In this activity, students are introduced to feasible regions defined by constraints.

Materials List

- graph paper (several sheets per student)
- rulers (one per student)
- red dice (one per group)
- white dice (one per group)

Technology

- graphing utility

Student Outcomes

After completing the following exploration and discussion, students should be able to:

✳ determine experimental and theoretical probabilities

✳ write and graph a system of linear inequalities

✳ determine the feasible region for a system of linear inequalities

✳ identify the corner points of the feasible region.

teacher note

You might wish to discuss the differences between discrete and continuous solution sets. Students should be able to graph and interpret both types.

Exploration

a. Sample data:

Roll No.	White Die	Red Die	Sum	Win?
1	2	6	8	no
2	2	2	4	yes
3	2	3	5	yes
4	5	6	11	no
5	3	5	8	no
6	5	3	8	no
7	4	5	9	no
8	4	1	5	no
9	2	2	4	yes
10	2	6	8	no
			Total Wins	3

b. Using the sample data given in Part **a,** the experimental probability of winning is 3/10 = 30%.

c. The following table shows one method for determining the sample space for the game.

		White Die					
		1	2	3	4	5	6
	1	lose	lose	lose	lose	lose	lose
	2	win	win	win	win	win	lose
Red	3	win	win	win	win	lose	lose
Die	4	win	win	win	lose	lose	lose
	5	win	win	lose	lose	lose	lose
	6	lose	lose	lose	lose	lose	lose

d. As shown in Part **c,** there are 36 possible outcomes, 14 of which result in a win. The theoretical probability of winning is 14/36 ≈ 0.39.

Discussion

a. There are more possible losing rolls than winning rolls, which means that players are more likely to lose. The probability of losing is 22/36; the probability of winning is 14/36.

b. Because rolls are determined by chance, there is no strategy that increases the probability of winning.

c. The graph is a set of 36 discrete points whose coordinates are the integers from 1 to 6.

d. 1. The less-than-or-equals sign (≤) in the inequalities indicates that boundary points are included in the feasible region.

2. The solid boundary lines indicate that points on the boundary lines are included.

3. Sample response: If the boundary points are not to be included, the boundary line would be dashed.

e. Note: Students should realize that this graph will be a set of discrete points rather than a continuous region bordered by lines.

1. Sample response: Shading the feasible region would imply that points with decimal coordinates are possible outcomes in Roll-a-rama, when only those points with integer coordinates are possible.

2. Sample response: The feasible region can be represented by discrete dots at the points with integer coordinates [lattice points].

Warm-Up

1. Sample graphs:

a.

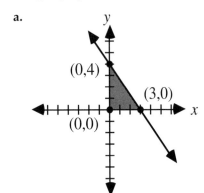

b.

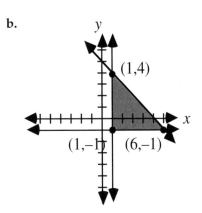

---

d. The points on the boundary lines of the feasible region in Figure 13-10 are part of the feasible region.

1. How do the inequalities that define the feasible region indicate that this is true?

2. How does the graph of the feasible region indicate that points on the boundary are included?

3. How would you change the graph if boundary points were *not* included in the feasible region?

e. The winning combinations for Roll-a-rama could be graphed as a feasible region.

1. Why might it be misleading to shade the feasible region for Roll-a-rama?

2. How might you represent the feasible region for Roll-a-rama?

Warm-Up

1. For each of the following systems of inequalities, graph the feasible region and identify the coordinates of its vertices.

a. $\begin{cases} x \geq 0 \\ y \geq 0 \\ 4x + 3y \leq 12 \end{cases}$ **b.** $\begin{cases} x \geq 1 \\ y \geq -1 \\ x + y \leq 5 \end{cases}$ **c.** $\begin{cases} 2x + 3y \leq 6 \\ x - 2y \geq -4 \\ y \geq -2 \end{cases}$

d. $\begin{cases} x \geq 3 \\ x \leq 5 \\ y \geq -2 \\ y \leq 4 \end{cases}$ **e.** $\begin{cases} x \geq 0 \\ y \geq 0 \\ y \leq 8 \\ 4x + 3y \leq 32 \end{cases}$ **f.** $\begin{cases} x - 2y \geq -10 \\ 7x + 5y \leq 44 \\ 7x + 4y \geq -16 \\ 3x - 7y \leq 28 \end{cases}$

2. Describe the constraints on the feasible region in each of the following graphs. **Note:** Each axis is marked in increments of 1 unit.

a.   **b.**

c.   **d.**

356   Module 13 ■ *Under the Big Top but Above the Floor*

c.

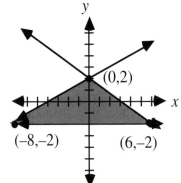

d.

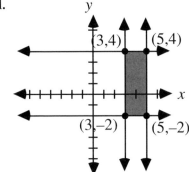

e.

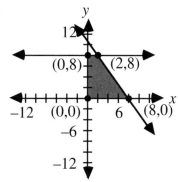

f.

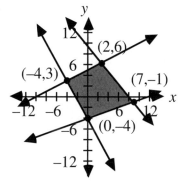

2. a. $\begin{cases} y \leq 0.75x + 1 \\ y \leq -0.75x + 1 \\ y \geq -2 \end{cases}$

b. $\begin{cases} y \geq 0.5x - 0.5 \\ y \leq -x + 4 \\ y \leq 2x + 1 \end{cases}$

c. $\begin{cases} y \leq -1.5x + 1 \\ x \geq -3 \\ y \geq -2 \\ y \leq 4 \end{cases}$

d. $\begin{cases} y \leq -0.5x + 0.5 \\ x \geq -4 \\ x \leq 3 \\ y \leq 2 \\ y \geq -4 \end{cases}$

Assignment

Problems suitable for use as assessment items are identified by an asterisk (*).

3.1 a. In these inequalities, x represents the number on the white die and y represents the number on the red die.

b. The constraint $x \geq 1$ corresponds with the fact that the roll of the white die cannot be less than 1. The constraints $y \geq 2$ and $y \leq 5$ correspond with the rule that specifies the range of winning numbers for the red die. The constraint $x + y \leq 7$ corresponds with the rule for the sum of a winning roll.

c. As shown in the following sample graph, the feasible region consists of discrete points:

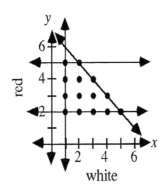

d. There are 14 possible winning rolls.

3.2 There are 4 winning rolls in these 10 games: (1,4), (3,2), (4,3), and (3,3). Students should identify these ordered pairs using the graph from Problem **3.1c.**

3.3 a. There are 22 possible losing rolls.

b. Sample response: The combinations (1,1), (6,5), and (4,4) are all losing rolls. These points are not included in the feasible region graphed in Problem **3.1c.**

3.4 Sample response: No. The y-intercept has coordinates (0,7) which indicates a roll of 0 on the white die and 7 on red die. Because these values are not included on either die, this point cannot be in the feasible region.

* 3.5 a. The number rolled on each die must be an integer from 1 to 6.

b. These constraints can be described by the following system of inequalities: $x \geq 1$, $x \leq 6$, $y \geq 1$, and $y \leq 6$, where x and y are integers. **Note:** Some students may report this solution as $1 \leq x \leq 6$ and $1 \leq y \leq 6$.

3.6 Sample response: If the constraint on the sum of the two dice is changed to $x + y \leq 8$, there will be a 50% chance of winning.

✳ ✳ ✳ ✳ ✳

Assignment

3.1 You can identify the winning combinations in Roll-a-rama by graphing a system of linear inequalities on a coordinate plane. The inequalities that define the constraints on a winning roll can be written as follows:

$$\begin{cases} x \geq 1 \\ y \geq 2 \\ y \leq 5 \\ x + y \leq 7 \end{cases}$$

a. What do x and y represent in these inequalities?

b. Describe the rule of the game that corresponds with each constraint.

c. Graph this system of inequalities on a set of coordinate axes and determine the feasible region.

d. Identify the number of points in the feasible region that represent winning rolls.

3.2 While playing Roll-a-rama, Sharline recorded each roll as an ordered pair in the form (white die, red die). In 10 games, she obtained the following rolls: (1,4), (3,2), (6,2), (4,4), (2,1), (4,3), (5,1), (3,3), (1,6), and (5,3). How many games did she win? Justify your response using your graph from Problem **3.1c.**

3.3 a. How many different losing combinations are there in Roll-a-rama?

b. List at least three of these losing combinations. Use your graph from Problem **3.1c** to explain why they do not represent winning rolls.

3.4 Is the point where the line $x + y = 7$ intersects the y-axis in the feasible region for Roll-a-rama? Explain your response.

3.5 a. What are the constraints on the region that includes all possible rolls in Roll-a-rama?

b. Write inequalities to describe these constraints.

3.6 Rewrite the rules for "Roll-a-rama" so that the probability of winning is the same as the probability of losing. To check your rules, play the new game several times and record your results.

✳ ✳ ✳ ✳ ✳

3.7 Graph the feasible region for each of the following systems of inequalities and label the vertices.

a. $\begin{cases} w \geq 0 \\ t \geq 0 \\ 2w + 3t \leq 10 \end{cases}$

b. $\begin{cases} x \geq -1 \\ y \leq 2 \\ y \geq x - 1 \end{cases}$

3.7 Sample graphs:

a.

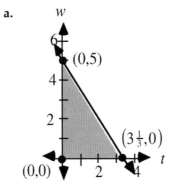

b.

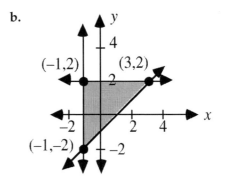

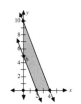

3.8 a. Describe the constraints on the feasible region shown in each of the following graphs:

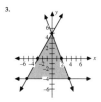

b. List the coordinates of the corner points for each feasible region in Part a.

3.9 A furniture manufacturer makes upholstered chairs and sofas. On average, each chair requires 4 hr to assemble and each sofa requires 8 hr to assemble. The company's carpenters can provide a total of no more than 124 hr of assembly work per day. Each chair also requires 2 hr to upholster, while each sofa requires 6 hr to upholster. According to contract, the company must guarantee at least 72 hr of work per day for the upholsterers.

a. Write a system of inequalities that describes the numbers of chairs and sofas that the company can build and upholster in one day.

b. Graph the feasible region described by the system you wrote in Part a and identify the coordinates of the corner points. Use the horizontal axis to represent the number of chairs and the vertical axis to represent the number of sofas. **Note:** Save your graph for use in Problem **4.3.**

3.10 A group of friends would like to order two large pizzas with extra toppings and some soft drinks. Each pizza costs $10.00. Each extra topping costs $0.50, and each soft drink costs $1.00. The group has $30.00 to spend.

* 3.9 a. In the following system of inequalities, c represents the number of chairs and s represents the number of sofas:

$$\begin{cases} c \geq 0 \\ s \geq 0 \\ 4c + 8s \leq 124 \\ 2c + 6s \geq 72 \end{cases}$$

b. The following sample graph identifies the coordinates of the corner points. Students should save this graph for use in Problem **4.3.**

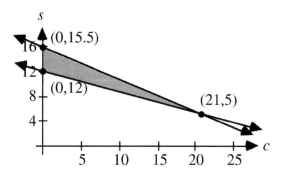

3.10 a. The constraints can be described by the following system of inequalities, where t represents the number of toppings and s represents the number of soft drinks. **Note:** In this context, both t and s must be integers.

$$\begin{cases} s \geq 0 \\ t \geq 0 \\ s + 0.5t \leq 10 \end{cases}$$

Sample graph:

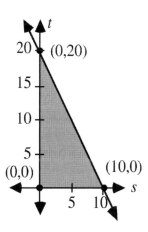

b. The coordinates of the corner points are (10,0), (0,0), and (0,20).

3.8 a. 1. $\begin{cases} x \geq 0 \\ y \geq 0 \\ y \leq -2.5x + 5 \end{cases}$

2. $\begin{cases} x \geq 0 \\ y \geq 0 \\ y \geq -2.5x + 5 \\ y \leq -2.5x + 10 \end{cases}$

3. $\begin{cases} y \geq -4 \\ y \leq \dfrac{5}{3}x + 5 \\ y \leq -2.5x + 5 \end{cases}$

b. 1. (0,0), (2,0), and (0,5)
2. (0,5), (0,10), (4,0), and (2,0)
3. (0,5), (−5.4,−4), and (3.6,−4)

ACTIVITY
4

In this activity, students write a system of inequalities to represent the constraints on a problem. Using the corner principle, they then find a solution that optimizes an objective function.

teacher note

A brief assessment of the mathematical content in Activities **3** and **4,** for use at your discretion, appears in the Teacher Resources for this module.

Materials List

- graph paper (several sheets per student)
- rulers (one per group)
- Roll-a-rama template (one per group; a blackline master appears in the Teacher Resources for this module)

Technology

- graphing utility

Student Outcomes

After completing the following exploration and discussion, students should be able to:

✴ write a system of linear inequalities to represent the constraints of a problem

✴ write an objective function for a problem

✴ use the corner principle to optimize an objective.

Exploration

a. Sample graph:

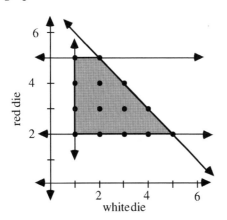

---

a. Graph the feasible region that shows the possible numbers of toppings and soft drinks that the group can order.

b. Identify the coordinates of the corner points.

ACTIVITY
4

In Roll-a-rama, each winning player receives a second roll of the dice. If the player also wins on this second roll, a score is determined based on the number showing on each die. The score is calculated using the following rules:

- the number on the white die is multiplied by 2
- the number on the red die is multiplied by 3
- the two resulting numbers are added.

The object of the second roll is to obtain as high a score as possible. This score (S) can be determined by the equation $S = 2x + 3y$, where x represents the number on the white die and y represents the number on the red die. This is called an **objective function,** because finding the best value of S is the objective.

Exploration

In this exploration, you use an objective function to help determine the maximum and minimum scores in Roll-a-rama.

a. As noted in the previous activity, players roll one red die and one white die in Roll-a-rama. To win,

- the number on the red die must be at least 2 but no more than 5
- the sum of the two dice must be less than or equal to 7.

The winning combinations can be described by a feasible region for a system of inequalities. On a copy of the Roll-a-rama template, graph the lines that define this feasible region.

b. Use the objective function to find the value of S for each roll in the feasible region. Record this information in a table with headings like those in Table **13-3.**

TABLE 13-1 ■ *Score for Each Winning Roll*

Winning Roll (x,y)	Score (S)
(1,2)	8

---

b. A completed table is show below.

Roll	Score	Roll	Score	Roll	Score
(1,2)	8	(2,2)	10	(3,2)	12
(4,2)	14	(5,2)	16	(1,3)	11
(2,3)	13	(3,3)	15	(4,3)	17
(1,4)	14	(2,4)	16	(3,4)	18
(1,5)	17	(2,5)	19		

c. **Note:** In Parts **c–e,** students graph five lines, each with a slope of –2/3. The middle three lines represent the solutions to Part **c.** The line with the greatest *y*-intercept is the solution to Part **d.** The line with the least *y*-intercept is the solution to Part **e.** Sample graph:

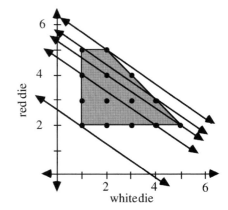

c. 1. Select two points in the feasible region with the same value for S. Draw the line that passes through these two points.

2. Write the equation of this line in the form $y = mx + b$.

3. Repeat Steps **1** and **2** for the remaining points in the feasible region.

d. 1. Use the information in Table **13-3** to identify the maximum value for S.

2. Substitute this value for S in the objective function $S = 2x + 3y$. Solve the equation for y.

3. Graph this equation on the template.

e. In Roll-a-rama, you want to find the greatest value of the objective function. In other situations, you might want to find the least value of an objective function. Repeat Part **d** for the minimum value for S.

Discussion

a. Where are the maximum and minimum values for S located on your graph from the exploration?

mathematics note

The **corner principle** helps you find the maximum or minimum values for an objective function in problems that involve a system of linear inequalities (and where the corner points are part of the feasible region). According to this principle, the maximum and minimum values of an objective function occur at corner points of the feasible region.

b. 1. What similarities did you observe among the lines graphed in Parts **c–e** of the exploration?

2. How are the equations of the lines related to the equation for S?

c. What must a player roll to obtain the greatest possible score?

Warm-Up

1. Determine the maximum and minimum value of the objective function for each set of corner points given below.

a. $V = 3x - 2y$; (2,3), (–1,2), (–4,–1), (0,–1)

b. $V = -3x + 4y$; (2,3), (–1,2), (–4,–1), (0,–1)

c. $V = -2x - y$; (2,3), (–1,2), (–4,–1), (0,–1)

The score is 14 for the points with coordinates (4,2) and (1,4). An equation of the line through these points in slope-intercept form is:

$$y = -\frac{2}{3}x + \frac{14}{3}$$

The score is 16 for the points (2,4) and (5,2). An equation of the line through these points in slope-intercept form is:

$$y = -\frac{2}{3}x + \frac{16}{3}$$

The score is 17 for the points (1,5) and (4,3). An equation of the line through these points in slope-intercept form is:

$$y = -\frac{2}{3}x + \frac{17}{3}$$

d. 1. The maximum score of 19 occurs with a roll of (2,5).

2. Students should obtain the following equation:

$$y = -\frac{2}{3}x + \frac{19}{3}$$

3. A sample graph is shown in Part **c** above.

e. 1. The minimum score of 8 occurs with a roll of (1,2).

2. Students should obtain the following equation:

$$y = -\frac{2}{3}x + \frac{8}{3}$$

3. A sample graph is shown in Part **c** on the previous page.

teacher note

In the exploration, the points on the parallel lines that intersect the feasible region are solutions to the objective function. The slope of each parallel line is the same; therefore the x-and y-coefficients remain the same. This means that the greater the y-intercept of the parallel line, the greater the value of the objective function. In this case, the corner point (2,5) produces the maximum value and the corner point (1,2) produces the minimum value for the objective function. These maximum and minimum values always occur at a corner point of a feasible region.

Discussion

a. The location of the maximum is (2,5). The location of the minimum is (1,2). Both of the points are corners of the feasible region.

b. 1. The lines are parallel (they have the same slope).

2. Each equation can be written in the form of the objective function ($S = 2x + 3y$) with a value substituted for S.

c. A player must roll a 2 on the white die and a 5 on the red die.

Warm-Up

1. a. The maximum value of 2 occurs at the corner point (0,–1). The minimum value of –10 occurs at the corner point (–4,–1).

b. The maximum value of 11 occurs at the corner point (–1,2). The minimum value of –4 occurs at the corner point (0,–1).

c. The maximum value of 9 occurs at the corner point (–4,–1). The minimum value of –7 occurs at the corner point (2,3).

2. **a.** The maximum value of 10 occurs at the corner point (4,–2). The minimum value of –22 occurs at the corner point (–4,–2).

b. The maximum value of 15 occurs at the corner point (3,1). The minimum value of –7 occurs at the corner point (–1,–1).

c. The maximum value of 2 occurs at the corner point (2,–2). The minimum value of –22 occurs at the corner point (–4,–2).

d. The maximum value of 9 occurs at the corner point (3,–1). The minimum value of –28 occurs at the corner point (–4,–4).

3. **a.** The maximum value of 15 occurs at the corner point (3,0). The minimum value of 0 occurs at the corner point (0,0).

b. The maximum value of 28 occurs at the corner point (6,–1). The minimum value of 3 occurs at the corner point (1,–1).

c. The maximum value of 26 occurs at the corner point (6,–2). The minimum value of –44 occurs at the corner point (–8,–2).

Assignment

Problems suitable for use as assessment items are identified by an asterisk (*).

4.1 a. The constraints can be represented as follows: $x + y \leq 100$, $x \leq 60$, $y \geq 10$, and $x \geq 0$. **Note:** Students should include the constraint $x \geq 0$ as part of the system, since a negative number of prizes cannot be purchased.

b. Sample graph:

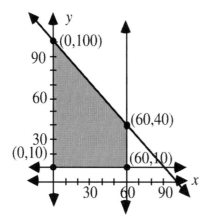

c. Answers will vary. Because prizes cannot be bought in fractional amounts, the coordinates of these points must be integers. The x-values represent the number of small prizes, and the y-values represent the number of large prizes.

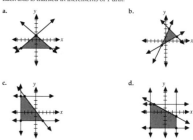

2. For each of the following feasible regions, use the corner principle to find the maximum and minimum values of the objective function $V = 4x + 3y$. **Note:** Each axis is marked in increments of 1 unit.

a. b.

c. d.

3. For each of the following systems of inequalities, use the corner principle to find the maximum and minimum values of the objective function .

a.
$\begin{cases} x \geq 0 \\ y \geq 0 \\ 4x + 3y \leq 12 \end{cases}$

b.
$\begin{cases} x \geq 1 \\ y \geq -1 \\ x + y \leq 5 \end{cases}$

c.
$\begin{cases} 2x + 3y \leq 6 \\ x - 2y \geq -4 \\ y \geq -2 \end{cases}$

Assignment

4.1 Sharline and Anton are designing a new game for the Dantzig High carnival. They already have selected two different prizes from a catalog, and need only to decide how many of each to buy. The small prizes cost 25 cents each; the large ones cost 75 cents each.

According to carnival guidelines, the game may offer no more than 100 prizes. To make the game attractive to players, Sharline and Anton want to buy at least 10 of the large prizes and no more than 60 of the small prizes.

a. Write a linear inequality for each constraint in this situation. Let x represent the number of small prizes and y represent the number of large prizes.

b. Graph your system of linear inequalities on a coordinate plane. Identify the coordinates of the vertices.

c. List the coordinates of three points in the feasible region. What does each point mean in terms of buying prizes?

> d. Sharline and Anton have decided to charge $1.00 to play the game and give each player a prize. Because they have no other expenses, their **profit** is the money they take in minus the cost of the prizes.
>
>   1. What is their profit on each small prize?
>
>   2. What is their profit on each large prize?
>
> e. Because Sharline and Anton wish to maximize profit, write an equation that describes the amount of profit (P) for each point (x,y) in the feasible region.
>
> f. Use the corner principle to find the coordinates of the point that maximizes P. Assuming that 100 people play the game, how many of each prize should they buy?
>
> 4.2 Imagine that you are responsible for managing the concession stand at the carnival. Your budget for purchasing pizza and canned soft drinks is $160.00. A six-pack of soft drinks costs $3.00. A 12-serving pizza costs $10.00. The number of soft drinks you order should not exceed the number of slices of pizza.
>
>   a. The concession stand sells pizza for $1.50 per slice. Soft drinks cost $1.00 each.
>
>   Assuming that the concession stand sells everything you purchase, write an equation that describes the profit from pizza and soft-drink sales, where p represents the number of pizzas and s represents the number of six-packs of soft drinks.
>
>   b. How many six-packs and how many pizzas should you order? Explain your response.
>
>   c. If each customer buys at most one piece of pizza and one can of soda, what is the greatest number of customers you can serve while earning the maximum profit? What is the least number? Explain your responses.
>
> ★ ★ ★ ★ ★
>
> 4.3 The furniture company described in Problem **3.9** earns a profit of $50.00 on each chair and $80.00 on each sofa.
>
>   a. Write an equation that describes the company's profit from sales of sofas and chairs.
>
>   b. Using your graph from Problem **3.9**, determine the number of sofas and chairs the company should make each day to maximize profit.

d. **1.** The profit on each small prize is $0.75.
  2. The profit on each large prize is $0.25.

e. $P = 0.75x + 0.25y$

f. The maximum profit ($55.00) occurs at the point with coordinates (60,40). Anton and Sharline should buy 60 of the small prizes and 40 of the large prizes. **Note:** When applying the corner principle to locate this point, students should evaluate the objective function at every vertex.

* 4.2 a. One possible equation is $P = 3s + 8p$, where P represents profit in dollars, s represents the number of six-packs and, p represents number of pizzas. **Note:** Students should recognize that this equation must be expressed in terms of six-packs and whole pizzas. Profit is described in terms of single soft drinks and single servings of pizza.

b. The system of inequalities that describes the constraints in this situation is shown below:

$$\begin{cases} s \geq 0 \\ p \geq 0 \\ 3s + 10p \leq 160 \\ 6s \leq 12p \end{cases}$$

The following sample graph shows the feasible region described by this system.

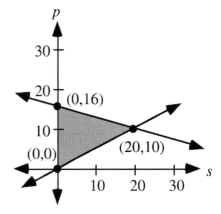

The maximum profit of $140.00 occurs at the corner point (20,10). This indicates that 20 six-packs and 10 pizzas should be ordered.

c. Sample response: By ordering 20 six-packs and 10 pizzas, there are 120 soft drinks and 120 slices of pizza available. If each customer bought both a soft drink and a pizza, you would serve 120 customers. If each customer bought only one or the other, you would serve 240 customers.

4.3 a. One possible equation is $P = 50c + 80s$, where P represents profit in dollars, c represents the number of chairs, and s represents the number of sofas.

b. The maximum profit of $1450 occurs when the company makes 21 chairs and 5 sofas.

4.4 a. The system of inequalities that describes the constraints in this situation is shown below, where s represents the number of scientific calculators and g represents the number of graphing calculators:

$$\begin{cases} s \geq 0 \\ g \geq 0 \\ s + g \leq 240 \\ 10s + 20g \leq 3200 \end{cases}$$

Sample graph:

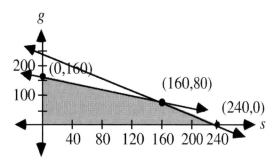

b. $P = 9s + 15g$

c. The maximum profit of $2640 occurs at the corner point (160,80). The company should make 160 scientific calculators and 80 graphing calculators.

4.4 Imagine that you are a production manager at an electronics company. Your company makes two types of calculators: a scientific calculator and a graphing calculator.

a. Each model uses the same plastic case and the same circuits. However, the graphing calculator requires 20 circuits and the scientific calculator requires only 10. The company has 240 plastic cases and 3200 circuits in stock. Graph the system of inequalities that represents these constraints.

b. The profit on a scientific calculator is $9.00, while the profit on a graphing calculator is $15.00. Write an equation that describes the company's profit from calculator sales.

c. How many of each type of calculator should the company produce to maximize profit using the stock on hand?

Summary Assessment

Instead of having a game booth, the Dantzig High Pep Club has decided to sell "Spirit Animals" at the carnival. The following illustration shows a Spirit Animal.

Spirit Animals are made from pompons and come in two sizes: small and large. Small animals require 1 pompon, and large animals require 3 pompons. The club has 270 pompons.

Seven members of the club have agreed to work for 30 min each making animals. It takes 1 min to make a small animal and 1.5 min to make a large animal.

The club plans to sell large animals for 90 cents each and small animals for 65 cents each. The club paid 5 cents for each pompon. Your job is to help the Pep Club maximize their profit.

1. Choose variables to represent the numbers of each size of Spirit Animal the club can make.

2. The project is limited by the number of pompons available. Consider how many pompons are needed for each size of animal. Write the linear inequalities for these constraints.

3. The number of minutes that members can work on the project is also limited. Consider how much time is needed to make each size of animal. Write the linear inequalities for these constraints.

4. Graph the linear inequalities from Problems **2** and **3** on a coordinate plane and shade the feasible region.

5. What is the profit on each size of animal?

6. Assuming that club members sell every animal they make, write an equation to describe the club's profit.

7. How many of each size of Spirit Animal should the Pep Club make to maximize profit?

8. Describe the steps you used to find the maximum profit.

teacher note

An additional assessment, for use at your discretion, appears in the Teacher Resources for this module.

Summary Assessment

1. **Note:** The assignment of x and y to the two sizes of Spirit Animals will affect the appearance of the system of inequalities but will not change the maximum profit. In the following sample responses, x represents the number of large animals and y represents the number of small animals.

2. $3x + y \leq 270$, $x \geq 0$, and $y \geq 0$

3. $1.5x + y \leq 210$, $x \geq 0$, and $y \geq 0$

4. Sample graph:

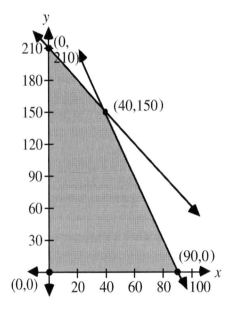

5. The profit for large animals is $0.90 - 3(\$0.05) = \$0.75$ each. The profit for small animals is $0.65 - \$0.05 = \$0.60$ each.

6. $P = 0.75x + 0.60y$

7. The maximum profit of $126.00 occurs at $(0,210)$. The Pep Club should make 210 small animals and no large animals.

8. Answers will vary. Students should describe generating inequalities to define a feasible region, identifying the vertices of the feasible region, evaluating the objective function for each of the vertices, identifying the vertex that produces the maximum profit, and interpreting the meaning of the coordinates of that vertex.

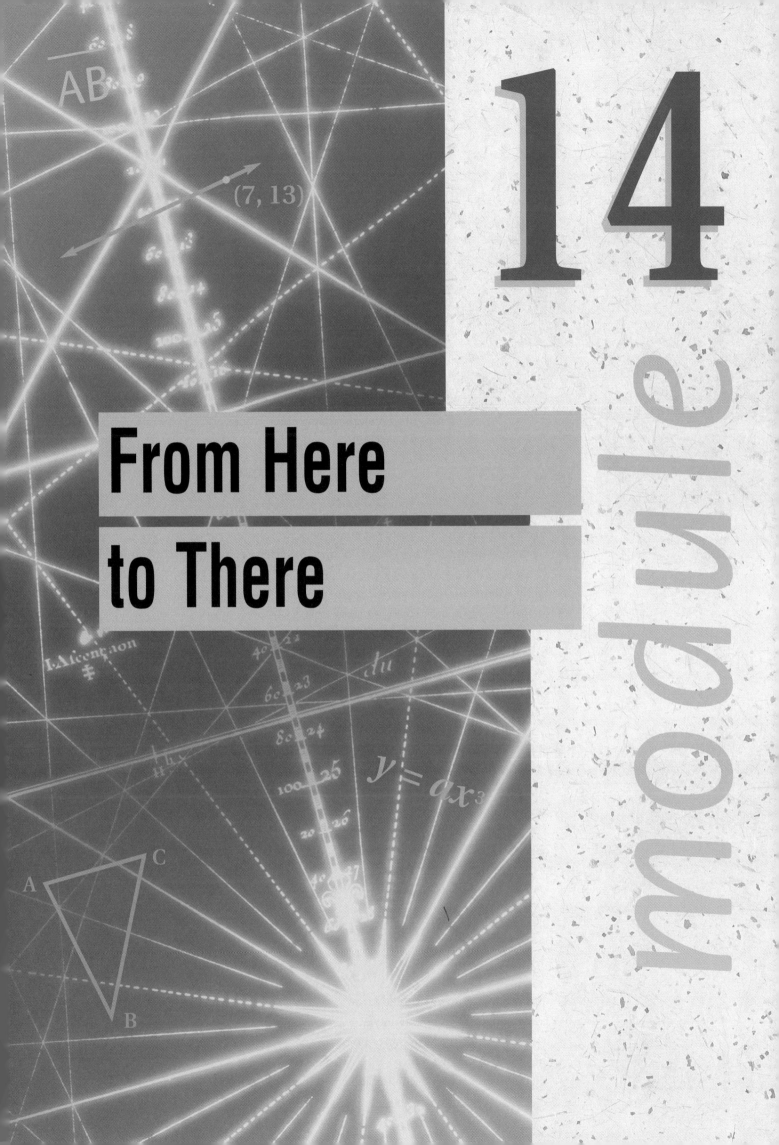

From Here to There

14

module

Overview

Students investigate the use of three-dimensional coordinate systems in the context of topographic maps.

Introduction:	Students are introduced to topographic maps, contour lines, and how to interpret them.
Activity 1:	Students create a three-dimensional model and its corresponding topographic map. They then plot points on a three-dimensional coordinate system.
Activity 2:	Students use the Pythagorean theorem to develop and apply the distance formula for two points in three dimensions.
Activity 3:	Students develop topographic profiles and use them to find distances between two points.

Objectives

In this module, students will:
* create and interpret topographic maps (1, 2, 3)
* create and use three-dimensional coordinate systems (1, 2, 3)
* plot points in three-dimensional space (1, 2)
* apply a three-dimensional coordinate system to a topographic map (1)
* identify points in space using ordered triples (1, 2, 3)
* determine geometric representations when one variable or more is fixed in an ordered triple (1)
* create a possible topographic map given a profile of the terrain (1, 3)
* describe a locus of points that satisfy a given condition (2)
* calculate distances between points in three dimensions using the Pythagorean theorem (2)
* develop a distance formula in three dimensions (2)
* apply the distance formula for points in three dimensions (2, 3)
* coordinatize locations given a reference point (2, 3)
* interpret the terrain between two points on a topographic map (2, 3)
* develop a profile given a segment connecting two points on a topographic map (3)
* analyze how changing the scale affects the profile (3)
* describe how the distance between two points on a topographic map can be approximated using a profile (3)
* use right-triangle trigonometry to determine the measures of angles and sides of right triangles (3)
* determine angles of elevation (3).

Prerequisites

For this module, students should know:
* how to interpret scale drawings
* how to describe the locations of points in space
* the Pythagorean theorem
* how to calculate trigonometric ratios and their inverses

* how to convert between units of measure
* how to apply the distance formula in a coordinate plane.

 Flashbacks, for use at your discretion, appear in the Teacher Resources for this module. These brief problem sets provide a review of some prerequisite skills for each activity.

Planning Guide

Activity	Materials	Technology	Time Line
Introduction and Activity **1**	■ ruler ■ glue ■ unlined paper ■ straightedge ■ cardboard ■ utility knife ■ tape ■ three-dimensional graph paper (optional) ■ three-dimensional coordinate system (optional) ■ rectangular box (optional)	■ none	3 days
Activity **2**	■ ruler ■ three-dimensional graph paper (optional) ■ three-dimensional coordinate system (optional) ■ rectangular box (optional)	■ none	3 days
Activity **3**	■ straightedge ■ topographic map ■ graph paper ■ lined notebook paper ■ three-dimensional coordinate system (optional)	■ none	2 days
Assessment Activities	■ ruler ■ lined notebook paper	■ none	3 days **Total: 11 days**

teacher note

This module focuses on the plotting and interpreting of points in the form (x,y,z) on a two-dimensional model of a three-dimensional coordinate system.

Following the exploration in Activity **1,** you might wish to demonstrate how to plot and interpret ordered triples on three-dimensional graph paper. A template for three-dimensional graph paper appears in the Teacher Resources for this module. Students should understand that plotting must be done neatly and accurately for a two-dimensional representation of a point in space to be interpreted correctly.

If students have difficulty visualizing the position of a point in space using a two-dimensional model, it might be helpful to employ a three-dimensional model, such as a rectangular box. When using a box, one corner can be designated as the origin. After designating the x-; y-, and z-axes, students then should be able to identify the coordinates of the other corners of the box.

A blackline master of a topographic map also appears in the Teacher Resources. As an alternative, you may use a topographic map of a region near your school. Topographic maps can be purchased at many sporting goods stores. They also might be available at the local library or in some government offices.

Introduction

Students are introduced to topographic maps and their uses.

Student Outcomes

After completing the following discussion, students should be able to:

✳ interpret topographic maps

✳ describe the three-dimensional characteristics of terrain depicted on a flat map.

Discussion

a. A topographic map shows the terrain from a perspective above the earth's surface.

b. The quantities represent elevation above sea level.

c. Sample response: The contour line at *A* should read 800 m because it represents the next level in elevation. **Note:** Some contour maps do not follow a fixed interval rigidly.

d. Sample response: The ratio of the change in elevation between two consecutive contour lines to the distance between them describes the slope of the terrain. If the ratio is small, the terrain has a gentle slope. If the ratio is large, the terrain is steep.

e. 1. Sample response: I would make an estimate based on the location of the point within the two contour lines. For example, if the point were halfway between the 100-m line and the 200-m line, I would estimate that its elevation is about 150 m.

 2. Sample response: The terrain between the two lines could have a very gradual slope for most of the distance and then rise sharply as it nears the second contour line. For example, a cliff 50 m high might not show up at all on a map with 100-m contour intervals.

f. Sample response: The north side is steeper than the south side because the space between the contour lines is narrower. The V-shaped pattern of the lines may indicate a ridge.

Introduction

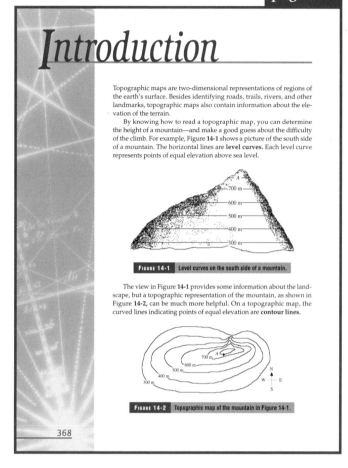

Topographic maps are two-dimensional representations of regions of the earth's surface. Besides identifying roads, trails, rivers, and other landmarks, topographic maps also contain information about the elevation of the terrain.

By knowing how to read a topographic map, you can determine the height of a mountain—and make a good guess about the difficulty of the climb. For example, Figure 14-1 shows a picture of the south side of a mountain. The horizontal lines are **level curves**. Each level curve represents points of equal elevation above sea level.

FIGURE 14-1   Level curves on the south side of a mountain.

The view in Figure **14-1** provides some information about the landscape, but a topographic representation of the mountain, as shown in Figure **14-2**, can be much more helpful. On a topographic map, the curved lines indicating points of equal elevation are **contour lines**.

FIGURE 14-2   Topographic map of the mountain in Figure **14-1**.

368

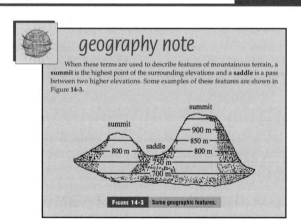

geography note

When these terms are used to describe features of mountainous terrain, a **summit** is the highest point of the surrounding elevations and a **saddle** is a pass between two higher elevations. Some examples of these features are shown in Figure **14-3**.

FIGURE 14-3   Some geographic features.

Discussion

a. From what perspective does a topographic map show the earth's surface?

b. In Figure **14-1**, what do the quantities expressed in meters represent?

c. In Figure **14-2**, what is the elevation at contour line *A*?

d. On a topographic map, moving from one contour line to the next consecutive line indicates a constant change in altitude. However, the contour lines themselves might not be evenly spaced.

 What is indicated by the space between two consecutive contour lines? Explain your response.

e. 1. How would you estimate the elevation of a point between two contour lines?

 2. What physical characteristics of the terrain could make this estimate inaccurate?

f. How does the south side of the mountain in Figure **14-1** compare with its north side?

ACTIVITY 1

In this activity, you create a topographic map for a three-dimensional surface of your own design. To investigate some of the features of your map, you use a three-dimensional coordinate system.

Exploration

When trying to visualize a mountain from a topographic map, it might help to build a three-dimensional model of the terrain. In this exploration, you build a model that contains a saddle, a summit, a cliff, and a lake. At the same time, you create a topographic map of your model on a coordinate plane. **Note:** Read the instructions in Parts **a–g** before beginning your model.

a. Draw a pair of coordinate axes on a large sheet of paper (at least 60 cm by 28 cm).

b. 1. On a sheet of cardboard slightly smaller than the paper in Part **a**, sketch the outline of the base of a mountain, such as the example shown in Figure **14-4**. Cut out this base.

| FIGURE 14-4 | Outline of the base of a mountain. |

2. Trace the outline of the cardboard base on the coordinate plane, as shown in Figure **14-5**. This is the first contour line of your topographic map.

| FIGURE 14-5 | Coordinate plane with first contour. |

370   Module 14 ■ *From Here to There*

ACTIVITY 1

To help visualize three-dimensional landscapes from two-dimensional representations, students build a three-dimensional model of a mountain and construct the corresponding topographic map.

teacher note

A brief assessment of the mathematical content in Activity **1,** for use at your discretion, appears in the Teacher Resources for this module.

Materials List

- large sheets of paper, at least 60 cm by 28 cm (one per group)
- clear adhesive tape or quick-drying glue
- ruler or straightedge (one per group)
- thick cardboard (several sheets per group; cardboard boxes are a good source)
- utility knife (one per group)

---

teacher note

During the exploration, you might wish to display several photographs of mountains and lakes.

Following the exploration, students might find it helpful to create a model coordinate system using card stock, labeling the xy-, xz-, and yz-planes as shown below.

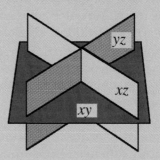

A template for this model, along with a template for three-dimensional graph paper, is included in the Teacher Resources for this module.

- three-dimensional graph paper (optional)
- three-dimensional coordinate system (optional)
- rectangular box (optional)

Student Outcomes

After completing the following exploration and discussion, students should be able to:

✳ build a three-dimensional model of a landscape

✳ create a topographic map with a rectangular coordinate system

✳ interpret data from a topographic map

✳ determine three-dimensional coordinates for points on a topographic map.

Exploration

a–f. Students create a three-dimensional cardboard model of a mountain that includes a cliff, a summit, a lake, and a saddle. The model consists of 10 layers of cardboard shapes, each representing the terrain at a given elevation. While building the cardboard model, students also create the corresponding topographic map.

Note: You might wish to remind students to read the instructions for the entire exploration before beginning their models.

g. Students create a scale for their model and topographic map using the thickness of the cardboard to represent 100 m.

h–i. Students use ordered pairs and ordered triples to describe the summits of their mountains.

Discussion

a. Sample response: Our cliff is represented by several contour lines that converge to form one line. Our lake is represented by a shaded region. Our saddle is represented as the lowest elevation between two summits. Our summit is located inside the region defined by the highest contour line.

b. Sample response: An ordered triple indicates not only the location of the summit, but also its height.

c. Differences in methods might produce a variety of measurements for similar sheets of cardboard. For example, students who directly measure one layer may get significantly different results from students who measure five layers and divide by 5.

c. 1. Trace the outline of the base on another sheet of cardboard. Using the tracing as a guide, draw the next contour of the mountain. As shown in Figure **14-6,** make this contour slightly smaller than the base.

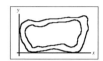

top view   side view

FIGURE 14-6   Cardboard with first and second levels.

2. Cut out this second level and place it on the coordinate plane inside the outline of the base. Trace the outline of the second contour on the plane, as shown in Figure **14-7.**

FIGURE 14-7   Topographic map of first two levels.

d. Trace the outline of the second level on another sheet of cardboard to create a guide for the third contour. Then tape or glue the second level to the base in the same relative position as the contour lines on the coordinate plane.

e. Cut out the third level and place it on the coordinate plane inside the second contour. Trace the outline of the third contour on the plane.

f. Repeat the process described in Parts **d** and **e** until you have created a complete model of a mountain along with its topographic map. Your model should consist of 10 layers of cardboard; the map should have 10 contour lines. Both should include the following geographic features:

1. a lake   2. a summit

3. a saddle   4. a cliff at least half as high as the summit.

g. Measure the thickness of one layer of cardboard. Let this distance represent 100 m in elevation and 100 m along the x- and y-axes on your topographic map.

h. Use your map to identify an ordered pair (x,y) that represents the location of the summit.

i. Identify an ordered triple (x,y,z), where z represents elevation, that designates the location of the summit.

mathematics note

Three-dimensional coordinate systems typically are represented by graphs like the ones shown in Figure **14-8.** The x- and y-axes determine the xy-plane. The z-axis is used to help depict points above, below, or on the xy-plane. The x- and z-axes determine the xz-plane, while the y- and z-axes determine the yz-plane.

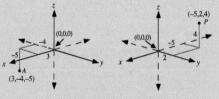

FIGURE 14-8   Three-dimensional graphs.

The coordinates of a point in this type of three-dimensional coordinate system form an **ordered triple,** (x,y,z). For example, the coordinates of point A in Figure **14-8** are $(3,-4,-5)$. In other words, the x-coordinate of point A is 3, the y-coordinate is -4, and the z-coordinate is -5, which indicates that point A is located 5 units below the xy-plane. Similarly, the coordinates of point P are $(-5,2,4)$, which means that its x-coordinate is -5, its y-coordinate is 2, and it is located 4 units above the xy-plane.

The **origin** is the point where the three axes intersect. The origin has coordinates $(0,0,0)$ because at that point $x = 0$, $y = 0$, and $z = 0$.

Discussion

a. Describe how the cliff, lake, saddle, and summit are represented on your topographic map.

b. Why does an ordered triple provide more information about the summit than an ordered pair?

c. Compare the method you used to find the thickness of one layer of cardboard with the methods used by others in your class.

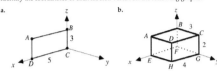

d. Describe the z-coordinate of all the points that represent the surface of your lake.

e. Describe how to draw a path that provides a gradual ascent from the lake to the summit on your topographic map.

Warm-Up

To complete the following problems, assume that the orientation of each coordinate system is as shown in Figure **14-8**.

1. **a.** Is the z-coordinate of a point above the xy-plane positive or negative?

   b. What is the x-coordinate of a point on the yz-plane?

   c. If the y-coordinate of a point is positive, what is its relationship to the xz-plane?

2. Describe the location of a point with coordinates $(-5,-4,-6)$ on a three-dimensional coordinate system.

3. Identify the coordinates of each labeled vertex on the following graphs.

   a.   **b.**

Assignment

1.1 Using your cardboard model from the exploration, locate a point on the top of the cliff. Locate another point at the bottom of the cliff, directly below the first one. Label the two points C_1 and C_2.

   a. Identify an ordered triple for each point.

   b. How do the coordinates of the ordered triples $C_1(x_1,y_1,z_1)$ and compare $C_2(x_2,y_2,z_2)$?

   c. What geometric figure is formed by the set of all points with coordinates (x,y,z) where the x- and y-coordinates are held constant? Explain your response.

   d. Where are the points that correspond to ordered triples such as C_1 and C_2 located on a topographic map?

---

d. Students should recognize that all points on the surface of the lake share the same z-coordinate.

e. Students should suggest drawing a path that contains relatively long segments from one elevation to the next.

Warm-Up

1. The following responses assume that the axes are oriented as shown in Figure **14-8**.

   a. When a point is located above the xy-plane, its z-coordinate is positive.

   b. The x-coordinate of a point on the yz-plane is 0.

   c. If the y-coordinate of a point is positive, it is located to the right of the xz-plane.

2. Sample response: When viewed from the first octant, the point $(-5,-4,-6)$ is below the xy-plane, behind the yz-plane, and to the left of the xz-plane. A sample sketch follows.

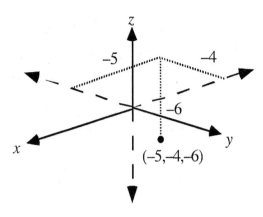

3. **a.** A (5,0,3); B (0,0,3); C (0,0,0); D (5,0,0)

   b. A (4,0,2); B (0,0,2); C (0,3,2); D (4,3,2); E (4,0,0); F (0,0,0); G (0,3,0); H (4,3,0)

teacher note

In Problems **1.3** and **1.6**, the precise shapes of contour lines cannot be determined from the information given. As a result, student responses may vary greatly. You might wish to ask several students to present their maps to the class, and defend their reasoning.

Assignment

Problems suitable for use as assessment items are identified by an asterisk (*).

1.1 **a.** Answers will vary. The ordered triples should have the same x- and y-coordinates.

   b. Sample response: The x- and y-coordinates are the same. The z-coordinates differ.

   c. The figure is a vertical line.

   d. Sample response: These points are represented by the same point on the topographic map.

1.2 **a.** Answers will vary. The ordered triples should have the same z-coordinate.

  b. Sample response: The x- and y-coordinates are different while the z-coordinates are identical.

  c. The figure is a horizontal plane.

1.3 Student maps may vary greatly. Sample response:

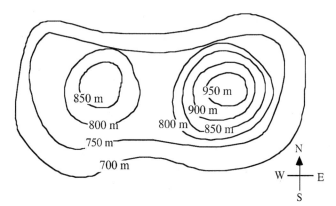

* **1.4** **a.** Sample response: Point A is on a cliff 300 m high because there is no visible space between the contour lines. Point B is in a ravine or gully at an elevation between 600 and 700 m.

  b. The coordinates of A are $(400, 500, z)$, where $800 \leq z \leq 1100$. The coordinates of B are approximately $(500, 150, z)$, where $600 \leq z \leq 700$.

✴ ✴ ✴ ✴ ✴

1.5 Student maps should resemble a series of concentric circles. The elevations of the contour lines will vary.

1.2 Using your cardboard model from the exploration, label two points L_1 and L_2 on opposite shores of the lake.

  a. Identify an ordered triple for each point.

  b. How do the coordinates of the ordered triples $L_1(x_1,y_1,z_1)$ and $L_2(x_2,y_2,z_2)$ compare?

  c. What geometric figure is formed by the set of all points with coordinates (x,y,z) where the z-coordinate is held constant? Explain your response.

1.3 The diagram below shows the north side of a mountain. Draw a topographic map that might represent this terrain.

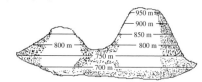

1.4 Use the topographic map below to complete Parts **a** and **b**.

  a. Describe the features of the terrain at points A and B.

  b. Identify the locations of points A and B using ordered triples.

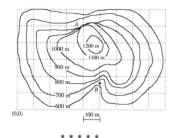

✴ ✴ ✴ ✴ ✴

1.5 Create a topographic map for a right circular cone using at least five contour lines and your own grid system.

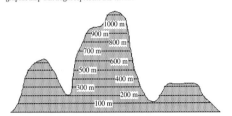

1.6 The diagram below shows the south side of a mountain range. Draw a topographic map that might represent this terrain.

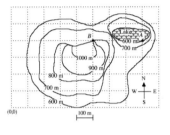

1.7 Use the topographic map below to complete Parts **a** and **b**.

 a. Describe the features of the terrain around points *A* and *B*.

 b. Identify the locations of points *A* and *B* using ordered triples.

ACTIVITY 2

In previous modules, you calculated distances in one or two dimensions. Finding the distance from the base of a mountain to its summit, however, could require the use of three-dimensional coordinates.

Module 14 ■ *From Here to There* 375

1.6 Student maps may vary greatly. Sample response:

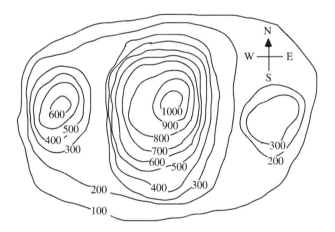

1.7 **a.** Sample response: Point *A* is on the shore of a lake at an elevation of 600 m. Point *B* is somewhere on a cliff 200 m high.

 b. The ordered triple for point *A* is (800, 400, 600). The ordered triple for point *B* is (500, 400, z), where $800 \leq z \leq 1000$.

ACTIVITY 2

Students work with simple three-dimensional spaces to discover the distance formula in three dimensions. They then use this equation to determine distances on topographic maps.

Materials List

■ rulers (one per student)

■ three-dimensional graph paper (optional)

■ three-dimensional coordinate system (optional)

■ rectangular box (optional)

teacher note

Templates for three-dimensional graph paper and a three-dimensional coordinate system are included in the Teacher Resources for this module.

You might wish to conduct Parts **c** or **d** of the exploration as a class activity. To help students visualize the scenario, you may use a rectangular box, designating one of its diagonals as the segment with the given endpoints. Ask students to identify the coordinates of the other corners of the box, to determine the lengths of the sides of the box, and, finally, to find the length of the diagonal.

Student Outcomes

After completing the following exploration and discussion, students should be able to:

✳ plot points on a three-dimensional coordinate system

✳ use the Pythagorean theorem to determine the distance between two points in three dimensions

✳ develop a formula for finding the distance between ordered triples.

Exploration

a. 1. $P_1(0,0,0)$, $P_2(3,4,0)$, $P_3(3,4,2)$

2. $\sqrt{3^2 + 4^2} = 5$

3. 2

4. $\sqrt{2^2 + 5^2} \approx 5.39$

b. 1. The coordinates of P_2 are (6,3,0). The horizontal distance is $\sqrt{(6-0)^2 + (3-0)^2} = \sqrt{45} \approx 6.71$. The vertical distance is $(4-0) = 4$. The distance from P_1 to P_3 is therefore:

$$\sqrt{\left(\sqrt{45}\right)^2 + \left(4\right)^2} = \sqrt{61} \approx 7.81$$

2. The coordinates of P_4 are (6,0,4). The distance from P_1 to P_4 in the xz-plane is $\sqrt{(6-0)^2 + (4-0)^2} = \sqrt{52} \approx 7.21$. The distance from P_4 to P_3 is $(3-0) = 3$. The distance from P_1 to P_3 is:

$$\sqrt{\left(\sqrt{52}\right)^2 + \left(3\right)^2} = \sqrt{61} \approx 7.81$$

3. Regardless of the triangle used, the distance from P_1 to P_3 is the same.

c. 1. Sample graph:

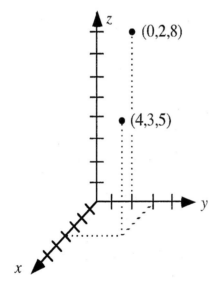

2. The horizontal distance is $\sqrt{(4-0)^2 + (3-2)^2} \approx 4.12$. The vertical distance is $|8-5| = 3$, so the distance is $\sqrt{(4.12)^2 + (3)^2} \approx 5.10$.

d. Students derive the distance formula for two points in three dimensions. See the solution to Discussion b.

mathematics note

As Figure **14-9** demonstrates, the Pythagorean theorem can be used to derive a formula for the distance between any two points, (x_1,y_1) and (x_2,y_2), on a coordinate plane.

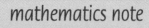

FIGURE 14-9 Distance between two points on a coordinate plane.

According to the **distance formula**, the distance d between (x_1,y_1) and (x_2,y_2) is:

$$d = \sqrt{(x_2 - x_1)^2 + (y_2 - y_1)^2}$$

For example, consider the points (–2,5) and (–4,–6). Using the distance formula, the distance between these two points can be found as follows:

$$d = \sqrt{(-4 - (-2))^2 + (-6 - 5)^2}$$
$$= \sqrt{(-2)^2 + (-11)^2} = \sqrt{125} \approx 11.18$$

Exploration

In this exploration, you develop a method for finding the distance between any two points in a three-dimensional coordinate system.

Figure **14-10** shows a three-dimensional coordinate system and three points, P_1, P_2, and P_3. Each unit on the coordinate system represents 1 m. Each edge of the rectangular prism in Figure **14-10** either coincides with or is parallel to one of the axes.

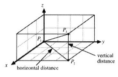

FIGURE 14-10 A three-dimensional coordinate system.

a. One way to find the length of the segment with endpoints P_1 and P_3 is through the following steps.

1. Identify the coordinates of P_1, P_2, and P_3.

2. Find the distance between P_1 and P_2. This is the horizontal distance between P_1 and P_3.

3. Find the distance between P_2 and P_3. This is the vertical distance between P_1 and P_3.

4. Use the fact that triangle $P_1P_2P_3$ is a right triangle to find the distance between P_1 and P_3.

b. The three-dimensional coordinate system in Figure **14-11** shows two right triangles $P_1P_2P_3$ and $P_1P_3P_4$, with right angles at P_2 and P_4. The coordinates of P_3 are (6,3,4), $\overline{P_2P_3}$ is parallel to the z-axis, and $\overline{P_3P_4}$ is parallel to the y-axis.

1. Find the coordinates of P_2, a point in the xy-plane. Use these coordinates to find the distance from P_1 to P_3.

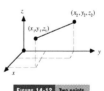

FIGURE 14-11 Two right triangles.

2. Find the coordinates of P_4, a point in the xz-plane. Use these coordinates to find the distance from P_1 to P_3.

3. Compare the distance found in Step **2** with the distance in Step **1**.

c. Draw and label a three-dimensional coordinate system.

1. Plot the two points with coordinates (4,3,5) and (0,2,8).

2. Find the distance between these two points. *Hint:* Draw right triangles.

d. The three-dimensional coordinate system in Figure **14-12** shows the locations of two points with coordinates (x_1,y_1,z_1) and (x_2,y_2,z_2). Find the distance between the two points.

FIGURE 14-12 Two points.

Discussion

a. How many times did you use the Pythagorean theorem to find the distance between P_1 and P_3 in Figure **14-10**?

b. How would you find the distance between any two points (x_1, y_1, z_1) and (x_2, y_2, z_2)? Express your method using a mathematical formula.

c. Describe how you could find the distance between points A and B on the topographic map in Figure **14-13**.

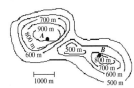

FIGURE 14-13 A topographic map.

Warm-Up

1. Find the distance between each of the following pairs of points.
   a. (9,14) and (4,1)
   b. (–12,8) and (7,–4)
   c. (–3,–6) and (–9,8)

2. Draw and label a three-dimensional coordinate system.
   a. Plot the two points with coordinates (5,0,2) and (2,2,4).
   b. Find the distance between these points.

3. Draw and label a three-dimensional coordinate system.
   a. Plot the two points with coordinates (3,4,2) and (5,4,0).
   b. Find the distance between these points.

---

teacher note

In Problems **2** and **3**, some students might use the distance formula developed in Part **b** of the discussion. Others might use right triangles to determine the distance. Each sample graphs shows one set of right triangles that could be used to determine the distance between the two given points.

Warm-Up

1. **a.** $d = \sqrt{(9 - 4)^2 + (14 - 1)^2} \approx 13.9$

   b. $d = \sqrt{(-12 - 7)^2 + (8 - (-4))^2} \approx 22.5$

   c. $d = \sqrt{(-3 - (-9))^2 + (-6 - 8)^2} \approx 15.2$

2. **a.** Sample graph:

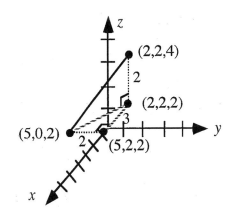

   b. The distance between the two points is:

   $$\sqrt{(2 - 5)^2 + (2 - 0)^2 + (4 - 2)^2} \approx 4.12$$

3. **a.** Sample graph:

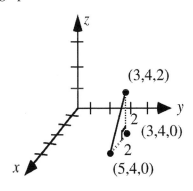

   b. The distance between the two points is:

   $$\sqrt{(3 - 5)^2 + (4 - 4)^2 + (2 - 0)^2} \approx 2.83$$

Discussion

a. The Pythagorean theorem is applied two times.

b. The distance formula for two points in three dimensions is:

$$\text{distance} = \sqrt{(x_2 - x_1)^2 + (y_2 - y_1)^2 + (z_2 - z_1)^2}$$

The distance between two points in a coordinate plane is:

$$\text{distance} = \sqrt{(x_2 - x_1)^2 + (y_2 - y_1)^2}$$

In three dimensions, the square of the difference between the z-coordinates is added to the sum of the squares of the differences between the x- and y-coordinates under the radical.

c. Sample response: Use the scale on the map to determine the horizontal distance between the points, and the contour lines to determine the vertical distance. Then use the Pythagorean theorem to find the actual distance between them.

Assignment

Problems suitable for use as assessment items are identified by an asterisk (*).

2.1 a. Sample response:

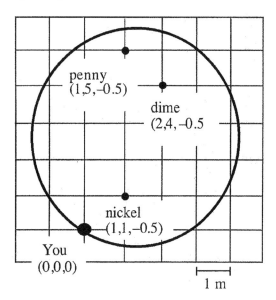

b. The distance to the nickel is:

$$\sqrt{(1)^2 + (1)^2 + (-0.5)^2} = 1.5 \text{ m}$$

The distance to the dime is:

$$\sqrt{(2)^2 + (4)^2 + (-0.5)^2} = 4.5 \text{ m}$$

The distance to the penny is:

$$\sqrt{(1)^2 + (5)^2 + (-0.5)^2} \approx 5.1 \text{ m}$$

2.2 a. The set of points is a sphere with a radius of 3 cm and center at the given point.

b. The set of points is a right circular cylinder whose height corresponds to the length of the segment and whose base has a radius of 3 cm. At each end of the cylinder is a hemisphere with a radius of 3 cm.

c. The set of points is a plane perpendicular to the plane containing the two parallel lines. It intersects the plane containing the two lines halfway between them.

d. The set of points is two parallel planes 6 cm apart, one on each side of the given plane.

Assignment

2.1 At the local wishing well, you throw in three coins—a dime, a nickel, and a penny. They land in the well as shown in the following diagram.

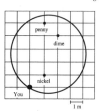

a. The depth of the water in the well is 0.5 m. If the surface of the water is the *xy*-plane and you are at the origin, identify the location of each coin as an ordered triple.

b. Determine the distance from yourself to each coin.

2.2 Describe the set of all points in space that are:

  a. 3 cm from a point   **b.** 3 cm from a segment

  c. equidistant from two parallel lines   **d.** 3 cm from a plane.

2.3 The figure below shows a topographic map of the terrain surrounding a lake, including four houses designated *A*, *B*, *C*, and *D*.

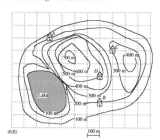

Module 14 ■ *From Here to There*   379

Use the map to find the distance between each of the following pairs of houses:

a. *A* and *B*

b. *B* and *C*

c. *C* and *D*

d. *A* and *D*.

2.4 The following diagram shows a topographic map of a region of the ocean floor. In this case, the contour lines represent distances below the surface of the ocean. For example, –850 indicates 850 m below sea level. The ocean floor for this region is 1000 m deep.

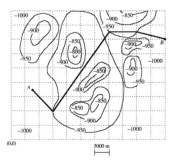

a. The captain of a submarine must navigate from point *A* to point *B* along the path shown. Assume that the submarine is 10 m above the floor at each point along the path. What are the coordinates of point *A*, point *B*, and each point where the path turns?

b. The submarine must travel no closer than 10 m but no more than 25 m above the ocean terrain. What is the total distance the sub will travel from point *A* to point *B* along the given path?

* * * * *

2.5 The topographic map below shows the routes taken by two skiers traveling down a mountain from point *A* to point *B*. Create a story for each skier's descent. In each story, include a description of the terrain and the approximate distance traveled. Assume that the terrain between contour lines is smooth, with no drops or rises other than those indicated on the map.

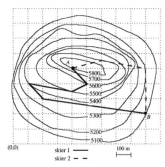

2.6 Use the map in Problem **2.5** to complete Parts **a–c** below.

a. **1.** Find the vertical distance between points *A* and *B*.

2. Find the horizontal distance between points *A* and *B*.

3. Find the distance between *A* and *B* using the Pythagorean theorem.

b. **1.** Determine the coordinates of points *A* and *B*.

2. Find the distance between *A* and *B* using the coordinates of the points.

c. Compare your results in Parts **a** and **b**.

ACTIVITY
3

Microwave signals are used in a variety of applications, including telephone transmissions. Because microwaves travel in a straight line and weaken considerably over distances greater than 5 km, engineers must place microwave repeaters along the transmission path to receive and relay signals.

---

* **2.3 a.** $\sqrt{(700-300)^2 + (200-700)^2 + (200-200)^2} \approx 640$ m

b. $\sqrt{(800-700)^2 + (600-200)^2 + (300-200)^2} \approx 424$ m

c. $\sqrt{(800-700)^2 + (600-400)^2 + (300-500)^2} \approx 300$ m

d. $\sqrt{(300-700)^2 + (700-400)^2 + (200-500)^2} \approx 583$ m

* **2.4 Note:** Topographic maps of the ocean floor come in several styles. Some show the distance of features above the continental shelf, some indicate the depth of the water using positive numbers and some (like the one shown in the problem) indicate the distance from sea level using negative numbers.

a. The approximate coordinates of the points along the sub's route are: (7500,17500,–990), (15000, 10000,–940), (35000,37500,–940), (45000,37500,–940), and (55000,35000,–990).

b. The distance traveled is approximately

10,607 + 34,004 + 10,308 + 10,000 = 64,919 m.

✳ ✳ ✳ ✳ ✳

2.5 Answers will vary. Students should mention that skier 1 traveled down a gentler slope than skier 2. The distance traveled by skier 1 is about 1615 m. The distance traveled by skier 2 is approximately 909 m.

2.6 **a.** **1.** 700 m

2. about 580 m

3. about 909 m

b. **1.** The coordinates of *A* are (400,500,5800). The coordinates of *B* are (900,200,5100).

2. about 911 m

c. The two estimates should be reasonably close.

ACTIVITY
3

Students continue to work with topographic maps, developing profiles of the terrain between two locations.

teacher note

A brief assessment of the mathematical content in Activities **2** and **3**, for use at your discretion, appears in the Teacher Resources for this module.

Materials List

- topographic map
- ruler or straightedge (one per group)
- lined notebook paper or graph paper
- three-dimensional coordinate system (optional)

teacher note

A blackline master of a topographic map and a template for the three-dimensional coordinate system appear in the Teacher Resources for this module.

Student Outcomes

After completing the following exploration and discussion, students should be able to:

✳ draw and interpret a profile given a segment connecting two points on a topographic map

✳ describe how changing its scale affects a profile.

teacher note

In Part **e** of the exploration, students are asked to consider the scales on their profiles. In Figure **14-16**, for example, the horizontal scale is 2 km for each of the given units, and the vertical scale is 100 m between each set of dotted lines. To make these scales the same, the length that represents 2 km on the horizontal axis also must represent 2 km on the vertical axis. In this case, the lines corresponding to each contour would be drawn much closer together. The resulting profile would appear much flatter.

Exploration

Students obtain an image of the landscape between two locations by developing a profile of the terrain. **Note:** The profile may not be to scale, because the lines on the notebook paper might give a different scale than the one on the map.

a. Profile segments should begin and end on contour lines with different elevations. Students will obtain more interesting profiles if there are several changes in elevation between endpoints.

In this activity, you use a topographic map to create a **profile** of mountainous terrain. Profiles can help provide a visual image of the landscape between two points on a topographic map.

geography note

A **profile** shows a vertical cross section or "side view" of the terrain. For example, Figure **14-14** shows a profile of a mountain valley.

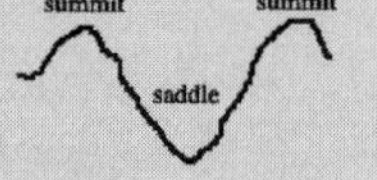

FIGURE 14-14 A profile of a mountain valley.

Exploration

a. 1. On a topographic map provided by your teacher, label two points at least 10 km apart and located on different contour lines.

   2. As shown in Figure **14-15**, connect the points with a **profile segment**.

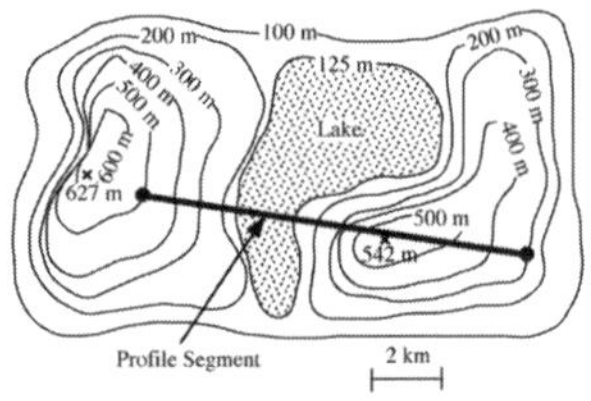

FIGURE 14-15 Profile segment drawn on a topographic map.

b. 1. Label the top line of a sheet of notebook paper with the highest elevation crossed by the profile segment.

2. Determine the change in elevation between consecutive contour lines on the map. This change in elevation is the **contour interval** (*I*). In Figure **14-15**, for example, the contour interval is 100 m.

3. Label each successive line on the notebook paper with an elevation *I* units less than the line above it. Continue this process until a line has been labeled with the lowest elevation crossed by the profile segment.

c. 1. Place the top edge of your notebook paper along the profile segment, as shown in Figure **14-16**.

2. At each point where a contour line crosses the profile segment, draw a segment perpendicular to the profile segment. Extend each perpendicular segment to the line on the notebook paper that represents the same elevation as the corresponding contour line.

3. Mark the intersections of the perpendicular segments and their corresponding lines on the notebook paper.

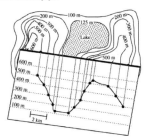

FIGURE 14-16 Creating a profile.

d. Connect the points of intersection with a smooth curve. This curve represents a profile of the terrain between the two points you located on the map.

e. Compare the vertical scale on the profile with the horizontal scale. If they are different, make a sketch of the profile using the same vertical and horizontal scales.

f. Describe any similarities or differences you observe in the two profiles in Parts **d** and **e**.

b–d. Refer to Figure **14-14** in the student edition.

e. Students should realize that a difference in horizontal and vertical scales will affect the appearance of the profile.

f. Students may notice that terrain which appeared to have a steep slope in their first profiles actually has a more gradual incline.

Note: By using the same scale, students can determine the distance between two points simply by measuring with a ruler. If the scales are not the same, they must use the Pythagorean theorem to calculate the distance.

Discussion

a. Sample response: A profile allows you to see elevation changes and to compare the steepness of the inclines.

b. Sample response: No. You would only be able to draw a series of isolated dots representing points on a profile segment.

c. Sample response: Microwaves can't travel through the ground. You have to consider any obstructions that exist, and the distance between the points.

   For example, the map below is overlaid with circles with radii of 5 km. Based only on this map, it would appear that two repeaters are necessary: one at the top of the eastern peak and one somewhere in the intersection of the two circles.

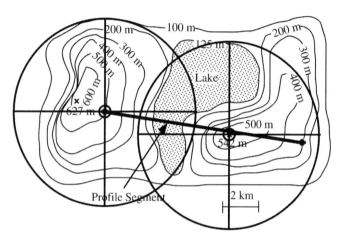

   Considering a profile of the terrain, however, a third repeater may be necessary between the eastern peak and the receiver because of an obstructed path.

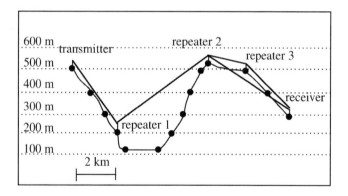

d. Sample response: Measure the distance between the points on the profile and use the horizontal scale to convert the measured distance to approximate the actual distance. (This ignores the vertical distance.)

e. Sample response: Yes, if the vertical scale and horizontal scale of the profile are the same. If this is true, you can use right-triangle trigonometry to determine the angle of elevation. If the scales are not the same, the right triangle formed will not be similar to the actual triangle. Because they are not similar, the corresponding angles might not be congruent.

Discussion

a. What information does a profile provide about a landscape?

b. Given a profile between two points, could you recreate the topographic map from which it was derived? Why or why not?

c. Microwaves travel in a straight line and the distance between repeaters must be less than 5 km along an unobstructed path.

   Imagine that the two points you located in the exploration are the sites of a microwave transmitter and receiver, respectively. Describe how you could use the profile and topographic map to help locate appropriate sites for microwave repeaters.

d. Describe how the distance between two points on a topographic map can be approximated using a profile of the terrain.

e. Could you use a profile to determine the angle of elevation between two points (the angle formed by the segment joining the two points and a horizontal line)? Explain your response.

Warm-Up

1. Draw a right triangle, labeling all sides and vertices. Choose one acute angle and write the formulas for the three trigonometric ratios relative to that angle.

2. Determine the unknown measure in each triangle below.

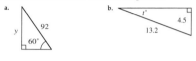

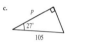

Warm-Up

1. Answers will vary. Sample response:

$$\sin\angle A = \frac{a}{c} \qquad \cos\angle A = \frac{b}{c} \qquad \tan\angle A = \frac{a}{b}$$

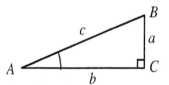

2. **a.** $\sin 60° = \dfrac{y}{92}$

   $y \approx 79.7$

   b. $\sin t° = \dfrac{4.5}{13.2}$

   $t \approx 20°$

   c. $\cos 27° = \dfrac{p}{105}$

   $p \approx 93.6$

   d. $\cos h° = \dfrac{5}{8}$

   $h \approx 51°$

Assignment

3.1 The figure below shows a profile of a mountain landscape.

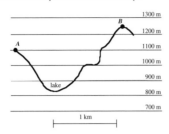

a. What is the elevation of the summit?

b. Approximately how tall is the cliff?

c. At what elevation is the lake?

d. What is the distance from point *A* to point *B*?

e. **1.** Sketch a profile of this mountain on a coordinate grid, using the same scale for both the horizontal and vertical axes.

   2. Use the ordered pairs that describe the locations of points *A* and *B* to verify the distance found in Part **d**.

3.2 Imagine that a microwave transmitter is located at point *A* on the profile in Problem **3.1**. A receiver is located at point *B*.

a. Using the distances found in Problem **3.1**, sketch a right triangle like the one in the diagram below to model this situation.

b. In the diagram, what trigonometric ratio is defined by *BC/AB*? Explain your response.

c. Using the trigonometric ratio you identified in Part **b**, determine the angle necessary to transmit a microwave signal directly from *A* to *B*.

Assignment

Problems suitable for use as assessment items are identified by an asterisk (*).

* 3.1 a. The elevation of the summit is approximately 1250 m.

b. The cliff is about 100 m tall.

c. The elevation of the lake is approximately 830 m.

d. The following right triangle can be used to model this situation.

Using the Pythagorean theorem, the distance from *A* to *B* is:

$$\sqrt{(150)^2 + (1750)^2} \approx 1756 \text{ m}$$

e. If students locate the origin at point *A*, the coordinates of *B* are (1750,150) and the distance formula yields the same equation as given in Part **d**. No matter where the origin is placed, however, the distance between the points remains the same.

3.2 a. Sample response:

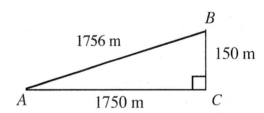

b. Because the sine of an acute angle in a right triangle is the ratio of the length of the leg opposite the angle to the length of the hypotenuse, $BC/AB = \sin\angle BAC$.

c. $\sin^{-1}(150/1756) \approx 4.9°$

* **3.3 a.** Answers will vary. The map below shows two possible locations for the repeaters.

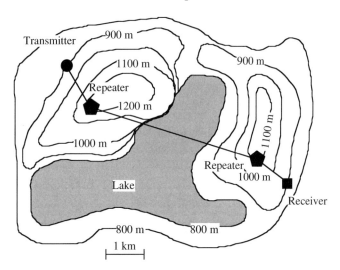

b. 1. Students should create profiles to show that signals are not obstructed by mountains. They also may use measurements to demonstrate that the distances between towers are less than 5 km.

2. Students determine the distance between towers using the distance formula. One method of accomplishing this places the origin of a three-dimensional coordinate system at the transmitter, aligning the x-axis with the segment connecting the transmitter and the first repeater. Using kilometers as the units on all axes, the coordinates of the transmitter are $(0,0,0)$ and the coordinates of the repeater are $(0,1.3,0.3)$. The distance between them is about 1.3 km.

To find the distance between the two repeaters, the origin may be located at the first repeater, the x-axis aligned with the segment connecting the two, and the process repeated. For the sample locations shown above, the distance between the two repeaters is about 4.7 km. The distance between the second repeater and the receiver is about 1.1 km.

3.4 In the sample response given in Problem **3.3,** the total distance traveled by the signal is about 7.1 km. The time, in seconds, is therefore:

$$7.1 \text{ km} \bullet \frac{1000 \text{ m}}{1 \text{ km}} \bullet \frac{1 \text{ sec}}{3 \bullet 10^8 \text{ m}} = 2.4 \bullet 10^{-5} \text{ sec}$$

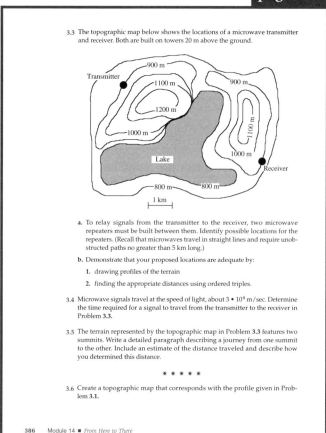

3.3 The topographic map below shows the locations of a microwave transmitter and receiver. Both are built on towers 20 m above the ground.

a. To relay signals from the transmitter to the receiver, two microwave repeaters must be built between them. Identify possible locations for the repeaters. (Recall that microwaves travel in straight lines and require unobstructed paths no greater than 5 km long.)

b. Demonstrate that your proposed locations are adequate by:

1. drawing profiles of the terrain

2. finding the appropriate distances using ordered triples.

3.4 Microwave signals travel at the speed of light, about $3 \bullet 10^8$ m/sec. Determine the time required for a signal to travel from the transmitter to the receiver in Problem **3.3**.

3.5 The terrain represented by the topographic map in Problem **3.3** features two summits. Write a detailed paragraph describing a journey from one summit to the other. Include an estimate of the distance traveled and describe how you determined this distance.

* * * * *

3.6 Create a topographic map that corresponds with the profile given in Problem **3.1**.

3.5 Estimated distances will vary, depending on the route chosen and where students locate the peaks. For example, some routes may cross the lake, while others go around it. Some students may create profiles of the terrain along their paths.

✳ ✳ ✳ ✳ ✳

3.6 Answers will vary. Students should show that the profile segment intersects the topographic map at the appropriate locations.

3.7 The figure below shows a profile of a valley.

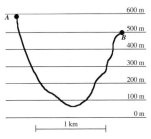

a. What is the elevation of the lowest part of the valley shown in the profile?

b. What is the distance from point *A* to point *B*?

Research Project

The U.S. Geological Survey (USGS) has published topographic maps of nearly the entire United States. Obtain a topographic map of a region near your school.

a. Identify several key features of the terrain. In a paragraph, describe how contour lines help characterize these features on the map.

b. Create a profile of the terrain.

c. Determine the straight-line distance and angle of elevation between the two highest points on the map.

3.7 a. The elevation at the lowest part of the valley is about 70 m.

b. The distance between points *A* and *B* is:

$$\sqrt{(90)^2 + (1500)^2} \approx 1503 \text{ m}$$

Research Project

Student responses should demonstrate their understanding of contour maps and describe the methods used to find the distance and angle of elevation between the two highest points.

Note: As an alternative to the tasks described in the student edition, you may ask students to create a topographic map of a portion of the classroom.

teacher note

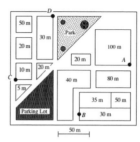

An additional assessment, for use at your discretion, appears in the Teacher Resources for this module.

Summary Assessment

1. a. The profile at the bottom of the page shows that there is an unobstructed line of sight between *A* and *C*.

   b. The distance between *A* and *C* is about 206 m.

   c. This situation can be modeled by the following right triangle:

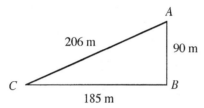

   Because $\sin\angle BAC = 185/206$, the measure of $\angle BAC$ is about 64°. Measured from horizontal, the angle of the transmitter is $90 - 64 = 26°$. **Note:** If the horizontal and vertical scales on their profiles are congruent, students can measure the angle of elevation using a protractor.

Summary Assessment

The diagram below shows a map of a business district in a large city. Each polygon not otherwise labeled represents a building in the district. Each measure indicates the height above street level of the corresponding building. Use this map to complete Problems 1 and 2 below.

1. The local telephone company plans to build a microwave transmitter on the top of the building at point *A*. The transmitter will send signals to a receiver located on the top of a building at point *C*.

   a. Determine whether or not there is an unobstructed line of sight between points *A* and *C* by creating a profile of the terrain.

   b. Determine the distance between points *A* and *C* using the coordinates of ordered triples.

   c. Determine the angle of elevation (measured from the horizontal) necessary to transmit the signal directly from point *A* to point *B*.

2. A cable television company is trying to determine the most cost-efficient way to relay signals from its headquarters at point *B* to a substation at point *D*. The company has two choices: burying a cable underground, or installing a system on the roofs of buildings to transmit signals through the air.

   a. Burying a cable underground will cost $450 per meter. To minimize the disruption of traffic, the cable may not pass under more than three streets and must run alongside buildings.

      1. Determine a possible route between points *B* and *D*.

      2. Calculate the cost of this plan.

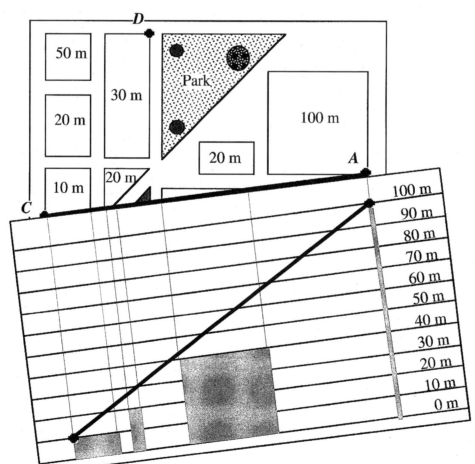

b. The transmitters required to send the signal through the air cost $35,000 each. The repeaters cost $15,000 each. The path between a transmitter and a repeater must be unobstructed by other buildings. If a transmitter or repeaters must be located on the roof of a building not already owned by the company, the space must be purchased for $3000.

1. Use a profile to determine the number and location of the transmitters and repeaters necessary to relay signals between points *B* and *D*.

2. Calculate the cost of this plan.

c. Write a letter to the president of the company describing both options. Include appropriate maps and profiles, a summary of the costs of each plan, and a report of your recommendations.

2. a. 1. The shortest route for the cable, along with a possible path for microwave signals, is shown on the map at the bottom of the page.

2. The distance along the route shown above is about 215 m. Total cost is 215 • 450 or about $96,750.

b. 1. Using a profile, students should determine that direct transmission of the signal from *B* to *D* is not possible. Using the path shown in Part **a** above, transmission requires two transmitters, two receivers, and the purchase of space on the 80-m building.

2. Total cost is 2(35,000) + 2(13,000) + 3000 or $99,000.

c. Answers will vary. Based on the sample responses given in Parts **a** and **b,** burying a cable underground will cost slightly less than transmitting the signal overhead.

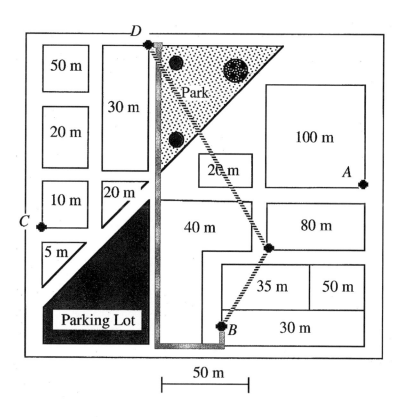

Going in Circuits

Overview

This module encourages students to analyze complicated problems involving many choices in a systematic manner. Students explore Hamiltonian circuits and use algorithms to plan a tour for a hypothetical rock band.

Activity 1:   Students are introduced to some terms and definitions of graph theory.

Activity 2:   Students use tree diagrams and the fundamental counting principle to determine the number of possibilities in different problem settings.

Activity 3:   Students use various algorithms in their attempts to find optimal solutions to problems.

Objectives

In this module, students will:

* receive an introduction to graph theory, including weighted graphs, Hamiltonian circuits, and digraphs (1, 2)
* use tree diagrams to organize information and solve problems (2)
* use the fundamental counting principle (2, 3)
* use factorial notation (2, 3)
* solve problems involving Hamiltonian circuits (3)
* examine and develop algorithms for solving problems (3).

Prerequisites

For this module, students should know:

* how to interpret scale drawings
* how to evaluate algebraic expressions
* how to read and interpret data tables
* how to use tree diagrams.

 Flashbacks, for use at your discretion, appear in the Teacher Resources for this module. These brief problem sets provide a review of some prerequisite skills for each activity.

Planning Guide

Activity	Materials	Technology	Time Line
Activity **1**	■ metric rulers ■ Hamilton High template	■ none	3 days
Activity **2**	■ metric rulers ■ map of United States (optional)	■ none	2 days
Activity **3**	■ state map	■ none	3 days
Assessment Activities	■ none	■ none	3 days **Total: 11 days**

teacher note

A blackline master of the Hamilton High template appears in the Teacher Resources for this module.

Introduction

This introduction describes the constraints involved in a scheduling problem. Students use the information given to complete the exploration in Activity **1**.

   Note: To introduce students to some other applications of the mathematics in this module, you might wish to use the video *Trains, Planes and Critical Paths*, Module I.3 in the video series *For All Practical Purposes*.

ACTIVITY 1

This activity introduces students to some fundamentals of graph theory.

Materials List

- metric rulers (one per student)
- Hamilton High School template (one copy per group; a blackline master appears in the Teacher Resources for this module)

teacher note

The exploration requires many measurements and calculations, so students should work in pairs or small groups.

You might wish to create an overhead transparency of the Hamilton High School template for use in the following discussion.

Student Outcomes

After completing the following exploration and discussion, students should be able to:

✳ recognize a path in a graph

✳ recognize a circuit, specifically a Hamiltonian circuit

✳ draw a weighted graph.

Introduction

The map in Figure **15-1** shows the floor plan of William R. Hamilton High School.

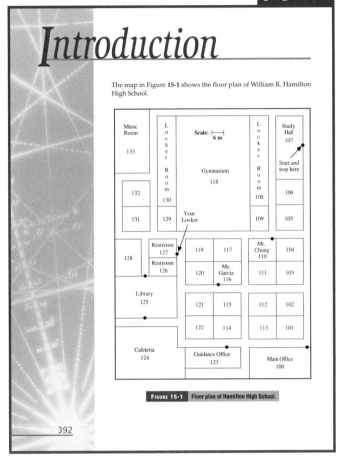

FIGURE 15-1 Floor plan of Hamilton High School.

As a new student at Hamilton High, you have a lot to do. To complete your first day on schedule, you must visit six different rooms during a 55-min study hall. The following list describes each room, the task involved, and the time required to complete the task.

- Main Office: fill out a new student information card (7 min)
- Guidance Office: make an appointment to talk to a counselor (1 min)
- Room 116: question Ms. Garcia about a science experiment (10 min)
- Room 110: talk to Mr. Chang about taking French (10 min)
- Library: find a book for an English assignment (15 min)
- Locker: pick up a notebook (1 min).

You may visit the rooms in any order. However, your route must satisfy the following requirements.

- You must start and stop in Study Hall, Room 107.
- You must visit all the rooms and accomplish all the tasks.
- You must return to Study Hall before the end of the class period (55 min).

   How can you find an efficient route to all these rooms and back to Study Hall? A situation such as this one, in which an appropriate solution makes good use of time or other resources, involves **optimization.**

ACTIVITY 1

It can help to organize the available information in a table or graph before beginning to solve an optimization problem.

   You can describe one possible route by representing each destination as a point, as shown in Figure **15-2.** This route leaves Study Hall, visits the locker first, then eventually returns to Study Hall. The diagram shows the sequence in which the rooms are visited, but it is not drawn to scale.

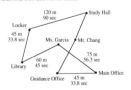

FIGURE 15-2 Possible route for completing study hall tasks.

Module 15 ■ *Going in Circuits*   393

Exploration

Figure **15-2** also shows the distances between some of the stops and the time required to walk those distances. The distances were determined by measuring the hallways on the map in Figure **15-1**, then using the map's scale to convert these distances to meters. The corresponding walking times were calculated using a rate of 4.8 km/hr.

a. 1. Use Figure **15-1** to find the distances along the hallways from the Guidance Office to Mr. Chang's room and from Mr. Chang's room to the Study Hall.

2. Using a walking speed of 4.8 km/hr, calculate the walking times for these trips.

3. Determine the walking time for the entire route.

4. Calculate the total time required to walk the route and complete all the tasks.

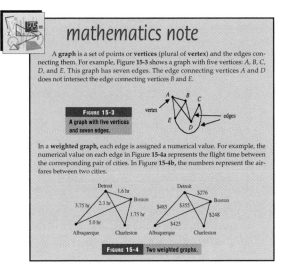

mathematics note

A **graph** is a set of points or **vertices** (plural of **vertex**) and the edges connecting them. For example, Figure **15-3** shows a graph with five vertices: *A, B, C, D,* and *E*. This graph has seven edges. The edge connecting vertices *A* and *D* does not intersect the edge connecting vertices *B* and *E*.

FIGURE 15-3
A graph with five vertices and seven edges.

In a **weighted graph,** each edge is assigned a numerical value. For example, the numerical value on each edge in Figure **15-4a** represents the flight time between the corresponding pair of cities. In Figure **15-4b**, the numbers represent the airfares between two cities.

FIGURE 15-4 Two weighted graphs.

Exploration

In this exploration, students fill in the missing information in Figure **15-2**. Students plan a route through the high school that takes less than 55 min and satisfies all the requirements described in the introduction. All paths must follow hallways. Students should measure distances on the template provided, convert these measurements to actual distances using the given scale, then calculate the corresponding walking times.

The table at the bottom of the page shows the distances and times used to calculate the sample responses. (You might wish to initiate a discussion about precision and accuracy of measurement.)

a. 1. The distance from the Guidance Office to Mr. Chang's room is 75 m. The distance from Mr. Chang's room to Study Hall is 63.8 m.

2. The walk from the Guidance Office to Mr. Chang's takes 56.3 sec. The walk from Mr. Chang's room to Study Hall takes 47.8 sec.

3. The total walking time for the route in Figure **15-2** is approximately 6 min.

4. The total time for the route after all tasks are completed is 50 min.

Mr. Chang	Ms. Garcia	Locker	Library	Guidance Office	Main Office	
63.8 m 47.8 sec	112.5 m 84.4 sec	120 m 90 sec	150 m 112.5 sec	150 m 112.5 sec	105 m 78.8 sec	**Study Hall**
	48.8 m 36.6 sec	56.3 m 42.2 sec	86.3 m 64.7 sec	75 m 56.3 sec	71.3 m 53.4 sec	**Mr. Chang**
		37.5 m 28.1 sec	60 m 45 sec	48.8 m 36.6 sec	75 m 56.3 sec	**Ms. Garcia**
			45 m 33.8 sec	67.5 m 50.6 sec	112.5 m 84.4 sec	**Locker**
				60 m 45 sec	105 m 78.8 sec	**Library**
					45 m 33.8 sec	**Guidance Office**

b. 1–2. Students may use several techniques to select a route. One possible route is shown in the following graph.

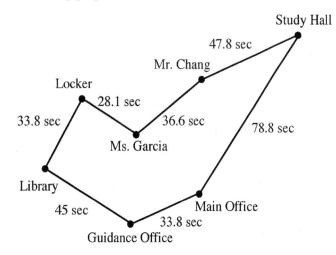

3. The total time for the sample route is 49.1 min.

Discussion

a. Sample response: The better route of the two is the one in Part **b,** because it takes less time to complete.

b. Answers may vary. Sample response: The route that satisfies all the requirements described in the introduction and takes the least amount of time is the best solution.

c. To be assured of finding the best solution to the problem (no matter what the criteria), students would have to try all possible solutions.

d. The vertices of the graphs in the exploration represent locations in Hamilton High School.

e. The edges of the graphs in the exploration represent distances or times between locations in Hamilton High School.

f. The graph from Part **b** of the exploration is a Hamiltonian circuit because it is a path that starts and stops at the same vertex, and visits each vertex exactly once.

g. Sample response: The sequence of vertices *A–B–D–C–E–B–A* is not a Hamiltonian circuit because vertex *B* is visited twice.

b. Find an acceptable route through Hamilton High School that takes less time than the one shown in Figure 15-2.

1. Display the route as a graph.

2. Weight the edges of the graph with the corresponding walking times.

3. Find the total time required to complete the route.

Discussion

a. Which route in the exploration do you think is the better one? Explain your response.

b. What characteristics do you think describe the best possible route?

c. How could you make sure that you found the best possible route?

mathematics note

A **path** is a sequence of vertices connected by edges in which no edge is repeated. Vertices, however, can occur more than once in a path.

In Figure **15-5**, for example, *A–B–D–C–E* represents a path in which no vertex is repeated, while *B–E–A–B–D* represents a path in which one vertex (*B*) is repeated.

FIGURE 15-5 A graph with five vertices.

A **circuit** is a path that starts and ends with the same vertex in which no intermediate vertex is repeated. For example, *E–B–D–C–E* and *A–B–E–A* in Figure **15-5** are circuits.

A **Hamiltonian circuit** is a circuit in which every vertex in the graph is visited exactly once. For example, *A–B–D–C–E–A* in Figure **15-5** is a Hamiltonian circuit.

d. What do the vertices of the graphs in the exploration represent?

e. What do the edges of the graphs in the exploration represent?

f. Explain why your graph from Part **b** of the exploration is a Hamiltonian circuit.

g. Why is *A–B–D–C–E–B–A* in Figure **15-5** not a Hamiltonian circuit?

Warm-Up

1. The diagram below shows a graph with six vertices: *A, B, C, D, E,* and *F.*

Use this graph to describe an example, if possible, of each of the following:

a. a path

b. a circuit that is not a Hamiltonian circuit

c. a path that is not a circuit

d. a circuit that is not a path

e. a Hamiltonian circuit.

Assignment

1.1 In the weighted graph below, the vertices represent cities. The numbers on the edges represent the time in minutes required to drive from one city to the next.

a. Find the path from *A* to *D* that uses the minimum amount of time.

b. Identify one Hamiltonian circuit in the graph. Determine the total time required for this route.

c. Identify another Hamiltonian circuit in the graph that results in a different total time.

d. Which of the circuits from Parts **b** and **c** makes more efficient use of time?

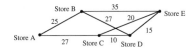

1.2 The following diagram shows a weighted graph in which the vertices represent stores in a mall and the numbers on the edges represent the time in seconds required to walk from one store to another.

a. Find the path from Store A to Store E that takes the least amount of time.

b. Identify a Hamiltonian circuit beginning with Store A. Determine the time required to walk the circuit.

c. Identify another Hamiltonian circuit in the graph that results in a different total time.

1.3 The following chart shows the distances in kilometers between some Alaskan cities.

	Valdez	Tok	Fairbanks
Anchorage	478	520	581
Fairbanks	584	333	
Tok	409		

a. The vertices in the diagram below represent the relative locations of the cities. On a copy of this diagram, draw all the possible edges between these vertices.

Fairbanks
•
     • Tok

•   •
Anchorage Valdez

b. Weight your graph from Part a using the distances between cities.

c. What is the shortest path on the graph?

d. Name one circuit in the graph that is not a Hamiltonian circuit.

e. Identify two Hamiltonian circuits that result in different total distances.

* * * * *

Warm-Up

1. a. Any number of vertices connected by edges is acceptable if no edge is repeated. Sample response: A–B–C.

b. Any circuit that does not visit all the points in the graph is acceptable. Sample response: A–B–D–E–F–A.

c. Any path that does not begin and end at the same vertex is acceptable. Sample response: A–B.

d. Because a circuit must be a path by definition, there are no circuits that are not paths.

e. The path must visit each vertex exactly once and return to the starting vertex. Sample response: D–F–A–B–C–E–D.

Assignment

Problems suitable for use as assessment items are identified by an asterisk (*).

1.1 a. The path from *A* to *D* that takes the least amount of time is *A–E–D*. This path requires 50 min.

b. One possible Hamiltonian circuit is *A–B–C–D–E–A*. The total time for this route is 180 min.

c. Another Hamiltonian circuit is *A–E–B–C–D–A*. The total time for this route is 240 min.

d. Of the two Hamiltonian circuits, the one with the lesser total time would be more efficient.

1.2 a. The path *A–C–E* requires 47 sec.

b. The circuit *A–C–D–E–B–A* takes 112 sec.

c. Sample response: The circuit *A–C–E–D–B–A* requires 114 sec.

* 1.3 a–b. Sample graph:

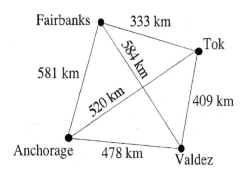

c. The shortest path on the graph is from Fairbanks to Tok.

d. Answers will vary. Sample response: *F–V–A–F*.

e. Sample response: Two Hamiltonian circuits that yield different total distances are: *F–T–A–V–F* (1915 km) and *T–F–A–V–T* (1801 km).

* * * * *

1.4 a. The six possible Hamiltonian circuits, where S represents the start, are: *S–J–K–L–S, S–L–K–J–S, S–J–L–K–S, S–L–J–K–S, S–K–L–J–S,* and *S–K–J–L–S.*

b. To make a selection, students should find the total time for each circuit identified in Part **a.** The table below shows the time in hours for each edge of the graph. The rate of 7 km/hr was used to estimate walking time on edges *S–K* and *J–K,* because one path goes over a mountain and the other goes through thick brush. The time for the path around the lake, *S–L,* was calculated using the rate of 9.6 km/hr.

	L	*K*	*J*
S	0.27	0.35	0.22
J	0.28	0.27	
K	0.22		

The following table shows the total time for each circuit.

Circuit	Total Time (hr)
S–J–K–L–S	0.97
S–L–K–J–S	0.97
S–J–L–K–S	1.07
S–L–J–K–S	1.17
S–K–L–J–S	1.07
S–K–J–L–S	1.17

The scouts in the competition should hope to be assigned one of the first two routes listed in the table above, as these should require less time to complete.

1.5 Answers will vary. The Hamiltonian circuit Seattle–Chicago–Washington, DC–Orlando–Los Angeles–Seattle is 11,555 km long. Sample graph:

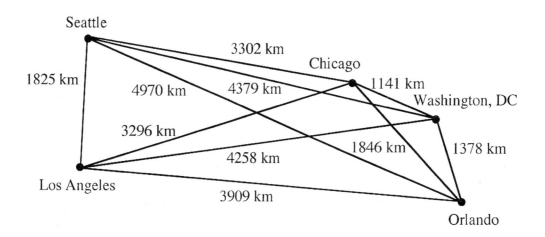

1.4 A scoutmaster has designed an orienteering competition for six scouts. Each scout will be assigned a different course. All six courses, however, start at the same point, visit three locations, then return to the starting point. The scouts must use maps and compasses to complete the assigned course in as little time as possible.

The diagram on the left shows the relative positions of the three locations and the starting point. It also shows the presence of some obstacles on the course, including a mountain, thick brush, and a lake. The weighted graph on the right shows the distances between the locations.

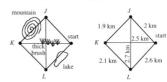

a. Each of the six possible routes is a Hamiltonian circuit. Identify the six routes.

b. Over easy terrain and around the lake, the scouts can travel at an average speed of 9.6 km/hr. Over rugged terrain, such as mountains or thick brush, the average speed is 7 km/hr.

If you were one of the six scouts participating in the competition, which route would you want to be assigned? Explain your response.

1.5 Create a weighted graph showing the distances between the following cities: Seattle, WA; Washington, DC; Orlando, FL; Los Angeles, CA; and Chicago, IL. Identify a Hamiltonian circuit that connects these cities, beginning in Seattle, and determine the total distance traveled. Compare this total with others in your class.

In the previous activity, you described two different routes through Hamilton High School. To determine the best route in this situation, you might be tempted to consider all the possible Hamiltonian circuits. However, this would mean taking the time to examine over 500 circuits.

In this activity, you investigate a method for quickly determining the number of possible solutions to a problem.

398   Module 15 ■ *Going in Circuits*

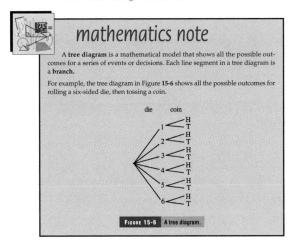

Exploration

Imagine that you are the manager of the most popular band in the nation. The members of the band are in Miami, Florida, and must fly to Los Angeles, California, to sign a recording contract.

There are two flights leaving Miami—one to Chicago, Illinois, and one to Kansas City, Missouri. From both Chicago and Kansas City, there are three flights going west—one to Denver, Colorado; one to Salt Lake City, Utah; and one to Las Vegas, Nevada. There are direct flights to Los Angeles from Denver, Salt Lake City, and Las Vegas.

a. A **directed graph** or **digraph** is a graph in which a direction is indicated on each edge. Draw a directed graph that shows the relative positions of the cities named above and the flights between them.

mathematics note

A **tree diagram** is a mathematical model that shows all the possible outcomes for a series of events or decisions. Each line segment in a tree diagram is a **branch**.

For example, the tree diagram in Figure **15-6** shows all the possible outcomes for rolling a six-sided die, then tossing a coin.

FIGURE 15-6 A tree diagram.

b. Draw a tree diagram to illustrate all possible routes from Miami to Los Angeles.

c. How many different routes are there from Miami to Los Angeles?

Module 15 ■ *Going in Circuits* 399

Student Outcomes

After completing the following exploration and discussion, students should be able to:

✳ draw and label digraphs

✳ draw tree diagrams

✳ use tree diagrams to count possibilities

✳ use the fundamental counting principle.

Exploration

a. Sample digraph:

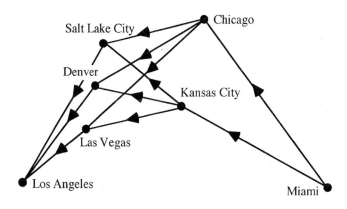

b. Sample tree diagram:

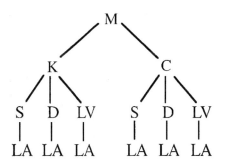

c. From the tree diagram above, there are 6 possible routes.

ACTIVITY

2

In this activity, students use the fundamental counting principle and factorials to determine the number of possibilities in several different problem settings.

Materials List

■ map of the United States (optional)

teacher note

To help students visualize the relative positions of the cities described in the exploration, you may display a map of the United States.

Discussion

a. Methods may vary. Sample response: The total was determined by counting the number of different routes in the tree diagram.

b. Sample response: Using a tree diagram would not work well. Adding more cities would add many more branches.

c. Because there are 2 routes from Miami, 3 each from Chicago and Kansas City, and 1 each from Salt Lake City, Las Vegas, and Denver, using the fundamental counting principle gives 2 • 3 • 1 or 6 routes.

Warm-Up

1. Sample tree diagram:

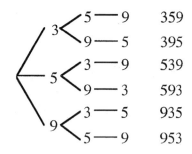

5 — 9	359
9 — 5	395
3 — 9	539
9 — 3	593
3 — 5	935
5 — 9	953

2. a. Using the fundamental counting principle, the number of arrangements is 3 • 2 • 1 = 6.

   b. Student diagrams should show 6 different arrangements.

3. 3 • 4 • 6 • 13 = 936

Assignment

Problems suitable for use as assessment items are identified by an asterisk (*).

2.1 a. Using the fundamental counting principle, there are 4 • 3 • 2 • 1 • 1 = 24 possible routes.

   b. Sample tree diagram:

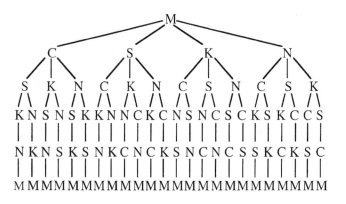

Discussion

a. Describe how you determined the number of different routes from Miami to Los Angeles.

b. Would your method work well if several more cities were involved?

mathematics note

The **fundamental counting principle** provides a method for determining the total number of outcomes for a series of events or decisions. If an event that can occur in *m* ways is followed by an event that can occur in *n* ways, then the total number of ways in which the two events can occur is *m* • *n*.

For example, consider rolling a six-sided die, then flipping a coin. The die has 6 faces and the coin has 2 sides. In this situation, the number of possible outcomes is 6 • 2 = 12.

c. Describe how the fundamental counting principle can be used to determine the number of different routes from Miami to Los Angeles.

Warm-Up

1. Draw a tree diagram that shows all the three-digit numbers that can be formed using the digits 3, 5, and 9, without repetition.

2. You and two of your friends would like to pose for a group picture.

   a. Using the fundamental counting principle, in how many ways can the group be lined up in a row?

   b. Draw a tree diagram to verify your answer to Part **a**.

3. A local coffee shop has begun offering a special lunch, which includes soup, salad, and bread. Customers can choose from 3 different soups, 4 different salads, and 6 different types of bread. They also can select from 13 different beverages. How many different lunch combinations, including beverages, are possible?

Assignment

2.1 As the manager of a band, you are planning a five-city tour to promote the band's new album. The tour will begin and end in Miami, with stops in Seattle, Washington; Kansas City, Missouri; Chicago, Illinois; and New York City. The band will visit each city only once and the order of the cities is not important.

   a. Determine the number of possible routes that the band can take on the tour.

   b. Draw a tree diagram to verify your answer from Part **a**.

   c. Describe the process you used to create the tree diagram in Part **b**.

mathematics note

An **algorithm** is a step-by-step process used to accomplish a task.

In a **brute force algorithm**, every potential solution to a problem is examined. For example, suppose that you wanted to determine the number of possible routes from your home to school. To solve this problem with a brute force algorithm, you could use a tree diagram to list every route.

2.2 On the first day of a new semester, your principal greets you with a list of the seven classes in your school day.

   a. In how many different ways could these seven classes be arranged?

   b. Why is a brute force algorithm not appropriate in this situation?

mathematics note

Factorial notation is often used to simplify the representation of the product of the positive integers from 1 to *n*. If *n* is a positive integer, then *n* **factorial** (denoted by *n*!) can be expressed as

$$n! = n \cdot (n-1) \cdot (n-2) \cdot \ldots \cdot 3 \cdot 2 \cdot 1$$

Zero factorial, or 0!, is defined as 1.

For example, the number of possible arrangements of the letters A, B, and C can be found using the fundamental counting principle as follows: 3 • 2 • 1 = 6. Using factorial notation, this can be represented as 3!

2.3 As part of the publicity for their tour, the band will appear on the cover of *Singer's Circuit* magazine. Before choosing a photo, the magazine editors want to look at samples with the four band members arranged in different orders.

a. If the band members stand side by side, how many different arrangements are possible?

b. Use factorial notation to represent the number of possible arrangements.

2.4 During its concerts, the band plays 10 songs in a set before taking a break.

a. In how many different orders can 10 songs be played?

b. If the band wants to play its current hit song first, how does this affect the number of possible orders for a 10-song set?

c. How would your answer to Part **b** change if the band chose to play its hit song fourth in the set?

d. If the band wants to play its hit song first and its shortest song second, how does this affect the number of possible orders for a 10-song set?

e. In how many different orders can n songs be played?

2.5 The band is planning several tours during the summer concert season. All of these tours begin and end in the band's hometown.

a. Use the fundamental counting principle to determine the number of possible tours involving each of the following numbers of cities:

1. 2 cities (the band's hometown plus one other city)

2. 3 cities (the band's hometown plus two other cities)

3. 4 cities (the band's hometown plus three other cities)

4. 10 cities (the band's hometown plus nine other cities).

b. Use the pattern you observe in your responses to Part **a** to develop a formula for calculating the number of tours possible for n cities if all tours begin and end in the band's hometown.

2.6 a. Determine the number of possible routes through Hamilton High School that begin and end in Study Hall and visit all six destinations described in Activity **1**.

b. Explain why it is not feasible to list all the possible routes.

✳ ✳ ✳ ✳ ✳

2.7 As captain of the softball team, Corrine must determine the order in which the team's nine players will bat. Use the fundamental counting principle to determine the number of different batting orders that Corrine could choose.

---

d. Because the band knows the first and second song they will play, there are $8 \cdot 7 \cdot 6 \cdot 5 \cdot 4 \cdot 3 \cdot 2 \cdot 1 = 8! = 40,320$ possible orders.

e. There are n! possible orders.

2.5 a. 1. $1 = 1! = 1$

2. $2 \cdot 1 = 2! = 2$

3. $3 \cdot 2 \cdot 1 = 3! = 6$

4. $9 \cdot 8 \cdot 7 \cdot 6 \cdot 5 \cdot 4 \cdot 3 \cdot 2 \cdot 1 = 9! = 362,880$

b. If there are n cities in a tour and the first city is known, there are $(n-1)!$ possibilities. **Note:** If students have trouble seeing this pattern, encourage them to examine more examples, such as 5-, 6-, 7-, and 8-city tours.

2.6 a. $6! = 720$

b. Sample response: Listing 720 routes would be very time consuming and the chance of making mistakes is high.

✳ ✳ ✳ ✳ ✳

2.7 $9 \cdot 8 \cdot 7 \cdot 6 \cdot 5 \cdot 4 \cdot 3 \cdot 2 \cdot 1 = 9! = 362,880$

---

c. Sample response: From a point representing Miami, draw a branch to each of the four remaining cities. From each of these four cities, draw a branch to each of the three cities not yet visited along the route. Continue this process until each city is connected to every other city. From each of the last points, draw a single branch to represent the trip back to Miami. The total number of routes can be found by counting the number of terminal branches.

2.2 a. $7 \cdot 6 \cdot 5 \cdot 4 \cdot 3 \cdot 2 \cdot 1 = 5040$

b. Sample response: It would take too much time to list 5040 different schedules.

2.3 a. Using the fundamental counting principle, there are $4 \cdot 3 \cdot 2 \cdot 1 = 24$ possible orders for the band members.

b. $4 \cdot 3 \cdot 2 \cdot 1 = 4!$

* 2.4 a. There are $10 \cdot 9 \cdot 8 \cdot 7 \cdot 6 \cdot 5 \cdot 4 \cdot 3 \cdot 2 \cdot 1 = 10! = 3,628,800$ possible orders.

b. Since the band knows the first song they will play, there are $9 \cdot 8 \cdot 7 \cdot 6 \cdot 5 \cdot 4 \cdot 3 \cdot 2 \cdot 1 = 9! = 362,880$ possible orders.

c. The order in which the numbers are multiplied makes no difference because multiplication is commutative. Playing the hit song fourth makes no difference in the number of possibilities.

2.8 a. $7! = 5040$

b. $\dfrac{9!}{7!} = \dfrac{362,880}{5040} = 72$ or $\dfrac{9!}{7!} = 9 \cdot 8 = 72$

c. Sample response:

$$200! = 200 \cdot 199 \cdot 198 \cdot 197 \cdot \cdots \cdot 1$$
$$= 200(199 \cdot 198 \cdot 197 \cdot \cdots \cdot 1)$$
$$= 200(199!)$$

d. Sample response:

$$\dfrac{100!}{95!} = \dfrac{100 \cdot 99 \cdot 98 \cdot 97 \cdot 96 \cdot 95!}{95!}$$
$$= 100 \cdot 99 \cdot 98 \cdot 97 \cdot 96$$
$$= 9,034,502,400$$

e. $\dfrac{n!}{(n-1)!} = \dfrac{n(n-1)!}{(n-1)!} = n$

2.9 a. $40 \cdot 39 \cdot 38 = 59,280$

b. It would take more than 10 days to try all the possible combinations.

In this activity, students use algorithms to find reasonable solutions to optimization problems.

teacher note

A brief assessment of the mathematical content in Activities **1**, **2**, and **3**, for use at your discretion, appears in the Teacher Resources for this module.

Materials List

- map of the United States (optional)
- state map (for Problem **3.7**; one per student or group)

Student Outcomes

After completing the following exploration and discussion, students should be able to:

✷ use the nearest neighbor algorithm to draw a weighted graph

✷ interpret weighted graphs

✷ evaluate the utility of a specific algorithm by considering the problem setting.

2.8 a. Find the value of 7!

b. Find the value of 9!/7!

c. Explain why it is possible to write 200! as 200(199!).

d. One way to find the value of 100!/95! is to calculate 100! and divide it by 95!
Describe another way to calculate the value of 100!/95!

e. Simplify the following expression:
$$\frac{n!}{(n-1)!}$$

2.9 On his first day at Hamilton High School, Marcus forgets the combination to his locker. In an attempt to jog his memory, he tries a few different combinations.

a. The combination to the lock consists of a sequence of 3 different numbers. Each of these numbers can be chosen from 40 different numbers. How many different combinations are possible?

b. If it takes 15 seconds to try each combination, how long would it take Marcus to try them all?

ACTIVITY 3

In Activity **2**, you identified the number of possible routes for your band's upcoming tour. As manager, however, you must also consider the time and expense associated with the tour. Selecting the shortest route possible, for example, might save both time and money.

Exploration

The stops on your concert tour include Miami, Seattle, Chicago, New York, and Kansas City. Table **15-1** below shows the distances in kilometers between these cities.

TABLE 15-1 ■ *Distances between Cities (in kilometers)*

	Seattle	Kansas City	Chicago	New York
Miami	4400	1997	1912	1757
New York	3875	1765	1147	
Chicago	2795	667		
Kansas City	2424			

Module 15 ■ *Going in Circuits*   403

a. Without using a brute force algorithm, plan a tour that starts in Miami, ends in Miami, visits each of the other cities exactly once, and travels as few kilometers as you think possible.

mathematics note

In a **greedy algorithm**, the choice made at each step is the best of all remaining choices. One greedy algorithm is the **nearest neighbor algorithm**. The steps for the nearest neighbor algorithm are described below.

- Starting with any vertex, draw an edge to its nearest vertex. In Figure **15-7**, for example, vertex A is connected to its nearest vertex, B.

FIGURE 15-7   Connecting the first vertex to the nearest vertex.

- Continue this process from the second vertex, drawing an edge to the next nearest vertex not yet visited, and so on, until all vertices have been visited. For example, Figure **15-8** shows edges drawn from B to C and from C to D.

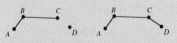

FIGURE 15-8   Continuing the nearest neighbor algorithm.

- To complete a Hamiltonian circuit, return to the original vertex. For example, Figure **15-9** shows an edge drawn from D back to A.

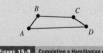

FIGURE 15-9   Completing a Hamiltonian circuit.

404   Module 15 ■ *Going in Circuits*

b. Use the nearest neighbor algorithm to draw weighted Hamiltonian circuits that start and stop in each of the five cities in Table 15-1.

c. 1. Compare the graphs of the five circuits.

   2. Determine which weighted graph represents the tour with the shortest total distance.

d. Compare the shortest tour found using the nearest neighbor algorithm to the tour you identified in Part **a**.

Discussion

a. 1. What advantages are there to using the nearest neighbor algorithm to find a short tour?

   2. What advantages are there to using a brute force algorithm to find a short tour?

b. Describe a situation in which the nearest neighbor algorithm would provide an appropriate method for solving a problem.

c. Describe a situation in which a brute force algorithm would provide an appropriate method for solving a problem.

d. In Part **b** of the exploration, you drew Hamiltonian circuits that started and stopped in each of five cities. Which of these circuits could you use to plan a tour that starts and stops in Miami? Explain your response.

Warm-Up

1. Write each of the following expressions in factorial form.

   a. $5 \cdot 4 \cdot 3 \cdot 2 \cdot 1$

   b. $22 \cdot 21 \cdot \cdots \cdot 3 \cdot 2 \cdot 1$

   c. $n \cdot (n-1) \cdot \cdots \cdot 2 \cdot 1$

2. Simplify each of the following.

   a. $5!/3!$

   b. $\frac{42!}{3!40!}$

   c. $\frac{n!}{(n-3)!}$

Exploration

a. Sample response: Start in Miami, travel to Kansas City, Seattle, Chicago, New York, and then back to Miami. The total distance traveled along this route is 10,120 km.

b. The following figures show the five Hamiltonian circuits created by the nearest neighbor algorithm.

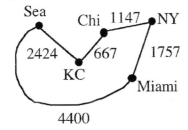

1. Starting in Miami: 10,395 km

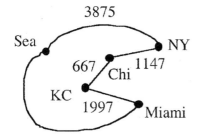

2. Starting in New York: 12,086 km

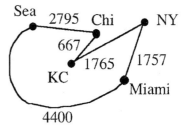

3. Starting in Chicago: 11,384 km

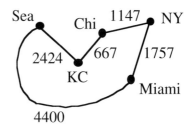

4. Starting in Kansas City: 10,395 km

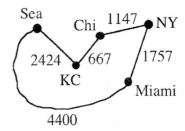

5. Starting in Seattle: 10,395 km

c. 1. The five circuits created using the nearest neighbor algorithm produce only three different graphs.

   2. The graphs produced by starting in Seattle, Miami, or Kansas City give the shortest total distance.

d. Answers may vary. For example, the tour described in the sample response to Part **a** results in a shorter total distance than the shortest one produced by the nearest neighbor algorithm.

   Students should realize that although the nearest neighbor algorithm yields a tour with a reasonably short distance, it might not produce the shortest possible tour. In this case, the nearest neighbor algorithm identifies only 5 of the 120 possible routes.

Discussion

a. 1. The nearest neighbor provides a relatively quick method to solve an optimization problem when there are too many possibilities to list.

   2. By checking all possible routes, a brute force algorithm guarantees finding the shortest distance.

b. The nearest neighbor algorithm should be used when a reasonable solution is acceptable or when it is not feasible to use a brute force algorithm.

c. A brute force algorithm should be used when it is important to find the best possible solution.

d. Sample response: Any of the five circuits may be used. Because a Hamiltonian circuit visits every vertex in a graph and starts and stops at the same point, it creates a closed path. Therefore, you can start and stop at any point on the circuit and still have a Hamiltonian circuit.

Warm-Up

1. **a.** 5!

   b. 22!

   c. $n!$

2. **a.** 20

   b. 287

   c. $n \bullet (n-2) \bullet (n-1)$

3. **a.** $10 \bullet 9 \bullet 8 \cdots \bullet 3 \bullet 2 \bullet 1 = 3{,}628{,}800$

   b. 10!

   c. $10 \bullet 9 \bullet 8 \bullet 7 = 5040$

   d. $10!/6! = 5040$

teacher note

Problems **3.1–3.3** demonstrate the usefulness of algorithms that yield a good solution in a reasonable amount of time, but might not yield the best possible solution.

To complete Problem **3.7**, students might require a map of your state.

Assignment

Problems suitable for use as assessment items are identified by an asterisk (*).

3.1 a–b. The following graph shows the weighted Hamiltonian circuit created by starting from Los Angeles and using the nearest neighbor algorithm. Of the six circuits created, this graph results in the shortest total distance: 11,302 km.

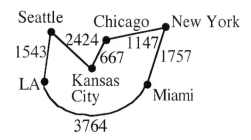

3. **a.** Use the fundamental counting principle to determine the number of ten-digit codes that can be created using the digits 0 through 9, without repetition.

   b. Use factorial notation to represent your response to Part **a**.

   c. Determine the number of four-digit codes that can be created using the digits 0 through 9, without repetition.

   d. Represent your response to Part **c** using factorial notation.

Assignment

3.1 The band would like to add Los Angeles, California, to the tour in the exploration. The following table shows the distances in kilometers between Los Angeles and the other five cities.

	Los Angeles
Miami	3764
New York	3945
Chicago	2808
Kansas City	2182
Seattle	1543

   a. Use the nearest neighbor algorithm to draw weighted Hamiltonian circuits that start and stop in each city on the tour.

   b. Determine which circuit results in the shortest total distance.

   c. Using the nearest neighbor algorithm, how many different routes did you have to check?

   d. If you used a brute force algorithm to select the shortest tour, how many routes would you have to check?

3.2 **a.** About how many seconds did it take you to generate and calculate the total distance of one circuit in Problem **3.1**?

   b. Using your response to Problem **3.1d**, about how long would it take you to check all the possible tours?

3.3 One of the band members suggests that this summer's tour begin with a send-off concert in your town, visit 24 other cities, then end with a homecoming concert in your town.

   a. Determine the number of possible 25-city tours that begin and end in the same town.

   b. Using the time you estimated in Problem **3.2**, determine the total time needed to check all the possible tour routes.

c. Students check six routes, one for each graph in Part **a**.

d. If the tour begins and ends in Miami, there are 5! = 120 possible routes. If the tour may begin and end in any of the six cities, there are 6! = 720 possible routes.

3.2 **a.** Sample response: It took about 50 sec to generate and calculate the total distance.

   b. Sample response: 120(50 sec) = 6000 sec or 1 hr, 40 min.

3.3 **a.** The number of possible 25-city tours that begin and end in the same town is 24! or approximately $6.2 \bullet 10^{23}$.

   b. Using an estimate time of 50 sec, $6.2 \bullet 10^{23}$ (50 sec) $= 3.1 \bullet 10^{25}$ sec or approximately $9.8 \bullet 10^{17}$ years.

3.4 Katherine works in the admissions office at Applegate University. As part of her duties, she leads prospective students on a walking tour of the campus. The diagram below shows the relative positions of the campus buildings.

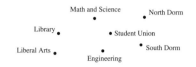

- Math and Science
- North Dorm
- Library
- Student Union
- Liberal Arts
- South Dorm
- Engineering

a. If she visits each of the seven buildings exactly once, in how many different ways can Katherine organize the walking tour?

b. Since new students live in South Dorm, Katherine likes to begin and end the tour there. How many ways are there to organize this tour?

c. The table below shows the distances in meters between buildings on campus. Use these distances and the nearest neighbor algorithm to graph a possible route for the walking tour you described in Part **b.**

	Student Union	South Dorm	North Dorm	Math/Science	Library	Liberal Arts
Engineering	20	40	55	40	50	45
Liberal Arts	55	90	100	60	20	
Library	50	85	90	40		
Math/Science	25	50	50			
North Dorm	40	30				
South Dorm	35					

Module 15 ■ *Going in Circuits* 407

mathematics note

The nearest neighbor algorithm is just one of many greedy algorithms that can be used to solve optimization problems. In the **cheapest link algorithm,** the cheapest (or shortest) action is taken at each stage, regardless of starting and stopping points.

Individual, disconnected edges may occur at various stages. If the cheapest remaining action completes a circuit that is not Hamiltonian, then the next best action is taken. When a Hamiltonian circuit is found, the algorithm is complete.

For example, Figure **15-10** shows the steps used to draw a Hamiltonian circuit with the cheapest link algorithm.

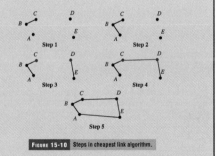

FIGURE 15-10 Steps in cheapest link algorithm.

In Step **3**, notice that *D* and *E* are connected even though these points are farther apart than *C* and *A*. This occurs because drawing an edge between *A* and *C* would complete a circuit that is not Hamiltonian.

3.5 **a.** Use the cheapest link algorithm to determine a possible route for the walking tour in Problem **3.4b.**

b. How does this tour compare with the one you identified in Problem **3.4c**?

3.4 **a.** There are 7! or 5040 ways to organize the walking tour.

b. There are 6! or 720 ways to organize this walking tour.

c. The following graph shows the route created by beginning and ending with South Dorm. The total distance traveled with this tour is 280 m.

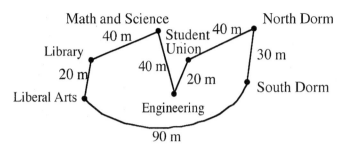

3.5 **a.** Using the cheapest link algorithm produces the route shown below. The total distance traveled is 275 m.

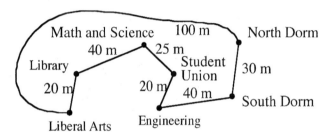

b. The distance traveled using this route is 5 m less than in the sample response given in Problem **3.4c.**

* 3.6 **a.** The circuit found using the cheapest link algorithm follows a route from Miami to New York to Chicago to Kansas City to Los Angeles to Seattle to Miami.

b. The total distance is 11,696 km.

c. The nearest neighbor algorithm resulted in a route with a total distance of 11,302 km, 394 km less than the distance in Part **b** above.

✳ ✳ ✳ ✳ ✳

3.7 Answers will vary. The following sample response uses the Montana cities of Kalispell, Missoula, Great Falls, Bozeman, and Havre. The tour begins and ends in Kalispell.

a. In the following sample table, distances are reported in kilometers.

	Havre	Bozeman	Great Falls	Missoula
Kalispell	420	468	367	185
Missoula	452	323	270	
Great Falls	182	298		
Bozeman	467			

b. There are 4! = 24 possible routes.

c–d. In this case, the routes produced by the two algorithms are the same: *K–M–G–H–B–K*. The total distance is 1572 km.

e. In general, both the nearest neighbor and cheapest link algorithms yield good solutions, but not necessarily the best one.

f. Using a brute force algorithm, the shortest possible route is 1408 km long. **Note:** Only 12 of the 24 circuits are unique. For example, *K–M–G–B–H–K* is the same as *K–H–B–G–M–K* because circuits do not have a direction.

Circuit	Distance	Circuit	Distance
K–M–G–B–H–K	1640	*K–G–B–M–H–K*	1860
K–M–G–H–B–K	1572	*K–G–H–M–B–K*	1792
K–M–B–G–H–K	1408	*K–G–M–H–B–K*	2024
K–M–B–H–G–K	1524	*K–G–M–B–H–K*	1847
K–M–H–G–B–K	1585	*K–H–G–M–B–K*	1663
K–M–H–B–G–K	1769	*K–H–M–G–B–K*	1908

3.6 **a.** Use the cheapest link algorithm to find a tour of the six cities in Problem **3.1** that begins and ends in Miami.

b. Calculate the distance covered by the tour.

c. Compare this distance with the distance found using the nearest neighbor algorithm.

✳ ✳ ✳ ✳ ✳

3.7 As the result of a stellar performance on the state math exam, your class has been awarded a trip to four interesting places in your state. Your class may choose both the places and the route, but the trip must start and end in your town.

a. Choose four destinations and create a table that shows the distances from each one to the others, including your town.

b. Determine the number of possible routes for your trip.

c. Use the nearest neighbor algorithm to plan your route. Determine the total distance traveled.

d. Use the cheapest link algorithm to plan your route. Determine the total distance traveled.

e. Is the shorter of the two routes necessarily the shortest possible route? Explain your response.

f. Use a brute force algorithm to support your response to Part **e**.

Summary Assessment

At 4:30 P.M., Jack and Jill leave their house to run some errands for their parents. They must stop by a friend's house, the music store, the bookstore, the newsstand, and the post office. As a reward, their parents have given them enough money to play video games at the arcade. The relative positions of these destinations are shown in the diagram below.

home
•
       arcade book
     •   store
 music   •
 store •
      post
friend's office
house
•   •
    newsstand

Each errand should take 5 min to complete and Jack and Jill must be home by 6:00 P.M. for dinner. The following table shows the walking time in minutes between the locations.

	Friend's House	Newsstand	Book Store	Post Office	Arcade	Music Store
Home	5.5	9.5	6.5	5.5	4.0	2.5
Music Store	3.0	6.5	6.0	2.5	2.5	
Arcade	5.0	5.5	3.5	2.0		
Post Office	3.0	4.0	5.5			
Book Store	8.5	5.5				
Newsstand	3.5					

1. Select a route that allows Jack and Jill to spend more time at the arcade. Draw a weighted graph to represent this route and indicate the order in which the edges were chosen.

2. The games at the arcade last about 5 min each. Using the route you selected in Problem **1**, how many games can Jack and Jill play?

3. Identify the algorithm you used to select a route. If you devised an algorithm of your own, describe its steps so that any student in the class could repeat your results.

4. If you had to find the quickest possible route that visited all these destinations, how many circuits would you have to check?

---

teacher note

An additional assessment, for use at your discretion, appears in the Teacher Resources for this module.

Summary Assessment

1. The cheapest link algorithm gives two possible routes. This occurs because three of the edges have the same time (2.5 min). In the sample graphs below, the dotted segments indicate the two choices at this step.

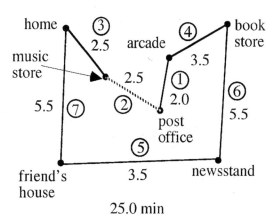

25.0 min

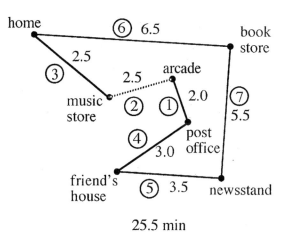

25.5 min

The nearest neighbor algorithm gives several possible routes. Student graphs will vary, depending on the decisions they make when two or more edges have the same time. The sample graph below was drawn by starting at Jack and Jill's home.

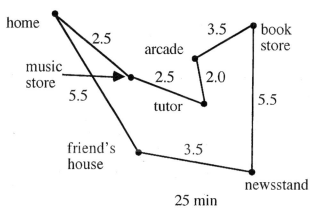

25 min

2. Sample response: Since there are 5 errands and each requires 5 min, this accounts for 25 min. Adding 25 min of travel time results in a total of 50 min. Jack and Jill have a total of 90 min for their trip. Therefore, they have 40 min remaining for the arcade, or enough for 8 games.

3. Answers will vary. Both the cheapest link and nearest neighbor algorithms yield reasonable solutions.

4. If using a brute force algorithm, there are a total of $6!/2 = 360$ possibilities.

Glossary

absolute value of a residual—measure of the distance from a data point to the linear model; in general, the smaller the sum of the absolute values of the residuals, the more closely a line approximates the data.

acceleration—the rate of change in velocity with respect to time; has both magnitude and direction.

acceleration (due to gravity)—a constant typically denoted by g; on earth's surface, the acceleration due to gravity is about 9.8 m/sec^2 in a direction toward the earth's center.

algorithm—a step-by-step process used to accomplish a task.

angle of incidence—angle formed by the normal and the incident ray.

angle of reflection—angle formed by the normal and the reflected ray.

Angle-Angle-Angle (AAA) property—if the angles of one triangle are congruent to the corresponding angles of another triangle, then the triangles are similar.

apothem—segment whose measure is the perpendicular distance from the center of a regular polygon to one of its sides.

area (of a regular polygon)—can be calculated by $A = [(1/2)as]n$, where n is the number of sides, a is the apothem, and s is the side length.

arithmetic sequence—a sequence in which every term after the first is found by adding a constant value (the constant difference) to the preceding term.

arithmetic series—the sum of the terms of an arithmetic sequence.

average velocity—can be calculated by dividing the change in position by the change in time. See *velocity*.

back-to-back stem-and-leaf plot—stem-and-leaf plot used to compare two sets of data.

base (of a cylinder or prism)—one of the congruent and parallel faces.

boundary line—a graph of a linear equation that forms a boundary of a solution set or feasible region; a solid boundary indicates that the points on the line are part of the solution set; a dashed boundary indicates that the points on the line are not part of the solution set.

box-and-whisker plot (or box plot)—displays the median, lower quartile, upper quartile, and outliers (if any) of a data set; the whiskers are segments that connect each end of the box to the farthest values which are not outliers.

branch—a line segment in a tree diagram.

brute force algorithm—an algorithm in which every potential solution to a problem is examined.

calorie—amount of energy required to raise the temperature of 1 mL of water 1°C. **Note:** the calorie-per-gram rating on most food labels measures *dietary calories;* each dietary calorie equals one kilocalorie.

central angle (of a circle)—angle formed by two rays drawn from the center of a circle.

central angle (of a regular polygon)—angle formed by rays drawn from the center of a circumscribed circle to two consecutive vertices of the polygon, dividing the polygon into congruent isosceles triangles; the measure of a central angle of a regular polygon with n sides is: $360°/n$.

cheapest link algorithm— a greedy algorithm in which the cheapest (or shortest) action is taken at each stage, regardless of starting and stopping points; individual, disconnected edges may occur at various stages; if the cheapest remaining action completes a circuit that is not Hamiltonian, then the next best action is taken; when a Hamiltonian circuit is formed, the algorithm is complete.

circuit (in graph theory)—a path that starts and ends with the same vertex in which no intermediate vertex is repeated.

coefficient (of a variable)—a number multiplied times a product of variables or power of variables in a term; the coefficients of x in the expression $ax^2 + bx + c$ are a, b, and c.

common difference—the constant value added to each term in an arithmetic sequence to form the next term.

common ratio—the constant ratio between any two consecutive terms in a geometric sequence.

complementary angles—two angles are complementary when the sum of their measures is $90°$.

congruent—exactly equal in size and shape; the symbol for congruence is $\cong$.

conjunction—combines two mathematical statements with the word *and*; can be represented as the intersection of two sets.

constant of proportionality—the constant in a direct proportion or an inverse proportion.

constraint—condition that limits the number of possible solutions to a problem.

contour line—a line that indicates elevation on a topographic map.

converse—the converse of a statement in the form "If A, then B" is the statement "If B, then A"; the converse of a true if-then statement may or may not be true.

corner point—an intersection of two or more boundary lines of a feasible region; also called a vertex.

corner principle—according to this principle, the maximum and minimum values of an objective function occur at corner points of the feasible region.

cosine (of an angle)— in a right triangle, the ratio of the length of the leg adjacent to the angle to the length of the hypotenuse.

cube root (of a number a)—a number b such that $b^3 = a$; denoted by $\sqrt[3]{a}$.

cylinder—a three-dimensional solid with bases that are congruent simple closed curves (non-polygons) in parallel planes.

density—ratio of an object's mass to its volume.

dependent variable—a variable for which values depend on the outcome of another variable.

dietary calorie—normally referred to as a Calorie with a capital C; equal to 1 kcal (the calorie-per-gram rating on most food labels measures dietary calories).

digraph (in graph theory)—a graph in which a direction is indicated on each edge; also called a directed graph.

dihedral angle—angle formed by two intersecting planes; the measure of a dihedral angle is the measure of the angle whose sides are the two rays formed by the intersections of the faces and a plane perpendicular to the edge.

direct proportion—a relation in which the ratio of two quantities is a constant; can be described by an equation of the form $y = mx$, where m is the constant of proportionality; the graph of a direct proportion always contains the origin because $y = 0$ whenever $x = 0$.

directed graph (in graph theory)—a graph in which a direction is indicated on each edge; also called a digraph.

displacement—the change in the position of an object; has both magnitude and direction.

distance (between two points in two dimensions)—can be found using the formula

$$d = \sqrt{(x_2 - x_1)^2 + (y_2 - y_1)^2}.$$

distance (between two points in three dimensions)—can be found using the formula

$$d = \sqrt{(x_2 - x_1)^2 + (y_2 - y_1)^2 + (z_2 - z_1)^2}.$$

distance (from a point to a line)—the distance along a path perpendicular to the line.

distance-time graph—displays the distance between two objects as a function of time.

distributive property (of multiplication over addition)—$a(b + c) = ab + ac$ or $(b + c)a = ba + ca$.

domain (of a relation)—the set of first elements in ordered pairs of the form (x,y).

equiangular polygon—a polygon for which all interior angles are congruent.

equilateral polygon— a polygon for which all sides are congruent.

event—a subset of a sample space.

expected value—the mean value of an experiment; calculated by adding the products of the value of each event and its corresponding theoretical probability.

experimental probability—(of an event) equals the number of times an event occurs divided by the total number of trials.

explicit formula—a rule for finding for calculating any specific term in a sequence.

exponential equation—an equation of the form $y = a \bullet b^x$, where $a > 0$ and either $0 < b < 1$ or $b > 1$.

exponential growth—change in a quantity or population that can be described by an equation of the form $y = a \bullet b^x$, where a represents the size of the initial population, b is the sum of two percentages—100 (representing the initial population) and r (representing the growth rate)—and x represents a time period.

exterior angle—an angle in the exterior of a polygon; the measure of an exterior angle of a *regular polygon* with n sides is $360°/n$.

factorial—a product of the positive integers from 1 to n; if n is a positive integer, then n factorial (denoted by $n!$) can be expressed as $n! = n \bullet (n-1) \bullet (n-2) \bullet \cdots \bullet 3 \bullet 2 \bullet 1$; zero factorial, or $0!$, is defined as 1.

fair game—game in which the expected value equals the cost of playing.

family (of functions)—a set of functions that have a common parent; for example, the parent of the family of quadratic functions is $p(x) = x^2$.

feasible region—a graph of the solution set of a system of linear inequalities.

first law of motion (Newton's)—an object in a state of rest or moving in a straight line at a constant speed will continue in that state unless acted on by a force.

force—a physical quantity that can affect the motion of an object (two familiar forces are gravity and friction); has both magnitude and direction.

frequency (of a data item)—number of observed occurrences of that item.

frequency table—table consisting of two columns; one displays data items, the other displays the number of observed occurrences of each item.

function—relation in which each element of the domain is paired with an element of the range and each element of the domain occurs in only one ordered pair; a function may be described by a rule or equation.

fundamental counting principle—if an event that can occur in m ways is followed by an event that can occur in n ways, then the total number of ways that the two events can occur is $m \cdot n$.

geometric sequence—a sequence in which every term after the first is found by multiplying the preceding term by a constant value (the common ratio).

geometric series—the sum of the terms of a geometric sequence.

graph (in graph theory)—a set of vertices (plural of vertex) and edges; each edge may connect a maximum of two vertices.

greedy algorithm—an algorithm in which the choice made at each step is the best of all remaining choices.

growth rate (of a population)—the percent increase or decrease in the population between two time periods.

Hamiltonian circuit (in graph theory)—a circuit in which every vertex in the graph is visited exactly once.

height (of a cylinder or prism)—perpendicular distance between the bases.

hertz (Hz)—international unit of frequency which represents one cycle per second.

histogram—graph that displays information using rectangles or bars of uniform width and scales with uniform intervals.

horizontal line—line with a slope of 0 and an equation of the form $y = c$.

hypotenuse—the longest side in a right triangle; the side opposite the right angle.

image—result of a transformation, such as a reflection; if point A is the preimage, then the image of a point A can be represented as A' (read "A prime").

incident ray—models the path that a light ray follows from an object to a reflective surface.

incoming angle—angle between the reflective surface and the incident (incoming) ray.

independent variable—a variable for which values do not depend on the outcome of another variable.

inequality—a mathematical sentence using one or more of the symbols $<$, $>$, $\leq$, or $\geq$; one way to describe a real-number interval.

infinite interval—a set of real numbers greater than or less than a given value; so called because it increases or decreases without bound.

instantaneous velocity—velocity at a particular instant in time.

interior angle—angle in the interior of a polygon.

interquartile range—difference between the upper quartile and the lower quartile.

interval (of real numbers)—set of all real numbers between two fixed endpoints; each endpoint may or may not be included in the interval.

interval notation—in interval notation, a square bracket,] or [, indicates that the endpoint is included in the interval; a parenthesis,) or (, indicates that the endpoint is not included in the interval.

inverse proportion—a relation in which the product of two quantities is constant; can be described by an equation of the form $xy = k$, where k is the constant of proportionality; the equation of an inverse proportion can also be written in the form $y = k/x$.

kilocalorie (kcal)—1000 cal; amount of energy needed to raise the temperature of 1 L of water 1°C.

lateral face (of a prism)—parallelogram formed by joining the corresponding vertices of a prism's bases.

least-squares line—the linear model that results in the least sum of the squares of the residuals; also called a linear regression.

leg (of a right triangle)—one of the two shorter sides in a right triangle; a side opposite an acute angle.

line of reflection— the perpendicular bisector of each segment connecting a preimage point to its corresponding image point under a reflection; every point on the line of reflection is its own image.

linear model—mathematical model that consists of a line or a linear equation.

linear regression—the linear model that results in the least sum of the squares of the residuals; also called the least-squares line.

lower quartile—median of the lower half of the data points.

mean absolute deviation—measure of spread that describes the average distance from the mean for the numbers in a data set.

measures of central tendency—the mean, median, and mode of a data set.

nearest neighbor algorithm—a greedy algorithm that starts with any vertex and draws an edge to its nearest vertex, then continues this process from the second vertex to the next nearest vertex not yet visited, and so on, until all vertices have been visited; to complete a Hamiltonian circuit, it returns to the original vertex.

net—a two-dimensional pattern without tabs that can be folded to make a three-dimensional solid.

newton (N)—a metric unit of force; the weight of an object in newtons is its mass in kilograms multiplied by $9.8 \text{ m}/\text{sec}^2$ (the acceleration due to gravity).

normal (of a reflecting surface)—the perpendicular line to the surface at the point of reflection.

nth root (of a non-negative number a)—a number s such that $s^n = a$; the non-negative nth root of a is denoted as $\sqrt[n]{a}$.

objective function—a function whose value is to be maximized or minimized.

optimization—the process of making the best use of time or other resources.

ordered triple—used to represent the coordinates of a point in a three-dimensional coordinate system; can be written in the form (x,y,z).

origin (of a three-dimensional rectangular coordinate system)—the point where the three axes intersect; has coordinates $(0,0,0)$.

outgoing angle—angle between the surface and the reflected (outgoing) ray.

outliers—extreme data values more than 1.5 times the interquartile range above the upper quartile or below the lower quartile.

parabola—the graph of a quadratic equation; has a vertex and is symmetric about a line known as the axis of symmetry.

path (in graph theory)—a sequence of vertices connected by edges in which no edge is repeated; vertices, however, can occur more than once in a path.

perpendicular bisector (of a segment)—the line perpendicular to a segment that divides the segment into two congruent parts.

pie chart (or circle graph)—graph consisting of circular regions divided into sectors that each represent a percentage of the whole.

point-slope form (of the equation of a line)—an equation of the form $y - y_1 = m(x - x_1)$, where m is the slope and the line passes through the point (x_1, y_1).

polygon—a union of coplanar segments intersecting only at endpoints; at most two segments intersect at any one endpoint and each segment intersects exactly two other segments. See *side; vertex*.

power equation—an equation of the form $y = ax^b$.

preimage—object prior to a transformation.

principal square root— the positive square root of a number, usually denoted by $\sqrt{a}$, although it also may be written as $\sqrt[2]{a}$.

prism—a three-dimensional solid determined by two congruent polygons in parallel planes whose corresponding vertices are connected by segments; the two congruent and parallel faces are the prism's bases; the parallelograms formed by joining the corresponding vertices of the bases are the prism's lateral faces; prisms are named by the polygonal shape of the bases.

profile—a vertical cross section or "side view" of terrain.

proportional—two ratios, a/b and c/d, where neither b or d equal 0, are proportional if $a/b = c/d$.

Pythagorean theorem—in a right triangle, the square of the length of the longest side (the hypotenuse) equals the sum of the squares of the lengths of the other sides (the legs).

quadratic expression (in a single variable)—an expression in which the greatest exponent on the variable is 2; also referred to as a second-degree expression; a quadratic expression in x can be written in the general form $ax^2 + bx + c$, where $a \neq 0$.

quadratic function—a function f in which $f(x)$ is equal to a quadratic expression in x; also called a second-degree function; can be written in the general form $f(x) = ax^2 + bx + c$, where $a \neq 0$.

range (of a data set)—measure of spread found by subtracting the least data value from the greatest data value.

range (of a relation)—the set of second elements in ordered pairs of the form (x,y).

rate—ratio of the change in one quantity to the change in another quantity.

recursion—the process of using a recursive formula.

recursive formula—a rule for calculating any term in a sequence by using the preceding term(s).

reflected ray—models the path of a light ray away from a reflective surface.

reflection (in a line)—a pairing of points in a plane so that the line of reflection is the perpendicular bisector of each segment connecting a preimage point to its corresponding image point; every point on the line of reflection is its own image.

regular polygon—a polygon in which all sides are congruent and all interior angles are congruent.

relation (between two variables)—a set of ordered pairs of the form (x,y).

residual—the difference between the y-coordinate of a data point and the corresponding y-value of a linear model.

saddle—a pass between two higher elevations.

sample space—the set of all possible outcomes for an experiment.

scale factor—the ratio of corresponding sides for two similar figures.

sequence—an ordered list; each item in the list is a *term* of the sequence.

side—segment of a polygon.

similar—two objects are similar if they have the same shape and the ratios of corresponding lengths are proportional; the ratio of corresponding sides is the scale factor; the symbol for similarity is $\sim$.

simple closed curve (in a plane)—a curve with no endpoints that does not intersect itself.

simulation—an experiment conducted to investigate real-world situations.

sine (of an angle)—in a right triangle, the ratio of the length of the leg opposite the angle to the length of the hypotenuse.

slope (of a line)—ratio of the change in vertical distance to the change in horizontal distance between any two points on a line; a vertical line has no slope.

slope-intercept form (of the equation of a line)—an equation of the form $y = mx + b$, where m is the slope and b is the y-intercept.

solution (to a system of linear equations)—a point where the graphs of all the lines intersect; the coordinates of this point satisfy all the equations in the system.

solution set (of an inequality)—all the points, or solutions, that make the inequality true.

square of a residual—the square of the distance from a data point to the model; in general, the smaller the sum of the squares of the residuals, the more closely a model approximates the data.

square root (of a non-negative number a)—a number s such that $s^2 = a$.

standard deviation—a measure of spread often represented by the Greek letter σ (sigma) and determined by the following formula, where μ represents the mean and n is the number of items in the set:

$$\sigma = \sqrt{\frac{(x_1 - \mu)^2 + (x_2 - \mu)^2 + \cdots + (x_n - \mu)^2}{n}}.$$

stem-and-leaf plot—displays the values in a data set in a stem-and-leaf arrangement; to simplify interpretation, data is usually ordered and a legend is included.

subscripted variable—a variable with a subscript, such as x_1 (read "x sub one").

substitution method—can be used to solve a system of linear equations; begins by solving an equation for one variable; the resulting expression is then substituted for that variable in another equation in the system; this process is repeated until a solution can be identified.

summit—the highest point of the surrounding elevations.

supplementary angles—two angles are supplementary when the sum of their measures is 180°.

surface area (of a prism)—the sum of the areas of the bases and lateral faces.

system of linear equations—a set of two or more equations whose graphs are lines; a solution to a system of linear equations is a point where all the lines intersect.

tangent (of an angle)—in a right triangle, the ratio of the length of the leg opposite the angle to the length of the leg adjacent to the angle.

template—a two-dimensional pattern with tabs that can be folded to make a three-dimensional solid.

term (of a sequence)—an item in an ordered list; may be represented by a subscripted variable of the form p_1 (read "p sub one"); the general or nth term may be represented by p_n.

tessellation—a pattern of repeated shapes that covers an entire plane without gaps or overlaps; also called a tiling.

theorem—a conjecture proven to be true for all cases.

theoretical probability—(of an event) equals the number of outcomes in the event divided by the total number of outcomes in the sample space.

tiling—a pattern of repeated shapes that covers an entire plane without gaps or overlaps; also called a tessellation.

tree diagram—a mathematical model that shows all the possible outcomes for a series of events or decisions; each line segment in a tree diagram is a branch.

trigonometric ratios—ratios of the lengths of sides in right triangles.

upper quartile—median of the upper half of the data points.

velocity—rate of change in position with respect to time; has both magnitude and direction. See *average velocity* and *instantaneous velocity.*

vertex (of a feasible region)— an intersection of two or more boundary lines; also called a corner point.

vertex (of a parabola)—occurs at the highest (or lowest point) in the graph of a quadratic function.

vertex (of a polygon)—intersection of two sides of a polygon; plural *vertices.*

vertex form (of a quadratic function)—a function of the form $f(x) = a(x - c)^2 + d$, where a, c, and d are real numbers and $a \neq 0$; the coordinates of the vertex are (c, d).

vertical line—line with no slope and an equation of the form $x = c$.

volume (of a cylinder or prism)—can be found by multiplying the area of a base by the height.

volume—amount of space occupied by an object; measured in units such as cubic centimeters (cm^3) or liters (L).

weighted graph (in graph theory)—a graph in which each edge is assigned a numerical value.

whiskers—segments that connect each end of the box in a box-and-whisker plot to the farthest values which are not outliers.

x-intercept—x-coordinate of the point where a line or curve intersects the x-axis.

y-intercept—y-coordinate of the point where a line or curve intersects the y-axis.

Selected References

Badawy, A. *Architecture in Ancient Egypt and the Near East.* Cambridge, MA: M.I.T. Press, 1966.

Bittinger, M. W., and E. B. Green. *You Never Miss the Water Till . . .* (The Ogallala Story). Littleton, CO: Water Resources Publications, 1980.

Britton, J., and D. Seymour. *Introduction to Tessellations.* Palo Alto, CA: Dale Seymour Publications, 1989.

Chartrand, G. *Introductory Graph Theory.* New York: Dover Publications, 1977.

Cohen, J. E. "How Many People Can the Earth Hold?" *Discover 13* (November 1992): 114–119.

Consortium for Mathematics and Its Applications (COMAP). *For All Practical Purposes.* New York: W. H. Freeman and Co., 1991.

Cozzens, M. B., and R. Porter. "Problem Solving Using Graphs." High School Mathematics and Its Applications Project (HiMAP). Module 6. Arlington, MA: COMAP, 1987.

Davidovits, J., and M. Morris. *The Pyramids.* New York: Hippocrene Books, 1988.

Dugan, J. T., and D. E. Schild. *Water-Level Changes in the High Plains Aquifer—Predevelopment to 1990.* U.S. Geological Survey Water Resources Investigations Report 91–4165. Lincoln, NE: U.S. Geological Survey, 1992.

Dugan, J. T., D. E. Schild, and W. M. Kastner. *Water-Level Changes in the High Plains Aquifer Underlying Parts of South Dakota, Wyoming, Nebraska, Colorado, Kansas, New Mexico, Oklahoma, and Texas—Predevelopment Through Nonirrigation Season 1988–89.* U.S. Geological Survey Water Resources Investigations Report 90-4153. Lincoln, NE: U.S. Geological Survey, 1990.

Eves, H., and H. Eves. *Introduction to the History of Mathematics with Cultural Connections.* Philadelphia, PA: Saunders College Publishing, 1990.

Farlow, S. J., and G. Haggard. *Finite Mathematics and Its Applications.* New York: Random House, 1988.

Frautschi, S., R. Olenick, T. Apostol, and D. Goodstein. *The Mechanical Universe.* Cambridge: Cambridge University Press, 1986.

Galilei, G. *Dialogues Concerning Two New Sciences.* Translated by H. Crew and A. di Salvio. Amherst, NY: Prometheus Books, 1991.

Garland, T. H. *Fascinating Fibonaccis: Mystery and Magic in Numbers.* Palo Alto: Dale Seymour Publications, 1987.

Gebhardt, S., and R. Matthews. *Nutritive Value of Foods.* Washington, DC: U.S. Government Printing Office, 1981.

Grünbaum, B., and C. G. Shephard. *Tilings and Patterns.* New York: W. H. Freeman and Co., 1987.

Guinness World Records 2005. New York: Bantam Dell, 2004.

Halliday, D., and R. Resnick. *Physics.* New York: John Wiley & Sons, 1978.

Iowa Academy of Science. *Physics Resources and Instructional Strategies for Motivating Students.* Cedar Falls, IA: University of Iowa, 1985.

Little, C. E. "The Great American Aquifer." *Wilderness 51* (Fall 1987): 43–47.

Kastner, W. M., D. E. Schild, and D. S. Spahr. *Water-Level Changes in the High Plains Aquifer Underlying Parts of South Dakota, Wyoming, Nebraska, Colorado, Kansas, New Mexico, Oklahoma, and Texas—Predevelopment Through Nonirrigation Season 1987–88.* U.S. Geological Survey Water Resources Investigations Report. Lincoln, NE: U.S. Geological Survey, 1990.

Macaulay, D. *Pyramid.* Boston, MA: Houghton Mifflin, 1975.

McArdle, W., F. Katch, and V. Katch. *Exercise Physiology: Energy, Nutrition, and Human Performance.* Philadelphia: Lea & Febiger, 1991.

McMahon, T., and J. T. Bonner. *On Size and Life.* New York: Scientific American Books, 1983.

Microflect Co. *Passive Repeater Engineering.* Salem, OR: Microflect, 1984.

Milgram, J. H., and R. G. Donnelly, R. J. Van Houten, and J. M. Camperman. *Effects of Oil Slick Properties on the Dispersion of Floating Oil into the Sea.* U. S. Department of Transportation Report No. CG-D-64-78. Springfield, VA: National Technical Information Service, 1978.

Murphy, J., and R. Smoot. *Physics: Principles and Problems.* Columbus, OH: Charles E. Merrill Publishing Co., 1977.

National Council of Teachers of Mathematics (NCTM). *Discrete Mathematics Across the Curriculum K–12.* Reston, VA: NCTM, 1991.

National Council of Teachers of Mathematics (NCTM). *A Core Curriculum: Making Mathematics Count for Everyone.* Reston, VA: NCTM, 1992.

Olson, M., G. K. Goff, and M. Blose. "Triangular Numbers: The Building Blocks of Figurate Numbers." *Mathematics Teacher* 76 (November 1983): 624–625.

Packal, E. *The Mathematics of Games and Gambling.* Washington, DC: Mathematical Association of America, 1981.

Page, L., and N. Raper. *Food and Your Weight.* Washington, DC: U.S. Government Printing Office, 1977.

Paulos, J. A. *Innumeracy: Mathematical Illiteracy and its Consequences.* New York: Vintage Books, 1988.

Paulos, J. A. *Beyond Numeracy: Ruminations of a Numbers Man.* New York: Alfred A. Knopf, 1991.

Reiss, M. *The Allometry of Growth and Reproduction.* Cambridge: Cambridge University Press, 1989.

Roman, S. *An Introduction to Discrete Mathematics.* New York: Saunders College Publishing, 1986.

Schmidt-Nielsen, K. *Scaling: Why Is Animal Size So Important?* Cambridge: Cambridge University Press, 1984.

Seymour, D., and M. Shedd. *Finite Differences: A Problem-Solving Technique.* Palo Alto: Dale Seymour Publications, 1973.

Sharkey, B. J. *Physiology of Fitness.* Champaign, IL: Human Kinetics Publishers, 1979.

Sundberg, J. *The Science of Musical Sounds.* San Diego, CA: Academic Press, 1991.

Trains, Planes and Critical Paths. Videocassette. Produced by the Consortium for Mathematics and Its Applications (COMAP). Module I.3 in the series *For All Practical Purposes: Introduction to Contemporary Mathematics.* Santa Barbara, CA: The Annenberg/CPB Project, 1989. 30 min.

United Nations, Department of Economic and Social Affairs. *World Urbanization Prospects: The 2003 Revision.* New York: United Nations, 2004. (United Nations publication, Sales No. ESA/P/WP.190.)

U.S. Bureau of the Census. *Statistical Abstract of the United States: 2005.* Washington, DC: U.S. Government Printing Office, 2005.

U.S. Congress, Office of Technology Assessment. *Coping with an Oiled Sea: An Analysis of Oil Spill Response Technologies.* OTA-BP-O-63. Washington, DC: U.S. Government Printing Office, March 1990.

U.S. Department of the Army. *Map Reading and Land Navigation.* Washington, DC: U.S. Government Printing Office, 1987.

Whitmer, J. *Spreadsheets in Mathematics and Statistics Teaching.* Bowling Green, OH: School Science and Mathematics Association, 1992.

Zwingle, E. "Wellspring of the High Plains." *National Geographic* 183 (March 1993): 81–109.